THE BIOCHEMISTRY AND USES OF PESTICIDES

THE BIOCHEMISTRY AND USES OF PESTICIDES

Structure, Metabolism, Mode of Action and Uses in Crop Protection

KENNETH A. HASSALL, PhD, FRSC

Senior Lecturer, Department of Biochemistry and Physiology, University of Reading

Second Edition

MACMILLAN

First edition published 1982 under the title
The Chemistry of Pesticides
Second edition 1990

Published by
MACMILLAN PRESS LTD
Houndmills, Basingstoke, Hampshire RG21 2XS
and London
Companies and representatives
throughout the world

Typeset by Latimer Trend & Company Ltd
Plymouth

Printed in Hong Kong

British Library Cataloguing in Publication Data
Hassall, Kenneth A. (Kenneth Arnold), *1924–*
The biochemistry and uses of pesticides.—2nd ed).
1. Crops. Pesticides. Chemical properties
I. Title II. Hassall, Kenneth A. (Kenneth Arnold),
1924–. Chemistry of pesticides
632′.95
ISBN 0–333–49789–9
ISBN 0–333–49790–2 pbk

Contents

Preface to the second edition   xi

Preface to the first edition   xiii

Introduction, acknowledgements and a disclaimer   xvi

1   General considerations   1

1.1   Some historical landmarks   1
1.2   The role of pesticides in agriculture   3
1.3   The size and scope of the pesticide market   5
1.4   Economic aspects of pesticide usage   7
1.5   Toxicological considerations   10
1.6   International arrangements relating to the safe use of
     pesticides   17
1.7   National arrangements for pesticide safety   19
1.8   Local and personal aspects of pesticide safety   21
     References   22

2   Physicochemical aspects of pesticide formulation and application   25

2.1   Target surfaces for pesticide applications   25
2.2   Plant leaf cuticle   26
2.3   The insect integument   28
2.4   Pesticide formulation and state of application   31
2.5   Fumigation   33
2.6   Application of solids as dusts or as granules   34
2.7   Application as liquids   39
2.8   Impact of machinery on formulation and application   44
2.9   Types of spray supplements   47
2.10   Chemistry of surfactants   50
2.11   Mode of action of surfactants   53
     References   56

3   Principles of pesticide metabolism   **57**

   3.1   Defence systems and their importance   57
   3.2   Enzymes responsible for the metabolism of pesticides   59
   3.3   Hydrolases   60
   3.4   Microsomal polysubstrate oxygenases   65
   3.5   Role of glutathione in pesticide degradation   73
   3.6   Other conjugation reactions   76
         References   79

4   Organophosphorus insecticides   **81**

   4.1   Introduction   81
   4.2   Structural diversity of organophosphorus insecticides   83
   4.3   Practical uses of organophosphorus insecticides   83
   4.4   Nervous systems, nerve cells and synapses   87
   4.5   Acetylcholinesterase: its action and inhibition   92
   4.6   Adverse and environmental effects of organophosphorus
         compounds   97
   4.7   Low-persistence contact poisons (subgroup 1)   100
   4.8   Loco-systemic compounds (subgroup 2)   102
   4.9   Systemic insecticides (subgroup 3)   112
   4.10 Organophosphorus compounds with a fumigant action
         (subgroup 4)   119
   4.11 Organophosphorus compounds used against soil organisms
         (subgroup 5)   121
         References   123

5   Carbamate insecticides, molluscicides and nematicides   **125**

   5.1   Introduction   125
   5.2   Structural diversity of carbamate insecticides   125
   5.3   Practical uses of carbamates   128
   5.4   Mode of action and side-effects of carbamate insecticides   131
   5.5   Aryl methylcarbamates (subgroup 1)   133
   5.6   Heterocyclic monomethyl- and dimethylcarbamates
         (subgroup 2)   140
   5.7   *N*-Methylcarbamate derivatives of oximes (subgroup 3)   144
         References   152

6   Organochlorine insecticides   **155**

   6.1   Introduction   155

6.2 Structural diversity and properties of organochlorine insecticides   156
6.3 Production figures and practical uses of organochlorine insecticides   157
6.4 Mechanism of normal axonic transmission   159
6.5 DDT and its analogues   163
6.6 Hexachlorocyclohexane (HCH, formerly BHC)   171
6.7 The chlorinated cyclodiene family   174
6.8 Secondary and environmental effects of organochlorine insecticides   178
     References   182

7 **Natural and synthetic pyrethroids**   **185**

7.1 Natural pyrethroids   185
7.2 Synthetic pyrethroids   190
7.3 Mode of action and side-effects   201
     References   205

8 **Other insecticides and similar compounds**   **208**

     Acylureas (benzoylphenylureas)   *208*

8.1 Special features and field uses   208
8.2 Mode of action of acylureas   210
8.3 Metabolism and persistence of acylureas   214

     Insect growth regulators   *216*

8.4 Juvenile hormone and methoprene   216

     Formamidine insecticides and acaricides   *217*

8.5 Behavioural characteristics, chemistry and uses   217
8.6 Mode of action of formamidines   219
8.7 Metabolism of formamidines   221

     Some other insecticides of plant origin   *222*

8.8 Nicotine, rotenone and their derivatives   222

     Other pesticides that harm invertebrates   *224*

8.9 Acaricides   224
8.10 Nematicides   228
8.11 The avermectins   230
8.12 Molluscicides   233
     References   235

9 Insect resistance to insecticides **237**

9.1 An overview 237
9.2 Importance of uptake and excretion 239
9.3 The role of hydrolases 240
9.4 Mono-oxygenase activity in relation to resistance 245
9.5 Glutathione-*S*-transferases and DDT dehydrochlorinase 247
9.6 Modification of the site of action 251
9.7 Cross-resistance 254
9.8 Management of resistance 256
 References 259

10 Fungicides: general principles; inorganic and heavy-metal fungicides **262**

10.1 Fungi and fungicides 262
10.2 Penetration of fungicides into fungi 266
10.3 Selectivity of fungicides 267
10.4 Copper fungicides: preparation, properties and uses 269
10.5 Copper fungicides: mode of action 273
10.6 Inorganic and organic mercury compounds 275
10.7 Organotin compounds 280
10.8 Sulphur and lime sulphur 281
 References 284

11 Non-systemic organic fungicides **286**

11.1 Classification of non-systemic fungicides 286
11.2 Dithiocarbamates: chemistry, uptake and uses 288
11.3 Dithiocarbamates: mode of action and metabolism 293
11.4 The phthalimide group 298
11.5 Dinitrophenol derivatives 302
11.6 Chlorine-substituted aromatic fungicides 305
11.7 Other non-systemic or poorly systemic fungicides 308
 References 312

12 Systemic fungicides **315**

12.1 Classification; advantages and disadvantages of systemic fungicides 315
12.2 Benzimidazoles 318
12.3 Oxathiins or carboxamides 327
12.4 Morpholine inhibitors of sterol synthesis 331
12.5 Inhibitors of C-14 demethylation of sterols 335

12.6   Hydroxyaminopyrimidine derivatives   347
12.7   Antibiotics   349
12.8   Phenylamides used against Oomycetes   350
12.9   Miscellaneous antifungal compounds   354
       References   358

13   Herbicides: general considerations   362

13.1   Introduction   362
13.2   Non-selective and selective herbicides   363
13.3   Weed control: an overview   368
13.4   Uptake of herbicides by leaves or by roots   369
13.5   Persistence of herbicides in soil   372
13.6   Situations involving the application of herbicides to soil   377
13.7   The use of mixtures of herbicides   379
13.8   Classification of herbicides   381
       References   382

14   Herbicides applied to foliage   383

       Type A: Herbicides that kill all foliage   384

14.1   Quaternary ammonium compounds   384
14.2   Glyphosate   390
14.3   Aminotriazole (amitrole)   395

       Type B: Herbicides selectively toxic to broad-leaf weeds   399

14.4   Phenoxyacetic acid derivatives   399
14.5   Auxin-like herbicides derived from benzoic acid   408
14.6   Bromoxynil and ioxynil   410
14.7   Bentazon   414

       Type C: Herbicides to control grassy weeds   415

14.8   Dalapon   415
14.9   Herbicides that selectively kill grasses post-emergence of
       crop   416

       *Type D: Herbicides to control wild oats and some other
       grasses in cereals*   422

14.10 Foliage-applied carbamates and amides   422
14.11 Other substances used post-emergence against grasses   425

*Type E: Herbicides to control broad-leaf weeds in various
dicotyledonous crops*   *428*

14.12   Phenoxybutyric acid derivatives   428
14.13   Dinitrophenol derivatives   429
14.14   Other herbicides occasionally applied to weed foliage; oils
and the concept of physical toxicity   431
References   436

15   Herbicides that are mainly soil-acting against seedling weeds   439

Type A: Inhibitors of photosynthesis   *440*

15.1   Urea herbicides   440
15.2   Triazine herbicides   447
15.3   Uracil and pyridazinone herbicides   454

Type B: Substances that act at, or before, cell division   *458*

15.4   Phenylcarbamate derivatives   458
15.5   Sulphonylurea herbicides   463

Type C: Herbicides that disrupt membranes   *468*

15.6   Diphenyl ethers with light-dependent action   468
References   472

16   Soil-applied herbicides often used in the absence of annual crops   475

Type A: Substances that disrupt lipid biosynthesis   *476*

16.1   Thiolcarbamates   476

Type B: Herbicides that affect meristematic growth   *483*

16.2   Dichlobenil and chlorthiamid   483
16.3   α-Chloroacetamides; other amides   485
16.4   Dinitroaniline herbicides   489
References   493

Epilogue   **495**

**Appendix: Some proprietary products containing active ingredients
mentioned in the text**   **503**

Index   **511**

Preface to the second edition

The first edition appeared in 1982 under the title *The Chemistry of Pesticides: Their Metabolism, Mode of Action and Uses in Crop Protection*. This largely rewritten second edition is published under the modified title, *The Biochemistry and Uses of Pesticides: Structure, Metabolism, Mode of Action and Uses in Crop Protection*. This modification reflects the dramatic progress that has been made in the last few years towards an understanding of how pesticides function, of how metabolism contributes to selectivity and safety, and of how the development of resistance is linked to biochemistry and molecular biology.

Since the appearance of the first edition, a deeper insight has been gained into causes of the neurotoxicity of several groups of insecticides. In addition, more use is being made of newer insecticides, which harm insects by altering behaviour or by interfering with the insect life cycle. The increased importance of substances such as the formamidines, insect growth regulators and avermectins has been recognised in this edition by allocation of an additional chapter to newer compounds. Similarly, since much new information has become available about the causes of resistance in insects, this subject is now considered in a separate chapter, rather than piecemeal under several groups of insecticides.

Very impressive advances have also been made in the last few years into an understanding of how fungicides work. This has permitted a more rational function-based classification than was hitherto possible, including a regrouping of the numerous types of substances used as systemic fungicides. An important aspect of some newer systemic fungicides is that they have not, so far, encouraged the development of resistance at the damaging rate characteristic of certain benzimidazoles and pyrimidines. On the other hand, there has been, for safety reasons, a decline in the use of several types of fungicides, including the formerly valuable dinitrophenols.

Several new groups of herbicides have been introduced, some of which are both of great practical value and have target sites that make them academically fascinating. The control of dicotyledonous weeds, made possible decades ago by, *inter alia*, phenoxyacetic acid herbicides, unfortunately also aggravated problems associated with the spread of perennial grasses. The relatively recent large-scale use of specific grass-killers has therefore been of great practical importance. Weedkillers that kill seedling weeds or act through the soil have so proliferated that it is now convenient to subdivide into two chapters the compounds considered in chapter 13 of the first edition. This division in large measure reflects differences in the agricultural uses to which the various soil-applied herbicides are put.

Finally, a short personal comment. With retirement now thrust upon me, I would like to say how pleasant it has been in the course of my life's work to have taught pesticide chemistry to so many good students (it is as a teacher, not a researcher, that I prefer to be remembered, and I hope I shall be invited to do similar work in the developing world after I leave Reading). However that may be, I am grateful to all who have stimulated my interest in pesticides and, thereby, in life itself. My thanks to all who have supported me in the preparation of this second edition, especially my wife, Maggie, who organised the chapter references and who encouraged me to persevere despite the trauma of losing both my parents in 1988. To these three I owe an unrepayable debt of gratitude, and to them I informally dedicate this book.

Reading, April 1989   Ken Hassall

Preface to the first edition

Few aspects of agriculture have advanced so rapidly or generated so much controversy as has the use of chemicals for crop protection. Such chemicals include insecticides, fungicides and herbicides, as well as several minor groups of compounds. All of these are here collectively termed *pesticides*—an unsatisfactory but useful umbrella term, from 'pest: anything noxious, mischievous or destructive'. In its early days the subject of pesticides involved little more than an enumeration of the toxic compounds used in agriculture, with lists of their chemical properties and practical uses. Such has been the progress in the subject that nowadays it is evident that an understanding of metabolism, persistence and mode of action is as essential for the safe and efficient use of pesticidal substances as it is for poisons and drugs of importance in medical toxicology.

A consequence of this progress has been that the subject has become more fascinating as it has become more complex. This book attempts to portray something of this fascination by demonstrating the multidisciplinary nature of the science of pesticides, with specific reference to substances used in crop protection. The agriculturist or his adviser normally has to handle and apply insecticides, fungicides and herbicides and will find it convenient for these three major types of agricultural pesticides to be considered under one cover. This (regrettably unusual) event is highly desirable scientifically and educationally since so many of the principles involved transcend the type of compound under discussion—the scientific aspects of formulation, application, disposition, metabolism and even mode of action, are extremely similar for insecticides, fungicides and herbicides, and one may suspect academic demarcation often separates what should naturally be united.

At least 3 per cent of the market value of agricultural crops in technologically advanced countries is spent on toxic chemicals and their application. This large sum is spent in an effort to minimise the effects of the army of pests that find large areas of monoculture a paradise for explosive reproduction. Some of us may regret the necessity for the use of pesticides on crops, but it is a necessity arising from the fact that man has opted out of the usual constraints placed upon species equilibrium; man neither wishes to limit his reproduction to two children per family nor wishes to take a cut in his (world-wide) standard of eating. Remove the chemicals and, in the present world situation, food will become scarcer for the poor nations and dearer for the rich. On the other hand, Rachel Carson and many others have pointed out that the use of toxic chemicals on crops can help to create some of the problems that perpetuate their use (the development of resistance and the destruction of competitors are two examples). They can also pollute the environment if used in the wrong place or at the wrong time, or in the wrong amounts.

Let me make quite clear that the comments above are not to be construed as an apologia; even though I am sometimes proud to wear a conservationist's hat, I have dedicated much of my life to teaching this subject and several well known names were former students at Reading. In short, in my considered judgement, chemical crop protection is both inevitable and desirable for the foreseeable future, albeit increasingly as part of integrated pest control. So, if such substances are to be used it is imperative that all who use them, or advise about their use, are aware of the hazards that can arise and of the metabolic factors that determine their persistence, activation or degradation.

A major purpose of this book is to meet the need just described, while demonstrating that the underlying principles are often of intrinsic interest to the pure scientist. It is thus designed to meet the needs of those in academic, commerical or international organisations who, while expert in some other discipline, have neither the time not the inclination to sieve through advanced texts for various types of basic information. In addition, most students studying agricultural disciplines now receive courses in crop protection chemistry. Pesticides also provide excellent examples of how molecules can be designed to fulfil predetermined objectives (biochemical and molecular pharmacology) and of the problems arising from the widespread use of toxic chemicals (environmental and pollution chemistry).

From undergraduate teaching in both Britain and East Africa, I have found the subject both intelligible and interesting to those with a standard in chemistry approximately equivalent to A Level in Britain (i.e. school chemistry to about 18 years of age). Clearly the book is not intended to deal with this wide subject exhaustively, for merely to list the *titles* of the articles on pesticide chemistry that have appeared in the last 10 years would occupy a space larger than this book. On the other hand, where chemistry (or biochemistry) is an essential vehicle to convey the rationale of structure, enzymic attack, or mode of action of a particular pesticide, chemical or biochemical discussion has not been sidestepped. However, recognising that long chemical names can break the continuity of presentation (and perhaps be rather off-putting to some non-chemists), chemical names have, wherever possible, been kept out of the main text but provided for reference as a part of the legend to figures. For rather similar reasons Latin names do not always accompany trivial names in the text although they have been used where ambiguity might arise. For others, cross-reference is possible through the index.

Substances used for crop protection vary from year to year but the fundamentals governing their choice, use and metabolism evolve much more slowly. Of the hundreds of chemicals in current use as pesticides only a relatively small number have been selected to illustrate these general principles, for a lengthy catalogue would obscure rather than enlighten—and would be, one imagines, profoundly tedious. The same would apply to lists of insect pests, pathogens and weeds together with the chemicals that have been used to control them. This is, in fact, something that is best done at the local level anyway, and in many countries Agricultural Ministries provide literature indicating how best to deal with local problems. In addition, excellent commerical literature exists on the practicalities of pest control and should always be sought and carefully read before handling any crop protection chemical. In the present book the principles already outlined are illustrated by reference to substances selected as representative of groups or of subgroups of pesticides and have been chosen to illustrate the widest range of structure–toxicity relationships and metabolic patterns as is reasonably possible within the space available.

No doubt these subjective choices will merit criticism. Nevertheless it is my hope that this book will be a stimulus to all who are concerned with scientific agriculture, whether as growers, governmental advisers or as representatives of commercial firms. In addition, I should regard it as a welcome bonus if its contents provide an appreciation of the subject of molecular biology, the fascination of which grows with each new discovery, and which often lies at the heart of pesticide metabolism, mechanism of action and the development of resistant strains of organisms.

Reading, May 1981   K. A. H.

Introduction, acknowledgements and a disclaimer

Pesticide science is a multidisciplinary subject and readers of this book are likely to be approaching it from a variety of scientific backgrounds. Consequently, although this book is an *introductory* text, suitable for use by undergraduates for whom the subject is but one part of a wider course, it is also expected that specialists, expert in their own field, may wish to set their own expertise in perspective or to superimpose a knowledge of pesticides upon their pre-existing expertise. Thus specialists in chemistry, biology, agriculture, entomology, plant pathology, ecology, food industries, soil science and toxicology may know far more about their chosen discipline than the present writer yet still acknowledge a need to broaden their horizon by reference to chapters dealing with matters in which they are *not* specialists. Thus, for any one reader, *introductory* does not necessarily mean *elementary*.

Many hundreds of active ingredients are in use, most of which are formulated and sold under several tradenames. With rare exceptions this book refers to active ingredients by their trivial (i.e. short) international names. Moreover, for larger groups of compounds, no attempt has been made to include all known members of each group. Instead, examples have been chosen to illustrate the overall properties and uses of members of the group. The number of known substances is so great that to do otherwise would reduce parts of this or any other book almost to the format of a telephone directory. That is not the present objective. Moreover, products come and go with the years, but many of the principles involved alter far more slowly. On the other hand, ample references at the ends of chapters suggest monographs that carry a wider range of names of active ingredients. In the appendix of this book the reader will find a list that cross-references the names of commercial products with the trivial names used for an active ingredient each contains (comment on the first edition demonstrated that this appendix was popular). I wish to add that, while it has been a pleasure to listen to advice from many quarters, the approach to my subject is exclusively my own and is, at least so far as I can diagnose myself, totally independent of any commerical influence, or, indeed, of influence or inducement from any source.

It is a pleasure to acknowledge the help provided by several colleagues in my own and other departments of the University of Reading, of Jealott's Hill Research Station (ICI, and also an associated Institute of the University of Reading) and of staff of the British Agrochemicals Association. Numerous reference texts and review articles have provided invaluable sources of information and, more importantly, have enabled decisions to be made with regard to balance and priorities of subject matter. I should like to make especial mention of the following (detailed references appear at the ends of appropriate chapters): *MAFF List of Approved Products for Farmers and Growers* (1985); *British Insecticide and Fungicide Handbook* (1976 and later); *Weed Control Handbook* (1978 and later); *Comprehensive Insect Physiology, Biochemistry and Pharmacology* (edited by Kerkut and Gilbert, 1985); *Metabolism of Pesticides* (Menzie, 1969 and later); *Progress in Pesticide Biochemistry and Toxicology* (edited by Hutson and Roberts, 1981 and later); *Pest Resistance to Pesticides* (edited by Georghiou and Saito, 1983); *Modern Selective Fungicides* (edited by Lyr, 1987); and *Biochemistry and Physiology of Herbicide Action* (Fedtke, 1982). The publishers and I also wish to thank VEB Gustav Fischer Verlag who have kindly given permission for the use of copyright material from *Modern Selective Fungicides* by H. Lyr, in particular the table on p.33, and figures 10.2 and 10.3, published by Longmans in 1987.

A few of the tables and figures in this book are based on data or ideas in books or reviews by other authors. These are acknowledged where they occur, but there are several authors to whom I am particularly indebted. Many of the toxicity data in table 1.2 appeared in *World Review of Pest Control* (1966) and were collated by Edson, Sanderson and Noakes. Some of the diagrams of jets and discs in figure 2.5 have been based on commercial literature or diagrams from *Pesticide Application Methods* by Matthews (1979). Some data in table 4.3 and later tables were derived from the *British Insecticide and Fungicide Handbook* (edited by Martin and Worthing) or (for herbicides) from the *British Weed Control Handbook* (edited by Fryer and Makepeace). Some of the data in table 5.1 are quoted from *Carbamate Insecticides: Chemistry, Biochemistry and Toxicology* (1976) by Kuhr and Dorough and some of those in table 6.2 are from a review by Kenaga in *Environmental Toxicology of Pesticides* (1972). Stereochemical representation of some pyrethroids is based on the method used by Leahey, editor of *The Pyrethroid Insecticides* (1985). Figure 12.4 is a simplification of diagrams by Schewe and Lyr in *Modern Systemic Fungicides* (1987). Aspects of steroid biosynthesis in figure 12.6 are partly based on diagrams by Kerkenaar in the same work (p. 168). Figure 12.9 is based on work by Gadher (1983) as quoted by Buchenauer, also in the same work (p. 210). Part of figure 13.2 is based on illustrations by Ashton in *Biodegradation of Pesticides* (1982). Figure 13.5 is patterned on a scheme of Fedtke in *Biochemistry and Physiology of Herbicide Action* (1982). Commercial products listed in the appendix were selected from a variety of sources of data, mostly commercial, together with products named in *Pesticides 1986: Pesticides Approved under the Control of Pesticides Regulations, UK*. I have used several diagrams and tables from two of my earlier works, namely *World Crop Protection*, vol. 2, *Pesticides* (1969, Iliffe) and *Biochemistry and Physiology of the Cell* (Edwards and Hassall, 1980, McGraw-Hill).

Finally, because of the nature of the subject a disclaimer is necessary. This book is for educational information, not for trade. Although every care has been taken to get facts right and to avoid printing errors, the ultimate responsibility in pesticide usage rests with the user, whose job it is to read the label on the container, to consult commercial or official advisers and to be acquainted with local rules and regulations. Consequently, notwithstanding any statement made in this book, **neither the author nor the publisher accepts any responsibility for any damage or accident of any sort whatsoever, arising from the use of any of the pesticidal compounds mentioned in this book.** It should also be pointed out that **mention in the book of the use of a compound, in no way implies that the substance in question may be legally used in a particular country or on a particular crop.** Substances that are now restricted or even banned in many countries still need to be mentioned in a book of this sort in order to explain why trouble has been taken by agrochemical firms, at great expense, to promote research leading to new-generation replacements for dangerous out-dated substances.

1 General considerations

1.1 SOME HISTORICAL LANDMARKS

The use of chemicals to control insects possibly dates back to classical Greece and Rome, for Homer mentioned the fumigant value of burning sulphur and Pliny the Elder advocated the insecticidal use of arsenic and referred to the use of soda and olive oil for the seed treatment of legumes. Pliny experienced the non-selective action of sulphurous fumes for he died when Vesuvius erupted in A.D. 79 ('sulphur and the gross air' in the words of his nephew, Pliny the Younger). The Chinese were employing moderate amounts of arsenicals as insecticides by the sixteenth century, and not long afterwards nicotine, in the form of tobacco extracts, was used to control the plum curculio. By the nineteenth century, both pyrethrum and soap had been used for insect control, and Forsyth described a combined wash of tobacco, sulphur and lime to combat insects and fungi (see Horsfall, 1956, frontispiece).

As in the twentieth century, chemical pest control was not without its competitors even in ancient times. Some mystical and legal anecdotes are entertainingly described by Ordish (1976). A method described by Mouffet and apocryphally attributed to Pliny would undoubtedly still be popular if it were totally reliable—caterpillars can allegedly be enticed off infected trees by persuading an unadorned maiden of appropriate charm to dance around the orchards. Those who favour the wisdom of age to the sallies of youth may prefer a legal indictment of 1485, when the High Vicar of Valencia 'commanded caterpillars to appear before him, gave them a defence counsel and, in judgment, condemned them to leave the area' (Ordish, 1976, p. 44).

The middle of the nineteenth century marked the beginning of the first systematic scientific studies into the use of crop protection chemicals. Work on arsenic compounds led to the introduction in 1867 of Paris green, an impure copper arsenite. It was used in the USA to check the spread of the Colorado beetle and by 1900 its use was so widespread that it led to the introduction of what was probably the first pesticide legislation in the world. Bordeaux mixture was in use in 1885 to control the downy mildew of vine, and by the turn of the century lime sulphur was employed both in Europe and California as a fungicide for use against diseases of fruit trees.

In 1896 a French grape grower, applying Bordeaux mixture to his vines, observed that the leaves of yellow charlock growing nearby turned black. This chance observation demonstrated the possibility of chemical weed control, and shortly afterwards it was found that iron sulphate, when sprayed onto a mixture of cereal and dicotyledonous weeds, killed the weeds without damaging the crop. Within a decade several other inorganic substances had been shown to act selectively at appropriate concentrations. Another important landmark before the First World War was the introduction in 1913 in Germany of the first organomercury seed dressings (prior to this, organomercury compounds had been used medically to combat syphilis).

In the years between the two world wars, both the number and the complexity of crop protection chemicals increased. Tar oil was, and still is, used to control eggs of aphids on dormant trees. Dinitro-orthocresol was patented in France in 1932 for the control of weeds in cereals, and in 1934 thiram, the first of several important dithiocarbamate fungicides, was patented in the USA.

The cosmopolitan nature of contributions to chemical pest control was even more evident after 1939. During the Second World War, the insecticidal potential of DDT was discovered in Switzerland and insecticidal organophosphorus compounds were developed in Germany. At about the same time, work was in progress in Britain and the USA that was to lead to the commercial production of herbicides of the phenoxyalkanoic acid group. In 1945 the first soil-acting carbamate herbicides were discovered by British workers and the organochlorine insecticide, chlordane, was introduced in the USA and in Germany. Shortly afterwards, the insecticidal carbamates were developed in Switzerland.

The decade 1950–60 saw the appearance of 'second-generation' organophosphorus insecticides, which were more selective and less toxic to higher animals than were earlier organophosphorus compounds. These were soon to be supplemented by a wide range of synthetic pyrethroids, pioneered by workers in Britain and Japan. Some of these synthetic pyrethroids, unlike the natural substances, are stable to light, and, quite recently, pyrethroids have been marketed for use in soil (ICI, 1986). Another advance has been the introduction of several substances, notably diflubenzuron, which affect insects by inhibiting an enzyme related to the synthesis of a component of their cuticles.

Systemic fungicides that have appeared since about 1960 include the benzimidazoles (e.g. benomyl), pyrimidines (e.g. ethirimol, triarimol), triazoles (e.g. hexaconazole) and the acylalanine derivative, metalaxyl. This period has also seen a considerable expansion of our knowledge of how some groups of fungicides work—in particular, the way in which certain substances block the biosynthesis of steroids.

Herbicides to appear between 1955 and 1960 included the important triazines (Switzerland) and quaternary ammonium compounds (Britain). Glyphosate, which, like the quaternary compounds, is inactivated by soil, was discovered soon afterwards by workers in the USA. From about 1960 the foliar-acting hydroxybenzonitriles (e.g. bromoxynil), the diphenyl ethers (e.g.

acifluorfen) and sulphonylureas (e.g. chlorsulfuron) were introduced. Diclo-fop-methyl and sethoxydim are examples of two relatively new groups of foliar herbicides that have aroused much interest; the reason for this is that they complement the phenoxycarboxylic acids in that they selectively control grasses growing in broad-leaf crops.

1.2 THE ROLE OF PESTICIDES IN AGRICULTURE

In many parts of the world, but especially in North America and Europe, dramatic changes in farming practice have occurred during the second half of this century. Not only have farms grown larger, but each has tended to specialise in one or a few crops. This has been partly a response to the need to use costly farm machinery efficiently and has been made possible by great advances in plant breeding as well as the use of fertilisers, irrigation and soil improvement techniques.

The resulting system of intensive agriculture has less use for crop rotation than had earlier systems, and crop rotation was, albeit accidentally, a quite useful way to control some pests. Moreover, intensive agriculture frequently leads to large areas where only one crop is grown. Such areas of monoculture are ideal targets for pests and diseases. The situation is, in fact, rather similar to that well known in the physical world, where disorder (entropy) tends to increase unless energy is expended to stop this happening. In the biological context, an area of monoculture is a metastable system and the ingress of insects, fungi and weeds to increase the disorder can be prevented in various ways. For example, theoretically weeds can be removed physically, and biological control methods to limit attacks by insects and fungi are being actively sought. However, at the present time, pesticides are the most frequently used method of control on most farms in most developed countries. Labour is often costly and scarce, and is hardly relevant to the weed problems of the prairies, to take an extreme example.

In consequence, the world food situation has been transformed in the last 40 years. Despite the embarrassment of too great a success in some areas, resulting in excess production of certain commodities, especially grain, the availability of these excesses has proved most valuable when emergencies have arisen in such areas as sub-Saharan Africa. There is now no scientific reason why anyone, anywhere in the world, should lack cereal foods. In practice, of course, it is not as simple as this, because problems relating to ease and cost of distribution, *inter alia*, are frequently superimposed.

Unfortunately, the successes of intensive agriculture have been bought at a price. Long gone are the euphoric days when pesticide experts came near to believing that there was little left for them to do (see, for example, Wheatley, 1987). On the negative side of the equation there are a number of complica-tions, some potentially dangerous. Pesticides of many types have led to the development of resistance in the target organism, sometimes to the point where the substance has had to be withdrawn or reformulated. Insecticides can sometimes be as damaging to the natural predators and competitors of phytophagous insects as they are to the target species. There are also ecological consequences, sometimes known, sometimes feared, of releasing pesticides into the environment, and the potential hazards to consumers of edible crops should residues still be present on or in the food at the time of consumption.

Since about 1980 the very success of modern agricultural methods in many developed countries has introduced a new perspective into the role of pesticides in crop protection. No longer is maximising yield the only goal, especially for those crops which are being locally overproduced. Instead, the emphasis has started to move towards the use of pesticides that are needed in much smaller quantities than those used heretofore, the use of more selective pesticides and the use of pesticides that are biodegradable and therefore less ecologically damaging. For example, some modern weedkillers are applied at one-twentieth of the amount per hectare that was necessary for their prede-cessors. In consequence, the tonnage used on the North American and European markets is no longer increasing at the rate of earlier years, even though the financial value of products on the world market still has much scope to increase.

The current role of pesticides in the developing world is less well defined. In many countries there are privately owned or national estates that grow cash crops. For these, where soil and climatic conditions are favourable, the role of pesticides may be similar to that in developed countries. Outside such estates, however, farming may be on a very small or subsistence level. In such cases weedkillers may be irrelevant, especially if family labour is available for hoeing. Insecticides and fungicides might still have a part to play but usually such use is limited by poverty. Pesticides to protect produce during storage in the hut or kraal would undoubtedly be valuable, in the author's experience.

It should also be added that non-agricultural uses of insecticides may have a profound agricultural significance for the control of insect vectors of human diseases. If diseases such as malaria, sleeping sickness, typhus and yellow fever sap men's strength and destroy their will to work, they will be inefficient farmers. Malaria is perhaps the most widespread debilitating disease of this kind, but the following extract from a publication of the World Council for the Welfare of the Blind illustrates poignantly the debilitating effect of onchocerciasis: 'In certain parts of Africa, near streams, in heavily infested areas, we find villages in which every adult is blind. In these villages, children are precious things, for they alone can see to lead about their elders for a few years until they themselves turn blind' (quoted from Hassall, 1969).

1.3 THE SIZE AND SCOPE OF THE PESTICIDE MARKET

The end of the Second World War in 1945 was marked by a couple of decades of rapid industrial expansion and a concomitant increase in prosperity in many industrialised countries. This was reflected in the market value of good-quality agricultural produce, and it became financially worth while for a farmer to protect his crops from the predations of insects and the effects of fungi and weeds. This happened at about the time that effective and relatively cheap organic pesticides were becoming readily available. The situation was to change in that second-generation pesticides were often more costly than the early ones—most pyrethroid and carbamate insecticides, for instance, are more expensive than organophosphorus compounds, and most of these are dearer than some organochlorine compounds (compare, for example, USDA, 1978, table 670). However, the success of first-generation pesticides had convinced farmers of the benefits accruing from the use of crop protection chemicals. It would, perhaps, be expedient to start enquiring soon about the source of raw materials for pesticides when oil becomes a precious commodity some time between 1995 and 2020.

The dramatic expansion of the world pesticides industry between 1945 and 1975 is illustrated by tonnages quoted by Green *et al.* (1977). In 1945 the tonnage was less than 0.13 million. It rose to 0.44 million by 1955, to about 1 million by 1965 and to 1.8 million in 1975. The growth is the more remarkable when it is recalled that cheap but heavily applied inorganic chemicals have in considerable measure been replaced during this period by organic chemicals of higher unit cost but which are applied at only a fraction of a kilogram per hectare. In financial terms it is estimated that, at retail prices, the world crop protection market has grown from $900 million* in 1960 to $7560 million in 1978 (Braunholtz, 1979). The world retail market value of agrochemicals in 1986 is estimated by Finney (1988) to be about $20 billion†.

The British Agrochemicals Association (BAA) have reported that the total sales of pesticides by the British pesticides industry rose from $238 million in 1976 to $1539 million in 1986 (BAA, 1987a). Of this $1539 million, about $639 million was generated by sales to the home market, comprising sales of herbicides, insecticides and fungicides (figure 1.1), as well as smaller quantities of seed dressings, growth regulators and other products. The predominant contribution of herbicides in 1986 is noteworthy, although the rate of growth of fungicide sales since about 1980, expressed in percentage terms, has been even more impressive.

Precise world production figures for individual pesticides are not readily available. The FAO Yearbooks give tonnages provided for many compounds by various countries, but uniformity of presentation does not exist; some

---

* For the sake of conformity, all text values are expressed as dollars, assuming $1.8 = £1.
† A billion is defined as being 1 000 000 000 throughout this book.

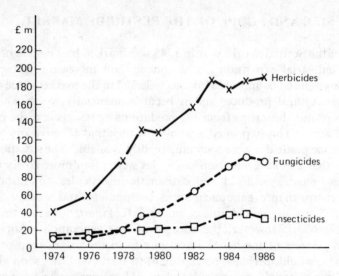

Figure 1.1   Wholesale value of UK sales of crop protection chemicals made by British manufacturers 1974–86

countries submit tonnages of formulations and others of active ingredients. Extraction of facts can be difficult, as is illustrated by the attempt by Smart (1987) to obtain data for organophosphorus compounds; Italy had submitted data to the FAO in terms of formulations, Denmark and Portugal in terms of active ingredients, and the UK had submitted no data at all.

The USA is responsible for about one-third of known world pesticide production, so breakdown of USA data could give some indication of the world pattern. Unfortunately, since about 1970, commercial secrecy has led to less and less disclosure of detailed production data, as the official statistical record shows (USDA, 1978; 1985). Instead, it is necessary to turn to a rather different criterion, namely usage (or estimates of usage) of pesticides by farmers in the USA (USDA, 1983). Such figures may distort the world situation because of local problems, especially in relation to weedkillers. Other than petroleum oils, some 225 000 tonnes of herbicides were employed; in decreasing order, the most used were alachlor, atrazine, butylate, metolachlor and trifluralin (the phenoxy group of herbicides being surprisingly low on the list). The most used fungicides, other than sulphur and copper compounds, were captan, maneb and systemic compounds. Of the insecticides, excluding petroleum oils, the ones used in greatest amounts were methyl parathion, terbufos, carbofuran and chlorpyrifos. According to McLaren (1986) the value of pesticides to the top 16 USA manufacturers in 1984 was about $6500 million. Another source of information (Agrochemical Service, produced once a year by Nat West Wood Mac) has estimated the current world market for all pesticides to be about 40 billion DM.

Eue (1985) lists the 10 leading countries in the herbicides market. The USA heads the list, possessing 46 per cent of the world herbicides market, five times the percentage contribution of the second country, France. In fact the nine most significant countries after the USA collectively share 37 per cent of the market. So, excluding the USSR and China, for which no figures seem to be available, 10 countries share 83 per cent of the herbicide market.

The post-war expansion in the development of new pesticides has probably ended, the reason being in part economic. It has been estimated that for every 8000 substances synthesised, only one is likely to be successfully marketed. Even when a winner is discovered, the cost of development is such that the innovating manufacturer is unlikely to break even financially for about a decade. Furthermore, the money tied up for these years is very great— nowadays it could exceed $18 million. Consequently, only the largest organisations are able to support the necessary research, development, toxicological studies and field trials essential to meet the stringent requirements for safety (and to demonstrate efficiency) demanded by governments in all the major pesticide markets in the world.

Finney (1988) described the prospects for sales and development of pesticides into the 1990s. By the early 1980s, commodity surpluses of several kinds were occurring in many developed countries. This resulted in decreasing farm incomes and also in millions of hectares being taken out of food production world-wide. Both of these factors have contributed to world agrochemical sales stabilising at about $20 000 million. Simultaneously, market penetration in many developed countries has, for certain crops, approached an upper limit. For example, 94 per cent of the total area used in the USA to grow soya beans is already sprayed with herbicides and 85 per cent of French vine-growing areas is already treated with fungicide. As profitability falls, agrochemical companies may be expected to invest less in new research, except in certain areas where market opportunities still exist (e.g. cost-effective nematicides, soil fungicides and substances capable of suppressing the development of resistance).

1.4 ECONOMIC ASPECTS OF PESTICIDE USAGE

On a global level it is probable that the current expenditure by farmers on pesticides is of the order of $20 000 million. In view of the fact that farmers have a reputation for hard-headedness, it must be assumed that they are convinced that this outlay provides an acceptable return on capital. Various estimates have been made which appear to demonstrate that this conviction is justified. Commonly quoted figures for benefit-to-cost ratio are four-fold overall in the USA, three-fold for cereal herbicides in West Germany and eight-fold for the control of aphids on sugar beet in West Germany (Braunholtz, 1979). Unfortunately, it is not easy to check the validity of such figures in individual cases, for each farmer's activities provide an uncontrolled experiment, and assumptions have to be made when predicting what losses a particular crop would have sustained had pesticides not been used. In an abnormally bad season, a pesticide may save the crop from being a write-off, and thus save the farmer from bankruptcy. Consequently, some farmers tend to regard money spent on pesticides as being in the same category as money spent on insurance. A slightly damaged crop (e.g. apples infested with codling moth) may be almost unmarketable, so that 'write-off', from a farmer's viewpoint, does not necessarily mean 'zero yield'. This is especially likely to be true where agreements exist for contract growing.

Despite these uncertainties, some useful guidelines exist concerning the economic use of pesticides. In general, the cost of additional control measures rapidly rises as the pest population falls; to control the final 10 per cent of a pest population costs about the same as it does to control the first 90 per cent. Therefore, unless the few surviving organisms really do cause serious damage, an uninformed farmer could well double his costs to little avail. Clearly, there is in every pest situation a break-even point where the costs of the control measures are such that they cancel out the market worth of the extra marketable produce arising from their use. This point of balance is termed the **economic threshold**. The ratio of the net profit arising from control measures to the cost of using those control measures is known as the **benefit-to-cost ratio**.

It follows from what has been said that, in an economic context, neither the percentage reduction in infestation compared to an unsprayed area nor the corresponding increase in yield are safe indices of economic acceptability. Nor, indeed, is the financial value of a yield over and above that typical of a similar untreated area. Some figures extracted from the work of Pareek *et al.* (1987) illustrate this point and are given in table 1.1. It is evident that the percentage of fruit infestation is lowest for fenvalerate and permethrin; similarly, both of these pyrethroids increased the value of the crop per hectare more than did any of the other substances employed. If, now, the cost of treatment is subtracted from the financial value of that increased yield, the net profit per hectare is obtained. This, divided by the cost of the treatment, gives the benefit-to-cost ratio, which appears in the final column. Clearly, in this example, fenvalerate gives greatest pest control and highest market value consequent on increased yield, but nevertheless compares unfavourably with carbaryl on a benefit-to-cost basis.

A similar approach by Jain *et al.* (1986) showed that, in relation to root knot nematode control in okra, a high dose of carbofuran gave a very poor return (a ratio of about 2) for all the extra work, whereas a low dose of aldicarb gave a benefit-to-cost ratio of almost 12. McGregor (1983), working upon the control of black pod disease in Papua New Guinea, used a bar-chart method to express his results in terms of economic threshold, benefits and costs.

In the case of herbicides, the problem is slightly different because the area that is not chemically treated usually has to be weeded mechanically or by

Table 1.1   **Relationship between the increase in yield resulting from the use of pesticides, the cost of treatment and the benefit-to-cost ratio (selected figures from a table in a paper by Pareek *et al.* (1987))**

Treatment	Fruit infestation (per cent)	Increase in yield of healthy fruit above control (Q/ha)	Value of increase in yield (at 150 Rs/Q)	Cost of treatment (Rs)	Net profit (Rs/ha)	Benefit-to-cost-ratio
Fenvalerate	2	42	6315	1425	4890	3.4
Permethrin	2	39	5871	1722	4148	2.4
Carbaryl	8	32	4882	453	4429	9.8
Malathion	53	6	915	313	601	1.9
Chlorpyrifos	65	5	802	990	(−188)	(loss)
Control	97	−		0		

hand. Such costs have to be offset against the costs of purchase and application of herbicides. Snaydon (1982) discussed the problem of weeds, weed control and crop yield. He concluded that too often the results of weed control are not considered in economic terms, and he quotes four cases where the average yield response was 2 per cent or less. On the other hand, Green *et al.* (1977) quote cases where the return per unit cost of herbicide was between two-fold and 13-fold in favour of the use of weedkillers.

Pesticides, together with mechanisation, fertilisers and irrigation, have helped to increase the productivity of farmworkers. In Europe and in the USA, one farmworker grows enough to feed about 60 people. Consequently, the (admittedly high) cost of growing food is shared by some 60 consumers, with the result that the average citizen of such countries may spend only 25 per cent of income on food, leaving plenty to spend on housing and luxuries. This excess spending capacity not only creates industries and employment but provides taxes to support an infrastructure that improves the quality of life— roads, sewers, piped water, hospitals and social services. It is to this all-pervading consequence of intensive agriculture, not the cost of food *per se*, that more attention should be directed (Hassall, 1985).

In contrast, where subsistence or peasant farming predominates, one farmworker may grow enough food for only 5–10 people, with the result that the cost, relative to income, is often very high for the average citizen. If 70 per cent of income is spent on food and much of the rest on other necessities, including housing, little excess purchasing power is left to sustain local manufacturing industries, or pensions, or pure water.

1.5 TOXICOLOGICAL CONSIDERATIONS

Any chemical substance may evoke one or both of two toxic effects. The first, the **acute effect**, is the one more readily comprehensible to the layman, and normally occurs shortly after contact with a *single dose* of poison. The magnitude of the effect depends on the innate toxicity of the substance and upon its method of application to a particular organism. Thus, a smaller dose of arsenious oxide than of sodium chloride will produce toxic symptoms in most animal species, and a drop of sulphuric acid is less dangerous on the skin than it is in the eye. Acute toxicity very often results from the disruption of an identifiable biochemical or physiological system and, in consequence, acute toxic responses are usually readily quantifiable.

A **chronic effect**, on the other hand, sometimes occurs when an organism is exposed to *repeated small and non-lethal doses* of a potentially harmful substance. Well known chronic responses to various irritants include silicosis, lung cancer, brain damage and necrosis of the liver or kidneys.

A frequently used measure of acute toxicity is the 50 per cent lethal dose, or LD_{50}. It is the amount of poison that kills half the organisms in a randomly chosen batch of a named species when applied in a particular way under stated experimental conditions. It is usually expressed in terms of milligrams poison per kilogram body weight of the experimental animals (mg/kg). Such a method of representation eliminates the variation of body weight between species. This is important, for most toxicological tests are done vicariously— the experimenter is not usually directly interested in the LD_{50} of a pesticide to, say, adult male rats, but employs this test species to obtain some indication of what the toxicity might have been had the substance been administered to man or to his livestock.

It will have been noted that in the previous paragraph the example referred to 'adult male' rats. This illustrates another important point, for sometimes male and female, or young and old, of a single species may vary greatly in their susceptibility to a particular poison. In the case of the rat, for example, the susceptibilities of males may sometimes be regarded as forming one distribution and those of the females a somewhat different one. Female rats are, in fact, on average more susceptible than males to a number of foreign compounds (or xenobiotics, as they are sometimes called). A useful survey of age, sex and species differences in the responses of animals to pesticides and other poisons has been provided by Brown (1980).

The LC_{50} is a somewhat similar concept to the LD_{50}. It is the concentration, usually in the air or water surrounding experimental animals, that causes 50 per cent mortality. It is therefore a convenient index for studying vapours inhaled by mammals or water-soluble pesticides in contact with fish; in neither of these cases is the amount of poison taken up by individual test organisms evident without additional investigation. In such cases, time of exposure has usually also to be taken into consideration. For example, time is an important factor in the use of phosphine to control grain weevils in stored products (Winks, 1986). Related terms are ED_{50} and EC_{50}, which are respectively, the 50 per cent effective dose and 50 per cent effective concentration, and are applicable when some criterion of toxicity other than death is adopted. The I_{50} is similarly the concentration that inhibits by 50 per cent an *in vitro* enzyme system.

To determine the LD_{50} of a substance, batches of animals are exposed to a range of doses and the percentage of organisms dying in each batch is recorded. The results can usually be represented by the (idealised) sigmoidal curve shown in figure 1.2a. The curve is steepest in the region of 50 per cent response so that a small change in concentration in this region of the curve causes a large change in percentage kill. The dose that kills half the organisms is thus a more sensitive index of toxicity than any other dose, and this is why the LD_{50} is usually adopted as a standard for comparing the relative toxicity of substances.

Acute toxicity data for numerous pesticides have been provided by several authors, including Edson *et al.* (1966) and Fairchild (1977). Some selected examples appear in table 1.2. It should be noted that compounds with *small* LD_{50} values are more toxic than those with large LD_{50} values, and that mg/kg (or µg/g) is equivalent to expressing a toxic dose as parts per million (ppm) body weight.

An empirical scale of assessment of levels of toxicity was introduced by Du Bois and Geiling (1959). It is a useful rule-of-thumb description as long as it is not raised to the level of a dogma*. On the scale they proposed, a substance with an LD_{50} of less than 1 mg/kg body weight is described as being *extremely* toxic and one with an LD_{50} lying between 1 and 50 mg/kg is *highly* toxic. The corresponding range for a *moderately* toxic material is 50 to 500 mg/kg and, for a *slightly* toxic substance, 500 to 5000 mg/kg.

In common with many other variable factors of a biological nature, the susceptibility of individuals of a population to a poison approximates to a normal distribution when the variable—in this case the applied concentration—is plotted on a logarithmic scale (figure 1.2b). As the concentration increases from $-\infty$ to $+\infty$, more and more organisms respond. For example, at -2σ, few respond, but at 0σ from the mean, half the population responds. In each case, the proportion of the whole population responding is the area to the left of the designated σ value expressed as a fraction of the total area under the curve. Thus the sigmoidal curve obtained in dosage–response tests and

---

* A limitation of this scale of assessment is illustrated by a recent incident. A cloud of hydrogen sulphide was released over a town in northern England. A police statement broadcast by the BBC said (quite rightly) that it was not dangerous. But it is interesting to speculate what the recipients of this comfort would have thought if they had been told (equally rightly) that hydrogen sulphide has an LD_{50} half that of the dreaded prussic acid, HCN! Why, then, is H_2S less dangerous than HCN in such circumstances? [*Answer*: because it has a strong smell.]

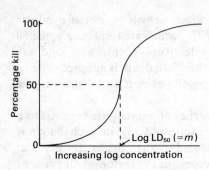
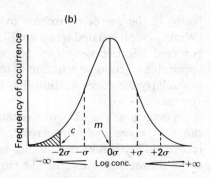

Figure 1.2   Statistical distribution of tolerances of individuals in a population to increasing amounts of a poison. (a) Relation of percentage response to the log of toxic concentration. (b) Normal distribution of responses to log concentrations

Table 1.2   Acute oral LD_{50} values of some pesticides to male rats (mg/kg)[a]

Insecticides		Fungicides		Herbicides	
Mevinphos	3	Bordeaux	700	2,4-D	300
Dichlorvos	25	Sulphur	(not toxic)	MCPA, MCPB	700
Parathion	5	Ethylmercury chloride	30	Paraquat	112
Malathion	1400	Phenylmercury chloride	60	Aminotriazole	1100
Fenitrothion	250	Thiram	375	Dalapon	6600
Azinphos methyl	10	Zineb	1000	Barban	600
Phorate	2	Captan	9000	Glyphosate	4320
Dimethoate	200	Dinocap	1000	Bromoxynil	190
Chlorfenvinphos	10	Binapacryl	150	Dinoseb	50
Bromophos	4000	Quintozene	1650	Diuron	3200
Coumaphos	100	Chloranil	4000	Linuron	1500
Fenchlorphos	1250	Dicloran	1500	Simazine	5000
Carbaryl	400	Dodine	1000	Desmetryne	1630
Other carbamates,		Benomyl	100[b]	Bromacil	5200
see table 5.1		Ethirimol	4000	Chlorpropham	3800
DDT	250	Tridemorph	650	Diallate	395
HCH (BHC)	125	Carboxin	3200	Trifluralin	5000
Methoxychlor	5000	Pyrazophos	140	Propachlor	710
Aldrin	40			Chlorthiamid	760
Pyrethrin	570				
Nicotine	70				

[a] Data (mostly for adult male rats) are from several sources, including commercial literature, Edson *et al.* (1966), Klingman and Ashton (1975), Fairchild (1977) and Brown (1980). Where discrepancies exist, lowest values are given.
[b] For wild birds.

shown in figure 1.2a is merely the summation of the area under the normal curve as the logarithm of the concentration increases from $-\infty$.

The normal distribution of tolerances allows statistical treatment of toxicity data. It enables, for example, the best estimate of the LD_{50} for a particular population to be calculated from the available data and permits confidence limits to be ascribed to it. The **probit analysis** method of Bliss, later extended by Finney (1964), is one of several methods commonly employed. In recent years the method has been computerised (see, for example, Crisp, 1982).

In contrast to acute toxic effects, which normally follow ingestion or contact with a single dose of appropriate size*, the long-term presence of small amounts of a poison in a living organism may (but does not necessarily) lead eventually to the appearance of chronic effects. The debilitating effects of blue asbestos or of coal dust are well known occupational hazards, where contact with these minerals causes physical damage to lung tissue. Possible chronic effects that could arise from long-term, low-level exposure to pesticides and many other substances include damage to the brain, to the liver (which detoxifies chemicals) or to the kidney (which attempts to excrete them in some form or other). Other possibilities are mutagenic effects (damage to chromosomes), teratogenic effects (thalidomide-like damage to the foetus), carcinogenic effects and immunosuppressive effects.

Much work has been done to discover whether repetitive intake of small quantities of highly stable and lipid-soluble substances results in indefinite linear accumulation with time. Without exception, at all doses of a magnitude at all relevant to the residue problem, a nearly constant internal level is eventually reached when an organism is exposed to a constant small daily intake. This implies that the various mechanisms which lead to detoxication and removal sooner or later balance the uptake, with the establishment of a **steady state** between uptake and elimination (figure 1.3). It is, in fact, not unusual for the presence of a poison to stimulate detoxifying systems and thus to accelerate the rate of its own decomposition or elimination. When this occurs, the internal level may actually fall after a certain period of time, even though the daily intake remains unchanged.

It is therefore evident that a constant daily intake does not cause continued accumulation until a dose capable of producing an acute response is reached. The main problem in predicting chronic toxic hazard relates to assessing the possible harmful effects of different steady-state concentrations. It is here that the scientific dilemma begins. All that can usually be said with reasonable certainty is that a higher internal steady-state concentration is likely to be more hazardous to a greater percentage of the population than is a lower internal concentration. Furthermore, when considering chronic effects that are only manifest after years of exposure, it is usually impossible to say

---

* There is really no such thing as a poisonous *substance* but only a poisonous *dose*. It is possible to kill oneself with salt if one has the mind to do so.

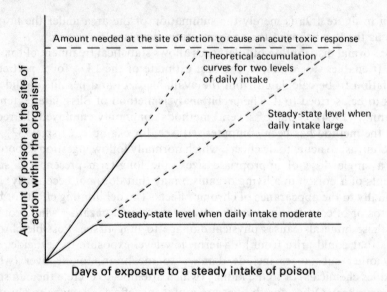

Figure 1.3 Chronic toxicity: relation of internal steady-state concentrations to levels of intake

whether or not there is a given internal concentration (and therefore a corresponding external daily dose) below which no damage whatsoever occurs in any one individual of the population. Science, in such matters, cannot prove a negative. However, even if such a dose could be demonstrated to exist for that one individual, for statistical reasons it could not be assumed that the same dose would be safe in another individual.

By the very nature of a long-term effect, it is difficult to quantify the sort of damage that is, or might be, happening in any particular circumstance. If we all died when exactly 70 years old, it could be said authoritatively that someone who died at 68 years had had his lifespan shortened. Even then, however, it might not be possible to say that this truncation resulted exclusively from, say, liver necrosis. Even if liver necrosis were the cause of death, it would probably not be possible to disentangle the individual contributions of the multifarious environmental and self-inflicted pollutants to which the deceased person had been exposed over much of a lifetime.

In order to assess the potential chronic toxic hazard of a pesticide, individuals of a suitable animal species are fed varying amounts of the substance and the highest concentration having 'no effect' on any of the organisms in that batch of animals is determined. This is known as the **threshold daily dose**. Numerous observations are made both during the long-duration feeding trial and by autopsy examination when the animals are eventually sacrificed. The kinds of data it is desirable to collect in chronic toxicity tests include changes in body weight, in the intake of food and in the composition of blood, urine and faeces. The activities of enzymes in serum, liver and other tissues are also investigated. Behavioural changes are often studied and, after death, histological examinations are made of liver, kidney, lung and brain.

In order to arrive at a figure for the **acceptable daily intake** (ADI) for man, a threshold daily dose (mg/kg day) is determined using an appropriate animal species, and this is then divided by a **safety factor**. The latter is often 100, but it may vary from 10 to 1000 or more, and it must be admitted that the reasons given for such variation sometimes seem pragmatic or arbitrary. Despite these limitations, the acceptable daily intake figures are of practical value as guidelines and are taken into consideration by the scientific advisers of many governments when tolerance limits for pesticide residues on crops are under consideration.

The safety factors mentioned above comprise two components. The first of these is for inter-species variation; it allows for the possibility that man (or, where applicable, domestic or farm animals) may be more susceptible than the test species on which the threshold daily dose was determined. Secondly, there is an intra-species component of a statistical nature. The threshold for one human being may be far lower than for another, and safety factors must take into account possible adverse effects on highly susceptible individuals rather than the response of people of average susceptibility. The ADI values of a number of pesticides have been published jointly by the World Health Organisation and the Food and Agriculture Organisation of the United Nations. Safety factors, ADIs and other aspects of the evaluation of health hazards have been reviewed by Sharratt (1977) and Vettorazzi (1977).

In practice, the ramifications of chronic effects can be wider than those just described, for the distinction between acute and chronic effects, including subclinical effects, can often be blurred. For example, animal experiments have been performed in which doses are below those that bring about immediate death but are sufficiently near to the LD_{50} to cause short-term symptoms. Not surprisingly, *post mortem* examination in such cases often reveals lesions, which are absent when long-term experiments are done at doses not far removed from the threshold daily intake (compare Ecobichon and Joy, 1982, p.101).

One situation of importance for which such animal studies can be relevant is that of a spray operator who is exposed to pesticides, gets a single or a repeated dose, develops (mild) symptoms at the time but then apparently recovers. Follow-up medical checks sometimes reveal that biochemical or physiological abnormalities may persist for years; for example, an enzyme activity may remain depressed or haematological changes may not return to normal for some time, even though no clinical symptoms are evident (Tocci *et al.*, 1969).

As well as chronic toxicity tests with animals, it is possible to use microorganisms to monitor potential pesticides and drugs for mutagenic and carcinogenic effects. Mutagenic effects are those which damage chromosomes and interfere with cell division, and, for this reason, mutagens are often also carcinogens (cancer is most prevalent in cells which divide rapidly). The **Ames test**, of which there are many modifications, is the best-known test for mutagens. Essentially, strains of, say, *Salmonella* are isolated in which a genetic change has occurred such that they cannot grow on some chosen growth medium which lacks some known growth factor. Such organisms are so chosen that, should further mutation occur (e.g. a base pair get reversed), the defective strain will regain its ability to grow on the chosen growth-factor-deficient growth medium. If such organisms are exposed to mutagens, more colonies are therefore found on the chosen growth medium than are found in the unexposed controls.

A modification of particular value in studying pesticides (which are known to be metabolised by microsomal enzymes) is the *Salmonella*/microsome mutagenicity test (McCann and Ames, 1977). An example of the use of the Ames test in pesticide work is the studies of Wildemauwe *et al.* (1983), who detected mutagenicity in dicofol, toxaphene and pirimiphos-methyl. An extra modification by Swiss workers concerned with residues in food was designed to avoid false-positive results arising from interference by other food constituents (Aeschbacher *et al.*, 1987).

A more recent concern has been the possibility that some pesticides might be immunotoxic or in some other way affect immunocompetence in higher animals. Aspects of this problem have been discussed by Devens *et al.* (1985), and an assay to screen for immunotoxic effects of pesticides has been described by Rodgers *et al.* (1986).

Finally, it is a regrettable fact that three different levels of hazard associated with pesticides are often confused by the popular media, so it is appropriate that a distinction should be drawn now. One level refers to the manufacture, transport, storage and dilution of concentrated products; incidents at this level are industrial accidents, in the same category as those which can occur in the plastics or petroleum industries. Accidents at this level can be very serious (e.g. Bhopal, Seveso).

The second relates to hazards arising at the spray-tank level, when diluted products are being applied to crops; these are analogous to risks incurred by workers in many industries (fishing, fire service, mining); as in these industries, good practice can minimise personal injury. It should be noted that, if things go wrong, the farmworker is exposed to a 'functional' concentration of the pesticide, namely one of the same order as that which is needed to kill insects, fungi or weeds. Numerous minor accidents do occur at this level, but few are fatal in developed countries where operators are trained and safety legislation is enforced (see section 1.7). In some other countries the situation is regrettably different. Also at this level of hazard are accidents resulting from the consumption of pesticide-treated grain or pulses, which, of course, are exclusively intended for sowing; in this case, too, a functional concentration is being consumed.

Thirdly, there are potential hazards associated with the presence of pesticide residues in food at the time of consumption. In most cases, residues are a small fraction of their 'functional' concentrations because they are separated in time and in space from their application—for example, seed-treated grain may be put into soil in spring whereas the crop is harvested from above ground in the autumn (Hassall, 1985). If residue levels are indeed harmful, only chronic toxic effects would be expected. It is not easy to show whether such effects do or do not occur in a small proportion of the population, but the risk is clearly minimised by ensuring that the initial application of the pesticide is done at the right time and in the right way. This can be achieved if international recommendations are followed and national legislation is enforced. These aspects of safety are described in the next two sections.

1.6 INTERNATIONAL ARRANGEMENTS RELATING TO THE SAFE USE OF PESTICIDES

In response to international concern about food quality, the United Nations established a commission to determine guidelines to safeguard the consumer and to issue certain recommendations. This commission, formed in 1962, is the Codex Alimentarius Commission and comprises about 120 member nations.

The Codex Committee on Pesticide Residues (CCPR) is one of its several committees. The governmental representatives on this committee are concerned with the impact on food quality of residues of pesticides. It is advised by a subcommittee of scientific experts. One of its functions is to agree on internationally acceptable maximum limits of pesticide residues in food, not only to safeguard the consumers but also to facilitate the movement of food across state frontiers. Clearly, if a group of nations harmonise their national legislation on pesticide residues, problems relating to levels of residues in imported commodities should not arise.

The CCPR thus establishes Codex Maximum Residue Limits (MRLs) for pesticides in foods. Essentially, the MRL for a named compound is the highest concentration that may be present on a commodity at the time of marketing. These MRLs are themselves arrived at from estimated figures for acceptable daily intakes (ADIs) for each pesticide (see section 1.5) after taking into account the proportion of each type of food in a total diet of a 'typical' consumer. Evidently, a number of snags and uncertainties are inherent in this empirical approach, but, luckily, actual residue levels are usually so far below the MRL levels that the ADI is seldom challenged. An account of the operation of the CCPR and of the methods by which MRL are set has been provided by Boardman (1986).

The first issue of the *Guide to Codex Maximum Limits for Pesticide Residues* was published in 1978 (FAO/WHO, 1978). This Codex document divides foods into classes, each of which is given a reference number suitable for computerisation. For example, A01 represents vegetables, A02 comprises fruits and A03 includes the grasses. Similarly, each pesticide (more precisely, its active ingredient) is given a code number. Thus, having established an ADI value for a particular pesticide, an MRL can be recorded for each commodity, as is illustrated in table 1.3.

Altogether, over 2000 residue–food combinations have been proposed by the CCPR. However, less than half the participating countries have so far been able to accept the recommendations. Even those countries that have notified the commission of their position have not necessarily fully accepted all the recommendations. It follows that international harmonisation is still far from complete. Consequently, international trade still runs into problems and, in some countries, consumers may well be exposed to residue intakes above ADI limits (FAO/WHO, 1985).

Obstacles inhibiting full use of Codex MRLs are of several kinds. First, national legislation or regulations may take time to be amended. Secondly, a country may fear that conformity might be to the disadvantage of local growers; for example, if the MRL for a substance is lower than the nationally used figure, a conforming substance could enter the country with ease, perhaps replacing the country's own products on its home market. Thirdly, Codex limits are based on a notion of what, in the view of experts, ought to be achievable when 'good agricultural practice' has been pursued. Unfortunately, what constitutes good agricultural practice is not uniquely definable, for such practice depends to some extent on what is possible under particular climatic and soil conditions (e.g. insect problems are often exacerbated in

Table 1.3   Partial Codex entry for fenitrothion (FAO/WHO, 1978)

ADI: 0.005 mg/kg body weight
Residue: fenitrothion plus its oxygen analogue

Classification no.	Commodity (alphabetical)	Maximum residue limit (mg/kg)
A02.1001	Apples	0.5
C	Bread (white)	0.2
A01.0404	Cabbage	0.5
B07.2500	Meat	0.05
B07.2800	Milk	0.05
A02.0910	Oranges	0.2
A01.0620	Peas	0.5
A01.0128 etc.	Potatoes	0.05

warmer climates, and greater use of insecticides may be essential). Finally, underlying any meaningful acceptance of MRLs is the prerequisite that means must exist to monitor, sample and analyse food or crops for residues. In some parts of the world appropriate laboratories to monitor residues on home-grown or imported foods may not exist, nor may the infrastructure allow representative samples to be reliably and honestly collected from docks, warehouses or fields.

The Codex Committee on Pesticide Residues has, however, responsibilities far wider than those relating to MRLs, for it issues recommendations relating to safety which cover the registration, usage, storage and analysis of pesti-cides. Associated with this work, the FAO (United Nations, Rome) issued in 1985 a series of booklets designated as 'Guidelines'. The contents of these books cover many aspects of good management of pesticides. One, for example, deals with guidelines for the registration and control of pesticides (FAO, 1985a) and another makes recommendations concerning the packaging and storage of pesticides (FAO, 1985b). A third is concerned with the disposal of waste pesticides and unwanted pesticide containers (FAO, 1985c). A publication outlining and recommending an international code of conduct for the distribution and use of pesticides also appeared in 1985 (FAO, 1985d), and in 1986 a booklet appeared giving guidelines on how to design trials to provide data for pesticide registration (FAO, 1986).

1.7 NATIONAL ARRANGEMENTS FOR PESTICIDE SAFETY

Individual countries usually require that, for registration as an approved pesticide, a formulation be tested for stated uses in the field and for various aspects of safety. When used on crops, safety aspects often include the establishment of (national) residue tolerance limits, using criteria more or less similar to those employed by the scientific advisers to the Codex Committee on Pesticide Residues. Where resources are limited, a country may adopt the Codex MRLs of appropriate compounds and use them as the national tolerance limits. Needless to say, adopting national tolerance limits is a time-consuming and deceptive exercise in futility unless the national law is backed up by effective means to enforce it (including analytical facilities).

In the USA, the Environmental Protection Agency was established in 1970, one of its functions being to take over from a pre-existing organisation the licensing and monitoring of pesticides. It has the authority to register pesticides and to assign the tolerance limits, which appear in a Federal Register of Tolerance Limits now comprising several thousand entries. The Federal Insecticide, Fungicide and Rodenticide Act (FIFRA) was rewritten in 1972 and legislated to regulate the marketing, registration and labelling of pesticides and their containers as well as to provide Federal control over the certification for competence of those who use such chemicals.

The US Food and Drugs Administration retains the responsibility to sample foods to determine levels of pesticide residues and to take enforcement action where necessary to prevent the sale of food with residues above tolerance. Problems arising as a result of inevitable delays before analytical results are available have been highlighted by the US Natural Resources Defense Council (Mott and Broad, 1984). The National Research Council is concerned with the promulgation of information relating to the safe use of pesticides. The Occupational Safety and Health Act helps to protect workers who handle poisonous chemicals. The Federal Aviation Administration controls aspects of safety relating to aerial spraying of pesticides. On the ground, transport and storage are regulated by several Acts, one of which is the Federal Environmental Pesticide Control Act. A detailed consideration of pesticide safety legislation is to be found in the *Pesticide Handbook* of the Entomological Society of America (ENTOMA, 1977; or later). Individual States in the USA have enacted legislation which controls local pesticide usage.

In Europe, the EEC is moving towards a similar approach to both that of the Codex and that of the USA. The first Directive (to sovereign Governments) was in 1981 and was concerned with the marketing of specified organochlorine and organomercury pesticides. Another Directive established tolerances for residues on fruit and vegetables. Other Directives (enacted or in the process of enactment) relate to residues on cereals and to the harmonising of pesticide registration schemes in the member States of the EEC. Such harmonisation would allow the commercial product of a company that successfully obtained EEC clearance in one country to circulate freely in all countries of the Community.

In order to be in a position to conform with the EEC Directives, the Voluntary Approval Scheme hitherto operative in the UK has been discontinued. A Food and Environment Protection Act was passed in 1985, the relevant Control of Pesticides Regulations appearing in 1986. Various restrictions and controls are being phased in, in stages. Since October 1986 only products approved by the Ministry of Agriculture can be supplied and stored; each must be appropriately labelled and only used for the specified approved uses. As from January 1987, advertising is controlled and, in addition, those who store pesticides must have a certificate of competence (or be supervised by such a person). More controls came into force in 1988; certain pesticides are only approved for use by professionals and restricted to use on certain crops and types of land. Finally, as from 1989, certificates of competence will be required by contractors applying pesticides (or be supervised by such a person). Also, as from 1989, the use of adjuvants will be controlled and tank mixing of pesticides will have to conform to published lists of permitted mixtures (BAA, 1986).

1.8 LOCAL AND PERSONAL ASPECTS OF PESTICIDE SAFETY

In most developed countries legislation has been, or is being, enacted to ensure that local storage depots are secure and that those who handle pesticides are suitably trained for the task. In such countries, farmworkers often have strong trade unions which ensure that the law is not disregarded either by workers or by their employers. Such safety does not always exist in countries with weaker mechanisms of control, poorer law enforcement or lower levels of literacy. For this reason it is appropriate to illustrate how easily things can go wrong if rules relating to storage, handling and spraying are not obeyed.

Except where strong alternative controls exist, it is highly desirable that district depots should hold stocks of pesticides and distribute them to individual farmers (the latter, ideally, being given permission by a trained official to purchase formulations containing named active ingredients only). This obvious precaution can be blatantly disregarded; for example, the author has seen home-labelled bottles of aldrin concentrate on shelves, above eye-level, in a food shop in a developing country. Such products were side by side with food, could be purchased by anyone, and if an unskilled shop assistant spilt the contents of such a bottle in his eye he would die; similarly, if the contents of a spilt bottle landed on pulses seen drying on the floor, the consequences to the food purchaser could be disastrous. Frankly, while such practices continue, thoughts about residue laboratories to enforce Codex residue limits are a nonsense. Methods of preventing storage emergencies have been published by the British Agrochemicals Association (BAA, 1985).

When handling concentrated pesticides or diluting them to spray-tank concentrations, it is essential to wear suitable dress and to wash thoroughly as soon afterwards as is possible. In many countries the protection that must be provided for workers handling named substances is dictated by statute. In any case, it is most desirable always to wear overalls, eye-shields and gloves; for more toxic or volatile substances respirators may also be essential. Work by Putnam *et al.* (1983) showed the importance of wearing gloves when making dilutions; working with nitrofen, they showed that the amount entering the body when handling a wettable powder formulation was 220 times greater if gloves were not worn than when they were worn. They also found that the risk arising from the dilution of an emulsifiable concentrate was reduced to one-tenth if the concentrate was pumped from container to tank instead of poured into it.

The safe disposal of a container emptied of its contents is clearly of importance to avoid risks to farm personnel, animals, wildlife and water-courses. Essentially, there should never be such a thing as a dirty, empty, discarded can or drum. When empty, a container should be washed with water and the contents added to the spray tank. This obvious and economically desirable precaution is often disregarded in all countries, but especially in developing countries. The author has seen a pile of containers 3 m high and

5 m long, dripping liquid organophosphorus insecticide and evaporating unpleasant vapour into the air of a North African citrus grove.

The precautions to take when actually applying pesticides are obvious; namely, no drinking, smoking or eating during the operation. Equally obviously, all animals and non-essential personnel should be kept out of the area being treated. Similarly, aircraft used for spraying should never overfly inhabited areas but, if need be, make a detour after take-off and upon landing. All spray operators should not only wash but bathe immediately a pesticide application is completed. The British Agrochemicals Association have issued booklets that contain guidelines for applying crop protection chemicals (BAA, 1987b).

The precautions recommended above do not constitute a complete list. A more comprehensive list concerning storage, spillage, weather conditions and special precautions is to be found at the beginning of the (now defunct) list of *Approved Products for Farmers and Growers* (MAFF, 1985). The author would, however, like to add a cautionary footnote. Many accidents involving pesticides arise from petty dishonesty. Only too distressingly often an employee has transferred pesticide to an empty bottle (e.g. a soft-drink bottle emptied at lunchtime), taken it home, placed it within reach of a child who has drunk the 'lemonade' father brought home from work.

Several sources of information exist on the subjects of occupational hazards and on the medical procedures to be adopted should accidents occur; the Approved Products brochure mentioned above is one of them (MAFF, 1985). One of the major risks nowadays is exposure of farmworkers to organophosphorus insecticides; the regulation of such residues for farmworker protection has been reviewed by Popendorf and Leffingwell (1982). Occupational hazards relating to the use of pesticides have been collated by Turnbull (1985). Finally, the British Department of Health and Social Security has issued notes for the guidance of medical practitioners who encounter cases of pesticide poisoning (DHSS, undated).

REFERENCES

Aeschbacher, H. U., Wolleb, U. and Porchet, L. (1987). *J. Fd Safety*, **8**, 167
BAA (1985). *Preventing Storage Emergencies*. British Agrochemical Association, 4 Lincoln Court, Lincoln Rd, Peterborough PE1 2RP, UK
BAA (1986). *Phasing-in of EEC Regulations* (four-page booklet). Address as above
BAA (1987a). *British Agrochemicals Association, Annual Report and Handbook, 1986/1987*. Address as above
BAA (1987b). *Guidelines for Applying Crop Protection Chemicals* (one booklet for ground crops and another for fruit). Address as above
Boardman, R. (1986). *Pesticides in World Agriculture*. Macmillan, Basingstoke
Braunholtz, J. T. (1979). *Chem. Ind.*, no. 22, Nov. 17
Brown, V. K. (1980). *Acute Toxicity in Theory and Practice*. Wiley, Chichester

Crisp, C. E. (1982). In *Biodegradation of Pesticides*, eds F. Matsumura and K. Murti. Plenum, New York

Devens, B. H., Grayson, M. H., Imamura, T. and Rodgers, K. E. (1985). *Pestic. Biochem. Physiol.*, **24**, 251

DHSS (undated). *Pesticide Poisoning: Notes for the Guidance of Medical Practitioners.* HMSO, London

Du Bois, K. P. and Geiling, E. M. K. (1959). *Textbook of Toxicology.* Oxford Univ. Press, Oxford

Ecobichon, D. J. and Joy, R. M. (1982). *Pesticides and Neurological Diseases.* CRC Press, Boca Raton, FL

Edson, E. F., Sanderson, D. M. and Noakes, D. N. (1966). *Wld Rev. Pest Control*, **5**, 143

ENTOMA (1977). *Pesticide Handbook, 27th Edition for the Year 1977/78.* Entomological Society of America, 4603 Calvert Rd, Box AJ, College Park, Maryland 20740, USA

Eue, L. (1985). *Weed Sci.*, **34**, 155

Fairchild, E. J. (1977). *Agricultural Chemicals and Pesticides: A Sub-file of the Registry of Toxic Effects of Chemical Substances.* US Dept Health, Education and Welfare, Public Health Service, Center for Disease Control, National Institute for Occupational Safety and Health, Washington DC, USA

FAO (1985a). *Guidelines for the Registration and Control of Pesticides.* FAO, Rome

FAO (1985b). *Guidelines for the Packaging and Storage of Pesticides.* FAO, Rome

FAO (1985c) *Guidelines for the Disposal of Waste Pesticide and Pesticide Containers on the Farm.* FAO, Rome

FAO (1985d). *International Code of Conduct on the Distribution and Use of Pesticides.* Annex to Resolution/85, C85/25—Rev.1. FAO, Rome

FAO (1986). *Pesticide Residue Trials to Provide Data for the Registration of Pesticides and the Establishment of Maximum Residue Limits.* FAO, Rome

FAO/WHO (1978). *Joint FAO/WHO Food Standards Programme. Codex Alimentarius Commission*, CAC/PR 1–1978, *Guide to Codex Maximum Limits for Pesticide Residues*, First Issue, FAO, Rome

FAO/WHO (1985). *Report of the 16th Session of the Codex Alimentarius Commission*, Geneva, 1985, published as Alinorm 85/24A—Add. 2, *Recommended National Regulatory Practices to Facilitate Acceptance and Use of Codex Maximum Limits for Pesticide Residues in Food.* FAO, Rome

Finney, D. J. (1964). *Probit Analysis*, 2nd edn. Cambridge Univ. Press, Cambridge

Finney, J. R. (1988). *Proc. Br. Crop Prot. Conf., Pests and Diseases*, p. 3

Green, M. B., Hartley, G. S. and West, T. F. (1977). *Chemicals for Crop Protection and Pest Control.* Pergamon, Oxford

Hassall, K. A. (1969). *World Crop Protection*, vol. 2, *Pesticides* (see p. 16). Iliffe, London

Hassall, K. A. (1985). *Environmentalist*, **5**, 105

Horsfall, J. G. (1956). *Principles of Fungicidal Action.* Chronica Botanica, Waltham, MA

ICI (1986). *Force Technical Data; Pyrethroid Soil Insecticide PP993.* Imperial Chemical Industries, Plant Protection Division, Fernhurst, Haslemere, Surrey GU27 3JE, UK

Jain, R. K., Paruthi, I. J., Gupta, D. C. and Dhanker, B. S. (1986). *Trop. Pest Managem.*, **33**, 192

Klingman, G. C. and Ashton, F. M. (1975). *Weed Science: Principles and Practices.* Wiley, New York

McCann, J. and Ames, B. N. (1977). In *Origins of Human Cancer*, eds H. H. Hiatt, J. D. Watson and J. A. Winsten, p. 143. Cold Spring Harbor Lab., New York

McGregor, A. J. (1983). *Trop. Pest Managem.*, **29**, 129

McLaren, J. S. (1986). *Pestic. Sci.*, **17**, 559

MAFF (1985). *Ministry of Agriculture, Fisheries and Food, UK Approved Products for Farmers and Growers*, Reference Book 380 (85). HMSO, London

Mott, L. and Broad, M. (1984). *Pesticides in Food: What the Public Needs to Know.* Natural Resources Defense Council Inc., 25 Kearny St, San Francisco, USA

Ordish, G. (1976). *The Constant Pest.* Peter Davies, London

Pareek, B. L., Sharma, G. R. and Bhatnagar, K. N. (1987). *Trop. Pest Managem.*, **33**, 192

Popendorf, W. J. and Leffingwell, J. T. (1982). *Res. Rev.*, **82**, 125

Putnam, A. R., Willis, M. D., Binning, L. K. and Boldt, P. F. (1983). *J. Agric. Fd Chem.*, **31**, 645

Rodgers, K. E., Leung, N., Imamura, T. and Devens, B. H. (1986). *Pestic. Biochem. Physiol.*, **26**, 292

Sharratt, M. (1977). *The Evaluation of Toxicological Data for the Protection of Public Health*, p. 105. Published for the Commission of the European Communities. Pergamon, Oxford

Smart, N. A. (1987). *Res. Rev.*, **98**, 99

Snaydon, R. W. (1982). *Proc. Br. Crop Prot. Conf., Weeds*, p. 729

Tocci, P. M., Mann, J. B., Davies, J. E. and Edmundson, W. F. (1969). *Ind. Med.*, **38**, 188

Turnbull, G. T. (1985). *Occupational Hazards of Pesticide Use.* Taylor and Francis, London

USDA (1978). *Agric. Statist.* (see pp. 470, 471). United States Department of Agriculture, Washington DC

USDA (1983). *Outlook and Situation.* United States Department of Agriculture, Washington DC

USDA (1985). *Agric. Statist.* (see p. 419). United States Department of Agriculture, Washington DC

Vettorazzi, G. (1977). *The Evaluation of Toxicological Data for the Protection of Public Health*, p. 207. Published for the Commission of the European Communities. Pergamon, Oxford

Wheatley, G. A. (1987). *Ann. Appl. Biol.*, **111**, 1

Wildemauwe, C., Lontier, J.-F., Schoofs, L. and van Larebeker, N. (1983). *Res. Rev.*, **89**, 129

Winks, R. G. (1986). *J. Stored Prod. Res.*, **22**, 85

2 Physicochemical aspects of pesticide formulation and application

2.1 TARGET SURFACES FOR PESTICIDE APPLICATIONS

The cuticle of plant leaves is frequently treated with pesticidal sprays or dusts. It may be a target by proxy, as when the purpose of spraying is to hit insects or fungi that live on or in the crop plants. Alternatively, leaf cuticle may be a direct target, an *intermediate* barrier that must be penetrated before a herbicide can reach its ultimate objective such as weed chloroplasts or meristems. Similarly, the cuticle of an insect represents an intermediate target for an insecticide, a barrier that must be reached and breached before the active ingredient can penetrate to its site of action, which is frequently some part of the nervous system. Fungal hyphal walls and spore walls are similarly intermediate targets for fungicides.

Soil is structurally a very different intermediate target. Rich in silicates, a typical soil in some ways resembles an ion-exchange column with fixed negative charges. By successive adsorption and elution, many substances move downwards at different rates. Damp soil contains a continuous aqueous phase and persistence in soil of a pesticide of low aqueous solubility is often (but not always) greater than that of one that is highly soluble. The situation is, however, usually more complex than this. For example, soil contains air spaces, and the volatility of the active ingredient may be a factor of importance. The chemical stability of the pesticide in the presence of water and its biochemical stability in the presence of soil microorganisms must also be taken into consideration. A proportion of all compounds applied to soil is strongly bound within the latticework of clay minerals and adsorbed onto soil organic matter.

The physicochemical characteristics of waxy cuticular surfaces contrast with those of soils. Consequently, the conditions which favour deposition and persistence of a particular pesticide on a leaf may be different from those which are most favourable for its use in soil. This is one reason why a pesticide manufacturer may **formulate** the same active ingredient in a variety of ways (section 2.4).

In this chapter, the structure of plant leaf cuticle and insect cuticle will be considered; factors associated with soil structure are more conveniently discussed in chapter 13. Later sections of the present chapter deal with application methods in relation to the physical state of the application system. To ensure that the best use is made of an active ingredient, it is often necessary to add supplementary substances to mixtures containing such ingredients. The closing sections of the chapter describe the main groups of these supplements or adjuvants and their mode of action.

2.2 PLANT LEAF CUTICLE

An important physical characteristic of the surface of foliage is the existence of a more or less substantial waxy, and therefore hydrophobic, barrier, which diminishes water loss and simultaneously restricts access of aqueous solutions (figure 2.1). This protective layer is deposited outside the cellulose walls of epidermal cells and merges into them. It varies in thickness and composition in different plant species and in different parts of the same plant.

Young parenchymatous cells are initially separated by a middle lamella comprising salts of pectic acid. The primary cell wall is thin and largely consists of cellulose and pectin (a methyl ester of pectic acid). Consequently, few intermolecular ionic forces exist and the young cell wall is elastic, with macromolecular chains able to glide over one another to accommodate extension growth. The thicker secondary cell wall becomes increasingly important as the cell ages, providing strength at the expense of flexibility. Although variable in composition, it contains cellulose, pectins, pectates and hemicelluloses. Unless 'waterproofed' in some way, even secondary cell walls are permeable to water and probably to most substances dissolved in it. Inside the cell wall lies the delicate plasmalemma, a lipoprotein membrane that normally prevents cell solutes from escaping outwards.

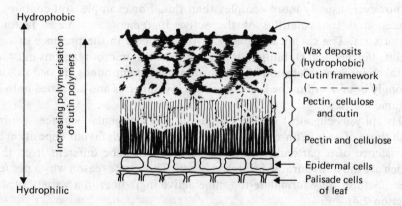

Figure 2.1   Structure of leaf cuticle in transverse section (after Hassall 1969)

Figure 2.1 shows diagrammatically the structure of plant leaf cuticle. Cuticle is not an amorphous structure but comprises several components organised into a latticework of considerable complexity, and usually between 5 and 20 μm in thickness. A major component of the non-polar region is cutin; this forms a sponge-like lattice, within the compartments of which platelets of waxy material are deposited. Cutin is a crosslinked polymer of various hydroxy and carboxylic acids, insoluble in most solvents. The degree of polymerisation varies, being highest towards the outside of the leaf and least where the cuticle merges into the cellulose cell wall. Permeability to water is inversely correlated with the degree of polymerisation, so the internal cutin is more permeable to aqueous solutions than is the cutin towards the outside.

Cuticular wax is variable in composition, but in most plants is predominantly composed of straight-chain alkanes or alkanes carrying terminal hydroxyl or carboxyl groups. The hydrocarbons normally contain an odd number of carbon atoms, 21–35 altogether, whereas the acids and alcohols contain even numbers of carbon atoms, the commonest numbers being 20–24. The outermost layer of the cuticle is often a very thin deposit of soft wax, of microcrystals, or of both; this layer, when present, is readily damaged by external solvents. Most of the cuticular wax is, however, embedded in the interstices of the outer region of the cuticle and is not readily removed by immersing the leaf in organic solvents.

Stomata, trichomes (hairs) and hydathode channels are intrusive structures in the cuticles of most leaves. Hydathodes provide channels through the cuticle along which outward-moving water can pass, but they probably do not play an important role in the uptake of pesticidal solutions. Hairs are of some importance in relation to the availability of pesticides, in that they can, when present at appropriate density, form a mesh which prevents spray droplets from running off the leaf, and so allows a toxicant to be deposited in larger amounts than it would be on glabrous leaves. Stomata do not provide entry points for aqueous solutions, or for solutions containing only small quantities of detergents. Some oily liquids can, however, enter the stomata, probably via the sensitive guard cells, and cause extensive damage to the cells lining the stomatal cavity.

The preceding paragraphs and figure 2.1 show that leaf cuticle is a system in which hydrophilic and hydrophobic properties are elegantly balanced. This balance is of importance in the chemistry of crop protection, for it implies that the undamaged cuticle is normally a barrier to the ready ingress of ions and of most water-soluble molecules. Conversely, however, small non-polar molecules, whether of active ingredient or of an oily carrier containing dissolved lipophilic toxicant, might well gain access to the outer region of the cuticle by physical sorption. This enables an absorbed pesticidal deposit to persist on the plant under conditions where wind and rain would remove a superficial deposit.

Since pesticides of different kinds are applied to foliage for different reasons, the degree of penetration that is desirable also varies. Sometimes, a measure of sorption is desirable for insecticides and fungicides (e.g. for malathion, section 4.8). Such local internal movement—a 'blotting-paper' effect—in the cuticular wax is sometimes known as **loco-systemic** or **persistent** contact action. In contrast, some substances remain as superficial deposits possessing an entirely local **contact** action, while others, with a **systemic** action, penetrate right through the cuticle and are transported around the plant.

Leaf cuticle represents a macroscopic barrier to the free movement of many pesticides, but there are ubiquitous, if less obvious, microbarriers to be surmounted. These are the lipoprotein membranes which surround all living cells. They are sometimes regarded as consisting of lipoprotein double layers (protein, lipid, lipid, protein), although more recent evidence favours a more indefinite fluid membrane. The fluid membrane is visualised as being composed of lipid penetrated in places by proteinaceous 'plugs' as well as being, in part, coated with protein. Such membranes are dynamically semipermeable, their properties varying with the physiological state of the cell. They probably act as barriers to the free entry of many types of poisons, although selective permeability is lost if they are damaged by intruding molecules.

Numerous factors affect the foliar absorption and redistribution of pesticides, but their effects can seldom be fully quantified. Many aspects of the physical chemistry of penetration into higher plants have been described in detail in the monograph by Hartley and Graham-Bryce (1980, pp. 544–657). More recently, the work of Stevens *et al.* (1988) is typical of many studies to be found in the literature. In their article, the second of a series, these authors measured the uptake by the foliage of four crops of 14 pesticides dissolved in aqueous acetone. Only 4 per cent (mean value) entered the leaves in the two or three minutes that it took for the deposited droplets to evaporate to dryness; on the other hand, the percentage of the applied dose in leaves 24 h after application varied from 1 to 97 per cent. Uptake usually decreased as the melting point increased; it also tended to decrease as the aqueous solubility of the pesticide increased. Furthermore, when a high level of uptake was achieved, it was usually found that the substance possessed an oil/water partition coefficient, P, that was neither very large nor very small (optimal log $P = 0$–2.0).

2.3 THE INSECT INTEGUMENT

The outermost living layer of the insect body is called the **epidermis**. It secretes a non-living, but structured, protective **cuticle** on its outer surface. The cuticle and epidermis, together with any modified epidermal structures within them, are known as the insect integument (figure 2.2).

The insect cuticle covers the whole exterior of the insect body and also lines

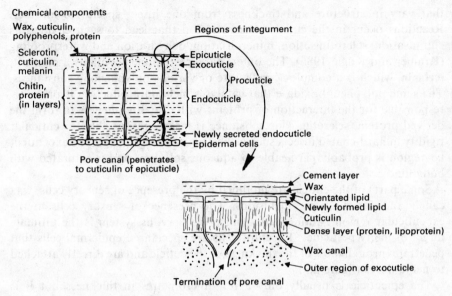

Figure 2.2 Structure of insect integument in transverse section, with enlargement of epicuticular region (from Hassall 1969)

the gut and the cavities of the spiracles, although its thickness varies greatly from insect to insect and from one part of an insect to another. It is a secretion, rich in proteins, and in most insects comprises two main regions. These are the **procuticle**, a thick inner layer consisting largely of glycoproteins, chitin and tanning agents, and the **epicuticle**, a thin outer layer that is rich in lipids and lipoproteins.

The procuticle is secreted in distinct layers by the epidermal cells and often represents 90 per cent or more of the total thickness of the cuticle. **Chitin** is its most distinctive component and may account for 60 per cent of the total cuticular weight. It is a stable and water-insoluble polymer of several hundred residues of *N*-acetylglucosamine. It contains β-linkages similar to those that render molecules of cellulose resistant to attack by most enzymes (exceptions are some bacterial hydrolases). Chitin, together with sclerotinised proteins, helps to provide strength while preserving a measure of flexibility to the insect's exoskeleton. Chitin is, however, not responsible for the impermeability of cuticle to many types of water-soluble compounds. Such impermeability is largely a consequence of the presence of wax in the extremely thin layer of the epicuticle (figure 2.2).

The procuticle can conveniently be considered as comprising a more hydrophilic inner region of **endocuticle** and a more lipophilic outer region of **exocuticle**, although it is, in fact, a single entity, consisting of merging layers that vary in structure and thickness from one insect species to another. Reactions occur in the cuticle after secretion that lead to such changes as chitinisation, sclerotinisation, mineralisation, dehydration and waterproofing (Kramer and Koga, 1986). The outer, darker exocuticle contains a pigment, **melanin**, which is a complex condensate of various polyphenolic substances. The same polyphenol oxidase that catalyses melanin production is probably responsible for the interaction of proteins with dihydric phenols to form the derived protein, **sclerotin**. This substance is largely responsible for cuticular rigidity in hard-coated insects such as beetles. Although tough, the exocuticular region is probably permeable to aqueous solutions and is saturated with body fluid.

Some parts of the cuticle are modified by the presence of sensory cells, wax canals and various other inclusions. The presence of sensory cells in the exocuticular region is noteworthy, since the nervous system is the ultimate target of many pesticides. Receptor cells are specialised epidermal cells that penetrate through most of the thickness of the cuticle and are directly attached to nerve fibres (figure 2.3).

The epicuticle is usually only a few micrometres in thickness but it is nevertheless the part of the cuticle of greatest significance in insecticide chemistry. Two of the three main regions of a typical epicuticle (figure 2.2) are extremely lipophilic and have no counterpart in the skins of vertebrates. The outermost cement layer is not continuous over the whole waxy surface and is sometimes entirely absent. It is only about 0.1 μm thick and consists of highly tanned lipoproteins.

The waxes in the central layer of the epicuticle are of crucial importance in relation to insecticide uptake and selectivity, for they are largely responsible for the water-impervious nature of the total cuticle. Waxes of different chemical composition, and therefore possessing different physicochemical properties, are present in different organisms. Such differences could well determine how readily an insecticide penetrates the cuticle of a particular sort of insect at some stated temperature. The wax of the cockroach epicuticle, for example, melts at 30°C, while that of the blood-sucking bug, *Rhodnius*

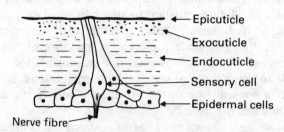

Figure 2.3 Modification of insect cuticle in the region of a sensory cell (from Hassall 1969)

prolixus, melts above 50°C. The ability of a lipid-soluble substance to penetrate into these two species of insect might therefore be expected to differ considerably at, say, 40°C.

The inner layer of the epicuticle is penetrated by wax canals that, via the wider pore canals, penetrate right through the procuticle down to the epidermal cells. It is through these that the wax originating from the (living) epidermal cells is eventually deposited in the wax layer of the epicuticle. This inner layer consists mainly of protein but it is also rich in polyphenols and cuticulin. The latter is a lipoprotein tanned with quinones and polyphenols.

It will be evident from the foregoing account that the insect cuticle in some ways resembles plant cuticle. In both cases, the inner layer of the protective barrier is less waxy, less rich in lipoprotein and less cross-polymerised than the outer region, and is more or less freely permeable to water and to solutes dissolved in it. The lipid, hydrophobic nature of the outermost layers of both leaf and insect cuticles is of importance in plant protection chemistry, for many pesticides, when applied to leaves, are suspended or dissolved in water. A 'water-off-a-duck's-back' problem can clearly arise in such circumstances and is overcome by formulating in the presence of surfactants (section 2.10).

There can be no doubt about the ease with which certain insecticides in suitable formulation can gain access to the bodies of many insects. As well as the remarkable and nearly instantaneous knock-down effect of natural pyrethroids (section 7.3), a comparison of the LD_{50} values of insecticides applied topically and by injection, first to insects and then to mammals, shows that, with a few exceptions, insect cuticle gives little protection against oil-soluble substances. Thus the values for the ratio

$$\frac{\text{Cuticular (or Dermal) } LD_{50} \text{ (ppm body weight of insect (or mammal))}}{LD_{50} \text{ by injection (ppm body weight of insect (or mammal))}}$$

$$= \frac{C \text{ (or } D)}{I}$$

are often small for insects (C/I), whereas the D/I values for mammals are frequently many times larger. For example, the C/I ratio for DDT applied to cockroaches is about 1.5 but the D/I ratio for rats is about 167. For lindane, the C/I ratio for the cockroach is 1.2 whereas the D/I ratio is 14 for the rat and 30 for the rabbit. Again, the C/I ratio found when pyrethrins are applied to the cockroach or Japanese beetle is about 1.0 whereas the D/I value when applied to the rat is approximately 9 (Edson *et al.*, 1966; Metcalf, 1955).

2.4 PESTICIDE FORMULATION AND STATE OF APPLICATION

With the exception of many substances used as fumigants, few active ingredients can be conveniently and effectively used without subjecting them to some grinding, mixing or dissolving process. The preparation of the active material in a form convenient for its intended use is known as **formulation**. Most active ingredients are biologically very active and it would be difficult to spread them evenly over a field at a rate of less than about a kilogram per hectare if they were not diluted in some way. In addition, many are greasy, organic substances insoluble in water, so simply mixing such substances with water in the spray-tank would be very inefficient. A common maxim is that no active ingredient can perform more adequately in the field than its method of formulation will allow.

Furmidge, a leading British formulation scientist, defined formulation in the following way: 'formulation is a vehicle which allows the active ingredient to be transported to its site of action in the biological system that is to be modified or destroyed' (Furmidge, 1982). The formulator must always have in mind the 'availability' factors mentioned above (the substance must not separate out before use, it must reach the surface to be sprayed and some of it must stay there in a suitably dispersed form). In addition, however, the formulator must never disregard the complications or hazards the formulation could cause during its manufacture, its transportation, its storage and its application. Hence formulation may be influenced by toxicity, flammability, volatility, etc., and thus formulation and packaging frequently need to be carefully planned as a joint concept.

In later sections, some of the principal methods of formulation will be described in more detail. Briefly, however, an active ingredient (AI, or sometimes a.i.) may be applied in the dry state, or in a liquid phase, or as a vapour. It should be noted that the effective state of the active ingredient at the time of application, or indeed at the time of attacking the target organism, has little to do with its own physical state before formulation. Thus a liquid AI may be sorbed onto a solid support and a solid active ingredient may be dissolved in a liquid, while several soil-acting pesticides possess a fumigant action in the soil.

When applied in the dry state, the AI may be formulated as a **dust** or as **granules** or **pellets**. When the AI is applied in the presence of a liquid (i.e. as a spray), water is usually one of the liquids present. For this purpose two major formulations are **wettable powders** (WP) and **emulsifiable concentrates** (EC). In addition, a few pesticides are sufficiently soluble in water to be usable as an **aqueous solution** and others can be formulated as **suspension concentrates** (SC), which flow readily when mixed with water in the spray-tank. Increasingly, low-volume applications are becoming more popular, and this involves a rather different formulation technology. Sometimes the active ingredient may be dissolved in a non-aqueous liquid (to avoid hydrolysis before use). The formulation is either used without any further dilution or else is such that the solvent mixes with water when added to a small amount of it.

Many thousands of different formulations made by 27 of the major USA and European pesticide companies are listed in a *Crop Protection Chemicals*

Reference Book (Anon, 1988). Each has an Environmental Protection Agency registration number and information is given on the percentage of active ingredient and on the nature of inert ingredients. Another useful source of information, offering advice on formulation to officials in countries that import active ingredients in order to formulate them locally, has been issued by the United Nations (UNIDO, 1983).

2.5 FUMIGATION

When an active ingredient is applied as a vapour, the process is termed **fumigation**. Within moderate limits, the concentration (c) required for a given level of response is inversely related to the time (t) of exposure; therefore,

$$c \times t = \text{constant} \tag{2.1}$$

The advantage of using a toxicant in the form of a vapour is that it can penetrate to every crevice of a system that constitutes a continuous gaseous phase. However, the successful use of fumigants also implies the requirement for an enclosed space; once that enclosed space is opened up, the toxic vapour rapidly disperses. This is not necessarily a disadvantage, for a notable use of fumigants is to protect food during storage and transportation. Holds of ships and freight wagons can be readily sealed, and since such vehicles often contain foodstuffs on their way to market, the use of a non-persistent active ingredient (e.g. methyl bromide) is an advantage in that it presents a low residue hazard to the consumer.

The need for an enclosed space limits the usefulness of fumigation in the protection of growing crops, but fumigation of greenhouses is of considerable value to horticulturists. As well as using true gases or vapours, it is possible to place volatile solids upon the steam pipes in greenhouses. The solid then volatilises to form a vapour, which usually condenses to a suspension of colloidal solid particles; this has almost the same penetrative power as a true vapour. The 'false fumigant' condition can also be achieved by smoke generators; the oxidant in smoke generators is often a carbohydrate and a chlorate. Active ingredients that have been formulated in this way include lindane, captan, azobenzene and pyrethroids. Similarly, aerosol preparations produce a suspension of tiny droplets of liquid and this mist also simulates the true gaseous state. For the fumigation of grain, 'fumigation tablets' can sometimes be used. An example is aluminium phosphide, which slowly emits phosphine (PH_3) on contact with the moist atmosphere in a sealed grain store.

Soil restricts the diffusion of volatile toxicants and it is possible to fumigate soil by the use of a special injection device, which can be plunged into the soil at regular intervals of distance and delivers a predetermined dose of a volatile liquid to a specified depth. Partial soil sterilants such as 'D-D' mixture (dichloropropene plus dichloropropane) and dibromochloropropane can be administered to soil in this way, to control some nematodes and soil fungi.

Some compounds of relatively low volatility are so toxic that they are able to vaporise in the soil air space to an extent that enables them to reach a concentration great enough to kill soil pests by vapour contact. Both aldrin and lindane (chapter 6) probably control wireworms and leatherjackets by a predominantly fumigant action. Triallate may similarly kill wild oats by fumigant action (chapter 16).

Aerosols that contain pesticides are commonly employed by home gardeners. Pyrethroid aerosols are used in the home against flies and mosquitoes, and malathion and pirimicarb aerosols are also used for small-scale application purposes. In principle, the active ingredient is dissolved in a solvent and the resulting solution is atomised through a jet by means of a gas under pressure or a liquid that is gaseous at atmospheric pressure. Originally, a common formulation contained 1–10 per cent active ingredient, 1–10 per cent kerosene (or other high-boiling-point solvent) and about 80–98 per cent w/v of a fluorocarbon propellant. The mixture was enclosed in a container under pressure exerted by the vapour of the fluorocarbon. Nowadays the fluorocarbon is usually replaced, for environmental reasons, with another volatile liquid such as butane or, more usually, by compressed carbon dioxide, which is non-flammable. In the former case a low-boiling-point hydrocarbon replaces the volume originally occupied by the fluorocarbon; upon release through the jet the low-boiling-point solvent evaporates, leaving either a colloidal suspension of the active ingredient or a mist comprising minute droplets of the active ingredient dissolved in the high-boiling-point solvent.

2.6 APPLICATION OF SOLIDS AS DUSTS OR AS GRANULES

The preparation of pesticidal **dusts** or **powders** has been described by Polon (1973). Usually, a suitable sorptive material is impregnated with a concentrated solution of the pesticide. The solvent is then evaporated and the powder diluted with a large bulk of the same sorptive substance. To minimise transportation costs, the process may be done in two stages, the primary concentrated dust being shipped to a local depot prior to secondary dilution and packaging. An alternative method of preparation is to mill 1–10 per cent of the active ingredient with the sorptive diluent.

The minerals whose particles are impregnated with pesticides are of two kinds. The **clays** include kaolinite and attapulgite (fuller's earth) and the **silicas** include talc, diatomite and pumice. Such absorptive diluents are often referred to as **fillers** or **carriers**. Most dusts are so prepared that almost all the particles are less than 50 μm diameter and the majority normally lie within the range of 3 to 30 μm. Although small particles are often more efficient than larger ones, they are also a greater inhalation hazard, and suitable face masks should be worn by all who handle dry powders (mineral particles may be abrasively damaging to lung epithelia, even if the pesticide is innocuous).

The application of dusts to foliage, in contrast to their use for soil or seed treatment, is not often done on a large scale. The reason for this is that not more than 10–20 per cent of the applied material normally adheres to dry foliage, although retention is much improved if the dust is applied when the plant leaves are damp with dew. Other problems relate to the tendency for dusts to be blown to neighbouring crops in all but the calmest weather, and to the tendency for the particles to cake under humid conditions. In addition, deposited dusts are often vulnerable to wind and rain occurring shortly after application, although small particles ($<$ 10 μm) adhere much more tenaciously than large ones.

In countries where water is scarce and the weather predictable, dusting may be the preferred method of foliage application. Dusting appliances are usually turbine blowers, which are relatively light, cheap and manoeuvrable compared to medium-volume spray machines, and the process of dusting is usually more rapid than that of spraying a similar acreage. However, fine particles tend to clump together when blasted out of a dusting machine, and technical difficulties exist in designing dusting machines that dispense powder evenly.

The method of formulation may greatly influence the effectiveness of the dust, for, within reasonable limits, the number of particles per unit area of foliage is more important than the weight of active ingredient per unit area. Consequently, a finely ground mixture of toxicant with a suitable diluent operates more efficiently than one that is less finely milled or less well mixed. On the other hand, particles smaller than about 20 μm may not settle out on warm days because of the effect of convection currents, and electrical forces may influence, favourably or adversely, the foliar deposition and retention of particles.

A recent example of the satisfactory use of a dust for pest control has been reported by Al-Samarraie *et al.* (1989). To control the lesser date moth (*Batrachedra amydraula*), these authors used a dust comprising a 1:1 mixture of wheat flour and pollen grains, to which any one of several active ingredients was added. The preparation was dusted on to the female clusters of date palms at the time of pollination. Fenitrothion and chlorpyrifos proved to be the most effective of the active ingredients employed and the method of application was claimed to be less environmentally polluting than was the use of high-pressure sprays.

Pesticidal dusts are often applied to soils. Particle size may also be significant for dusts used in this way since the rate of volatilisation of a substance with an appreciable vapour pressure increases with the degree of dispersion. As was seen above, some dusts applied to soils function, at least in part, by evaporation of the active ingredient into the soil air spaces, and, for all substances, dispersion is improved by decrease in particle size. Many insecticides and soil-acting herbicides can be applied in this way. In some cases the dust is sprinkled in trenches before placing tubers (e.g. potatoes) or in holes before transplanting seedlings (e.g. brassicas). In others, the dust is scattered around row crops (e.g. for control of carrot root fly). Some insecticides and herbicides are dispersed as dusts on the surface of the soil and then tined into the soil to an appropriate depth. Dusts may well be more convenient than surface-applied sprays for many of these purposes, and most of the disadvantages associated with foliage application of dusts are not applicable.

Granular formulations are occasionally used for treatments above ground level, an important example being their lodgement in the leaf funnels of maize as an ideal means for the control of the stem borer. Nevertheless, they are most commonly employed for ground-level application, especially for application through a standing crop. This minimises wastage and avoids possible phytotoxicity. Granules are safer to handle and more convenient to apply than liquids and are consequently often sold in sprinkler tins for domestic use in Britain. Granule application is less affected by wind and air currents than is the application of dusts and of some sprays, and they can be placed rapidly but accurately on the top of the ground around individual plants. This procedure is particularly useful for the control of insects that lay eggs near the base of the stem (e.g. carrot root fly) and for weed control near fruit bushes and similar established crops. Granular formulations sometimes make it possible for root-systemic action to be exploited for substances that are poorly systemic when applied to foliage. Moreover, for appropriate types of pest control, granules are often the preferred formulation for application by aircraft. An example is to bounce granules through foliage to swampy ground to control mosquito larvae.

With the exception of leaf application, granular formulations are thus convenient and efficient for many purposes. They do, however, suffer the disadvantage of being rather expensive. This is, to some degree, a reflection of the costs of manufacture, but additionally, they usually contain only 5–20 per cent of active ingredient and so are, in terms of active ingredient, costly to transport.

Granules can often be usefully applied to cultivated soil before a crop is sown, the application often being followed by tining, rotavation or watering. When tillage is to be minimised, weed problems can be serious; in such circumstances, a favoured procedure is to kill visible weeds by spraying before a crop is present (or visible) but to suppress growth of later-developing weeds, especially perennials, by slow-release granules (e.g. Schreiber *et al.*, 1987). Such a procedure to control late-developing weeds avoids a separate passage of spray machinery over a standing crop during the growing season. It is also possible to combine the application of granules with some other activity. For example, it is easier in seed furrows to sow seeds and to apply granules simultaneously than it is to sow seeds and to spray liquid at the same time. Similarly, it is possible to apply granules and fertiliser at the same time, as, for example, when herbicides are used prior to planting corn (e.g. Buhler, 1987).

The inert carrier of a granular formulation may be chosen for its sorptive capacity, its hardness or its density. Often, but not always, the carrier is an inert mineral with a porous reticulum that can be impregnated with a solution of an active ingredient. Inert supports include crushed and sieved silicate minerals such as attapulgite, kaolin, vermiculite and limestone. Less frequently, granules are made by aggregating dusts by adding a solution containing an adhesive to the dust contained in a rotating drum. If the release of an active ingredient from an otherwise satisfactory granule is too rapid, the manufacturer can provide the already treated granules with a plastic coating to delay or decrease escape of the toxicant.

Not all carriers in granules are, however, minerals. Another type of carrier has been described by McGuffog *et al.* (1984). A thermoplastic matrix with a micropore structure is extruded as a strand and then pelletised. The granular formulation is produced by incorporating the active ingredient, together with adjuvants called porosity modifiers, into the thermoplastic matrix. These Australian workers incorporated several pesticides into such granules, one being the insecticide chlorpyrifos. For this and many other substances, a typical release pattern is illustrated in figure 2.4; the soil concentration, after a delay, builds up rapidly and then declines, rapidly at first, then more slowly, but in such a way that an effective soil concentration may persist for 20 weeks or more. An equation often used to express rate of leaching from granules into soil is as follows:

$$\text{Amount leached per unit area} = \frac{kR\alpha}{Dp\rho} \qquad (2.2)$$

where R = volume of rain per unit area, D = granule diameter, p = percentage of AI in formulation at any moment, ρ = granule density and α = amount of AI applied per unit area.

A third type of granule employs the principle of incorporation of the active ingredient into a starch–xanthate, a starch–calcium or a starch–borate capsule. White and Schreiber (1984) have described the use of starch-encapsulated trifluralin, a herbicide that would rapidly lose its activity if applied in the form of an emulsifiable concentrate. Starch granule formulations of thiolcarbamate herbicides have also been successfully used by Schreiber *et al.* (1987).

Evidently, the commercial development of granule technology provides an alternative to persistent pesticides such as organochlorine compounds by enabling pesticides that would otherwise be rapidly destroyed in soil or lost by volatilisation to retain activity for long enough to be agriculturally useful. The principle is that the matrix of the granule can be so modified during manufacture, or the surface so coated, that the active ingredient is released neither too fast nor too slowly into the soil. This process is sometimes called **controlled release** of toxicant, although, in most cases, the term **delayed release** would probably be more appropriate.

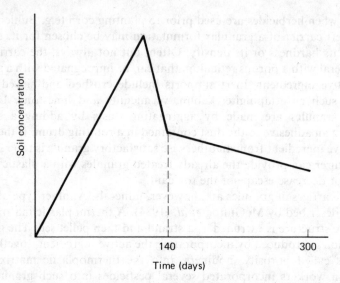

Figure 2.4   Release of toxicant from granules: soil concentration of chlorpyrifos released from thermoplastic granules into the soil (from McGuffog *et al.*, 1984)

There is another, quite different, use for granular formulations. It relates to the safe use of highly toxic substances, especially by the small-scale user of pesticides. Granular formulations are considerably safer than dusts or sprays for such hazardous substances as aldicarb (section 5.7) and paraquat/diquat (section 14.1). For example, they cannot be accidentally inhaled, as dusts can, nor splashed, as can happen for liquid concentrates. Soft granules are prepared from a mineral or other support into which a water-soluble pesticide soaks and from which it readily emerges as the granules disintegrate upon being added to a large volume of water. In order to make soft granules from (mineral) supports, the furnace 'firing' of hard granules is omitted (compare the preparation of pottery from clay).

Many granular formulations contain particles that are mostly within the range 0.3–1.0 mm diameter (the apposite British regulations require that not more than 4 per cent by weight should be able to pass through a 0.25 mm sieve). This means that there may well be many millions of granules per kilogram. However, as would be expected, any granular formulation will contain a range of particles of different sizes. A granular formulation is thus described by a double mesh number; one of these typifies a mesh with pores so large that all the particles pass through, the other a mesh with pores so small that all the particles are retained. For example, a '20/60 mesh' granular formulation will have granules of such a size that all will pass through a 20 mesh sieve and none will pass through a 60 mesh sieve. The relationship

Table 2.1 **Relationship between sieve mesh, particle size and approximate number of particles per kilogram of a granular formulation**

Mesh size of sieve	Size of particle that just passes through (mm)	Approximate number[a] of particles per kilogram (millions)
8	2.36	0.2
15	1.08	1
20	0.83	4
30	0.54	12
40	0.40	40
60	0.25	100
80	0.20	300

[a] The actual number may vary several-fold according to the precise nature of the carrier, its degree of hydration, etc.

between sieve mesh, pore size and the approximate number of particles per kilogram is shown in table 2.1.

When granules are applied to soil they are not necessarily randomly distributed, for, as was seen earlier, placement techniques are often to be preferred to broadcast treatments. The rate at which the pesticide escapes from a given formulation is largely determined by the extent of leaching by rain water. Leaching, in its turn, is influenced not only by the duration and intensity of the rain but also by the temperature. The rate of release will normally decrease with depletion and thus with the passage of time. The degree of control over effective release from granules also depends upon the extent of adsorption of the active ingredient on soil particles and the rate at which it decomposes once it reaches the soil. Hartley and Graham-Bryce (1980) have provided a detailed account of the physical principles that determine pesticide behaviour when granules are applied to soils.

2.7 APPLICATION AS LIQUIDS

The method most frequently employed for applying pesticides is to spray them as aqueous solutions or suspensions. In the latter case, the active ingredient is often dissolved in an organic solvent that is emulsified in the water or sorbed onto a finely divided solid. Such conventional sprays usually involve the application of 10 or more litres of fluid per hectare, and that fluid contains water (table 2.2). Increasingly, however, following the advent of suitable machinery, ultra-low-volume (ULV) applications, involving less than 4 litres per hectare, are becoming possible. For this method of application, the active ingredient is usually dissolved in a small volume of an oily organic solvent,

Table 2.2   Application volumes and common methods of impulsion of spray droplets

| Volume | Rate | | Carried or impelled by |
	(l/ha)	(gal/acre)	
Ultra-low (ULV)	1–5	< 1	Air or centrifugal energy
Very low	> 10	> 1	Air
Low	150	13	Air
Medium	350	31	Water/air
High	> 900	> 80	Mass of water

with or without cosolvents to increase the solubility of the active ingredient or to improve penetration into leaves. The formulation requirements are very different for conventional and ULV purposes, and are considered separately below.

(a) Conventional applications

In a few cases, a conventional formulation may consist of a water-soluble, water-stable active ingredient dissolved in water, to give a concentrated solution to which the manufacturer adds various adjuvants (section 2.9). Spreading agents are one such group and are added to ensure that the droplets spread on a waxy target surface. Aminotriazole and dalapon (chapter 14) are examples of water-soluble, stable active ingredients. Another possibility is for the water-soluble (but perhaps not totally stable) active ingredient to be dissolved in a water-miscible solvent such as isopropanol or butoxyethanol. This method of approach ensures that detrimental attack by water cannot occur during the period between manufacture and use by the purchaser. Monocrotophos is an example. In both cases, the spray operator dilutes the concentrate to perhaps 0.1 to 1.0 per cent by addition of the correct amount of water in the spray-tank.

More frequently, the formulation is either a wettable powder (WP) or an emulsifiable, concentrated (EC) liquid. These abbreviations are often found, sometimes without explanation, in pesticide literature. A wettable powder comprises an active ingredient, an inert solid and various supplementary substances, or adjuvants, the purpose of which is to ensure that the active ingredient is eventually able to be as effective as possible. Wettable powders tend to adhere to leaves less well than do oily preparations but they have the advantage that packaging and transportation can be cheaper (freight charges in some countries are higher for flammable organic liquids). Oily formulations, including emulsifiable concentrates, soak into leaves and so are more resistant to rain and provide more permanent deposits than are obtained with wettable powders.

Wettable powders are solids that disperse when stirred into water in the spray-tank. They are thus quite different from dusts, which are applied dry. Wettable powders consist of an active ingredient, which may be a solid or a liquid, as well as one or more adjuvants in the form of spreading and dispersing agents (section 2.9) and a solid, inert diluent or filler. The latter is usually a porous mineral such as a clay or diatomaceous earth, but may be a more alkaline substance such as calcium or magnesium carbonate. Fillers are needed because many organic substances are greasy and the particles would tend to stick together (which would be incompatible with the requirement for high availability and good dispersion). On the other hand, the amount of filler should be kept to a minimum because the particles are abrasive to equipment and because dilution of an active ingredient adds to transportation costs per unit active ingredient. A typical wettable powder contains about 50 per cent active ingredient, 47 per cent filler and 3 per cent adjuvants. The active ingredient normally remains strongly adsorbed on the filler when the wettable powder is suspended in water, thus ensuring that it, too, remains well dispersed. The particles of wettable powders are typically between 1 and 10 μm in diameter.

Emulsifiable concentrates are the main oil-based conventional formulations nowadays. This type of formulation produces a single-phase mixture. To make this type of formulation, a requirement is that it must be possible to make a moderately concentrated solution of the toxicant in a liquid mixture containing an oil and one or more oil-soluble emulsifiers and other adjuvants. When poured into water the single-phase mixture forms an emulsion with particles that are less than 8 μm in diameter. In practice, an emulsifiable concentrate normally contains a mixture of two emulsifiers, namely one that is of the non-ionic polyethylene oxide type and the other an anionic detergent. It has been found that such a mixture gives better results than either emulsifier used separately. A possible reason for this is that anionic detergents increase in solubility as the temperature is raised whereas non-ionic detergents become less soluble. In addition, the stability of emulsions is maximised by the use of an emulsifier mixture that possesses the optimal hydrophilic–lipophilic balance (HLB) for the particular active ingredient and organic liquid carrier (section 2.11).

The movement from higher to lower volumes of water in spray mixtures has had, as an inevitable consequence, a change in the method of impelling droplets to their target surface (table 2.2). At high volume, the water functions as a carrier, for the mass and velocity of the water droplets that leave the spray-tank are able to overcome air resistance and carry the spray to its target. When, as with medium- and low-volume application, less water is present, the droplets are impelled from the jet by a blast of air produced by the use of high-powered fans. A second but related consequence of lowering water volume is that when high air pressure is used to provide droplet momentum, the average droplet size is lower than is the average for droplets from most high-volume spray machines. Since the concentration of the mixture in the spray-tank normally rises as the volume applied falls, the ground area covered per tank filling is roughly the same for high- and low-volume applications.

(b) Ultra-low-volume (ULV) systems

This type of application system involves the application of less than about 5 litres of fluid per hectare. More definitively, formulations made for this purpose are intended to be used without further dilution or other modification by the spray operator. The formulation contains up to 40 per cent of active ingredient, and since no water (or, very occasionally, no extra water) is added, the spray comprises a fine mist of finely dispersed droplets containing a high concentration of pesticide. Table 2.3 summarises some of the characteristics of ULV and conventional hydraulic systems; the table is based upon one quoted by Furmidge (1982).

Aqueous formulations of a few herbicides have been applied by ULV systems but, much more typically, a ULV formulation comprises a solid or liquid active ingredient dissolved in a suitable organic solvent. Usually, but not always, cosolvents are also present, to improve solubility of active ingredient as well as to increase leaf penetration or to decrease volatility. The organic solvent used for a ULV formulation must be able to dissolve the active ingredient, but, in addition, it should provide a solution that is not too viscous, is not too volatile and is not phytotoxic. In practice, it is unusual for all these ideals to be realised in any one formulation.

Table 2.3   Differences between conventional and ULV sprays (after Furmidge, 1982)

Conventional sprays	ULV sprays
Spray prepared by diluting a concentrated formulation	Formulation used undiluted
Pesticide in sprayed liquid seldom exceeds 1 per cent	Pesticide in sprayed liquid usually 20–40 per cent
Typical spray volume applied is 100–350 l/ha	Typical spray volume applied is 1–2 l/ha
Spray liquid predominantly aqueous, with suspended oily drops or powder	Spray liquid non-aqueous in most cases
Adjuvants include spreaders, emulsifiers, stabilisers	Adjuvants include substances to modify solubility of AI or which are added to adjust volatility, viscosity or freezing point of mixture

Ultra-low-volume application can be a valuable technique in tropical areas where water supply is limited. Moreover, and more generally, in the absence of bulk liquid, ULV application allows lighter, often hand-held equipment to be used instead of the heavy tractor-trailed spray-tanks needed for higher application volumes. This in turn leads to reduced fuel costs and less damage to emerged crops during mid-season spraying. Lighter equipment can also be put into operation within a few minutes of a favourable weather forecast and thus gives greater versatility of response than does more cumbersome equipment. Another type of advantage relates to safety; the spray applier no longer has to dilute the formulation, a practice that can lead to error or spillage. Some ULV formulations now arrive in sealed units, which are fitted into the spraying apparatus (see below); if this facility were developed more generally, it could greatly reduce pesticide handling accidents, especially in developing countries. A further aspect of ULV technology is that it is closely linked to controlled droplet-size application (CDA). When the range of size of droplets being sprayed at any one time is limited, and is furthermore under the control of the spray operator, there are considerable theoretical and practical advantages with regard to safety and efficiency of application.

Some disadvantages of ULV formulation are that it is inflexible, that evaporation problems can occur before droplets reach their target and that the distribution of droplets on a full canopy of crop may be imperfect. Inflexibility exists in the sense that, with conventional systems, the operator can alter spray concentration by simply adding more or less water. With ULV formulations, the manufacturer must decide the best dose in terms of litres per hectare and design a formulation accordingly. If, for example, local pests are more tolerant than expected, all that the operator can do is to cover less than the prescribed area with the contents of one container. A second problem relates to the fact that evaporation from numerous very small droplets can be rapid, and, if so, must be slowed down by addition of a suitable adjuvant. A general rule is that formulations are designed so that less than 50 per cent of the volume of a formulation should be lost before droplet impaction. The theoretical superiority of ULV systems is undeniable, but whether ULV does work better than conventional methods, or allows a smaller quantity of active ingredient to be applied per hectare using currently available equipment, remains controversial; perhaps relative efficiency depends on the nature of the crop canopy and the type of target being aimed at, as well as limitations in currently available equipment.

Ultra-low-volume techniques have not always provided dramatic proof of their superiority. In part, this is because spray drift problems require that droplets larger than the optimal size (150 μm for herbicides, 50 μm or less for insecticides) have to be used. On the other hand, as Abdelbagi and Adams (1987) have pointed out, although application efficiency increases as droplet size decreases within the limits stated above, droplets less than about 50 μm lack momentum and the efficiency of impaction on foliage is low. If a crop has a dense canopy of growth, many of the pests within that canopy may survive ULV spraying whereas they may be reached by higher-volume sprays.

A technique advanced to meet some of the difficulties mentioned above involves the release of droplets that are electrostatically charged. It has been found, in particular, that deposition on the lower (abaxial) side of leaves is usually higher when droplets are electrostatically charged. This is because even a droplet of low terminal velocity may be deposited, whereas when sedimentation force is the only one operating, abaxial surfaces, upon which pests often live, may receive little spray. Conversely, the use of charged droplets can exacerbate problems relating to the penetration of a dense crop canopy. At later stages of crop development, although charged droplets lead to total deposit, the toxicant tends to be preferentially deposited on the upper and outer leaves of the crop, rather than lower down and underneath, where many of the pests survive. In consequence, a great improvement in results over those achieved by conventional techniques is not always apparent (Adams and Palmer, 1986; Cayley *et al.*, 1984).

2.8 IMPACT OF MACHINERY ON FORMULATION AND APPLICATION

In a book that is essentially chemical in orientation it would be inappropriate to deal in depth with the construction and operation of spray equipment, or with details of boom mounting or types of nozzles. The same applies to varieties of spray patterns, important though these are to efficient use of active ingredients. Nor shall we be considering the physics and mathematics of droplet deposition and retention, or the effect of wind speed on rate of droplet sedimentation. For a more advanced treatment of such subjects the reader should consult the textbook on application methods by Matthews (1979) or the British Crop Protection Council symposium on spraying systems (Walker, 1980). Detailed aspects of the physical chemistry of pesticide behaviour are to be found in the monograph by Hartley and Graham-Bryce (1980). Nation (1982) has provided a short but useful review of the development of ULV with special reference to sprayer design and provisions for boom stabilisation, and Spillman (1984) has described more mathematical aspects of the impaction of spray droplets and of how their angle of descent is altered by wind and droplet size. The results of a survey carried out at Long Ashton Research Station in which conventional and ULV systems were compared are also worthy of study (Hislop *et al.*, 1984).

Despite these omissions, it is evident that available technology must greatly influence the chemistry of formulation and the efficacy of application, as well as have repercussions on various aspects of safety. Consequently, in this section there follows a very brief account of the range of machines that can be used to apply conventional or ULV formulations.

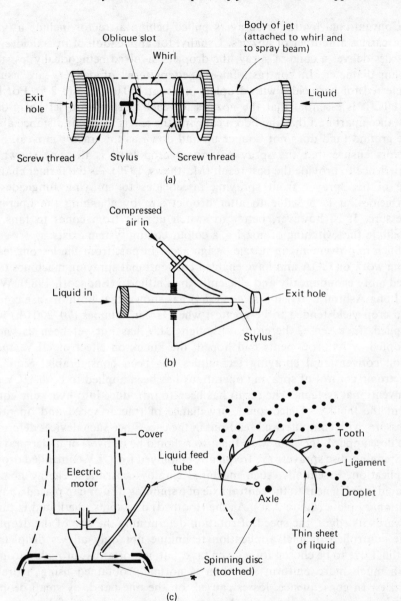

Figure 2.5 Spray delivery systems. (a) An exploded diagram of a simple jet; the body is attached to the spray beam and to a whirl with oblique slots which produce a vortex; the cap is hollow, with a central hole, through which liquid emerges. (b) Features of an atomising jet; liquid is forced into the central tube; compressed air causes liquid to vortex from the stylus through the exit hole. (c) Rotary disc droplet producer; at correct speed, film of liquid on the disc is forced outwards by centrifugal force, giving ligaments which disintegrate to form droplets of nearly uniform size

Conventional hydraulic sprayers pulled behind a tractor include a boom that carries a number of nozzles. Usually, for application of insecticides, the nozzles deliver a cone of spray, the droplets involved being ideally less than 50 μm diameter. In contrast, fan-shaped patterns of delivery are usually preferred for herbicides with droplets of about 150 μm (figure 2.5). For best results, it is essential that the nozzles for each purpose are set an optimal distance apart and that the boom carrying the jets is the right distance above the ground (and does not bounce up and down as the tractor moves). Such factors ensure that the spray pattern at crop level is the one shown by experience to provide the best result (Matthews, 1979). As the farmer changes use of his sprayer from spraying insecticides to spraying fungicides or herbicides, it is possible to alter droplet size by changing the operating pressure. It is, however, better to switch nozzles from cones to fans. To facilitate the switching of nozzles, a colour coding system exists.

Such improvements in nozzle design arose in part from the lessons learnt from work on CDA and have enabled conventional spraying machines to be used more economically and efficiently than hitherto (Endacott, 1983). Work at Long Ashton by Hislop *et al.* (1984) has shown that both disease control and crop yield tended to be greatest when larger volumes (70–200 l/h) were applied. In a sense, therefore, although ULV has not yet been as widely adopted as its proponents had hoped, the knock-on effect of ULV studies upon conventional spraying techniques has been considerable. Similarly, electronic control of spraying operations has been applied to both ULV and conventional systems. The result has been to introduce into hydraulic equipment the facility of electronic surveillance of tractor speed and operating pressure, with computerised read-out in the cab. Since such devices determine the dose applied, they can warn the driver should he be over- or underspraying.

Spinning-disc sprayers are frequently employed for ULV controlled droplet application. Essentially, such machines employ centrifugal energy nozzles. Liquid is fed in near to the central axle of a spinning disc or cup placed above a stationary plate (figure 2.5c). As the (toothed) disc spins, the liquid is thrust towards its edges, the speed of rotation determining the size of the droplets. The controlled droplet application technique not only allows droplets of optimal size to be chosen for a given task, but, importantly, provides droplets of a much more uniform size than is normally obtained using hydraulic nozzles. In consequence, losses caused, on the one hand, by small droplets drifting away or, on the other, by large droplets running off foliage, can be minimised.

Most spinning-disc machines have horizontal discs or cups but a French design has vertical spinning discs, the upward-moving droplets being collected and recycled (Nation, 1982). Spinning discs only work efficiently when the volume of liquid is restricted so that the system is not flooded. Arnold (1983) evaluated 14 spinning-disc sprayers, listing the good and weak points of each type. Matthews (1979) has described the design of the disc and its power supply, illustrating (for a given machine and formulation) the relationship between rotational speed of the disc, the flow rate to the disc and the median diameter of the droplets. Tractor-mounted sprayers with spinning-disc nozzles have also been developed. To overcome targeting problems in dense crops, tractor-mounted booms carrying disc nozzles have been fitted with air streams around the nozzles to blow spray droplets within the canopy of the crop.

The advent of ULV, and, with it, small droplet application, led to the introduction of systems for providing electrostatically charged droplets. In Britain, in the period 1970 to 1975, workers, first at Sheffield University and later at Rothamsted Research Station, devised spinning-disc machines charged at high potential so as to deliver droplets carrying a high electrostatic charge. Such charges should assist deposition, especially on the abaxial sides of leaves (which are often undersprayed when sedimentation is the force governing deposition). While theoretically applicable to all spray techniques, in practice electrostatic effects seldom work efficiently on the larger droplets characteristic of hydraulic systems and hydraulic machinery cannot easily be adapted to provide the necessary charge.

Electrostatic charges can be something of a mixed blessing, however, because, while they do frequently improve deposition of pesticides on leaves, they can exacerbate problems of penetration of crop canopy. In particular, when the crop is advanced in growth and has a dense canopy, the heavier pesticide deposits tend to be on the outer and upper part of the canopy whereas the pests are all too often sheltering lower down and underneath. Hence the greater deposit may not be in the right place to give maximal crop protection, a fact that may help to explain why a great improvement in efficiency over that achieved with conventional sprayers is not always apparent (Adams and Palmer, 1986).

The 'Electrodyn' sprayer marketed by ICI Ltd is unique in that the replacement refill bottle containing pesticide comes complete with a pre-set nozzle, so no handling or adjustment of any kind is required. Such 'closed' systems have a great advantage from the point of view of safety, and, if they can be made cheap enough, could be ideal for use under the conditions found in developing countries. In the case of the Electrodyn, less than one litre per hectare is often required for good pest control. Its handle contains batteries and a high-voltage generator and the earth field electrode surrounds the holder of the bottle–nozzle complex. Another advantage under conditions found in the developing world is that there are no moving parts to wear out.

2.9 TYPES OF SPRAY SUPPLEMENTS

Despite the advent of ULV techniques, water is still present in greater or lesser quantity for most agricultural spraying operations. For reasons of availability, cheapness and lack of phytotoxicity, water is an excellent, even an essential, spray component. In most other ways, unfortunately, it is almost the worst possible choice for a carrier when the primary purpose is to deposit a pesticide on a waxy surface. Water has low affinity for such surfaces and so tends to run off, with wastage of the active ingredient. Its high surface tension (78 dyn/cm) is a further cause of difficulty, for small droplets of water thus tend to be spherical and to bounce off a lipophilic surface. To minimise these difficulties, various **spray supplements** or **adjuvants** must be present in the majority of spray mixtures to enable the active ingredient to be utilised as effectively as possible.

Two types of supplements, the **emulsifiers** and the **dispersing agents** or **stabilisers**, operate at the spray-tank level, enabling heterogeneous mixtures to be kept thoroughly mixed (a process often assisted by mechanical stirring and circulation). Another type of supplement, the **spreading agent** or **wetting agent**, operates at the moment of impact; it reduces surface tension and so increases the contact between the spray droplets and the sprayed surface. These three types of supplement all have surfactant properties (section 2.10).

The retention of a droplet by a lipid surface is influenced by several interacting physicochemical factors, including droplet size, surface tension, volatility of carrier and, if relevant, the presence of an acquired electrostatic charge. In the absence of a spreader, droplets larger than about 250 µm but smaller than about 2.5 mm bounce off leaves and almost no residue is left. However, the percentage retention of water droplets by waxy surfaces increases suddenly as the size of the droplet falls below about 100 µm. Retention is also affected by the surface tension of the aqueous carrier. If too little spreader is present, the contact between an aqueous spray and a lipid surface is so poor that most of the droplets bounce off; if too much spreader is present, the droplets (especially when application involves medium to high volumes of liquid) may tend to flatten and coalesce, so that much is lost by run-off. Another possibility, favoured by high impact velocity, is that a large droplet may explode into many smaller droplets upon impact, and many of the latter then bounce off. The surface tension of aqueous sprays should probably not exceed 50 dyn/cm if adequate retention is to be assured.

Leaves of different types of plants retain or reflect aqueous droplets to different extents. In the case of herbicides, this difference can sometimes be exploited to achieve a greater selectivity of action. This is particularly true for weed control in some legume and brassica crops, although, naturally, some types of weeds will also have highly reflective leaves. If, therefore, the amount of wetting agent is sufficiently low to ensure reflection from leaves of crop plants but little reflection from those of most kinds of weeds, any selectivity possessed by an active ingredient can be accentuated. In this respect it should be noted that it is possible to select dispersing agents that do not reduce surface tension greatly and thus wettable powders as well as water-soluble concentrates can be used to exploit differences in reflection by different species of plants.

To maximise deposition on leaves thus requires the presence of the optimal amount of spreading agent. Except at high application volumes (> 500 litres per hectare) droplets do not overlap and coalesce. Thus for lower application volumes it is possible to use much spreading agent so that the droplets spread out on the leaves, almost to the point of incipient run-off, and then dry *in situ*. This ensures that any oily residue is sorbed into the cuticle.

After deposition, emulsions will break. At higher volumes of application the rate at which this occurs may well determine how much active ingredient remains on the leaf. If breaking occurs rapidly enough, the oily disperse phase (and any dissolved pesticide it contains) will be left behind when the water runs off the leaf.

The **sticking agent** is another type of spray supplement of occasional importance. Stickers are substances that improve the adhesion of deposited residues; they are of particular importance for use with active ingredients that are deposited upon, rather than sorbed within, the wax of the leaf surface. Among the numerous materials that have been used as stickers are casein, flour, oils, gelatin, gums, resins and synthetic polymers.

Humectants are sometimes added to a spray mixture to increase the length of time between the application of the droplets and their evaporation to dryness. This interval of time is occasionally of considerable importance, especially when penetration to some target is a prerequisite for success. An example is the penetration of crevices of bark so that the active ingredient is able to reach overwintering eggs; another is the need to penetrate the 'wool' produced by woolly aphids in order to kill the insects underneath. Fungal mycelium can regenerate from the smallest strands, so, in this case also, total wetting before the last of the water has evaporated may greatly improve performance. Water-soluble organic liquids such as propylene glycol are often employed as humectants because the tendency of water molecules to escape becomes less as the solution becomes more concentrated with respect to the propylene glycol.

Synergists and activators enable a fixed amount of certain toxicants to be more poisonous than they would be if applied alone under otherwise identical conditions. **Synergists** act at the biochemical level, often by inhibiting the microsomal oxidases (section 3.4) that inactivate many, but not all, toxic substances. If the enzymes are inactivated, the toxic substances persist longer at the site of action, and can therefore do greater damage. **Activators** often alter the physical state of the applied spray mixture, allowing better access of the active ingredient to its target. One example is the use of a bisulphate to alter the degree of ionisation of active ingredients that are weak acids. Figure 2.6 depicts a scheme showing components that may be present in spray mixtures, with some of the ways in which they interact with one another.

One or several of the foregoing supplements or adjuvants are present in conventional spray mixtures, where water is present. Adjuvants are, however, also necessary to modify the physicochemical properties of a pesticide–solvent

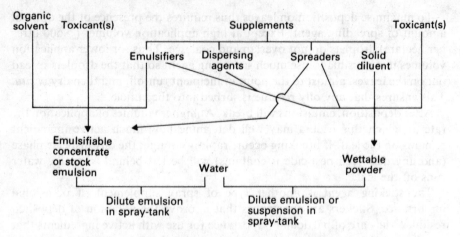

Figure 2.6   Possible components of spray mixtures

mixture used in many ULV preparations. Surfactants of various kinds are often present, but in addition, as we have already seen, ULV formulations often need to contain components which ensure that the mixture is not too viscous nor too volatile. Gillard (1987) has discussed the role of adjuvants for both conventional and ULV formulations.

2.10 CHEMISTRY OF SURFACTANTS

It was seen in the previous section that emulsifiers, stabilisers and spreading agents increase the availability of an active ingredient before and at the moment of impact. These three types of spray supplements share an important physicochemical attribute, namely their molecules are able to separate preferentially at lipophilic–hydrophilic phase boundaries. For electrical reasons, surface activity results in the stabilisation of emulsions and suspensions. In addition, the presence of surfactant molecules at phase boundaries pushes apart close-packed water molecules and so causes a marked reduction of aqueous surface tension. To justify and illustrate these assertions, it is necessary to review briefly the chemical structure of surface-active substances.

Surfactants (soaps and detergents) are divisible into three main groups. The first of these, the **anionic surfactants**, is the group to which soap belongs. Compounds of this type are characterised by the possession of a long non-polar portion to the molecule with a compact hydrophilic, ionised group at the end:

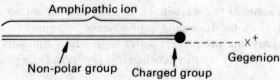

These compounds are termed anionic surfactants because the ion that separates at surfaces, the **amphipathic ion**, carries a negative charge (compare Cl^-, SO_4^{2-}). The balancing ion, or gegenion (German 'counter'), carries a positive charge.

Anionic surfactants are of several kinds. Among them are the sulphated alcohols and sulphonated hydrocarbons:

$C_{12}H_{25}$–O–SO_2O^- – – – Na^+ Sulphated alcohol (e.g. Dreft®)

R_2CH–O–SO_2O^- – – – Na^+ Sulphated alcohol (e.g. Teepol®)

$C_{12}H_{25}$–C_6H_4–SO_2O^- – – – Na^+ Sulphonated hydrocarbon (e.g. Dispersols®)

An advantage possessed by many anionic surfactants is that they can be readily synthesised from natural oils or from petroleum products and are therefore competitively priced. They do, however, suffer two major disadvantages. The first of these is that the amphipathic ions can react with metal ions to form insoluble compounds—solubility is a prerequisite for surface activity. Interfering metal ions may be present in hard water or be a part of certain active ingredients. Similarly, amphipathic ions may react with hydrogen ions with the formation of acids, which in some cases (e.g. soap) are only slightly ionised and are in consequence poor surfactants. Secondly, most anionic surfactants are of low solubility in hydrocarbon oils. Branched-chain surfactants tend to be more powerful in action and more persistent in the environment than those with straight chains, and for this reason are termed 'hard' detergents.

The second group comprises substances the amphipathic ion of which carries a compact positively charged group. Compounds with molecules of this sort are known as **cationic surfactants**. Representative examples are quaternary ammonium compounds and quaternary heterocyclic compounds such as pyridinium derivatives:

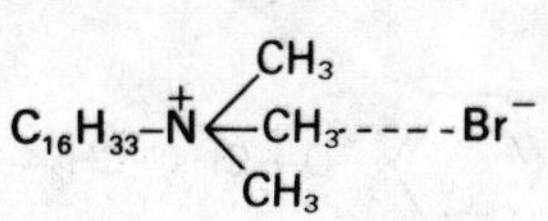

$C_{16}H_{33}$–$\overset{+}{N}$$\begin{smallmatrix}CH_3\\ CH_3 \\ CH_3\end{smallmatrix}$ – – – – Br^- A tetraalkylammonium salt (cetyl trimethyl ammonium bromide)

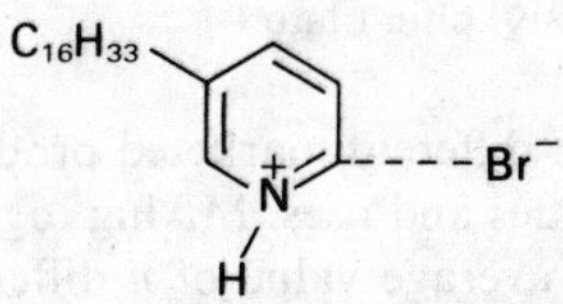

An alkylpyridinium salt (cetyl pyridinium bromide)

The group $C_{15}H_{31}CH_2$– is a cetyl group; the long carbon chain confers hydrophobic qualities, which counterbalance the hydrophilic charged nitrogen atom and lead to separation of the ion at water/non-water phase boundaries. Cetyl alcohol is often made by the reduction of palmitic acid, $C_{15}H_{31}COOH$, which itself is obtained by hydrolysis of natural fats and oils.

Cationic surfactants are sometimes expensive but they have the advantage that, being positively charged, the amphipathic ion cannot interact with cations in water or with cationic active ingredients. In practice, many anionic surfactants also work quite well in hard water because their heavy metal salts are fairly soluble. It is essential to avoid mixing a formulation containing an anionic detergent with one containing a cationic detergent, for the two oppositely charged amphipathic ions interact; both are then precipitated as a slimy oil and both the formulations are ruined.

The third group is the **non-ionic surfactants**. A major reason for the increasing popularity of some of these compounds in recent years is that they are more soluble in hydrocarbons and similar oily liquids than are most ionic detergents. As was seen in section 2.7 this property has greatly simplified formulation of liquids by making it possible to make single-phase emulsifiable concentrates to replace the earlier two-phase stock emulsions, which often possessed low storage potential.

Many non-ionic surfactants are **polyethylene oxide** derivatives formally derived as follows:

$$RO-\text{\textcircled{H}} + n\begin{bmatrix} CH_2-CH_2 \\ \diagdown O \diagup \end{bmatrix} \longrightarrow RO\text{\textopenbracket}CH_2-CH_2-O\text{\textclosebracket}_n\text{\textcircled{H}} \qquad (2.3)$$

Early members of the group included the Tween® series of compounds introduced by the Atlas Chemical Co. where R in (2.3) is an ester containing sorbitol anhydride united with various fatty acids. For instance, Tween 40 contains isomers of polyoxyethylene sorbitan monopalmitate (figure 2.7).

Other series exist with different aliphatic groups, R, attached to polyoxyethylene chains. A particularly valuable series for pesticide formulation is a condensate containing a phenol substituted with an alkyl group containing a long carbon chain:

Branched-chain
nonyl group
$$C_9H_{19}-\hspace{-0.3em}\left\langle\bigcirc\right\rangle\hspace{-0.3em}-O\text{\textopenbracket}CH_2-CH_2-O\text{\textclosebracket}_n H$$

Polyoxyethylene nonyl phenolate

The mean value of n varies considerably in different marketed products, and gives to each product its distinctive properties and uses. Mixing together two such non-ionic surfactants, for which the average value of n differs widely, often results in a mixture with a field performance superior to that achieved using either separately. Their surface-active properties depend on a balance of

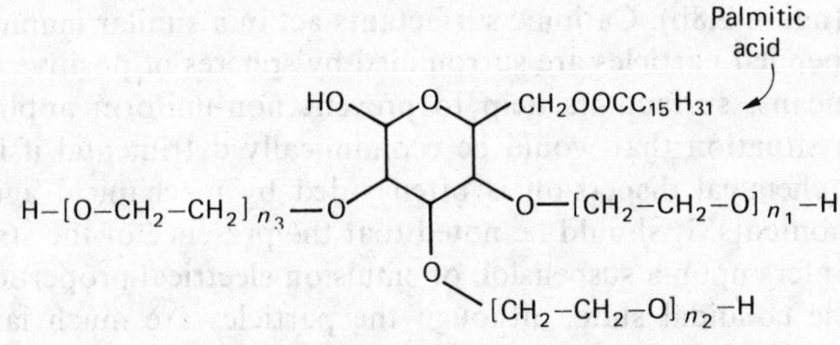

Figure 2.7 The structure of a Tween®, a polyoxyethylene sorbitan monopalmitate

hydrophilic properties (a property of the regularly occurring oxygen atoms) and hydrophobic properties (a function of the $C_9H_{19}-$ group and of the regularly occurring C_2H_4- groups). Other pesticide formulations often contain a mixture of a branched-chain anionic surfactant and a non-ionic surfactant, for again the mixture often proves superior to either used by itself. A ratio of four parts of non-ionic surfactant to one of ionic surfactant is frequently used, especially when emulsifying properties are of primary importance. Other polyoxyethylene oxide surfactants are used as wetting agents; one reason for this is that, as the water evaporates after deposition of droplets, the surfactant is left behind as a viscous deposit, the solvent properties of which help a systemic pesticide to penetrate leaves.

More recently, **dimethylsilicones** have been used as spreading agents. These substances are remarkably good wetting agents, working very effectively at very low concentrations, presumably because the oxygen atoms are attracted to the water while the two methyl groups, by hydrophobic escape, lead to the molecule being orientated along the interface.

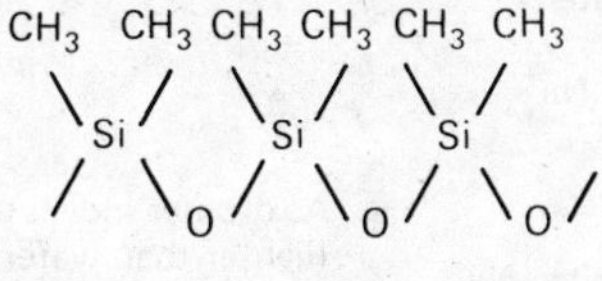

Polydimethylsilicone

2.11 MODE OF ACTION OF SURFACTANTS

On adding an anionic surfactant to a suspension of solid particles or of oil droplets in water, the amphipathic ions orientate themselves in the way shown in figure 2.8a. Since each suspended particle becomes surrounded, in effect, by a sphere of negative charges, the tendency of the suspended particles to separate out under the influence of gravity is opposed by the electrical charges upon them (figure 2.8b). Cationic surfactants act in a similar manner, except that the suspended particles are surrounded by spheres of positive charges.

By this means, surfactants help to prevent non-uniform application of pesticides, a situation that would be economically detrimental if it were to occur. This chemical dispersion is often aided by mechanical agitation of spray-tank contents. It should be noted that the presence of the **stabiliser** or **emulsifier** confers upon a suspension or emulsion electrical properties characteristic of the colloidal state, although the particles are much larger than colloidal particles. In addition, of course, the electrical charges are artificially induced whereas those of colloids are inherent in the colloidal state itself.

Spreaders are surfactants that operate at the moment of impact, and they function for the following reason. The compact stereochemistry of water molecules allows them to approach one another very closely, with the result that the forces of cohesion between them are very great (compare the inverse square law). The magnitude of these forces is manifest at the surface as a high surface tension. The latter can be regarded as an elastic film which, by contracting, causes a water droplet to assume as nearly spherical a shape as its size and environment will allow.

When a spreading agent is added to water, the molecules separate preferentially at the surface, thrusting the close-packed water molecules apart. The high forces of cohesion of water molecules are thereby partly replaced by the lower forces of adhesion between water molecules and surfactant molecules. The consequence of the presence of a spreader in an aqueous spray droplet is, therefore, to make the droplet 'sag' more than it would have done in the absence of surfactant (figure 2.9). This increases the area of contact between spray and sprayed surface; that is to say, it increases wetting and spreading. As was seen in section 2.10, an optimal quantity of a particular surfactant gives

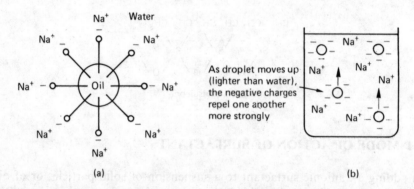

As droplet moves up (lighter than water), the negative charges repel one another more strongly

(a)   (b)

Figure 2.8   How a surfactant stabilises an emulsion. (a) Amphipathic ions of anionic detergent separate at the surface of an oil droplet and water. (b) Each droplet thus acts as though surrounded by a sphere of negative charge, so droplets repel one another

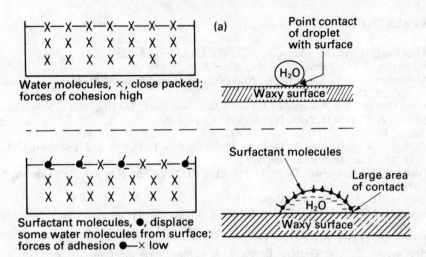

Figure 2.9 Effect of surfactants on surface tension. (a) Because of high forces of cohesion, there is little contact between droplet and surface in the absence of surfactants. (b) The area of contact increases when lower forces of adhesion replace the high forces of cohesion

maximal retention in any particular set of circumstances. The physical chemistry of coverage and of spreading, including mathematical aspects of the contact angle and of the rate of spreading, have been discussed by Hartley and Graham-Bryce (1980, p. 402).

The choice of an appropriate surfactant, or mixture of surfactants, for a particular purpose is still a rather empirical procedure, for optimal amounts have to be found by trial and error. However, a system has been developed for classifying surfactants that allows some level of selection of detergents for particular work. The system is called the **hydrophilic–lipophilic balance** (HLB) system.

All surfactants contain hydrophilic (water-loving) and lipophilic (oil-loving) groups, and the balance between their opposing effects can be measured. The lower the HLB value, the more lipophilic (or hydrophobic) the product is. Typical values range from 2 to 18, those of low HLB tending to be oil-soluble while those of high HLB tend to be water-soluble. In the Span® series, for example, Span 60 (sorbitan monostearate) has a value of 4.7 and Span 20 (sorbitan monolaurate) a value of 8.6. Similarly, in the Tween® series, Tween 85 (polyoxyethylene sorbitan trioleate) has an HLB value of 11 and Tween 20 (polyoxyethylene sorbitan monolaurate) a value of 16.7. Once a body of data has been built up, it is possible, within certain limits, to predict the right mixture of surfactants to provide an appropriate combination of emulsifying (or stabilising) and spreading properties to optimise the availability of active ingredient for any desired use in the field.

REFERENCES

Abdelbagi, H. A. and Adams, A. J. (1987). *Crop Prot.*, **6**, 226

Adams, A. J. and Palmer, A. (1986). *Crop Prot.*, **5**, 358

Al-Samarraie, A. I., Al-Hafdh, E., Abdul-Majed, K. and Basumy, M. A. (1989). *Pestic. Sci.*, **25**, 227

Anon (1988). *Crop Protection Chemicals Reference Book*, 3rd edn. Wiley, New York

Arnold, A. C. (1983). *Trop. Pest Managem.*, **29**, 105

Buhler, D. D. (1987). *Weed Sci.*, **35**, 412

Cayley, G. R., Etheridge, P., Griffiths, D. C., Phillips, F. T., Pye, B. J. and Scott, G. C. (1984). *Ann. Appl. Biol.*, **105**, 379

Edson, E. F., Sanderson, D. M. and Noakes, D. N. (1966). *Wld Rev. Pest Control*, **5**, 143

Endacott, C. J. (1983). *SPAN*, **26**, 113

Furmidge, C. G. L. (1982). Quoted from an invited lecture given to M.Sc. crop protection students, Reading University, March 1982

Gillard, G. (1987). *Pestic. Sci.*, **19**, 323

Hartley, G. S. and Graham-Bryce, I. J. (1980). *Physical Principles of Pesticide Behaviour*. Academic Press, London

Hassall, K. A. (1969). *World Crop Protection*, vol. 2, *Pesticides*. Iliffe, London

Hislop, E. C., Cooke, B. K., Herrington, P. J., Western, N. M., Jones, K. G. and Woodley, S. E. (1984). *Long Ashton Res. Sta. Rep.*, *1984*, pp. 44–8

Kramer, K. J. and Koga, D. (1986). *Insect Biochem.*, **16**, 851

McGuffog, D. R., Plowman, N. and Anderson, T. P. (1984). *Proc. Br. Crop Prot. Conf., Pests and Diseases*, p. 429

Matthews, G. A. (1979). *Pesticide Application Methods*. Longmans, London

Metcalf, R. L. (1955). *Organic Insecticides*. Interscience, New York

Nation, H. J. (1982). *Proc Br. Crop Prot. Conf., Weeds*, p. 983

Polon, J. A. (1973). In *Pesticide Formulations*, ed. W. Van Valkenburg, p. 143. Marcel Dekker, New York

Schreiber, M. M., White, M. D. and Shasha, B. S. (1987). *Weed Sci.*, **35**, 407

Spillman, J. J. (1984). *Pestic. Sci.*, **15**, 97

Stevens, P. J. G., Baker, E. A. and Anderson, N. H. (1988). *Pestic. Sci.*, **24**, 31

UNIDO (1983). *Advice on Formulation of Pesticides for Developing Countries*. United Nations Industrial Development Organisation, Vienna. Sales No. E83.1133. From UN Sales Section, New York, USA

Walker, J. O. (1980). *Spraying Systems for the 1980s. Proceedings of a Symposium held at Royal Holloway College, London, March 1980. Br. Crop Prot. Council, Monogr. 244*, ed. J.O. Walker. BCPC Publications, 144–150 London Road, Croydon CR0 2TB, UK

White, M. D. and Schreiber, M. M. (1984). *Weed Sci.*, **32**, 387

3 Principles of pesticide metabolism

3.1 DEFENCE SYSTEMS AND THEIR IMPORTANCE

All living organisms possess defence mechanisms intended to protect them from the deleterious effects of small quantities of many sorts of foreign compounds, including pesticides. If a toxic substance enters an organism more quickly than it can be eliminated (with or without prior metabolism), it will accumulate until a toxic concentration is reached at the site of action. Numerous anatomical, physiological and biochemical factors interact to determine how much of a particular substance penetrates in unit time, how it is distributed in the body, how rapidly and by what route it is metabolised and by what mechanism it is excreted. The importance of metabolic changes described in this chapter must be considered in this overall context, and particularly in relation to differences in the nature of such intermediate barriers as insect cuticle, vertebrate skin and plant waxes (chapter 2).

Enzymes that metabolise foreign compounds serve two related functions. In the first place the metabolic changes so alter the molecular structure that usually (but not invariably) the product is less harmful than the original substance. Secondly, these same changes render many substances more soluble in water and more polar, thereby increasing the rate of elimination from the body.

Most substances used as pesticides are not very soluble in water and their oxidation or hydrolysis (or both) leads to the **insertion** or the **uncovering** of polar groups. Such reactions are **primary** metabolic reactions. Often, but not always, the products of these primary reactions undergo **secondary** changes whereby they are conjugated with endogenous substances to form molecules that are more readily excreted. In some measure, the nature of the conjugating substance is characteristic of the organism or even of the phylum (section 3.6). In higher animals, these changes facilitate the transportation of metabolites of pesticides in blood, which in turn leads to their eventual excretion. Despite obvious differences in detail, analogous processes occur in invertebrates and in plants.

The preceding paragraphs explain the rationale underlying the near-universality of foreign-compound metabolism in organisms as diverse as moulds and man. However, the need for a pre-existing defence mechanism that is versatile enough to cope with any one of an almost infinite range of foreign compounds requires that the enzymes concerned should, in general, be of very low substrate specificity. It will be seen later that this flexibility sometimes causes the system to misfire so that it is not unknown for the organism to become its own executioner. Indeed, this accidental self-destructiveness has occasionally been exploited in the design of specifically insecticidal or herbicidal chemicals.

The majority of the enzymes responsible for the primary metabolism of foreign compounds are hydrolases and oxygenases. The primitive function of these enzymes was presumably to catalyse steps in the normal metabolism of various endogenous compounds. In the case of the oxygenases, exogenous lipophilic substances also fit their surfaces, perhaps because lipophilic properties and van der Waals bonding are more important than precise stereochemical fitment. Whether or not this is so, it is unlikely that those interested in evolutionary philosophy will contemplate the possibility of 'precognitive evolution' whereby enzymic defence mechanisms against specific poisons came into being millions of years before those poisons were an environmental hazard. There must be some more rational explanation.

Before considering some of the enzymes involved in pesticide metabolism, it is necessary to indicate why this subject is of fundamental importance to all concerned with chemical pest control. In the first instance, metabolism plays an important (but not an exclusive) role in relation to **selectivity** of action of pesticides, and thus plays a part in determining the safety of these compounds to man and to farm animals. If evolution had taken a different turn, an intelligent insect could certainly have devised selective mammalicides. Secondly, the level of metabolism is a factor determining the **persistence** of pesticides in soil, in plants and in animal bodies, and therefore contributes significantly to the reduction of environmental pollution. Once pesticides have undergone primary metabolic changes, most of them can be completely degraded by microorganisms of various kinds. In some cases, bacteria are known that can use the carbon skeletons as a source of food. Finally, and often detrimentally from a farmer's point of view, metabolic factors are frequently implicated in the mechanism leading to the development of pest **resistance**. If organisms—especially fast-breeding ones such as insects—are exposed to doses of a pesticide insufficient to wipe out the whole population, the surviving organisms, by interbreeding, can give rise to a more resistant population than the original one. It is sometimes found that this greater resistance can be attributed at least in part to increased levels, or efficiency, of a pesticide-inactivating enzyme compared with what was, on average, present in individuals of the original population. In some cases, the location of a gene coding for an enzyme associated with resistance has been identified on a specific chromosome.

3.2 ENZYMES RESPONSIBLE FOR THE METABOLISM OF PESTICIDES

Hydrolytic enzymes are widely distributed in various tissues of plants and animals and in different parts of individual cells. In vertebrates, hydrolases present in blood plasma are capable of attacking a wide range of extraneous esters, although the natural substrates of these esterases remain uncertain. In addition, membrane-bound hydrolases exist in the **microsomal** fraction obtained on differential centrifugation of a tissue homogenate, and soluble hydrolases are present in the cytosol. The various kinds of hydrolases and their roles in pesticide detoxication are considered in section 3.3.

Enzymes capable of oxidising foreign compounds occur in most cells of most organisms, but, for higher animals, the dominant site of such oxidative metabolism is in the endoplasmic reticulum of liver cells. The oxidative reactions can readily be studied *in vitro* by homogenising liver cells, centrifuging the homogenate at $10\,000\,g$ for 30 min and then recentrifuging the $10\,000\,g$ supernatant fluid at $100\,000\,g$ for an hour (compare Edwards and Hassall, 1980, p. 8). The $100\,000\,g$ pellet contains the remains of the endoplasmic reticulum and is known as the microsomal fraction of the cell. The microsomal pellet is resuspended and portions added to a buffered solution containing NADPH and pesticide. Metabolites are usually recognised by chromatography.

Microsomal enzymes are of several kinds. Those responsible for the oxidation of drugs, pesticides and other foreign molecules must of necessity be able to act upon a wide range of substrates and are consequently known as **microsomal polysubstrate mono-oxygenases**. As will be seen in section 3.4, mono-oxygenases are of more than one sort, but the principal type contains a haem protein called cytochrome P_{450}.

Less is known about the oxidative systems in plants and in invertebrates than is known about those in warm-blooded vertebrates, but systems capable of performing in a similar manner to vertebrate mono-oxygenases are undoubtedly present. The *level* of mono-oxygenase activity, and indeed the activity of other enzymes that metabolise foreign compounds, varies considerably between species in both the plant and the animal kingdoms, but, with some exceptions, the *types* of primary metabolites produced under aerobic conditions are remarkably constant from phylum to phylum.

Reduction of certain types of pesticides can also be effected by microsomal and other enzymes. Reduction reactions are, however, more evident in a reducing milieu, such as occurs in the gut of vertebrates, in the mud beneath ponds and in certain types of soils. In each of these cases, microorganisms can reduce suitable pesticides; for example, nitro groups can be reduced to amino groups.

Conjugation processes usually require cooperation between membrane-bound enzymes in the microsomes and other enzymes and cofactors present in the cytosol. For example, **glucuronic acid** conjugates of metabolites are common in higher animals (section 3.6) and the enzyme that facilitates the conjugation is a membrane-bound microsomal enzyme. However, before it can operate, the glucuronic acid must first be activated, and this is brought about in two steps, each of which involves an enzyme in the cytosol. In addition, the endogenous conjugating substances (in the example above, a glucuronic acid derivative) are water-soluble compounds.

3.3 HYDROLASES

Many pesticides contain ester, amide or phosphate linkages, which are more or less readily attacked by hydrolases. Examples are the organophosphorus, pyrethroid and carbamate insecticides, the dithiocarbamate and dinitrophenol fungicides, and the urea and carbamate herbicides. In contrast to the oxidases (section 3.4) and the transferases (sections 3.5 and 3.6), the hydrolases do not require any coenzymes although they occasionally need cations to activate them.

Hydrolases are present in all living organisms and play an important role in pesticide metabolism. Nevertheless, the situation is not as straightforward as was originally thought. Hydrolysable linkages are not necessarily the locus of initial metabolic attack and, if they are attacked, it does not necessarily follow that the enzymes that attack them are hydrolases. As an example, many organophosphorus insecticides contain alkoxy groups attached to the phosphorus atom (R–O–P) and these linkages look likely candidates for hydrolytic attack; in fact, while hydrolase action is possible, the end-product (H–O–P) can be formed by two quite different reactions, namely by oxidative *O*-dealkylation (section 3.4) and by the transfer of an alkyl or other group to glutathione (section 3.5).

A second difficulty relates to the naming and substrate specificity of hydrolases. The latter act *inter alia* upon R–O–P linkages ('phosphatases'), R–COOR′ linkages (carboxylesterases, carboxyesterases) and R–CONHR′ linkages (carboxyamidases). However, most of the enzymes responsible for these reactions have not been purified. Consequently, it often remains uncertain whether the hydrolytic reactions being studied are catalysed by one enzyme of low specificity (e.g. an enzyme with both esterase and amidase function) or by a mixture of two or more enzymes of higher specificity.

The classification of the enzymes responsible for pesticide hydrolysis is particularly unsatisfactory (see Walker and Mackness, 1983). Indeed, the classification of enzymes in subgroups 3.1.1.1 and 3.1.1.2 of the International Union of Biochemistry (1979) classification has been challenged (Junge and Krisch, 1973). For present purposes it is sufficient to divide esterases into two main groups termed **A-esterases** and **B-esterases**. The A-esterases are those that (in addition to whatever other hydrolytic reactions they catalyse) are able to hydrolyse organophosphates such as paraoxon at ordinary concentration levels, whereas B-esterases are under the same conditions inhibited by organo-phosphates.

Figure 3.1 illustrates why some esterases are blocked by a given organo-phosphate while others can hydrolyse it (i.e. treat it as a substrate). According to this explanation, both A-type and B-type esterases bind to the enzyme surface but the rate at which dephosphorylation occurs after the splitting reaction is complete differs considerably (compare section 4.5). The different rates of dephosphorylation of a given organophosphate by enzymes in the two subgroups may reflect a chemical difference at the site of action. For example, in the (more primitive?) B subgroup, a fairly stable enzyme phosphate could be formed as a result of the presence of a serine –OH group at the binding site, whereas the more weakly binding –SH group could be present in the A-esterases (Augustinsson, 1964). Attention is drawn to an account given in section 4.5 in a somewhat different context, where the mode of action of different organophosphates and carbamates on one particular esterase is considered in relation to the rate constants of various reactions involving these insecticides.

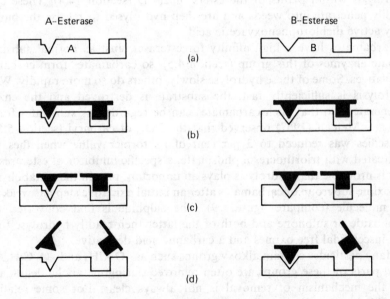

Figure 3.1 Postulated reason why A-esterases split, and B-esterases are inhibited by, organophosphates. (a) Phosphate-attracting site (left) may be slightly different in the two kinds of esterase. (b) Substrate attaches to both types of esterase. (c) Substrate is split by both types of esterase. (d) However, for the A type, both fractions leave the surface, allowing more enzyme action; but for the B type, one fraction, the phosphate, takes longer to depart and thus blocks the surface.

Up to 7 per cent of all microsomal proteins are membrane-bound esterases and these are predominantly of the B type. They do, however, also occur in serum and in pancreatic juice. A-type esterases in mammalian serum are largely associated with the high-density lipoprotein fraction (Walker and Mackness, 1987). The same authors could find no A-type esterase in a flour beetle. This is of interest, because others quoted by Walker and Mackness have reported that B-type esterases appear to be important in relation to the resistance of insects to organophosphorus compounds.

The following examples illustrate some of the hydrolytic processes referred to in later chapters. Malathion (figure 4.7) offers a straightforward instance in which the action of **carboxylesterase** leads to detoxication:

$$R-COO-C_2H_5 \xrightarrow[\text{H}_2\text{O}]{\text{carboxylesterase}} R-COOH + C_2H_5OH \tag{3.1}$$

The efficiency of this process in some higher animals helps to explain why malathion is of low toxicity to them (section 4.8).

A second important reaction that is mediated by carboxylesterase is the hydrolysis within plants of the esters of 2,4-D (section 14.4). These esters readily penetrate into weeds and are then hydrolysed to release the biologically active dichlorophenoxyacetic acid.

Carbamates have a high affinity for esterases. Just as normal substrates acylate enzymes of this group (section 4.5), so carbamates form carbamoyl derivatives. Some of these hydrolyse slowly, others do so more rapidly. Where hydrolysis is sufficiently fast, the substrate is destroyed and the enzyme regenerated, so that such carbamates can be regarded as substrates for the enzyme. Metcalf (1967) observed that the LD_{50} of carbaryl (section 5.5) to houseflies was reduced to 3 per cent of its former value when flies were pretreated with triorthocresol phosphate, a specific inhibitor of esterases.

It is probable that hydrolysis plays an important part in the metabolism of the oxime subgroup of carbamates after an initial oxidative step has weakened the molecule (compare figure 5.9). The sulphide is first converted to a sulphoxide or sulphone and both of the latter then readily hydrolyse to the non-insecticidal free oximes and a carbamic acid derivative.

Many pesticides contain alkoxy groups such as $-O-CH_3$ and $-O-C_2H_5$. The alkyl parts of these groups are often removed during metabolic degradation but the mechanism of removal is not always clear. For some relatively unstable compounds (e.g. dichlorvos, figure 4.15), hydrolytic removal may be of quantitative importance, but there is increasing evidence that small alkoxy groups in many compounds are removed by a **glutathione transferase** system (section 3.5). This system is, for example, probably responsible for a major proportion of the O-dealkylation of phorate (figure 4.12).

The **amide** linkage is somewhat similar to that in esters, and it is attacked by

amidases. Dimethoate is an important organophosphorus insecticide that is hydrolysed in this way:

$$CH_3O \diagdown \underset{CH_3O \diagup}{\overset{S}{\underset{\|}{P}}} - S - CH_2 - CO - NHCH_3 \xrightarrow[H_2O]{amidase} CH_3O \diagdown \underset{CH_3O \diagup}{\overset{S}{\underset{\|}{P}}} - S - CH_2 - COOH + CH_3NH_2$$

Dimethoate   Dimethoate acid

(3.2)

Propanil (section 14.11) is an important selective herbicide for the control of weeds in rice. It appears that rice plants contain an aryl carboxylamidase which protects them by catalysing the following hydrolysis:

$$C_2H_5CO-NH\underset{Cl}{\overset{Cl}{\bigcirc}} \xrightarrow[H_2O]{aryl\ carboxylamidase} C_2H_5COOH + H_2N\underset{Cl}{\overset{Cl}{\bigcirc}}$$

Propanil   Dichloroaniline

(3.3)

As was seen earlier, it is possible that some carboxylamidases are ordinary carboxylesterases capable of selecting amides as substrates. This possibility is of more than academic importance because the problems of cross-resistance between such compounds as malathion (an ester) and dimethoate (an amide) are likely to be more severe if the same enzyme attacks both molecular groupings. There is no doubt that crude carboxylesterases sometimes attack amide linkages. This could be due to the presence of two or more similar enzymes, but the esterase and amidase activities cannot usually be separated by purification.

Another complication of considerable importance relates to the possible role of hydrolases in insect resistance. Resistance to some insecticides is known to be associated with high levels of carboxylesterase. The assumption in such cases has usually been that the insecticide is inactivated by hydrolysis. However, instances have been reported where resistance appears to be correlated with a lower than usual carboxylesterase activity. The matter is, as yet, unresolved, but it seems possible that a mutant form of carboxylesterase exists which, while less effective than the non-mutant form against carboxylic esters, is a more potent attacker of some other types of hydrolysable linkage (Plapp, 1970).

Epoxide hydrolases (or **hydratases**, or **hydrases**) are present in the microsomal, the cytosolic and probably other parts of cells. In higher animals, they are particularly abundant in hepatic cells. They are of great importance because they destroy epoxides, and the latter can arise by autoxidation and peroxidation of endogenous ('natural') substances as well as by mono-oxygenase action upon foreign compounds that get into the body by mistake. Epoxides are highly active substances that directly, or indirectly after further oxidation, can do a great deal of damage by binding to DNA or to other cellular components. Elderly animals often respond less well to drugs, and also tend to develop more cancers, than do younger animals, possibly, and in part, because epoxide hydrolase activity diminishes in old age (Kaur and Gill, 1985).

Before considering pesticide metabolism in particular, attention should be drawn to the general position of epoxides in metabolism. Many, perhaps most, cyclic molecules containing one or mor double bonds have the potential to form epoxides within the body. More often than not, these are highly labile— so much so that for many years their role was not fully appreciated*. However, benzenoid, polycyclic and some heterocyclic substances form inter- mediate epoxides that are highly reactive and therefore potentially damaging to the cell. The role of the epoxide hydrolase is, in effect, to 'get in quick' and render them innocuous before they do irreparable harm, such as acting as mutagens or carcinogens.

Organic pesticides, in common with other organic substances, form epox- ides. A very few are stable enough to be isolated. Indeed, in two extreme cases, epoxides have been used as active ingredients. These are dieldrin and endrin. In view of what has been said above, it is ironic that these two substances are notoriously persistent precisely because they are poor substrates for epoxide hydrolase. They do, however, hydrolyse very slowly to the respective *trans*-dihydrodiols (figure 6.11).

More typically, the epoxide is unstable, indeed sometimes so transient that it cannot be isolated. In such cases, epoxide hydrolase often plays a role in the sequential biodegradation of the substance, usually by opening the epoxide bond with the formation of vicinal *trans*-diols (i.e. hydroxy groups on adjacent carbon atoms and facing in opposite directions). One such example is carbaryl (section 5.5). The insecticide can be metabolised by several routes; in one of these it is oxidised by microsomal oxidases to give carbaryl epoxide, and this is then converted to a *trans*-dihydrodiol by the action of epoxide hydrolase:

(3.4)

Carbaryl ring with aromatic character   Aryl epoxide   *Trans*-dihydrodiol

---

* The author synthesised a stable epoxide and discussed its use in the study of drug metabolism at a conference. Afterwards, at coffee, the diminutive author was approached by an even more diminutive delegate who showed great interest. So I asked him, 'Please forgive my asking, but who are you?' He replied, 'I'm Boyland, and I discovered them!'

3.4 MICROSOMAL POLYSUBSTRATE OXYGENASES

Tightly bound to the smooth endoplasmic reticulum, especially of hepatocytes in higher animals, are enzymes that are capable of inserting one of the two oxygen atoms from an oxygen molecule into an appropriate substrate, R–H. The other oxygen atom eventually forms part of a water molecule:

$$R–H + O_2 + [2H] \rightarrow R–OH + H_2O \tag{3.5}$$

Mono-oxygenases get their name from the fact that the atoms of the oxygen molecule are separated from one another and end up in different substances. They have also been known as mixed-function oxidases. A unique feature of the major mono-oxygenase system is the presence of a haem protein termed cytochrome P_{450}, which links electron flow to the reduction of the oxygen molecule by mechanisms that are still imperfectly understood. Similar but not necessarily identical systems appear to exist in organisms as diverse as vertebrates, insects and plants. A second polysubstrate oxygenase, often called FAD-containing oxygenase, appears to play an important but more limited role in pesticide metabolism and will be considered later; in common with the cytochrome P_{450} system, it has an absolute requirement for NADPH.

Considering first the cytochrome P_{450} mono-oxygenase system, the unique haem protein is named because of the position of a special spectral line formed when the cytochrome is poisoned with carbon monoxide. Cytochrome P_{450} is remarkable in that it is functionally a composite between mitochondrial cytochromes, for which iron can assume Fe^{3+} and Fe^{2+} forms, and haemoglobin, in which the iron remains in the ferrous state but can coordinate with one oxygen molecule per porphyrin group to form oxyhaemoglobin.

The main features of the mono-oxygenase system are summarised in figure 3.2, a scheme essentially similar to one proposed by Estabrook *et al.* (1971). The substrate, XH, probably becomes attached to the ferric form of cytochrome P_{450}. An electron from NADPH vicariously reduces the complex to the ferrous form. This, incidentally, explains the paradox that mono-oxygenase action requires the obligatory presence of a reducing agent. The oxidising agent, molecular oxygen, then attaches itself to the ferrous form of a cytochrome P_{450}–substrate complex. The bond between the two oxygen atoms is then weakened, possibly by addition of a second electron. An intramolecular electron shift then leads to the formation of a peroxide–XH–ferric P_{450} complex. This apparently loses an oxide ion to protons in the medium, leaving behind a highly active oxygen atom, which reacts with the XH attached nearby to form the metabolite, X–OH. The ferric form of cytochrome P_{450} is then ready to accept more substrate.

The enzyme that passes electrons from NADPH to cytochrome P_{450} is a flavoprotein. Thus the microsomal electron transport system comprises at

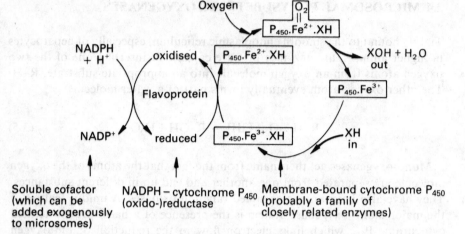

Figure 3.2 Proposed scheme for the oxidation of a foreign compound, XH, by the cytochrome P_{450} mono-oxygenase system

least three components reminiscent of those in the mitochondrion, namely a reduced pyridine nucleotide, a flavoprotein and a cytochrome. A cytochrome b_5 is also present in microsomes and may participate in this system, as may a non-haem iron protein.

The cytochrome P_{450} mono-oxygenase system from several sources has been solubilised and separated into three components. These are a cytochrome P_{450} fraction (or fractions), a flavoprotein fraction (this contains the NADPH–cytochrome P_{450} oxidoreductase) and a phospholipid fraction. In some cases these three fractions can be reassembled to give, when exogenous NADPH is added, a reconstituted, functional mono-oxygenase system. Such procedures revealed that cytochrome P_{450} is, in fact, not a single entity but a family of closely similar enzymes with slightly different substrate specificities and physical properties (see, for example, Johnson, 1980). Each enzyme in such a family is termed an **isozyme**. The isozymes in different organisms appear to be different, or at least to be present in different proportions. In the rat it has been shown that some forms are under hormonal control (Finnen and Hassall, 1984). Another example is provided by the work of Levi *et al.* (1988). Different cytochrome P_{450} isozymes were isolated from livers of mice and were then incubated with fenitrothion (section 4.8). This substance can oxidise in two ways—either to give fenitro-oxon or to give 4-nitro-*m*-cresol. It was found that the production ratio of these two metabolic products was characteristically different for each of the isolated isozymes. More recently, it has become evident that multiple forms of cytochrome P_{450} also exist in insects. For example, Moldenke *et al.* (1984) isolated two forms of cytochrome P_{450} from preparations made from the abdomens of houseflies and then successfully reconstituted the mono-oxygenase system. The two forms of cytochrome P_{450} metabolised different substrates at different rates; moreover, only one of the two forms appeared to *O*-demethylate a coumarin derivative (a qualitative difference such as this is always strong evidence for the existence of different cytochromes).

The cytochrome P_{450} mono-oxygenase system is rather specifically inhibited by a group of substances called **methylene dioxyphenols**, of which **piperonyl butoxide** is an important example. The significance of these substances to pesticide science was first evident in relation to pyrethroids, under which heading they are further discussed (section 7.3). Later, they were found to delay oxidative metabolism of carbamates (section 5.5) and of certain other pesticides. Other well known inhibitors of the cytochrome P_{450} mono-oxygenase system are n-octylamine and carbon monoxide.

Much of the work on the second polysubstrate oxygenase system was pioneered by Hodgson and his colleagues. Hajjar and Hodgson (1982) demonstrated that, in the presence of NADPH and oxygen, an FAD-dependent mono-oxygenase from pig liver microsomes could oxidise thioethers to sulphoxides. Unlike cytochrome P_{450} mono-oxygenase systems, these sulphoxidations were not inhibited by n-octylamine. Later, the systems in mouse and pig liver were purified (Smyser *et al.*, 1985) and the kinetic parameters, K_m and V_{max}, were determined for several organophosphorus and carbamate insecticides. It was found, as expected, that the enzyme–substrate affinity, as measured by K_m, varied widely but that the maximal velocity, V_{max}, was fairly similar for a range of thioethers. A one-to-one stoichiometry was found to exist between NADPH reduction and thioether oxidation, suggesting that this mono-oxygenase system (one proposal is shown in figure 3.3) was not responsible for the further oxidation of sulphoxides to sulphones which occurs *in vivo*.

Mono-oxygenase reactions of importance in pesticide metabolism are summarised in table 3.1. The cytochrome P_{450} system participates in at least the first four of these reactions, but the second enzyme system, often termed FAD-containing mono-oxygenase (Kulkarni and Hodgson, 1984), may be dominant in some of the reactions under headings 5(a) and 5(b). In reactions depicted under 1(a) and 1(b), a C–H bond is broken and an oxygen atom is interpolated (aliphatic and aromatic hydroxylation). Reactions of the second sort are analogous to the first but involve alkyl groups attached to oxygen or nitrogen atoms. The hydroxylation often, but not always, leads to unstable products, which split up to yield an aldehyde together with an alcohol (*O*-dealkylation) or an amine (*N*-dealkylation). Thirdly, oxygen can be attached to an olefinic bond to form an epoxide. This leads to the formation of the three-membered heterocyclic **oxirane** ring. Fourthly, an element (sulphur) in group 6 of the periodic table can be replaced by the more electronegative

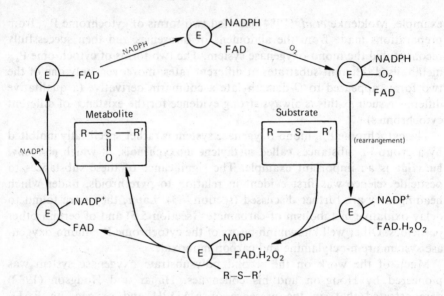

Figure 3.3 Proposed mechanism whereby a FAD-containing mono-oxygenase brings about the oxidation of a sulphide to a sulphoxide (after Kulkarni and Hodgson, 1984)

element oxygen. Reactions of the fifth kind lead to the coordination of oxygen atoms to thioether sulphur atoms to give sulphoxides or to amine nitrogen atoms to form unstable amine oxides. Sulphoxides can sometimes undergo further oxidation to sulphones.

Some of the reactions listed in table 3.1 will now be illustrated by cross-reference to insecticides, fungicides and herbicides that are encountered in later chapters.

Aliphatic hydroxylation is illustrated by the conversion of a methyl group, situated in the acid moiety of the pyrethrin molecule, to a hydroxymethyl group (section 7.3):

Hydroxylated pyrethrin

Other examples are the hydroxylation of the methyl group of the herbicide, bromacil (section 15.3), the oxidation of a propyl part of the trifluralin

Table 3.1 Oxidation reactions involving mono-oxygenases

Type of reaction	General representation
1 (a) Aliphatic hydroxylation	$R{-}CH_2{-}H \xrightarrow{[O]} R{-}CH_2{-}OH$
(b) Aromatic hydroxylation	$R{-}C_6H_5 \xrightarrow{[O]} R{-}C_6H_4{-}OH$
2 (a) O-Dealkylation	$R{-}O{-}CH_3 \xrightarrow{[O]} R{-}O{-}CH_2O{-}H \rightarrow R{-}OH$
(b) N-Dealkylation	$R{-}NH{-}CH_3 \xrightarrow{[O]} R{-}NH{-}CH_2O{-}H \rightarrow R{-}NH_2$
3 Epoxidation	$\mathrm{C{=}C} \xrightarrow{[O]}$ epoxide
4 Substitution of oxygen for sulphur	$\mathord{>}P{=}S \xrightarrow{[O]} \mathord{>}P{=}O$
5 (a) Formation of sulphoxides and sulphones	$R{-}CH_2{-}S{-}CH_3 \xrightarrow{[O]} R{-}CH_2{-}\overset{O}{S}{-}CH_3 \xrightarrow{[O]} R{-}CH_2{-}\overset{O}{\underset{O}{S}}{-}CH_3$
(b) Formation of amine oxides	$R{-}N(CH_3)_2 \xrightarrow{[O]} R{-}\overset{O}{N}(CH_3)_2$

molecule and the hydroxylation of the butyl side-chain of the fungicide, ethirimol (section 12.6):

Hydroxylated ethirimol

Ring hydroxylation is a common metabolic reaction for pesticides, since many contain aromatic or heterocyclic ring structures. Thus, in the presence of NADPH, carbaryl hydroxylates to give a mixture of 4-hydroxy- and 5-hydroxycarbaryl:

Hydroxylated carbaryl

Similarly, the herbicide, chlorpropham (section 15.4), is oxidised to phenolic derivatives in plants (Rouchaud and Meyer, 1982):

Chlorpropham   Hydroxylated chlorpropham

O-**Dealkylation** is quite common in pesticides but it can be brought about by at least three mechanisms. Care is thus necessary before attributing such a change to microsomal mono-oxygenases. The involvement of NADPH must, in particular, be demonstrated. One such example would appear to be the oxidation of the systemic fungicide, chloroneb (section 12.9), by the fungus *Rhizoctonia*:

Chloroneb

N-Dealkylation reactions are also common in pesticide metabolism since many pesticides are substituted amines or amides. The carbamate, carbofuran (section 5.6), is an example. For this compound the intermediate hydroxymethyl compound is fairly stable:

Carbofuran   N-Hydroxymethyl carbofuran

In the case of the herbicide, diuron, the reaction is similar but, since the product is unstable, the hydroxymethylation is followed by the elimination of the elements of formaldehyde:

Diuron   N-Demethyl diuron

Atrazine and many other triazine herbicides also undergo N-dealkylation:

Atrazine   N-Depropyl atrazine

In this group the reaction is of interest because partial resistance of some crops appears to exist when this N-dealkylation pathway is well developed.

Epoxide formation is a somewhat different type of NADPH-dependent reaction. As was mentioned in the previous section, epoxides are probably transitory intermediates in the metabolism of numerous unsaturated compounds. In the case of the organochlorine compound, aldrin, however, the epoxide is a stable product, which not only persists in the fat of organisms but is more toxic than the parent olefin:

Aldrin   Dieldrin

The transient epoxide of carbaryl was referred to earlier, at the end of section 3.3.

Oxidative desulphuration is a particularly important metabolic reaction for many thiophosphate insecticides. In this NADPH-dependent process, a sulphur atom is replaced by the more electronegative oxygen atom. Almost invariably, the oxidation results in a molecule that is a better cholinesterase inhibitor than was the original substance. In consequence, when this reaction occurs it can result, not in detoxication, but in activation of the pesticide. It is a common reaction in insects, which can thus be said to carry out **lethal metabolism**—they are, as it were, executed by their own 'detoxifying' enzyme system. A well known example is the activation of parathion to the highly toxic paraoxon:

Parathion   Paraoxon

Sulphoxidation is the oxidation of sulphide sulphur to sulphoxide. The reaction is probably catalysed by the FAD-containing mono-oxygenase system. An example is the oxidation of the systemic insecticide, demeton-*S*-methyl (section 4.9) to its sulphoxide:

Demeton-*S*-methyl   Sulphoxide of demeton-*S*-methyl

A second example is the sulphoxidation of the carbamate insecticide, aldicarb:

$$CH_3-S-C(CH_3)_2-CH{=}N-O-CONH-CH_3 \xrightarrow[O_2]{NADPH} CH_3-\underset{\underset{O}{\|}}{S}-C(CH_3)_2-\text{etc.} \longrightarrow CH_3-\underset{\underset{O\ \ O}{/\!/\backslash}}{S}-C(CH_3)-\text{etc.}$$

| Aldicarb | Aldicarb sulphoxide | Aldicarb sulphone |

In both of these cases, sulphoxidation is sometimes followed by further oxidation to a sulphone. As was mentioned earlier, it remains uncertain which enzyme system is responsible for the change.

3.5 ROLE OF GLUTATHIONE IN PESTICIDE DEGRADATION

Glutathione (GSH) is a tripeptide comprising residues of glycine, cysteine and glutamic acid. It is important in relation to the degradation of pesticides for a major metabolic pathway involves **glutathione-*S*-transferase** reactions.

Glutathione often forms a conjugate with the intruding foreign compound, whereas most other conjugating endogenous substances (section 3.6) take part in secondary reactions, which only occur after the original substance has undergone oxidation or hydrolysis. Several groups of glutathione-*S*-transferases are known, of which the three shown in table 3.2 are of considerable importance in pesticide detoxication. These transferases are present in the soluble cell fraction of mammalian liver and have molecular weights of the order of 45 000. It is of interest that the primitive function of these enzymes, if other than to detoxify poisons, remains unknown. Clark *et al.* (1984) have achieved up to a hundred-fold purification of glutathione-*S*-transferases from houseflies. As has long been known for vertebrates, they found that it was possible to separate several different groups of transferases with different substrate preferences and different subunit weights. Glutathione-*S*-transferases from plants are inhibited by triphenyltin chloride and by the oxirane derivative, tridiphane. It is of interest that the latter is a synergist of the herbicide, atrazine, presumably because it prevents decomposition of atrazine (section 15.2) by this mechanism (Lamoureux and Rusness, 1986).

Glutathione-*S*-epoxide transferases open the epoxide ring and insert glutathione by an addition reaction. They may be important in the destruction of carcinogenic oxides (Boyland, 1974). Benzene epoxides are not readily attacked unless the ring contains chlorine atoms, but naphthalene and phenanthrene epoxides are satisfactory substrates for these enzymes.

Among pesticidal compounds, dieldrin, endrin and heptachlor epoxide are all organochlorine epoxides, but their glutathione derivatives are only minor products in most of the species so far investigated. Epoxide transferases may,

Table 3.2   Three groups of glutathione-S-transferases of importance in pesticide degradation (GSH = glutathione)

Type	Name	Reaction examples
1	Glutathione-S-epoxide transferase	C_6H_5—$OCH_2 \cdot CH$—CH_2 (epoxide) $\xrightarrow{GSH}$ C_6H_5—$OCH_2 \cdot CH(SG) \cdot CH_2OH$
2	Glutathione-S-aryl transferase	(a) Cl-C_6H_3-NO_2 (3,5-Dichloronitrobenzene) $\xrightarrow{GSH}$ Cl-$C_6H_3(NO_2)$—S—G + HI (b) Diazinon: $(C_2H_5O)_2 P(S)$—O—[pyrimidine with $CH(CH_3)_2$, CH_3] $\xrightarrow{GSH}$ G—S—[pyrimidine with $CH(CH_3)_2$, CH_3] + $(C_2H_5O)_2 \cdot PS \cdot OH$
3	Glutathione-S-alkyl transferase	(a) CH_3I $\xrightarrow{GSH}$ CH_3—S—G + HI (b) Methyl parathion: $(CH_3O)_2 P(S)$—O—C_6H_4—NO_2 $\xrightarrow{GSH}$ $(HO)(CH_3O)P(O)$—O—C_6H_4—NO_2 + CH_3—S—G

however, play a role in the further metabolism of aromatic compounds that form epoxide intermediates (e.g. carbaryl, figure 5.3).

Glutathione-*S*-aryl transferases are present in animal liver and probably also in plants (Lamoureux and Davison, 1975). Considerable inter-species variation in the distribution of these enzymes exists, the activity in the female dog being, for example, some 40 times greater than the activity in adult humans (Walker, 1975). These transferases probably contain active thiol groups because they are blocked by alkylating agents and by mercuribenzoate. Typically, they unite with a substrate in such a way that hydrogen halide is eliminated (e.g. dichloronitrobenzene in table 3.2). A similar reaction occurs in plants to give rise to glutathione conjugates of atrazine and some other members of the chlorinated triazine subfamily of herbicides (section 15.2). It is of interest that maize and some other crops that are resistant to atrazine are well endowed with this enzyme system.

$$C_2H_5-HN-\underset{\text{Atrazine}}{\overset{Cl}{\triangle}}-NH-CH\overset{CH_3}{\underset{CH_3}{}} \xrightarrow[\text{aryl transferase}]{\text{GSH +}} C_2H_5-HN-\overset{S-G}{\triangle}-NH-CH\overset{CH_3}{\underset{CH_3}{}} + HCl$$

Atrazine

Glutathione complex with a dechlorinated atrazine residue

Another important reaction usually attributed to enzymes of this group is the combination of glutathione with the 'leaving group' of certain organophosphorus insecticides (section 4.5). The enzymes responsible are still ill-defined, but it is now evident that some of the reactions leading to detoxication of organophosphorus compounds originally ascribed to hydrolases are, in fact, glutathione-dependent. Thus diazinon is cleaved in the way shown in table 3.2. It should be noted that enzymes of this class lead to the union of glutathione with an aryl or heterocyclic group, which constitutes a sizable part of the original molecule of the pesticide.

The **glutathione-*S*-alkyl transferases** typically react with alkyl halides in the manner shown in example 3(a) of table 3.2. More important in relation to pesticide metabolism, however, these or similar enzymes can remove methyl groups from those organophosphorus insecticides that contain the CH_3-O-P group. In contrast to the aryl transferases above, they therefore catalyse reactions in which the glutathione becomes attached to what was a small part of the original molecule. Since the major part of the molecule remains unconjugated, the role of glutathione was overlooked in much of the earlier work and many such reactions were mistakenly attributed to hydrolytic cleavage. The glutathione-*S*-transferase reaction is particularly effective in the removal of methyl groups; ethyl and larger alkyl groups are removed much less readily, at least from organophosphorus compounds. Methyl parathion (table 3.2) and fenitrothion are demethylated, in part, by a glutathione-dependent mechanism. So, probably, are mevinphos and dichlorvos (chapter 4).

3.6 OTHER CONJUGATION REACTIONS

Primary oxidative, hydrolytic or reductive changes usually uncover or insert active groups such as hydroxyl or carboxyl, which make the molecules more polar. These polar groups may then undergo secondary **conjugation** with endogenous molecules, a process that further increases polarity and, in animals, facilitates excretion in urine or faeces. In plants, these more soluble substances are usually stored in the cell vacuoles, and deciduous plants get rid of them when leaves fall to the ground.

Conjugation reactions are classified according to the nature of the conjugating agent (table 3.3). **Glucuronides** are the principal conjugates in most terrestrial vertebrates. The donor of the glucuronic acid is uridine diphosphate glucuronic acid (UDPGA) and thus the reaction involves the transfer of glucuronic acid from one organic molecule to another. The enzymes, of which several exist with overlapping specificities, are termed **glucuronyl transferases**. They are largely associated with the microsomes.

Many insecticides, fungicides and herbicides are converted to glucuronic

Table 3.3   Conjugation reactions in vertebrates, invertebrates and plants

Endogenous conjugant	Type of organism[a]
Glucuronic acid	Mammals, birds, reptiles, terrestrial amphibians, some fish
Glucose	Higher plants, insects, some molluscs
Arginine	Arachnids, myriapods
Glutamic acid or glutamine	Arachnids, some myriapods
Glycine	Fish, crustaceans
Sulphate	Amphibians, echinoderms, some crustaceans, some molluscs, some insects
Others	Acetylation (fish, amphibia, a few insects) Phosphate (a few arachnids, some dipterans)

[a] Found in many investigated members—not necessarily true of every member of the group. Some organisms produce more than one type of conjugation product.

acid conjugates after primary metabolism by animal liver enzymes. In rats, for example, carbaryl is converted to 4-hydroxycarbaryl and 1-naphthol, and both of these are excreted mainly as **O-glucuronides** (figure 3.4). Dichlorvos (section 4.10) and resmethrin (section 7.2) are two other insecticides that can be ultimately converted to O-glucuronides.

The fungicide, ferbam (section 11.2), provides an example of a substance that is converted, in part, to an **S-glucuronide** in some animals:

$$\left[(CH_3)_2 N - \underset{\underset{S}{\|}}{C} - S \right]_3 \!\!\!-\!Fe \xrightarrow[\text{UDPGA transferase}]{\text{UDPGA +}} 3\ (CH_3)_2 N - \underset{\underset{S}{\|}}{C} - S - \text{glucuronic acid}$$

In contrast to most terrestrial vertebrates, insects and plants usually produce **glucose conjugates** (table 3.3). The mechanism resembles that for glucuronide formation but uridine diphosphate glucose (UDPG) replaces UDPGA as donor. The glucose becomes attached to alcoholic, thiol or amino groups by a β-glucoside linkage, the enzyme responsible being a glucose transferase. Glucosides, like glucuronic acid derivatives, are more polar and water-soluble than the parent aglycones (after the sugar of a glycoside is removed by hydrolysis, the non-sugar residue is termed an **aglycone**). A specific example of a substance that forms an **N-glycoside** is the herbicide, propanil (section 14.11), which is hydrolysed to 3,4-dichloroaniline in treated rice plants. This is then conjugated with glucose to form N-3,4-dichloro-phenylglucosylamine.

Sulphate esters are important in relation to the excretion of foreign compounds by amphibians and by many invertebrates. They are, in fact, ionised bisulphates, $R.O.SO_3^-$, rather than sulphates, $R.O.SO_2.OR'$. The formation of sulphate conjugates is catalysed by **sulphotransferases**. These enzymes are present in the soluble cell fraction of mammalian liver and kidney. They require the cooperation of a soluble cofactor, **3'-phosphoadeno-syl-5'-phosphosulphate** (PAPS). Sulphate esters of phenols formed by primary metabolism of pesticides occur in many higher animals, but usually as a minor pathway compared to glucuronide formation. For example, small amounts of sulphate conjugates of carbofuran derivatives are eliminated by several mammals. In insects, however, the route may sometimes be as important as glucoside production. Conjugation with sulphate is rare in higher plants.

Glycine conjugates occur mostly in vertebrates and are formed especially from aromatic pesticides, which, after primary metabolism, give compounds containing carboxyl groups. Thus chlorthiamid (section 16.2) breaks down to give dichlobenil, which, in turn, gives rise to 2,6-dichlorobenzoic acid or its hydroxylated derivatives. The latter then conjugate with glycine (figure 3.5). An interesting characteristic of those arachnids so far investigated (including ticks, spiders and scorpions) is that three other amino acids—arginine, glutamic acid and glutamine—are major conjugating agents (table 3.3).

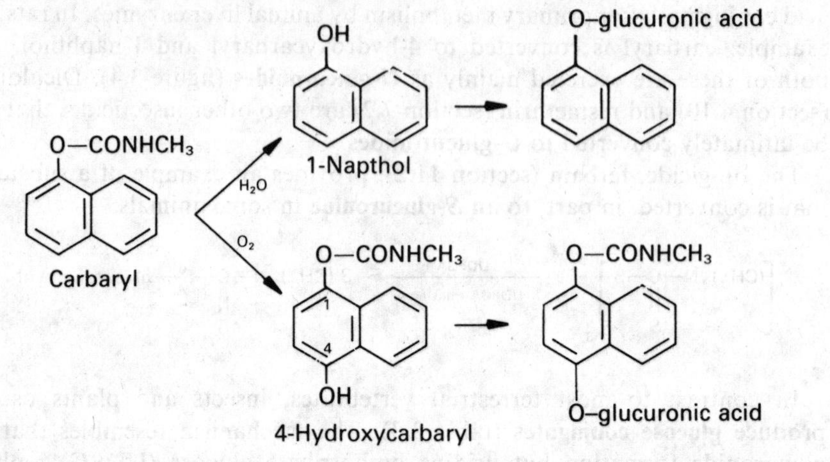

Figure 3.4   *O*-Glucuronide formation from hydrolytic and oxidative products of carbaryl

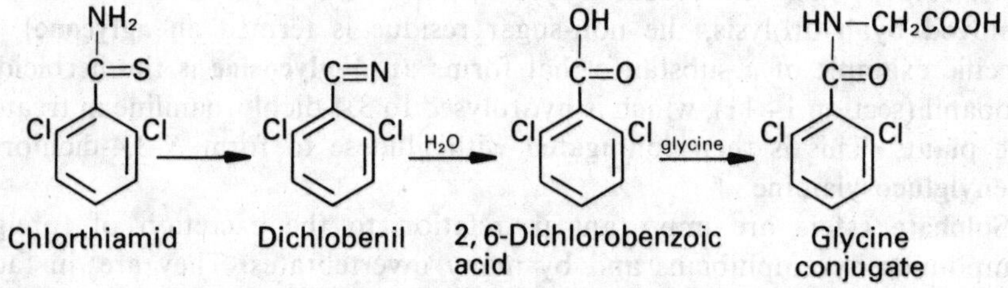

Figure 3.5   Glycine conjugates of chlorthiamid derivatives

Finally, it will be recalled that glutathione occupies a somewhat anomalous position in that it usually reacts with the initial foreign compound and not with a metabolite of that compound (section 3.5). However, glutathione conjugates can themselves undergo secondary changes, for excreted products in many organisms are not glutathione conjugates as such, but derivatives called **mercapturic acids**.

Glutathione is a tripeptide and it conjugates with foreign compounds to give complexes of the sort shown in figure 3.6. If the glycine and glutamic acid are hydrolytically removed, a cysteine derivative of the foreign compound remains (figure 3.6b). Acetylation of the amino group of the cysteine then frequently occurs so that the excreted material in many higher animals is an *N*-acetylcysteine derivative. This is called a mercapturic acid. In insects, glutathione conjugates tend to be either excreted unchanged or converted to cysteine rather than to acetylcysteine derivatives (Walker, 1975).

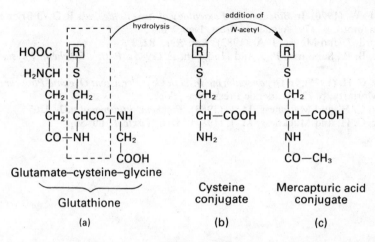

Figure 3.6 Structures of glutathione and mercapturic acid conjugates. (a) Glutathione, a tripeptide, conjugates with a pesticide residue, R. (b) A cysteine conjugate is formed on hydrolysis of (a). (c) *N*-Acetylation of (b) gives a mercapturic acid derivative

REFERENCES

Augustinsson, K. B. (1964). *J. Histochem. Cytochem.*, **12**, 744

Boyland, E. (1974). *Biochem. Soc. Trans.*, **2**, 167

Clark, A. G., Shamaan, N. A., Dauterman, W. C. and Hayaoka, T. (1984). *Pestic. Biochem. Physiol.*, **22**, 51

Edwards, N. A. and Hassall, K. A. (1980). *Biochemistry and Physiology of the Cell*, 2nd edn. McGraw-Hill, Maidenhead

Estabrook, R. W., Baron, J., Peterson, J. and Ishimura, Y. (1971). *Biochem. J.*, **125**, 3

Finnen, M. J. and Hassall, K. A. (1984). *Drug Metab. Dispn.*, **12**, 127

Hajjar, N. P. and Hodgson, E. (1982). *Biochem. Pharmacol.*, **31**, 745

International Union of Biochemistry (1979). *Enzyme Nomenclature: Recommendation 1978 of the Nomenclature Committee of the IUB*. Academic Press, New York

Johnson, E. F. (1980). In *Biochemistry, Biophysics and Regulation of Cytochrome P450*, eds J.-A. Gustafsson, J. Carlstedt-Duke, A. Mode and J. Rafter. Elsevier Biomedical Press, Amsterdam

Junge, W. and Krisch, K. (1973). *Mol. Cell. Biochem.*, **1**, 41

Kaur, S. and Gill, S. S. (1985). *Drug Metab. Dispn.*, **13**, 711

Kulkarni, A. P. and Hodgson, E. (1984). *Annu. Rev. Pharmacol. Toxicol.*, **24**, 19

Lamoureux, G. L. and Davison, K. L. (1975). *Pestic. Biochem. Physiol.*, **5**, 497

Lamoureux, G. L. and Rusness, D. G. (1986). *Pestic. Biochem. Physiol.*, **26**, 323

Levi, P. E., Hollingworth, R. M. and Hodgson, E. (1988). *Pestic. Biochem. Physiol.*, **32**, 224

Metcalf, R. L. (1967). *Annu. Rev. Entomol.*, **12**, 229

Moldenke, A. F., Vincent, D. R., Farnsworth, D. E. and Terriere, L. C. (1984). *Pestic. Biochem. Physiol.*, **21**, 358

Plapp, F. W. (1970). In *Biochemical Toxicology of Insecticides*, eds R.D. O'Brien and I. Yamamoto, p. 179. Academic Press, New York

Rouchard, J. and Meyer, J. A. (1982). *Res. Rev.*, **82**, 1

Smyser, B. P., Sabourin, P. J. and Hodgson, E. (1985). *Pestic. Biochem. Physiol.*, **24**, 368

Walker, C. H. (1975). In *Organochlorine Insecticides: Persistent Organic Pollutants*, ed. F. Moriarty, p. 73. Academic Press, New York

Walker, C. H. and Mackness, M. I. (1983). *Biochem. Pharmacol.*, **32**, 3265

Walker, C. H. and Mackness, M. I. (1987). *Arch. Toxicol.*, **60**, 30

4 Organophosphorus insecticides

4.1 INTRODUCTION

During the Second World War, German scientists under the direction of Gerhard Schrader were engaged on work with organophosphorus compounds that led eventually to the development of both the organophosphorus insecticides and the highly toxic nerve gases, tabun and sarin. The latter were, in fact, not used by either side in that war, but this association of organophosphorus insecticides with war gases was hardly an auspicious beginning for a group of compounds that was destined to become one of the main weapons in our armoury against insect pests of importance in agriculture, public hygiene and medicine. The earliest members of the group, marketed in the immediate post-war years, did little to allay these fears, for most of them were very toxic to vertebrates.

Altogether some 100 000 organophosphorus compounds have been screened for their possible insecticidal action, and over 100 have been marketed for this purpose. An important feature of the group is that different members possess very different physicochemical properties; in particular, they have different vapour pressures at room temperature and different solubilities in water. They also vary considerably in their chemical stability and their toxicity to mammals (table 4.1).

This wide spectrum of physicochemical and biological properties enables appropriate substances to possess a correspondingly wide range of uses in agriculture and in animal hygiene. Some are used as fumigants, others as contact poisons and yet others as systemic compounds. Some are used for crop protection early in the growing season, whereas some others are particularly valuable near harvest time. Those used early in the season must be sufficiently persistent to avoid the necessity of multiple application with its attendant increase in cost and effort. On the other hand, those used late in the season are specifically chosen because they do *not* persist very long; they must disappear sufficiently rapidly to ensure that negligible residues remain when the crop is harvested.

Table 4.1 Physicochemical and biological characteristics of some organophosphorus insecticides

Common name	Water solubility at 20–25°C (ppm)	Vapour pressure at 20°C (mmHg)	Persistence	Oral LD_{50} in male rats (mg/kg)	Systemic properties (by foliage application)[a]
Mevinphos	Miscible	Not given[b]	Short	7[c], 3[b]	Transient
Dichlorvos	10 000[d]	1.2×10^{-2}[e]	Short	25[f], 56[b]	No
Dimethoate	25 000[d]	8.5×10^{-6}[b]	Moderate	320[b]	Yes
Demeton-S-methyl	3 300[d]	3.6×10^{-4}[b]	Moderate	57[b]	Yes
Menazon	250[d]	1×10^{-6}[b]	Moderate	1950[b]	Slight
Malathion	145[b]	1.2×10^{-4}[e]	Short/Moderate	2800	No (LS)
Pirimiphos methyl	5[g]	1×10^{-4}	Moderate	2000	No (LS)
Fenitrothion	Almost insoluble	$\begin{cases} 6 \times 10^{-6}\text{[b]} \\ 5.4 \times 10^{-5}\text{[e]} \end{cases}$	Moderate	>250[b,e]	No
Bromophos	40[b]	1.3×10^{-4}[b]	Moderate	>3750[b]	No
Phorate	50	8.4×10^{-4}[b]	Moderate	2[b]	Yes
Vamidothion	33	Very low	Long	64[b]	Slight
Azinphos-methyl	30[e]	2.2×10^{-7}[b]	Long	16[e]	No (LS)

[a] LS = loco-systemic.
[b] British Crop Protection Council (1979).
[c] Price Jones and Edgar (1961).
[d] Mitchell et al. (1960).
[e] Matsumura (1975).
[f] Edson et al. (1966).
[g] ICI (1970).

4.2 STRUCTURAL DIVERSITY OF ORGANOPHOSPHORUS INSECTICIDES

Most organophosphorus insecticides have the following general structure:

$$
\begin{array}{c}
RO \\
 \searrow \\
 P \\
 \nearrow \searrow \\
RO X
\end{array}
\quad O \text{ or } S
$$

The two R groups are usually methyl or ethyl and are the same in any one molecule, while X is frequently a rather complex aliphatic, homocyclic or heterocyclic group. For reasons explained in section 4.5, X is often referred to as the **leaving group**. Sometimes the leaving group is such that a carbon atom in it is joined directly to the phosphorus atom but more often it is joined via an ester or thioester linkage, namely P–O–X or P–S–X.

Some of the more important variants of the basic molecular structure, a chemical naming system and some examples of insecticides possessing each structure are shown in table 4.2. Phosphates have four oxygen atoms arranged around the phosphorus. If one of these oxygen atoms is replaced by sulphur, the compounds are thiophosphates; and if two are replaced, they are dithiophosphates. If the sulphur is in the double-bond part of the molecule, the structure is that of a thionphosphate; the term *thion* (compare ket*one*) distinguishes the substance from one with a structure in which the sulphur atom is in the *thiol* position (compare alcoh*ol*). If a carbon atom of the leaving group, X, is attached directly to phosphorus, the compound is designated a phosphonate. The latter has thionphosphonate analogues. There are, in addition, a few instances where R–O–P is replaced by R–P or by R_2N–P.

The structural variability of organophosphorus compounds is reflected not only in their range of physical properties (table 4.1) but also in a considerable diversity of mechanisms by which they can be attacked by enzymes. This has two important consequences. First, species selectivity is sometimes achieved because the amounts or the activities of different enzymes vary from species to species. Secondly, a multiplicity of possible types and positions of attack by enzymes minimises the risk of a uniform development of tolerance to all organophosphorus compounds (chapter 9). The major types of enzymes that can attack various linkages in organophosphorus compounds are shown in figure 4.1.

4.3 PRACTICAL USES OF ORGANOPHOSPHORUS INSECTICIDES

Organophosphorus compounds have overtaken organochlorine compounds as the most-used insecticides, whether the criterion of usage is tonnage produced or wholesale value. In 1971 they were two or three times as

Table 4.2 Main chemical groups of organophosphorus insecticides

Main group		Examples
1. Orthophosphates	$\begin{array}{c} R-O \\ \\ R-O \end{array} \overset{\displaystyle O}{\underset{}{P}} O-X$	Chlorfenvinphos, dichlorvos, mevinphos, phosphamidon
2. Thionphosphates (phosphoro*thionates*)	$\begin{array}{c} R-O \\ \\ R-O \end{array} \overset{\displaystyle S}{\underset{}{P}} O-X$	Bromophos, diazinon, fenitrothion, parathion, pirimiphos (methyl and ethyl)
3. Thiolphosphates (phosphoro*thiolates*)	$\begin{array}{c} R-O \\ \\ R-O \end{array} \overset{\displaystyle O}{\underset{}{P}} S-X$	Demeton-S-methyl, oxydemeton-methyl, vamidothion
4. Dithiophosphates (phosphoro*thiolothionates*)	$\begin{array}{c} R-O \\ \\ R-O \end{array} \overset{\displaystyle S}{\underset{}{P}} S-X$	Azinphos-methyl, dimethoate, disulfoton, malathion, menazon, phorate
5. Phosphonates (isomeric phosphonates exist, as do related thiophosphonates)	$\begin{array}{c} R-O \\ \\ R \end{array} \overset{\displaystyle O}{\underset{}{P}} X$	Trichlorphon, butonate
6. Pyrophosphoramides	$\begin{array}{c} R_2N \\ \\ R_2N \end{array} \overset{\displaystyle O}{\underset{}{P}} O \overset{\displaystyle O}{\underset{}{P}} \begin{array}{c} NR_2 \\ \\ NR_2 \end{array}$	Schradan

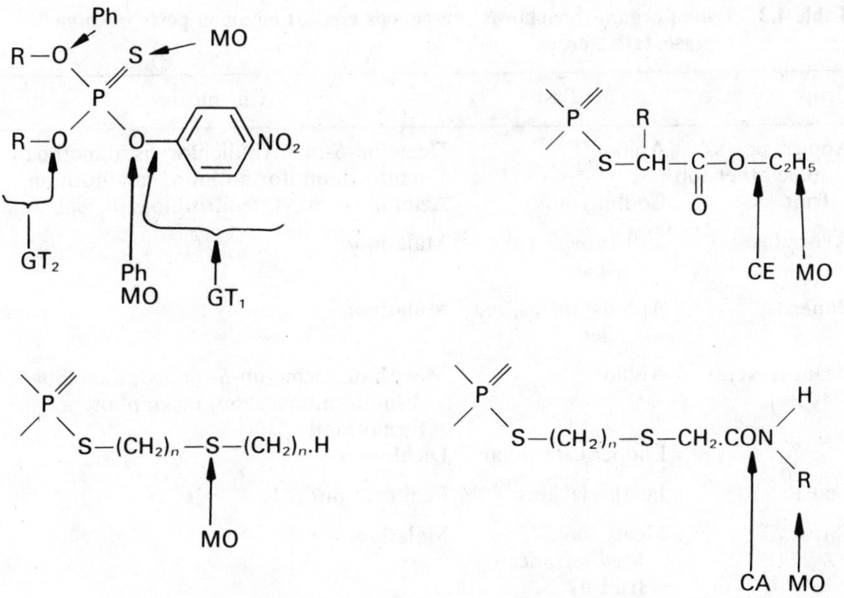

Figure 4.1 Enzymes that attack organophosphorus compounds. Ph, phosphatase/A-esterase; MO, microsomal mono-oxygenase; CE, carboxylesterase; CA, carboxylamidase; GT_1, glutathione-*S*-aryl transferase; GT_2, glutathione-*S*-alkyl transferase; R, usually alkyl, occasionally aryl (sometimes the adjacent oxygen is absent)

expensive as organochlorine compounds, but they have tended to replace organochlorine compounds as concern about the persistence and polluting effect of compounds such as DDT has increased. However, for the very reason that organophosphorus compounds are, in general, less persistent than organochlorine compounds, a greater number of applications to a crop may be necessary during the course of the growing season. Thus a price is exacted of the farmer, and hence indirectly of the consumer, for the privilege of growing organochlorine-free produce.

The majority of organophosphorus compounds are effective in the control of aphids and similar soft-bodied small insects, but many of the newer compounds have a wider range of uses. Some of these uses are listed in table 4.3, but only experience can determine the best substance to use for a particular purpose in a particular locality. In most countries, this information is available from governmental agricultural services as well as from commercial literature and sales representatives. Some of the compounds marketed for killing the more refractory insects possess certain disadvantages, such as somewhat high toxicity to vertebrates, or high persistence, or high cost.

Table 4.3   Use of organophosphorus compounds against common pests of some representative crops

Crop	Pest	Chemicals
Apples, pears, some other top fruit	Aphids	Demeton-*S*-methyl, dichlorvos, dimethoate, fenitrothion, formothion, vamidothion
	Codling moth	Azinphos-methyl, fenitrothion, phosphamidon
Avocados	Soft brown scale, thrips	Malathion
Bananas	Aphids, thrips, red spider	Malathion
Beans (several types)	Aphids	Malathion, demeton-*S*-methyl, dimethoate, disulfoton, menazon, mevinphos, formothion
	Looper caterpillar	Dichlorvos
Cereals	Leatherjackets	Fenitrothion
Citrus	Mealy bug, Mediterranean fruit fly	Malathion
	Red scale	Parathion
Coffee	Antestis bug	Parathion, trichlorphon
	Leaf miner, stem borer	Parathion
Maize	Aphids	Demeton-*S*-methyl
	Fruit fly	Phorate
	Stalk borer	Trichlorphon
Pea	Aphids, pea moth, thrips, weevils	Azinphos-methyl, fenitrothion
Potatoes	Aphids	As for beans; also oxydemeton-methyl
Stored grain	Weevils	Dichlorvos, malathion, pirimiphos-methyl
Sugar beet	Aphids (and virus)	As for potatoes; also mevinphos
Sweet potatoes	Leaf miners	Trichlorphon
Tobacco	Aphids	Dimethoate, malathion
	Leaf miners	Phosphamidon
Tomatoes	American bollworm	Mevinphos
	Aphids	Demeton-*S*-methyl, disulfoton, malathion, oxydemeton-methyl
	Red spider mite	Formothion, oxydemeton-methyl
Vegetables (various, e.g. beetroot, carrot, onion, parsnip)	Mangold fly	Dimethoate, formothion
	Aphids	Demeton-*S*-methyl, oxydemeton-methyl, disulfoton
	Carrot fly	Chlorfenvinphos, diazinon, phorate, disulfoton
	Celery fly	Malathion
	Onion thrips	Malathion

Killing pests can in some ways be compared to trying to keep law and order in a human society—the golden rule in the choice of a pesticide is never to use a powerful, undiscriminating weapon when a small selective one will do. Applying this rule, almost all organophosphorus compounds will control aphids and so, if the latter are the only problem, there is usually little need to employ one of the less safe or more costly members of the group.

It is possible to classify organophosphorus insecticides according to their practical uses, and such a classification is of more value in the present context than one based primarily on chemical constitution. Each subgroup in the following scheme is discussed in more detail in later sections of the chapter.

Subgroup 1. Compounds of low chemical stability soluble in water but more or less rapidly hydrolysed by it. They are used as **contact** insecticides. E.g. mevinphos, tetraethyl pyrophosphate, tetrachlorvinphos.

Subgroup 2. Compounds of moderate to high chemical stability, usually of low solubility in water but soluble in oil. These **persistent contact** or **loco-systemic** compounds soak into leaves but do not travel around the plant. The sprayed substance is activated before it reaches its site of action in insects. E.g. malathion, methyl parathion, diazinon, fenitrothion, trichlorphon.

Subgroup 3. Compounds of moderate to high chemical stability. Their oil/water partition coefficients are such as to enable them both to enter plants and to be translocated within them. These **systemic** compounds are activated before reaching their site of action in insects. E.g. dimethoate, demeton-methyl, phorate, formothion, disulfoton.

Subgroup 4. Compounds with sufficiently high vapour pressure and low chemical stability to enable them to be used as **fumigants**. E.g. dichlorvos.

Subgroup 5. Organophosphorus insecticides used against soil organisms. E.g. chlorfenvinphos, phorate, diazinon, bromophos.

4.4 NERVOUS SYSTEMS, NERVE CELLS AND SYNAPSES

The nervous system of insects is the target of several groups of insecticides and that of higher animals is often vulnerable should accidents occur. For this reason a brief description of how nerve cells function is essential to aid the minority of readers whose interest in pesticides has originated from non-biological disciplines. Differences do exist between the nervous systems of vertebrates and invertebrates and some of these are mentioned later. For the moment, it is probably sufficient to assume that basic elements in the nervous systems of mammals and insects are fairly similar.

The nervous system of higher animals comprises a central component of brain, spinal cord and nerves running to the periphery of the body, together with a separate but interrelated involuntary or autonomic system. The latter is responsible for the background control of activities that do not normally impinge on consciousness (e.g. secretions of glandular cells, the tone of muscles of the alimentary canal). This autonomic system comprises two subsections known as the sympathetic and parasympathetic systems, and these two systems sometimes modulate one another's activities. In contrast, the central nervous system (CNS) has functions which include (but are not limited to) the recognition of such external stimuli as sight, sound, touch and smell and organising appropriate responses to such stimuli.

Nervous tissue consists of nerve cells (neurons) accompanied by a variety of helper cells. The latter include interstitial cells, of which Schwann cells are one kind; they offer support, protection and possibly supply metabolites. When nerve cells aggregate together they form ganglia. The cell body of a neuron branches out into dendrites (figure 4.2), thus increasing the cell surface and allowing a large area for synaptic contacts with other neurons (see below). A further projection from a neuron is called the axon; it is down this that messages in the form of electrical signals are conveyed. The axon is often, but not always, protected and strengthened by being surrounded by Schwann cells. These are wound around the axon several times in such a way that the axon is surrounded by numerous layers of the plasmalemma of the Schwann cells. These are collectively known as the myelin sheath and provide electrical insulation except in the region of the nodes of Ranvier. Such nerves carry electrical signals faster than do nerves that are non-myelinated.

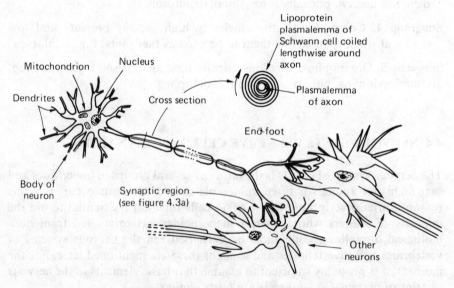

Figure 4.2 Structure of a nerve cell

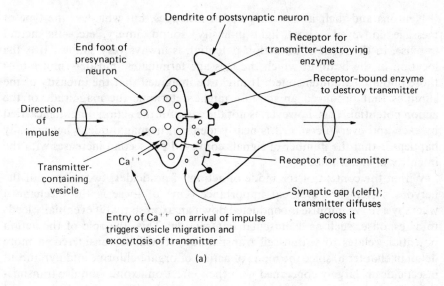

End foot of
presynaptic
neuron

Dendrite of postsynaptic neuron

Receptor for
transmitter-destroying
enzyme

Receptor-bound enzyme
to destroy transmitter

Direction
of
impulse

Receptor for transmitter

Transmitter-
containing
vesicle

Ca^{++}

Synaptic gap (cleft);
transmitter diffuses
across it

Entry of Ca^{++} on arrival of impulse
triggers vesicle migration and
exocytosis of transmitter

(a)

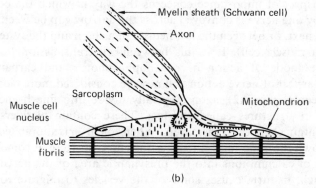

Myelin sheath (Schwann cell)

Axon

Sarcoplasm

Mitochondrion

Muscle cell
nucleus

Muscle
fibrils

(b)

Figure 4.3   (a) A synapse and (b) a neuromotor junction. The exocytotic movement of
vesicles containing acetylcholine is triggered by ingress of calcium ions;
when postsynaptic receptors are occupied, depolarisation of the nearby
membrane occurs

The axon ends in branches with numerous small swellings called end-feet,
which come into close contact with the dendritic areas of neighbouring
neurons. The minute gap (20–50 nm) between the end-feet of one nerve cell
and the dendritic area of another is termed a synapse (figure 4.3a). The
frequency of occurrence of synapses depends on the lengths of individual
axons, and these typically vary from a millimetre to a metre long. Gaps that
are rather similar to synaptic clefts occur when the last neuron in a sequence
comes into contact with, say, a muscle; here there is a neuromotor junction
(figure 4.3b).

Neurons and their axons carry coded messages, but whatever the type of message conveyed—about light intensity, sound, injury, etc.—the actual impulse, in the form of an action potential, is always very similar. It is the location in the brain at which the message terminates that determines how those impulses are interpreted. It might be imagined that the intensity of the stimulus that produced an impulse might determine the magnitude of the action potential. This, however, is not the case, for the action potential carried by each and every nerve cell is nearly identical in magnitude; what actually happens is that the number of signals conveyed per second increases with the intensity of the stimulus.

Within the context of the mode of action of pesticides, two aspects of the nervous system are of great importance. One of these is the mechanism whereby a nerve impulse is conducted down an axon so that it eventually leads to a response, such as a muscular contraction. This, the role of the action potential, relates to within-cell transmission; it will be considered in more detail in chapter 6, since the mode of action of organochlorine and pyrethroid insecticides is largely concerned with their effect on axonic impulse transmission. The other aspect of importance concerns the way in which the coded message carried by one nerve is conveyed across the narrow gap between one nerve cell and the next, or between the last neuron of a chain and the system it innervates (e.g. a muscle cell). It is this between-cell transmission that is implicated in the mode of action of organophosphorus and carbamate insecticides. This aspect of nerve action will now be considered more closely.

As has been seen (figure 4.2), axons typically divide into fine branches, which terminate in structures called end-feet. These contain bladders, or vesicles, which contain chemical transmitters. When a neuron is stimulated, an impulse passes down the axon until it reaches the end-feet. Here, it somehow triggers an influx of calcium ions into the presynaptic area of the nerve cell (figure 4.3a), which, in turn, causes some of the vesicles to migrate to the presynaptic membrane. The membranes of the vesicles and plasmalemma (the presynaptic membrane) fuse together, the transmitter thus being ejected into the 20–30 nm space between pre- and postsynaptic membranes. The chemical transmitter attaches itself to a specially designed region of the plasmalemma of the next nerve cell. This specialised region is called the receptor for the transmitter and comprises a particular sequence of amino acids in a protein that forms an integral part of the plasmalemma. When occupied by the transmitter, the postsynaptic cell responds by generating an action potential, which travels as a wave across the neuron and down its axon. Upon arrival at its ultimate destination, a similar gap exists between the end-feet of the final nerve cell and the membrane of the cell it innervates (e.g. a glandular cell or a muscle cell). This is termed a neuromotor junction (figure 4.3b), and the gap is bridged by a transmitter which crosses to a receptor on the plasmalemma of the effector cell and, on arrival, elicits an appropriate response.

The two principal synaptic and neuroeffector transmitters are noradrenaline (norepinephrine) and acetylcholine. One or other of these is usually stored in the presynaptic vesicles. In vertebrates, cholinergic nerve cells initiate a new signal by liberating acetylcholine at synapses whereas adrenergic neurons liberate noradrenaline. Acetylcholine is liberated at most neuroeffector junctions whatever the transmitter at the synapses. More than 20 other transmitters have been identified in various parts of the nervous systems of various species of animals, the role of most of which is still little understood.

It should be noted, in relation to the chemistry of pesticides, that a meaningful message requires that the transmitter must be removed (by sorption, diffusion or destruction) as soon as it has done its work. If this were not so, the impulse arising from the next stimulus would evidently be compromised on arrival at the blocked junction. It is rather like a Morse tapping key; no message is transmitted if the key is not depressed, nor is there a meaningful message if the key is continuously held down. Within the present context (namely, the mode of action of organophosphorus insecticides), the transmitter is acetylcholine. This is destroyed as soon as it has done its work by an enzyme, acetylcholinesterase, which is present at cholinergic junctions, usually in considerable excess.

The nervous system of invertebrates lies ventrally. In fully segmented insects there are typically a pair of fused ganglia per segment, joined to the ganglia in the adjacent two segments by bunched nerve fibres called connectives. From the ganglia of this primitive spinal cord, sensory, motor and autonomic nerves emerge. More usually, there are two ganglia in the head, three in the thorax and five in the abdomen, accompanied by connectives and emerging nerve fibres. The autonomic system is a single visceral system in insects and there are no synapses between the point of leaving the central nervous system and the effector cells in the viscera.

Table 4.4   Differences between the nervous systems of mammals and insects

Mammals	Insects
Dorsally located	Ventrally located
Brain present	Segmental ganglia in head region
Peripheral nerves are myelinated	Non-myelinated nerve fibres
All motor fibres are excitatory	Motor fibres excitatory or inhibitory
Peripheral autonomic ganglia are present	No peripheral autonomic ganglia
Typical motor end-plate	Numerous contacts
Cholinergic transmission in CNS and in some peripheral nerves	Only CNS is cholinergic
Neuromuscular junctions are cholinergic	Neuromuscular junctions are glutaminergic if excitatory or GABA-ergic if inhibitory
Pseudocholinesterases present	Pseudocholinesterases absent
Acetylcholinesterase in CNS, nerves, muscles, erythrocytes	Acetylcholinesterase in CNS only

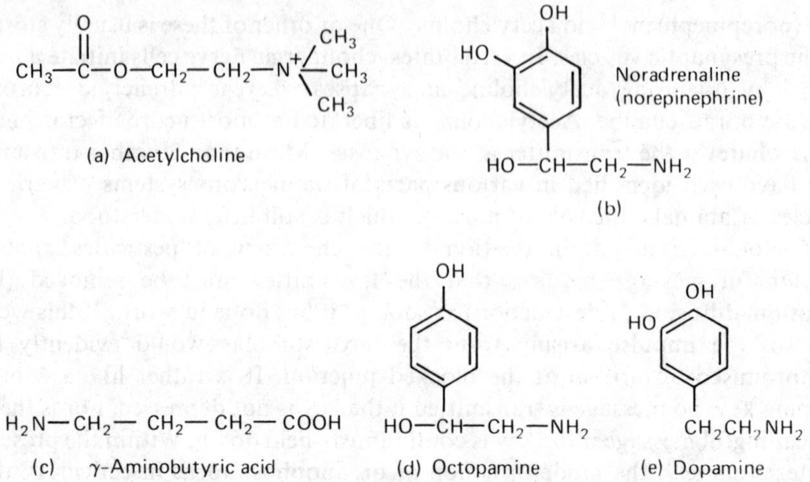

Figure 4.4   Structures of some neurotransmitters

The peripheral nerves of insects are not surrounded by myelin sheaths, a fact of possible importance in relation to the selective action of insecticides. Another difference is the absence of neuromotor junctions of the sort present in vertebrates; instead, the branches terminating the axons make individual contact with muscle cells. Moreover, although insect nervous systems do contain several pharmacologically distinct types of receptors, they are not all directly analogous to those in vertebrate synapses and neuromotor junctions. For example, glutamine appears to be the transmitter at excitatory neuro-motor junctions in insects, while, at inhibitory junctions, γ-aminobutyric acid (GABA) is the transmitter (Abalis *et al.*, 1983). Elsewhere, octopamine and serotonin play important roles; Kravitz *et al.* (1984) showed that if lobsters were injected with octopamine, they 'froze' into one stereotyped static posture, whereas, if injected with serotonin, they assumed an equally stereo-typed but different posture. The roles of invertebrate neurotransmitters have been reviewed by Leake and Walker (1980) and by Lund (1985). Some apparent differences between vertebrate and invertebrate nervous systems are summarised in table 4.4, and the formulae of common neurotransmitters appear in figure 4.4.

4.5 ACETYLCHOLINESTERASE: ITS ACTION AND INHIBITION

Acetylcholine binds to cholinesterase at two attachment sites. One of these, the **ester-forming site**, probably contains a serine residue in the protein chain, while the other, the negative or **anionic site**, may contain a glutamic acid residue (figure 4.5). The carbon atom of the carbonyl group of the substrate carries a slight positive charge and makes an electrophilic* attack on the hydroxyl group of the serine. This results in **acetylation** of the enzyme and in the splitting and deactivation of the acetylcholine. The free choline readily leaves the enzyme surface (figure 4.5b). The esteratic bond (EB) is weak and is rapidly hydrolysed during the **recovery stage** of the enzyme, the hydrolysis probably being facilitated by a basic histidine residue nearby. The surface of the enzyme is then free to accept another molecule of acetylcholine. It has been estimated that about 300 000 molecules of acetylcholine are destroyed by one molecule of enzyme per minute at 37°C.

Organophosphorus compounds have some structural similarity to the natural substrate, acetylcholine. The phosphate group is attracted to the esteratic site and the rest of the molecule is aligned by interaction with the numerous side-groups of amino acids, which form the total active area of the enzyme. Although most organophosphorus compounds have no positively charged groups to associate with the normal anionic site, they undergo a series of changes analogous to those described above. However, they **phosphorylate** the enzyme rather than acetylating it and the esteratic bond (EB) is relatively stable to hydrolysis (figure 4.5c). The stability of the bond depends on the nature of the phosphorylating entity, which is frequently either dimethyl phosphate or diethyl phosphate. It takes about 80 min for half the enzyme molecules to be dephosphorylated when dimethyl phosphate is attached to it, but some six times longer when it is phosphorylated by diethyl phosphate. These times are such that it takes up to a million times longer for a molecule of the enzyme to become operative again than it does when it undergoes the natural process of acetylation.

The ease with which the esteratic bond is formed (as distinct from being destroyed) depends on the stability of the P–X bond in the general structure shown at the start of section 4.2, and this stability depends on the electron-attracting capability of the group X. This is one reason why the various groups X in the many different organophosphorus insecticides are important. Other reasons are that they are attacked in different ways by enzymes capable of activating or destroying organophosphorus compounds, and that they influence the ease of access of the molecule to its potential site of action in insects and in vertebrates.

A somewhat more rigorous approach to the subject of cholinesterase inhibition and enzyme recovery follows, with the aid of minimal mathematics but utilising simple enzyme kinetics, based on the concept of the intermediate formation of an **enzyme–inhibitor complex**. These considerations apply equally to organophosphorus and carbamate insecticides (chapter 5). Both of these

*Electrophilic = 'electron-loving'; an attack by a slightly positively-charged centre in one molecule on a slightly negatively charged centre in another.

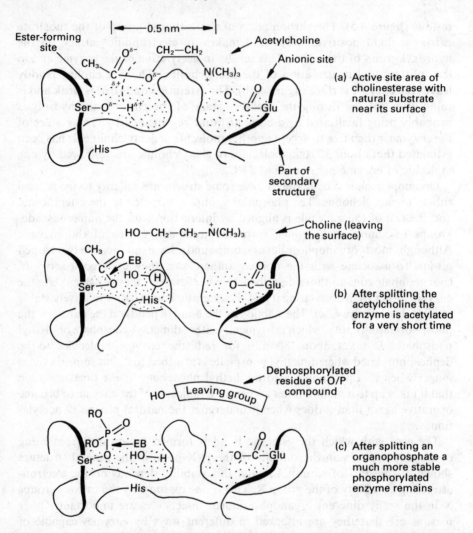

Figure 4.5 Cholinesterase: a representation of its secondary structure to illustrate how its active site is believed (a) to align acetylcholine, (b) to become transiently acetylated when it splits acetylcholine, (c) to become phosphorylated when it splits organophosphorus compounds. Ser, serine; Glu, glutamic acid; His, histidine; EB, esteratic bond (see text)

groups of compounds inhibit cholinesterase, but whereas organophosphorus compounds work by phosphorylating the enzyme, the carbamates often seem to compete with acetylcholine for the enzyme surface. The following account shows that the difference is, in fact, one of degree, depending on the relative magnitudes of certain rate constants.

Classical enzyme–substrate interactions (e.g. succinate dehydrogenase (E) and succinate (S)) can be represented by

$$E + S \underset{k_2}{\overset{k_1}{\rightleftharpoons}} ES \overset{k_3}{\rightarrow} A + B + E \qquad (4.1)$$

where k_1, k_2, k_3 are rate constants, ES is the enzyme–substrate complex and A, B are products of the reaction.

Analogously, if an inhibitor (IX) reacts with an enzyme (E) in an initially reversible manner, the reaction can be represented by

$$E + IX \underset{k_2}{\overset{k_1}{\rightleftharpoons}} E.IX \overset{k_3}{\underset{X}{\rightarrow}} EI \underset{H_2O}{\overset{k_4}{\rightarrow}} E + IH \qquad (4.2)$$

In this equation, E.IX represents the enzyme–inhibitor complex (at this stage the enzyme and inhibitor are not covalently linked), X is termed the leaving group, I is that part of the inhibitor molecule that eventually blocks the enzyme and EI is the inhibited enzyme (with the blocking group, I, attached covalently). The leaving group is released from the enzyme–inhibitor complex (E.IX) as the van der Waals forces of attraction are replaced by a covalent bond in a reaction governed by the rate constant, k_3.

The extent of **enzyme blocking** is thus determined by two separate factors, namely the rate at which the complex E.IX is converted to 'blocked enzyme' (EI) and the concentration of E.IX undergoing the change

$$\text{Rate of overall reaction} = k \, [\text{reactant}] = k_3 \, [\text{E.IX}] \qquad (4.3)$$

where square brackets indicate the molar concentration of the substance inside the bracket, and the overall reaction is that which leads to blocked enzyme (EI).

If either [E.IX] or k_3 is low, much of the enzyme may not be inhibited. Applying the law of mass action, the concentration of enzyme–inhibitor complex [E.IX] is often measured approximately by

$$K_D = \frac{k_2}{k_1} = \frac{[\text{E}][\text{IX}]}{[\text{E.IX}]} \qquad (4.4)$$

although this assumes that the distorting effect of k_3 is slight. The constant K_D is evidently the dissociation constant of the complex E.IX; it is often called the affinity constant (of enzyme for inhibitor), a large affinity of E for IX being reflected in a low value of K_D.

EI, the inhibited form of the enzyme, will be formed most rapidly from a fixed concentration of the enzyme–inhibitor complex (E.IX) when k_3 is high (equation (4.2)). An index that takes account of the contributions of both K_D and k_3 is the inhibition constant K_i. It is defined as

$$K_i = k_3/K_D \tag{4.5}$$

Clearly, the smaller K_D and/or the larger k_3, the larger is K_i; thus a large K_i value implies a high level of enzyme blocking.

Finally, it is necessary to refer to the rate of **unblocking** or **recovery** of the inhibited molecules of enzyme. This is, in the present context, the rate of hydrolysis of phosphorylated or carbamylated cholinesterase, a reaction governed by the rate constant k_4 (equation (4.2)).

When organophosphates inhibit acetylcholinesterase there is typically a very low concentration of enzyme–substrate complex (E.IX) present in the steady-state condition. The reverse reaction governed by k_2 is in consequence negligible. In addition, the compound EI is rather stable and the phosphorylated, inactive enzyme only dephosphorylates slowly. The rate of recovery depends on the nature of the dialkylphosphoryl moiety attached to the enzyme. The blocking action of the organophosphorus compounds should be compared and contrasted with that of the carbamates, another group of insecticides that possess an anticholinesterase effect. For carbamates (chapter 5) the rate-limiting step is the carbamylation of the enzyme (i.e. the rate at which E.IX is converted to EI). When the steady-state condition has been reached, a finite proportion of the enzyme is present in the form of the enzyme–carbamate complex (E.IX). Moreover, the inhibited enzyme (EI), which here is E–carbamate, is often hydrolysed moderately rapidly back to E, thus freeing enzyme, which can then participate in further reactions with natural substrate or with more carbamate. Consequently, in *in vitro* systems, carbamate inhibition can be partly reversed by addition of acetylcholine, i.e. there is competition between carbamate and acetylcholine for the enzyme surface.

In mammals, atropine is one of several drugs that can be used as antidotes to organophosphorus insecticide poisoning; it blocks the *in vivo* action of excess acetylcholine. Other types of drugs accelerate the rate at which dephosphorylation of the phosphorylated enzyme takes place. One of these, pralidoxime (PAM, pyridine-2-aldoxime methiodide), increases a million-fold the rate at which the reactivation reaction governed by the rate constant k_4 proceeds. This happens because of its strong nucleophilic properties; in effect, it has a more powerful affinity for the enzyme-bound phosphorus derivative than the latter has for the enzyme. However, if phosphorylated acetylcholinesterase is stored before the pralidoxime is added, the reversal of action is much slower because a chemical process termed 'ageing' has occurred. This process involves the removal of an alkyl group from the bound dialkylphosphate moiety, with the result that the vulnerability of the phosphorus compound to nucleophilic attack is greatly reduced.

4.6 ADVERSE AND ENVIRONMENTAL EFFECTS OF ORGANOPHOSPHORUS COMPOUNDS

It is convenient to divide the adverse effects of organophosphorus compounds on higher animals into three kinds: acute toxic effects; longer-term consequences following medically recognisable acute exposure; and chronic effects arising from long-term exposure to small quantities of one or more of these pesticides. Unfortunately, the important distinction between these possibilities has not always been clearly drawn. In addition, adverse effects of an environmental nature can also occur.

In cases of very mild short-term exposure to organophosphorus insecticides, the level of activity of blood or brain cholinesterase can be depressed without any obvious accompanying symptoms other than perhaps a headache and occasionally some of the symptoms of a common cold. Such symptoms are mostly caused by the effects of excess acetylcholine on receptors in the brain and might well pass almost unnoticed. Nevertheless, should someone be subjected to several such short-term exposures without knowing it, trouble can occur if, for any reason, the person has an operation involving anaesthesia associated with the use of muscle relaxants. Response to the (choline-based) relaxant may be excessive, so the hospital should be made aware that the patient could have suffered such exposure (DHSS, undated). If a worker is exposed to very small amounts on numerous occasions, this is tantamount to a chronic exposure, and is considered separately below.

When acute poisoning is more severe, a variety of symptoms are possible because excess acetylcholine has deleterious effects at different types of receptors in both the autonomic and the central nervous systems. For more detail, the account by Ecobichon and Joy (1982, p.166) is recommended. Essentially, however, when organophosphorus compounds inactivate acetylcholinesterase at muscarinic receptors for acetylcholine, symptoms of poisoning include cold sweating, salivation, nausea, bronchoconstriction and tightness of the chest, with a decrease in blood pressure. Very characteristically, the pupil of the eye contracts to a pin-point.

Elsewhere, other types of acetylcholine receptors, termed nicotinic receptors, exist. They are present both in neuromotor junctions (of somatic nerves) and in ganglia of the sympathetic autonomic system. At neuromotor junctions, the prolonged occupation of receptors by acetylcholine (e.g. after organophosphorus poisoning) causes twitching of muscles or muscular cramp. At autonomic ganglia, receptor occupation at sympathetic nerve synapses stimulates the release of adrenaline (epinephrine) from the adrenal gland; this adrenaline leads to increased blood pressure and increased restlessness. Thirdly, acetylcholine receptors in the brain respond to excess acetylcholine in a way that is manifest as tiredness and mental confusion; abnormal electroencephalograms are evident. Mental disturbances include anxiety, tension and impairment of memory.

These symptoms of malaise, exhaustion and confusion get steadily worse with increasing length of acute exposure because there is a corresponding progressive depletion in the acetylcholinesterase reserves. According to Bignami *et al.* (1975) the magnitude of neurological symptoms is inversely related to brain cholinesterase level once that level has fallen to about 50 per cent of normal for the individual (a difficulty is that the normal level in different members of a species can be very variable). At high exposure levels, tremors may become convulsions and drowsiness may precede coma. Death normally results from asphyxiation, caused jointly by bronchoconstriction, by decrease in blood pressure, by failure of the diaphragm muscles and by depression of the respiratory centre of the brain.

Should assistance be available when poisoning occurs, someone should immediately call for emergency help. Meantime, another helper should ensure that the respiratory air passage is free (mucilage, tongue and false teeth can block it). The patient should be kept quiet and inactive since activity exacerbates the problem. Any contaminated clothes should be cut off and all skin carefully washed. Artificial respiration can be a life-saving emergency measure. Medical workers on arrival can ameliorate the condition by giving drugs that block the action of the excess acetylcholine or reverse the inhibition of the acetylcholinesterase. Frequently atropine and pralidoxime (see section 5.4) are administered together. In the case of atropine, doses of 2 mg may be necessary every 20 min for many hours (DHSS, undated).

Another possible toxic response to organophosphorus poisons would be chronic responses following substantial but non-lethal acute toxic poisoning. Under this heading would be delayed effects following long after the disappearance of the characteristic acute symptoms, including acetylcholinesterase inhibition. Usually, acute symptoms last for 24–72 h, although tension, depression and anxiety may persist for a week or more. Levin and Rodnitzky (1976) quote examples of cases where manifestations of anxiety and irritability have persisted for months after the end of acute exposure. The same authors report that people who have suffered acute symptoms may suffer impaired vigilance and reduced concentration, with the result that they can be a safety hazard to themselves and to others. Many suffer from poor memories, slurred speech, insomnia and nightmares. Because many of the people concerned are workers with pesticides it is often impossible to be quite sure whether such effects are the after-effects of a single known incident, or whether after such an incident subclinical re-exposure leads to these apparently chronic responses.

Chronic effects are defined as those which occur as a result of continued exposure to small doses of a poison (or to several poisons with the same mode of action) but where no clinically observable acute symptoms had preceded them. When it is remembered that people occupationally exposed to organophosphorus insecticides are likely to encounter such chemicals quite often, and that mild symptoms of poisoning are difficult to quantify, it is not always possible, in practice, to distinguish between chronic consequences of a single, recognised acute event, and chronic symptoms following frequent but un-recognised subclinical acute exposures. In consequence, it remains uncertain whether truly asymptomatic workers can develop chronic complications. Of especial importance is the possibility that the mental acumen or reasoning capability of such people is impaired without their even knowing it. There have been, for example, many crashes involving pilots of aeroplanes used for spraying purposes; some of these accidents appear to have been associated with uncharacteristic risk-taking or slowness of reaction (Levin and Rod-nitzky, 1976; Levin *et al.*, 1975; Ecobichon and Joy, 1982).

The widespread use of organophosphorus compounds has stimulated research into the possibility that, at least in some species, they could have more general chronic effects unrelated to their anticholinesterase activity. Teratogenic (embryo-deforming) effects have been observed in avians treated with several organophosphorus compounds, but especially with diazinon. Introduction of malathion into the yolk sac of incubating eggs has similarly resulted in deformed chicks. These effects are apparently much less marked in mammals, although trichlorphon has caused embryonic abnormalities in mice and liver damage in cats. Chromosome abnormalities (mutagenic effects) have been observed to occur with greater than average frequency in human beings acutely poisoned by malathion. This has caused some concern, because mutagenic symptoms sometimes signal carcinogenic (cancer-producing) potential. Again, parathion and methyl parathion can cross the placental barrier of pregnant rats.

More recently, Pednekar *et al.* (1987) could find no evidence to suggest that two organophosphorus compounds, phosalone and malathion, were mutage-nic in the Ames *Salmonella* test, whether or not an activation system in the form of rat liver 9000 *g* supernatant supplemented with NADPH was added (the modification is known as the *Salmonella*/microsome mutagenicity test; see section 1.5). These Indian workers quoted three other groups of people that had come to similar conclusions, although, *inter alia*, Dulout *et al.* (1982) and Yadav *et al.* (1982) have reported various types of nuclear abnormalities in mice and in cultured cell lines. In addition, Van Bao *et al.* (1974) reported chromosomal breaks in the nuclei of human cells. The WHO (1986), in conjunction with other United Nations bodies, has reviewed the evidence for and against the involvement of various organophosphorus insecticides in mutagenesis, carcinogenesis and immunosuppressive events.

Publications dealing with the effects on birds of persistent pesticides, including some organophosphorus compounds, have been reviewed by Edwards (1973). Indirect effects of organophosphorus compounds on birds include behavioural changes in adult gulls, leading to decreased nest attentive-ness and frequent death of the chicks (White *et al.*, 1979). Similarly, starlings that had been exposed to organophosphorus compounds made fewer trips to feed their young (Grue *et al.*, 1982). It has also been observed that some birds in pesticide-contaminated areas tend to migrate during breeding, often with very unsuccessful second nestings. All of these changes are reminiscent of behavioural changes in humans referred to earlier.

Sublethal effects not obviously related to cholinesterase effects have also been reported to occur in fish. After 30 days' exposure to sublethal doses of demeton-methyl, Natarajan (1984) observed that succinate dehydrogenase activity and tissue respiration fell in the Indian freshwater fish, *Channa striatus*. Conversely, the lactate dehydrogenase activity was enhanced in several tissues, an observation construed as indicating that the metabolic balance in the tissues had been re-routed towards partial anaerobicity.

Some organophosphorus compounds not only inhibit acetylcholinesterase but, after a latent period during which any acute symptoms subside, engender a more persistent delayed neurotoxic effect, or neuropathy. Weakness in the legs develops after 1–4 weeks, with degeneration of the axons of neurons in the sciatic nerve. The cause of this delayed neuropathy is still imperfectly understood but there is evidence that a protein with esterase potential but of unknown function exists in the nervous system. This protein becomes the target for certain, but by no means all, organophosphorus insecticides and has now been termed **neuropathy target esterase** (Abou-Donia, 1981). Certain organophosphorus insecticides, including mipafox, leptofos and chlorpyrifos, are able to phosphorylate this protein. This eliminates the esteratic activity of the protein but is not, in itself, the cause of the neuropathological symptoms. Instead, upon continued contact or 'ageing' of the blocking process, some secondary and irreversible change takes place which leads to the neuropathy. Not all species show delayed neuropathy equally readily and it is a regrettable fact that human beings are among the more sensitive. The test animal used to study delayed neuropathy is the adult domestic hen.

4.7 LOW-PERSISTENCE CONTACT POISONS (subgroup 1)

In this and subsequent sections, an account will be given of the chemistry, biochemistry and uses of organophosphorus insecticides, based on the classification outlined in section 4.3.

Mevinphos (figure 4.6) is an important member of this small family of low-persistence contact organophosphates. **Tetraethyl pyrophosphate** (TEPP), one of the earliest commercially used organophosphates, also belongs to this group, although it is seldom used nowadays. TEPP (figure 4.6) is a water-soluble compound of low stability, but is of high toxicity to vertebrates—one drop of the concentrate, splashed into the eye, can be fatal. **Tetrachlorvinphos** (figure 4.6) is of relatively low persistence and probably qualifies for inclusion in this group. It is a relatively minor insecticide and acaricide used on certain types of bush fruit and brassicas. **Dichlorvos** could also be regarded as a member of this group were it not for the fact that its high vapour pressure

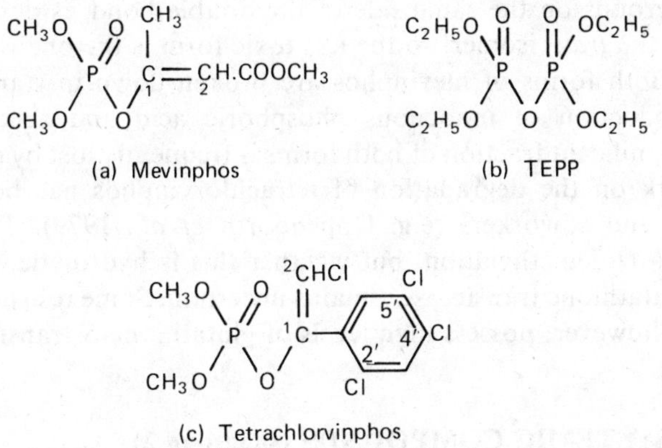

(a) Mevinphos

(b) TEPP

(c) Tetrachlorvinphos

Figure 4.6 Contact poisons of low persistence: (a) *cis, trans*-2-methoxycarbonyl-1-methylvinyl dimethyl phosphate; (b) tetraethyl pyrophosphate; (c) 2-chloro-1-(2′,4′,5′-trichlorophenyl)vinyl dimethyl phosphate

introduces a new feature and leads to it having different practical uses (section 4.10).

The water solubility and low hydrolytic stability of members of this group preclude the possibility of long persistence in a biological environment. In practice, therefore, field action must be almost immediate and this requires that action is primarily by direct contact with the pest. Some of them, including mevinphos, do additionally have a very short-term systemic action.

Mevinphos is one of the more toxic organophosphorus insecticides still in use (table 4.1). It is miscible with water and moderately soluble in lipids. Mevinphos usually persists only for a few days after application, a property that enables it to be used as an end-of-season spray. In Britain, it is recommended that three days should elapse between the last application and harvesting edible crops. It can also be employed in situations where a rapid kill is necessary, as, for example, when mechanical breakdown or weather conditions delay spraying to such an extent that a harmful insect population becomes established on a crop before action is possible.

Unlike substances in subgroups 2 and 3, mevinphos is probably the actual toxicant at the site of action; that is to say, enzyme systems in insects or plants do not 'activate' it by converting it to a more potent cholinesterase inhibitor. For this reason it possesses little selectivity between target species and any beneficial insects that happen to be in the vicinity at the time of spraying (contrast compounds in sections 4.8 and 4.9).

Mevinphos exists in *cis* and *trans* isomers. The *cis* isomer predominates in commercial products and, depending on the insect species, is 10–100 times as toxic as the *trans* isomer. The *cis* form, which has methyl and carboxymethyl

(COOCH$_3$) groups on the same side of the double bond, is destroyed more rapidly than the *trans* isomer, so the less toxic form is the one which persists the longer. Both forms of mevinphos are broken down in stages, with the eventual production of innocuous phosphoric acid and acetoacetate. In addition, a significant fraction of both forms is frequently lost by evaporation.

Much work on the degradation of tetrachlorvinphos has been done by Oppenoorth and coworkers (e.g. Oppenoorth *et al.*, 1979). The principal mechanism is *O*-demethylation, but whether this is hydrolytic, oxidative or involves a glutathione transferase remains uncertain. Some resistant strains of housefly do, however, possess high levels of glutathione-*S*-transferase.

4.8 LOCO-SYSTEMIC COMPOUNDS (subgroup 2)

Substances of this group are of low solubility in water but are soluble in lipids. Their chemical stability varies, but they characteristically persist for a few days to a few weeks after application to plant leaves. They are therefore also known as **persistent contact poisons**. Their lipophilic nature enables them to soak into the waxy cuticle of leaves and to diffuse short distances from the point of original contact, sometimes travelling as far as the lower surface of the leaf. This property has practical value, for it allows control of insects on low-growing plants (e.g. strawberries), where direct contact spraying would be impracticable. Once absorption has occurred, they are not readily removed by rain.

The low aqueous solubility of members of this group precludes the possibility of gross translocation, although radioactive labelling techniques have shown that minute amounts may be transported, especially after application to plant roots. Another characteristic of most, if not all, members of this family is that they undergo activation before they reach their site of action in the nervous system of the insect. Since activation is an oxidative process (see below), this renders the product more polar than the original molecule, so that it may possess some systemic action even where the original molecule does not.

The persistent contact or loco-systemic subgroup of organophosphorus insecticides is rather large. It can be conveniently subdivided into three principal families (as well as several minor ones). The three important subsections are here referred to as the malathion family, the parathion family and the family of compounds whose members contain a heterocyclic leaving group. Formulae of typical members are given in figures 4.7, 4.8 and 4.11, respectively.

Mammalian toxicity varies greatly from one compound to another. **Parathion** is a notoriously toxic liquid with an oral toxicity to rats of only 3–10 mg/kg body weight, and numerous accidents have occurred during the handling of the concentrate. **Methyl parathion**, which has been used extensively in the

USA, is somewhat less toxic, and its near relative, **fenitrothion**, is even safer, with an oral LD_{50} for rats greater than 250 mg/kg.

Some of the earlier-introduced members of the group were sufficiently persistent to cause residue problems especially when used on edible crops near to harvesting time. Many more recently introduced materials, on the other hand, are both less toxic and less persistent. Malathion, for example, has an LD_{50} to rats of 2800 mg/kg. It can be used, in appropriate cases, up to one or two days before harvesting, whereas the corresponding period for diazinon is two weeks, for azinphos-methyl, three weeks, and for parathion, four weeks.

(a) The malathion family

Malathion is one of the most generally useful loco-systemic compounds. As can be seen (figure 4.7), it is a dithiophosphate and the 'leaving group' is a succinic acid ester. It is principally used to control aphids and similar sap-sucking insects, although various weevils, small beetles, scale insects and red spider mites are often also susceptible. The technical material is a brownish liquid with a smell of garlic. Although somewhat expensive, it owes its popularity to the relative safety with which it can be handled, to its low persistence and to the possibility of application as an ultra-low-volume spray.

Malathion (figure 4.7) provides an elegant example of the way selective

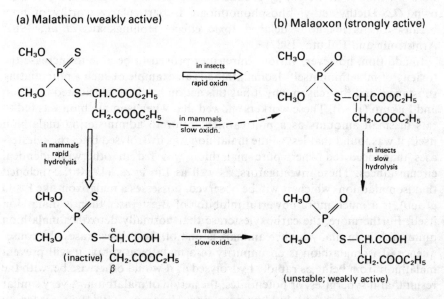

Figure 4.7   Malathion, its activation to malaoxon and its deactivation by carboxyl-esterase: (a) *S*-[1,2-bis(ethoxycarbonyl)ethyl] dimethyl phosphorothiolo-thionate; (b) *S*-[1,2-bis(ethoxycarbonyl)ethyl] dimethyl phosphorothiolate

action can sometimes be achieved by exploiting differences in the enzymic constitution of different organisms. Almost always, hydrolysis leads to detoxication, so organisms in which a **carboxylesterase** is particularly active are able to protect themselves from malathion by removing one of the ethyl groups from the succinic ester moiety. Fortunately, most vertebrates seem to be well endowed with this enzyme (or at least with an enzyme that has a similar ultimate effect). However, when the thion sulphur atom is replaced by oxygen, a much more powerful cholinesterase inhibitor, **malaoxon**, is formed. It so happens that most insects seem to possess a very active oxidative enzyme system. This can activate malathion by attacking the P–S linkage, so that the insect's own defence system actually helps to kill it. It is stressed that all insects and all vertebrates probably possess both an esterase and an NADPH-dependent oxidase system; it is the balance of the action of these two systems that varies from one organism to another. The breakdown of malathion is, in practice, more complex than shown in the figure, for further metabolic changes can remove both ethyl groups from the succinate moiety. There is also some evidence that a glutathione-*S*-methyl transferase (section 3.5) can remove methyl groups from one or both of the two methoxy groups.

In earlier years it was found that malathion occasionally appeared to be more toxic to higher animals than was to have been expected. Fukuto and his colleagues in the USA were among the first to establish that this variability was caused by traces of impurities present in the malathion. Some of these were low-molecular-weight by-products and possessed a high toxicity of their own. *O,S*-Diethyl ethyl phosphonothioate is particularly worthy of note because of its insidious delayed toxic effect (Hollingshaus *et al.*, 1981; Armstrong and Fukuto, 1987).

In addition, however, various impurities proved to be able to increase the toxicity of malathion itself. Isomalathion is an example of such a potentiating substance, and the reason why it has this action has been elucidated by Ryan and Fukuto (1985). These workers showed that when isomalathion was fed to rats in small amounts as a pretreatment prior to administering malathion itself, it was found that less of the malathion was hydrolysed by carboxylesterases than occurred when pure malathion was fed in otherwise identical circumstances. These investigators, as well as Lin *et al.* (1984b), concluded that isomalathion (which, it will be observed, possesses a malaoxon-like P=O group), is a much more powerful inhibitor of B-esterases than is malathion itself. Furthermore, the carboxylesterase that normally detoxifies malathion quite rapidly in many higher animals is one of these B-esterases. In consequence, if isomalathion is an impurity in a malathion spray, it will prevent malathion from being as rapidly hydrolysed as it would otherwise be, with the result that it synergises, or potentiates, the action of malathion. A very similar conclusion was reached by Imamura and Hasegawa (1984) in regard to another malathion impurity, *O,O,S*-trimethyl phosphorothioate. They showed that this substance inhibited the tissue carboxylesterases that normally detoxify malathion and, by so doing, compromised its safety in higher animals.

$$
\begin{array}{c}
CH_3O \\
 \\
CH_3O
\end{array}
\!\!\diagdown\!\!
\overset{\displaystyle O}{\underset{\displaystyle P}{}}
\!\!\diagup\!\!
\begin{array}{c}
 \\
S{-}CH_3
\end{array}
$$

*O,O,S-*Trimethyl phosphorothioate

The effect of impurities on the action of malathion has been described in some detail because it illustrates how complex the situation can become in view of the fact that organophosphorus compounds are hydrolysed by some esterases and yet strongly inhibit the action of others (section 3.3; also Kao *et al.*, 1985). Undoubtedly, similar complications could occur for other organophosphorus compounds (most have been less extensively studied than malathion) and interactions are to be expected not only when impurities are present but also, for example, when a spray operator comes into contact with more than one pesticide in a short timespan.

Within a decade of the introduction of malathion, several species of insects had developed **resistance** to it. For example, Spiller (1961) reported that by that time mosquitoes and houseflies had developed a 40–100 fold increase in tolerance under field conditions in both California and Florida. Sometimes, but not always, the development of resistance to malathion is associated with a simultaneous development of resistance to other organophosphorus compounds. This phenomenon is known as **cross-resistance**. On the other hand, strains of insects that have developed resistance to organochlorine insecticides such as DDT and dieldrin are usually initially susceptible to malathion.

Townend and Busvine (1969) reported that some malathion-resistant strains of insects show high carboxylesterase activity, thus providing a clue to the probable cause of this particular type of insect resistance. Dauterman and Matsumura (1962) observed that malathion-resistant strains of the mosquito *Culex tarsalis* showed cross-resistance to analogues of malathion which had propyl or isopropyl groups attached to the succinic acid instead of ethyl groups, but that there was no such cross-resistance to the carboxymethyl analogue. This was interpreted at the time as suggesting that the esterase did not readily remove methyl groups from –COOCH linkages. Later work by the Dauterman school has shown that the situation is not as straightforward as this, for a range of carboxylesterases is now known to exist. Not only do different members of this carboxylesterase family hydrolyse different carboxyalkyl esters at different rates (carboxymethyl usually being the slowest to react), but also different esterases attack preferentially the α and β carboxyethyl groups of malathion (see figure 4.7). Figures quoted by Lin *et al.* (1984a) illustrate these differences; not only is there a several-fold difference in the rates of hydrolysis of the esters studied (methyl, ethyl, propyl, isopropyl, butyl, amyl) but the ratio of the two possible mono-acids (the ethyl group coming from either of two positions) varies by more than 10-fold. Variability in carboxylesterase is likely to be a common event (section 9.3) and, as Lin and colleagues have pointed out, selectivity in some species is likely to be linked to the metabolic roles played by different carboxylesterases.

(b) The parathion family

The three principal members of this family are (or were*) **parathion**, **methyl parathion** and **fenitrothion**. Parathion is more persistent than methyl parathion and much more persistent than fenitrothion. Their mammalian toxicities were mentioned at the beginning of this section and their formulae appear in figure 4.8. Their agricultural uses are rather similar and wide ranging—in most localities they control aphids, capsids, leaf miners, sawflies and weevils. They also tend to have individual uses—thus parathion has been used for the control of mealy bugs, scale insects, root-knot nematodes and woodlice, whereas the less toxic fenitrothion is used against flour beetles, grain beetles and grain weevils. For some substances the problem of food residues can be minimised by spraying the insecticides onto the absorbent walls of the warehouse rather than admixing with the bulk of the food material.

The metabolism of parathion and its analogues illustrates how closely field safety is associated with minor variations in chemical structure, which, in turn,

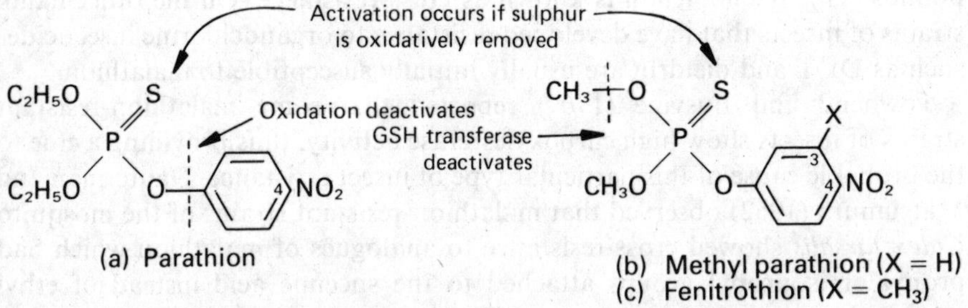

Figure 4.8 The parathion family of persistent contact insecticides: (a) diethyl 4-nitrophenyl phosphorothionate; (b) dimethyl 4-nitrophenyl phosphorothionate; (c) dimethyl 3-methyl-4-nitrophenyl phosphorothionate

*Please note that here, and throughout the book, the fact that reference is made to a pesticide does not imply that it is currently registered—or even manufactured—in any major country. Many dangerous substances are, in fact, still sloshing around the developing world. However, the main reason for mentioning certain, now notorious, substances is that the significance of second-generation pesticides cannot be appreciated out of context.

lead to changes in the balance established between the various pathways of metabolism. All three compounds shown in figure 4.8 are oxidised by mono-oxygenases in animals, insects and plants and are thereby changed to derivatives containing the P=O group, which are more powerful inhibitors of cholinesterase than was the original thionphosphate. Their degradation, however, follows different routes. Parathion is principally degraded by rupture of the P–O–phenyl linkage, whereas the two methyl analogues are not.

The rupture of the P–O–phenyl linkage of parathion is not a hydrolytic reaction but is an oxidative process mediated by an NADPH-dependent oxidase (compare figure 4.1). By contrast, methyl parathion and fenitrothion are principally destroyed in most species investigated by rupture of a P–O–CH$_3$ linkage:

$$
\begin{array}{ccc}
\text{CH}_3\text{---O} \diagdown \diagup \text{S} & & \text{H---O} \diagdown \diagup \text{S} \\
\quad\quad \text{P} & \xrightarrow[\text{GSH}]{\text{glutathione---}S\text{---}\atop\text{alkyltransferase}} \text{CH}_3\text{---SG} + & \quad\quad \text{P} \\
\text{CH}_3\text{O} \diagup \diagdown \text{O---aryl} & & \text{CH}_3\text{O} \diagup \diagdown \text{O---aryl}
\end{array}
\quad (4.6)
$$

Fenitrothion   (*S*-Methyl   Demethyl
glutathione)   fenitrothion

Fukami and Shishido (1966) found that rat liver could carry out this change five times as fast as a comparable insect system. It seems probable that this metabolic difference could be a factor contributing to the lower mammalian toxicity of these methyl analogues compared with parathion itself, for parathion does not readily de-ethylate in this manner. Rather similarly, it will be recalled that methyl parathion is normally more toxic to mammals than is fenitrothion, and this difference has been attributed to the more rapid metabolism of the latter compound.

Experiments by Baker *et al.* (1979) on whole perfused liver have provided a further insight into the higher animal's total defence mechanism against parathion (and probably many other organophosphorus compounds). In these experiments, perfusion fluid is recycled, the ingoing and exiting liquids being monitored for parathion. They showed that, in a single cycle, absorption of parathion was very high, varying at different parathion concentrations between 69 and 98 per cent of the dose. As the authors point out, the facility with which the liver is able to extract most of the toxicant reaching it is the most immediate and most protective of all mechanisms of defence.

More recently, Sultatos and Minor (1986) performed a similar perfusion experiment with parathion using mouse liver. Alteration in the flow rate of the perfusing liquid had little effect on the overall metabolic picture. The metabolites recognised and the presumed relationship between them are shown in figure 4.9.

When sulphur is removed from thionphosphates like parathion in *in vitro* systems, it becomes bound to microsomal macromolecules, sometimes to the detriment of microsomal enzyme activity. It is probable that such organic binding is in the form of hydrodisulphides (R–S–S–H). Eventually, in an *in vivo* situation, most of this organically bound sulphur is liberated and appears in the urine as sulphate and thiosulphate. The formation of inorganic sulphate is enhanced by the presence of reduced glutathione (Morelli and Nakatsugawa, 1979).

Fenitrothion, it will be recalled, is a favoured insecticide because it is often inactivated quite rapidly in higher animals. Metabolism in insects is normally much slower but in resistant insects the rate at which metabolism occurs by some pathways can be greatly increased.

This is well illustrated by the work of Ugaki *et al.* (1985) using a strain of houseflies that was susceptible to organophosphorus insecticides and another strain (Akita-f) that was some 3500 times more resistant. After topical application the fenitrothion was far more rapidly metabolised *in vivo* by the resistant strain than by the susceptible (SRS) strain. Parallel studies done on *in vitro* systems showed that the metabolic route involving the glutathione-*S*-methyl transferase system proceeded some 10 times faster in the resistant strain than in the SRS strain, while the routes catalysed by cytochrome P_{450} proceeded at double the speed (figure 4.10a). The transferase system removed an alkoxy methyl group (compare equation (4.6)) to give de(s)methyl fenitrothion. On the other hand, the cytochrome P_{450} system catalysed two reactions, one giving fenitrooxon (compare figure 4.9) and the other removing the leaving group to give, principally, 3-methyl-4-nitrophenol. Figure 4.10b appears to indicate that the rate at which fenitrooxon is formed decreases after a while, but in an experiment that demonstrates clearly the value of radio-

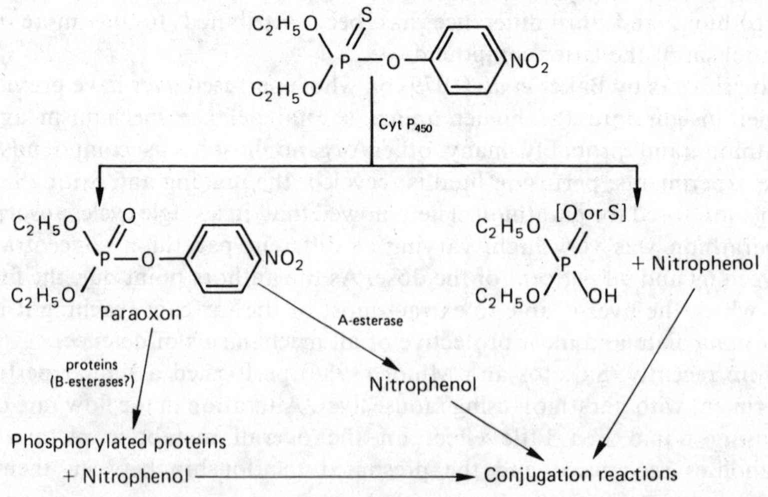

Figure 4.9 Metabolites of parathion when liver perfusion is done with mouse liver (after Sultatos and Minor, 1986)

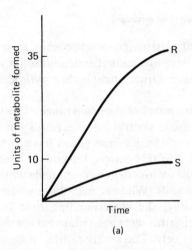
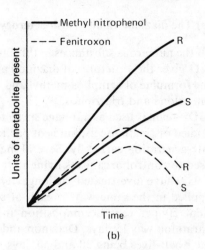

Figure 4.10 Metabolism of fenitrothion by susceptible (S) and resistant (R) strains of houseflies (after Ugaki *et al.*, 1985). (a) Formation of demethyl fenitrothion (R rich in glutathione-*S*-transferase?). (b) Formation and disappearance of fenitrooxon and of 3-methylnitrophenol (NADH-dependent)

labelled substrates in pesticide research, these Japanese workers showed that what was really happening was that the fenitrooxon was being further metabolised as fast as it was formed to nitrophenol and other products.

Excluding its effect upon cholinesterase, fenitrothion can have subtle effects on insect larvae, which can lead to distortions in later stages of development. Stewart and Philogène (1983) reviewed literature on such effects, which include depletion in larval food reserves and consequential alterations in the rate of growth. Working with the tobacco hornworm, these Canadian workers found that the larvae developed asynchronously and took longer to reach the stage of pupation. On the other hand, the development of pupae was completed more rapidly than was that of the controls. Perhaps unexpectedly, the adults laid more eggs than did control adults, but their lives were shorter.

It is well known that the effectiveness with which many pesticides protect stored grain varies with the moisture content of the kernels. As was mentioned earlier, fenitrothion is often used to protect stored grain. The relationship between moisture content and the effectiveness of fenitrothion in the control of several species of coleoptera that attack grain was investigated by Samson *et al.* (1987). They found that its effectiveness decreased 15-fold as the moisture content increased from 10 to 24 per cent. This effect was, in part, a function of the more rapid disappearance of fenitrothion at higher moisture content, but, in addition, the residual fenitrothion was seemingly less toxic. A probable explanation is that more residue accumulates in the pericarp, and less remains immediately available on the surface, when the moisture content of kernels is high.

(c) The diazinon family (with heterocyclic leaving groups)

Of the numerous substances in this family of persistent contact poisons, figure 4.11 gives the structures of diazinon and pirimiphos-methyl and, additionally, the formulae of azinphos-methyl and menazon. Others include chlorpyriphos, phosalone and triazophos.

Diazinon is used as a foliage spray for the control of the usual range of soft-bodied or small insects, but is of particular use to control cabbage root fly and late-generation carrot fly. Several members of the diazinon group have been used to control organisms living in the soil. For this reason, Laskowski *et al.* (1982) have investigated the longevity of four loco-systemic compounds when applied in the same way to each of several soils. Whereas malathion underwent 50 per cent decomposition in one day, the corresponding time for parathion was 15 days. Diazinon and chlorpyrifos were even more persistent, their half-lives being 30 and 60 days respectively. The ranking order of these four compounds (other compounds were also studied) was not affected by soil type, although the precise decomposition times would be expected to be different when different soils were used.

Reports occasionally appear with data that suggest that diet can alter the sensitivity of insects to particular pesticides. One such example, involving diazinon, has been reported by Riskallah *et al.* (1986). The tobacco budworm, *Heliothis*, is four times more tolerant of diazinon when fed on the leaves of wild tomatoes than when fed an artificial diet. The observation is of interest because analytical back-up suggested that the rate or route of metabolism had been altered as a consequence of the larvae having fed on the tomato leaves. It was concluded that the cytochrome P_{450} system had been induced (chapter 3) about three-fold. If this phenomenon occurred for other pests under field conditions, it would evidently hinder pest control.

Although the main effect of diazinon is its action on acetylcholinesterase,

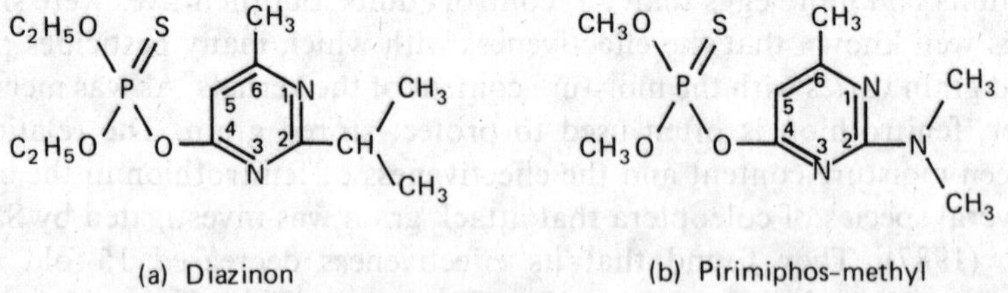

(a) Diazinon   (b) Pirimiphos–methyl

Figure 4.11 Persistent contact poisons with heterocyclic leaving groups: (a) diethyl 2-isopropyl-6-methylpyrimidin-4-yl phosphorothionate; (b) dimethyl 2-dimethylamino-6-methylpyrimidin-4-yl phosphorothionate. Others are azinphos-methyl: dimethyl *S*-(3,4-dihydro-4-ketobenzo-[*d*]-1,2,3-triazin-3-yl-methyl) phosphorothiolothionate; and menazon: dimethyl *S*-(4,6-diamino-1,3,5-triazin-2-yl-methyl) phosphorothiolothionate

various histopathological symptoms have been recorded in higher animals. The publication by Sastry and Sharma (1981) is particularly useful, for these authors have provided a histophotographic record of the changes which occur in the liver, stomach and gills of the Indian freshwater fish, *Ophiocephalus punctatus*, after exposure to a suspension of 0.4 mg/l diazinon. After 15 days the cytoplasm of hepatocytes was observed to vacuolate, many nuclei had enlarged and some of the cell membranes had ruptured.

Pirimiphos has been marketed as both the dimethyl and the diethyl analogues. Pirimiphos-ethyl is about 10 times more toxic to higher animals than is pirimiphos-methyl (figure 4.11b). The latter is a broad-spectrum insecticide with acaricidal properties. It is particularly valuable for the protection of stored products from mites, flour beetles, grain weevils and similar organisms. Its particular advantages are that it has a relatively low toxicity (2000 mg/kg body weight orally to rats), is moderately persistent on surfaces and has a vapour pressure that is sufficiently high to allow it, in some situations, to act as a fumigant. In Britain, pirimiphos-methyl is approved for use for direct admixing with grain, either as a dust or as an emulsifiable formulation. Alternatively, direct contact with stored produce can be avoided by spraying it onto the walls of storage areas or by treating storage sacks with it.

Cross-resistance to organophosphorus compounds is not absolute and it has been found that pirimiphos-methyl is quite useful against insects that have developed resistance to malathion. The reason for this may be that, unlike malathion, carboxylesterase is not involved in the metabolism of pirimiphos.

The metabolism of pirimiphos-methyl has been studied in ruminants and in poultry by Skidmore and Tegala (1986). This occurs quite rapidly both by hydrolysis and by *N*-dealkylation. Hydrolysis results in the splitting of the bond between the heterocyclic group and the phosphorothioate ester (see figure 4.11b) and NADPH-dependent *N*-demethylation leads to the group $-NHCH_3$ in position 2 of that formula. The use of liquid scintillation counting for labelled pirimiphos-methyl showed that primary metabolites are mostly conjugated and that about 90 per cent of the radioactivity is accounted for in products excreted in the urine within seven days. The same authors did, however, show that a significant proportion (40 per cent) of the small residual amount of radioactivity could not be removed from liver by the use of normal extraction techniques after slaughtering, indicating strong binding of one or more metabolites to tissue components.

Chlorpyrifos (figure 4.16c) has been used as a broad-spectrum insecticide, especially in the USA. Its efficacy and persistence in relation to the control of San José scale (*Quadraspidiotus perniciosus*) on peaches has been investigated by Howell and George (1984). At 0.6 g active ingredient per litre, effective residues remained on twigs, but not on fruit, for up to 80 days. The same authors reported that it was effective against climbing cutworms in apple and pear orchards. It does, however, interact in some way with constituents of tree bark, a process that increases its persistence to such an extent that it is probably only safe to use one spray per season. Chlorpyrifos is also the standard substance used in some areas to control the chinch bug, *Blissus insularis*, in lawns, but some strains of this bug have developed serious resistance to it. For example, Reinert and Portier (1983) studied 13 strains of *Blissus insularis* and found seven strains that had developed toxicity ratios in excess of 3.3×10^3.

Chlorpyrifos has been used to control domestic insects such as cockroaches and mosquitoes. Some formulations are also showing promise for use against pests that live in the soil. In Saudi Arabia, for example, an emulsifiable concentrate proved to be one of the three best methods for subterranean termite control (one litre diluted to 500 litres and applied to one hectare). The termite problem in Saudi Arabia can be severe (Badawi and Faragalla, 1986), leading to the loss of two-thirds of green-pepper plants. Treatment before sowing or before transplanting is better than other methods and reduces damage to less than 10 per cent. Factors influencing the persistence and effectiveness of chlorpyrifos in soil have been investigated by Getzin (1985).

Azinphos-methyl is particularly used in Britain to control codling, tortrix and winter moths, as well as a variety of other pests of top fruit, bush fruit and cane fruit. Unfortunately, red spider mites are tending to develop resistance to it. **Menazon** is a good aphicide, with slight systemic activity by foliage application, but it can enter roots quite readily.

Most, if not all, of the heterocyclic compounds are activated by mono-oxygenases with the formation of P=O (oxon) derivatives that are powerful inhibitors of cholinesterase. A common route of degradation for diazinon (and probably for other members of the group) involves the cleavage of the P–O–pyrimidine linkage by the action of an NADPH-dependent oxidase. This is analogous to the reaction undergone by parathion (figure 4.9). On the other hand, it is becoming increasingly clear that glutathione-*S*-aryl and -*S*-alkyl transferases often catalyse contributory, and sometimes major, detoxifying pathways. Thus Usui *et al.* (1977) isolated several glutathione-*S*-transferases from the fat bodies of female *Periplaneta americana*. These transferases had different but overlapping specificities, two being particularly active on diazinon and three on methyl parathion. As a result of genetic studies done on diazinon-resistant houseflies, Motoyama *et al.* (1977) concluded that gluta-thione-dependent enzymes are not a major biochemical mechanism respon-sible for housefly resistance to diazinon.

4.9 SYSTEMIC INSECTICIDES (subgroup 3)

These substances are soluble in lipids but they also usually possess a higher water solubility than substances in subgroup 2. Consequently, their partition coefficients are such that they pass through cuticular waxes and lipoprotein membranes to emerge in the phloem or xylem streams of sprayed plants. Most are of moderate stability and persist for a period of a few days to a few weeks within plants.

It should be noted that the word **systemic** can be used in slightly different ways, for a substance that does not readily enter through leaves may still enter through roots and be carried upwards in the transpiration stream. This can lead to different views about how systemic a particular substance is. In practice, those substances which enter predominantly through roots often have aqueous solubilities at the lower end of the range for the group, and almost all substances that readily enter foliage can also enter through the roots (although not necessarily easily reach roots through soil).

Systemic poisons have several important advantages over other types of persistent poisons. They are not, for example, susceptible to wash-off by rain. Furthermore, by virtue of their movement within plants, they give protection in regions away from the locus of application, as well as protection at a time removed from the time of application. They often tend to be transported towards regions of growth, giving protection to the vital and vulnerable tissue near meristems—they may, indeed, give protection to tissue not even differentiated at the time of spraying.

Since many systemic compounds have only a weak contact action, beneficial organisms in the vicinity at the time of spraying may not succumb even if the spray hits them. This opens up a new dimension in pest control, for, as Carson (1963) stressed, one of the principal objections to chemical pest control is that indiscriminate destruction of pests and predators can result in explosive reproduction (flare-up) of surviving pests. Their limited contact toxicity arises from the fact that the *sprayed substance* is often a weak cholinesterase inhibitor, the *actual toxicant* being formed by metabolic action within the plant (or sometimes after oral uptake by the insect). The metabolic activation can take several possible forms but it involves oxidation by mono-oxygenases in a manner analogous to examples encountered in section 4.8.

Systemic insecticides are used against a wide range of phytophagous insects but they excel as aphicides and some are used against red spider and other mites. Vicarious control of some aphid-borne virus diseases such as cucumber mosaic virus and beet virus yellows is also possible. Other common targets are bulb flies, sawflies, codling moth, leaf miners, weevils and woolly aphids.

Many systemic compounds fall into chemical families characterised by the presence of thioether and carbamate groups.

(a) The thioether family of systemic insecticides

The formulae of three members of the **thioether** family are shown in figure 4.12.

Phorate is one of the most toxic substances still used in crop protection (table 4.1). It can be applied to foliage to control capsids and aphids (and

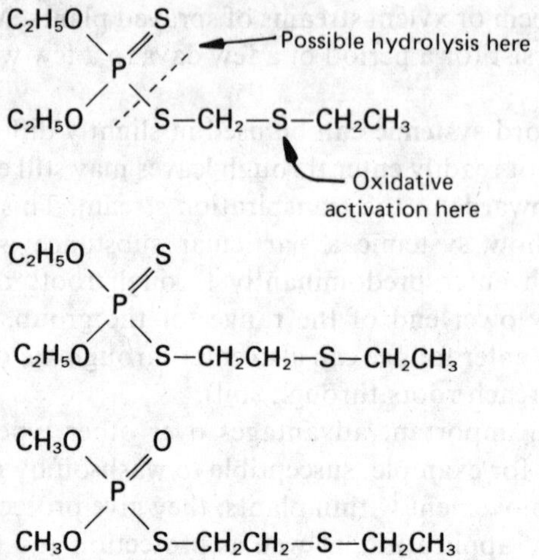

C_2H_5O S
   \P/
C_2H_5O $S-CH_2-S-CH_2CH_3$ ← Possible hydrolysis here

— Oxidative activation here

(a) Phorate

C_2H_5O S
   \P/
C_2H_5O $S-CH_2CH_2-S-CH_2CH_3$ (b) Disulfoton

CH_3O O
   \P/
CH_3O $S-CH_2CH_2-S-CH_2CH_3$ (c) Demeton–S–methyl

Figure 4.12 The thioether family of systemic insecticides: (a) diethyl S-(ethylthio-methyl) phosphorothiolothionate; (b) diethyl S-(ethylthioethyl) phosphorothiolothionate; (c) dimethyl S-(ethylthioethyl) phosphorothiolate

hence to reduce the incidence of roll virus of potatoes and yellows virus of sugar beet, both of which are aphid-borne). More usually, however, for reasons of safety, it is now applied in the form of granules to soil. Moreover, this is the way in which its rather low aqueous solubility can best be exploited to achieve systemic action. Granules are often applied prior to drilling of peas and beans to control weevil larvae and to control the larvae of carrot fly and frit fly. In view of the high toxicity, six weeks should elapse between application and harvesting of phorate-treated produce.

A major metabolic change undergone by compounds of this type is oxidation of the thioether sulphur atom to give sulphoxides and then sulphones:

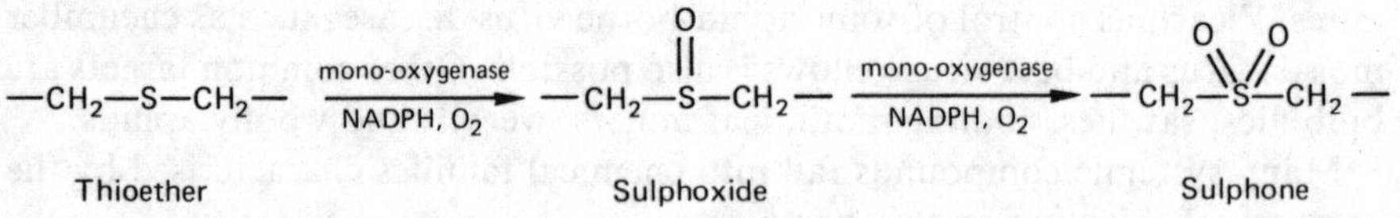

$$-CH_2-S-CH_2- \xrightarrow[\text{NADPH, O}_2]{\text{mono-oxygenase}} -CH_2-\overset{\overset{\text{O}}{\|}}{S}-CH_2- \xrightarrow[\text{NADPH, O}_2]{\text{mono-oxygenase}} -CH_2-\overset{\overset{\text{O O}}{\diagdown\diagup}}{S}-CH_2-$$

Thioether   Sulphoxide   Sulphone

(4.7)

Such changes can occur in insects, plants or higher animals. Yu (1985) investigated the sulphoxidation of phorate in the fall armyworm, *Spodoptera frugiperda*, and found that the reaction occurred most readily in the alimentary canal, the fat body and Malpighian tubules. The enzyme system concerned was located in the microsomes, was dependent upon NADPH, but was inhibited by piperonyl butoxide and by carbon monoxide. These observations strongly suggest that the reaction principally involves the cytochrome P_{450} system rather than the flavoprotein-dependent pathway (section 3.4).

When oxidation occurs to the sulphoxide and sulphone it is usually accompanied by an increase in mammalian toxicity and with an increased inhibitory effect *in vitro* upon acetylcholinesterase activity. For example, the dose of the sulphone of phorate that inhibits acetylcholinesterase by 50 per cent is only one-twentieth of that of phorate itself. For thionphosphate members of the group, such as phorate and disulfoton, there is some evidence that oxon formation, similar to that which converts parathion to paraoxon, also leads to activation.

Detoxication of members of the thioether family appears to be by the removal of the thioether moiety, principally but not exclusively by cleavage of the P–S (rather than the adjacent S–C) bond.

(b) The carbamate family of systemic insecticides

The second family contains substances that are essentially amides, for each molecule contains a substituted carbamic acid unit, –CONHR, in the leaving group. The structures of the two best-known members of the family are shown in figure 4.13.

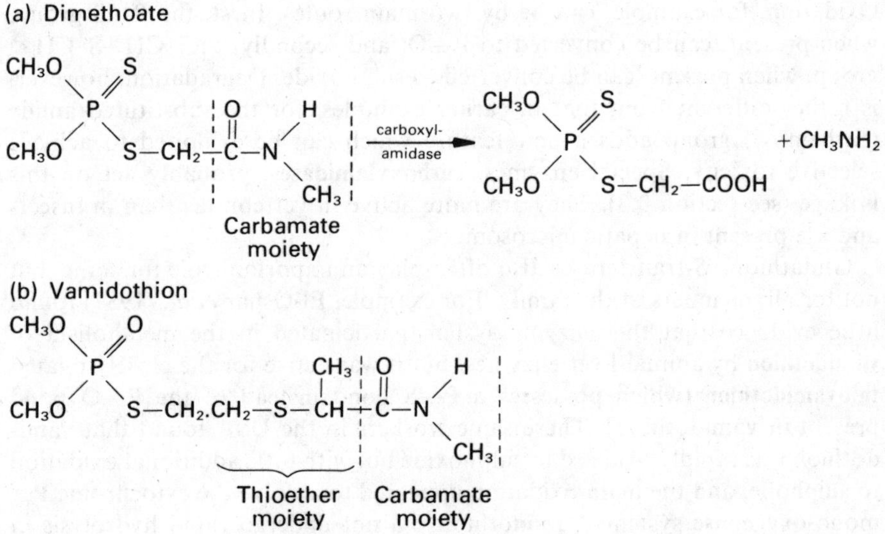

Figure 4.13 Systemic organophosphorus insecticides containing the carbamate group: (a) dimethyl *S*-(methylcarbamoylmethyl) phosphorothiolothionate; (b) dimethyl *S*-[2-(1-methylcarbamoylethylthio)ethyl] phosphorothiolate

Dimethoate is moderately soluble in water and has a much shorter half-life than substances such as phorate. For this reason the time interval between the last application and harvesting is only seven days. It has been used to control aphids on many crops, including many legumes, brassicas, beet, top fruit, cane fruit and bush fruit, tobacco and ornamentals. It also controls woolly aphids of apple, wheat bulb flies, pea midges, capsid bugs and beet leaf miners. It has also found use in farm animal hygiene, which probably reflects the fact that its LD_{50} is high compared to those of most organophosphorus insecticides that possess appreciable aqueous solubility (table 4.1). When correctly used, it does not seem to be unduly toxic to bees (Danka *et al.*, 1985). Not only was fruit set unaffected by pre-bloom sprays put on 2–18 days earlier but, using dislodged branches, it was shown that, on a visit-per-flower basis, bees paid fewer visits on the day that the spray was applied and for one succeeding day only, thereafter behaving normally.

The half-life of dimethoate in the absence of enzymes is greatly dependent on the ambient temperature and pH. Noble (1985) found that the half-life varied with pH from 206 days to 39 min at 25°C, and developed an equation representing the half-life as a function of pH and temperature. A practical recommendation arising from this work is that, when used for root dipping, dimethoate solutions should be on the acid side of pH 7 and the solution should not be above room temperature.

The metabolism of all members of the carbamate family of systemic organophosphorus insecticides probably follows well established patterns. Oxidation, for example, can be by two main routes. First, the P=S group, when present, can be converted to P=O; and secondly, the $-CH_2-S-CH<$ group, when present, can be converted to sulphoxide. Degradation, however, is rather different from that in earlier examples, for the substituted amide (carbamoyl) group adds a new feature which can be exploited to achieve selective toxicity. Special enzymes, **carboxylamidases**, probably act on this linkage (see section 3.3). They are more active in vertebrates than in insects and are present in hepatic microsomes.

Glutathione-*S*-transferases also often play an important role for some, but not for all, members of the family. For example, El-Oshar *et al.* (1987) found little evidence that this enzyme system participated in the metabolism of **vamidothion** by animal liver enzymes, but it was active for the closely related **thiovamidothion** (which possesses a P=S bond instead of the P=O bond present in vamidothion). These same workers in the USA found that vamidothion was rapidly oxidised to sulphoxide but with little additional oxidation to sulphone, and the main oxidation appeared to involve the cytochrome P_{450} mono-oxygenase system. Vamidothion did not undergo rapid hydrolysis in the *in vitro* systems under study.

(c) Other systemic organophosphorus insecticides

Phosphamidon (figure 4.14a) could possibly be classified in the previous section since it contains a double *N*-substituted carbamic acid moiety. However, its most striking characteristic is that it contains a vinyl group with an adjacent chlorine atom. These, together with its solubility in water, probably account for the fact that it is rapidly decomposed in alkaline solution and in the presence of enzymes in both plants and animals; its half-life within plants is often no more than two days. In contrast, toxic residues on plants may persist much longer than this; in Britain, the recommended safe period after spraying and before harvesting edible crops is three weeks. Animals often detoxify it by removing one of the methyl groups shown on the left of the formula while plants probably activate it to a more potent cholinesterase inhibitor by removal of one of the ethyl groups shown on the right-hand side. It is mainly used to control aphids on broad beans, field beans and peas as well as on beet and brassicas. It has also been used to kill sucking insects living on cotton and is a moderately effective acaricide (i.e. it kills phytophagous spider mites).

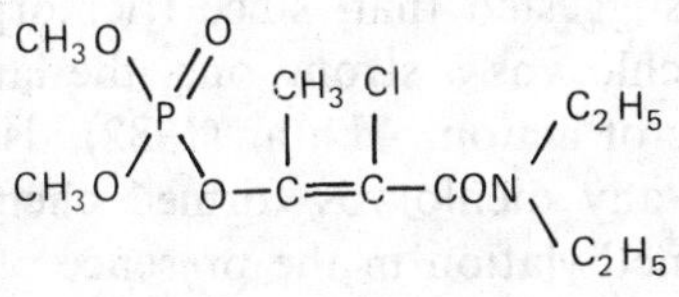

(a) Phosphamidon

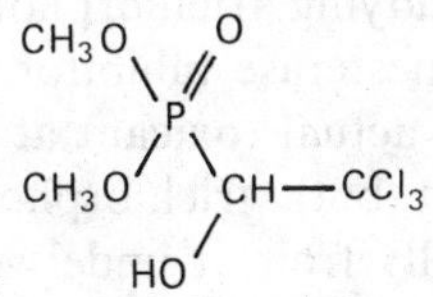

(b) Trichlorphon

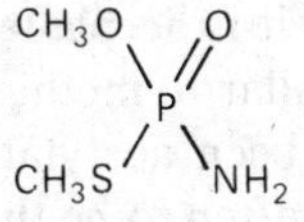

(c) Methamidophos

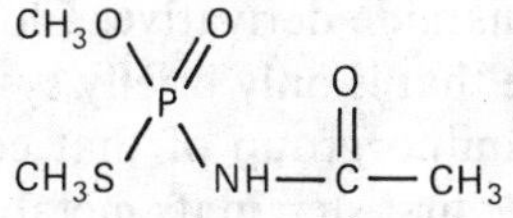

(d) Acephate (compare (c))

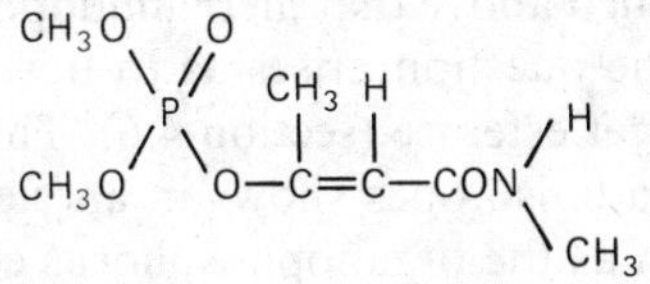

(e) Monocrotophos (compare (a))

Figure 4.14 Other systemic organophosphorus compounds

Dicrotophos is similar to phosphamidon except that it has a hydrogen atom instead of the chlorine, and methyl groups instead of the two ethyl groups. It is, like phosphamidon, soluble in water and not very stable. It is, however, much more toxic to animals. It has been used on elms in an attempt to control Dutch elm disease (which is spread by a beetle), as well as to control pests on cotton and soybeans.

Trichlorphon (trichlorfon) is a phosphonate with the structure shown in figure 4.14b. It is particularly useful against leaf miners, tortrix and cabbage root fly larvae (especially for late-season protection of Brussels sprouts). It has also been used against cockroaches and against organochlorine-resistant houseflies. Being of low mammalian toxicity it has been used against some parasites of domestic and farm animals.

Trichlorphon is somewhat soluble in water and of relatively low persistence; in consequence, the safe period after spraying and before harvesting can be as little as two days. In fact, under alkaline conditions, or when a solution is heated, it decomposes non-enzymatically. In addition, it is readily destroyed by hydrolases and probably by oxidases and conjugases as well. Akhtar (1982) showed that even in solutions containing only buffer, it is converted to a second insecticide, dichlorvos (DDVP; see section 14.10) in a reaction involving dehydrochlorination accompanied by molecular rearrangement. Earlier workers studying trichlorphon had suggested that, since trichlorphon is a weak cholinesterase inhibitor and dichlorvos a strong one, the latter could well be the actual toxicant at the site of action. Akhtar (1982) also demonstrated that both trichlorphon and any dichlorvos formed chemically or biochemically from it underwent demethylation in the presence of enzymes from the soluble (not microsomal) fraction of animal liver.

Methamidophos is another water-soluble and rather toxic systemic insecticide of quite short persistence (figure 4.14c). It will be seen that there is no 'leaving group' in the sense that that phrase is normally used, the molecule being a phosphonamide derivative. Closely related to it is **acephate**, a water-soluble substance that is only briefly systemic. It is similar to methamidophos except that the amino group of that compound has been acetylated (figure 4.14d). In fact, the first step in its metabolism appears often to be the removal of the acetyl group to give methamidophos (compare and contrast the relationship between trichlorphon and dichlorvos). The interaction of some analogues of methamidophos with acetylcholinesterase has been investigated by Vilanova *et al.* (1987). It was mentioned above that methamidophos has no conventional 'leaving group' and so the question arises as to how it blocks acetylcholinesterase or neuropathy target esterase (section 4.6). The work of Thompson and Fukuto (1982) using radioisotopes shows in an elegant way that it is the P–S linkage that is broken as the organophosphorus compound attaches itself to acetylcholinesterase. Vilanova *et al.* (1987) came to a similar conclusion when studying a series of alkyl homologues of methamidophos.

Monocrotophos (figure 4.14e) is one of the most poisonous substances marketed for use in crop protection. It is soluble in water, of short persistence and has been used to control pests of cotton, peanuts, tobacco and sugar cane.

4.10 ORGANOPHOSPHORUS COMPOUNDS WITH A FUMIGANT ACTION (subgroup 4)

Dichlorvos (figure 4.15) is the main practical example of an organophosphorus compound with a vapour pressure sufficiently high to enable it to act in the vapour phase. Its vapour pressure of 1.2×10^{-2} mmHg at 20°C is high compared with the lethal concentration needed to kill insects and is 10–1000 times higher than the vapour pressures of most other organophosphorus insecticides (table 4.1).

Dichlorvos was originally introduced to kill houseflies but has found horticultural application in greenhouses and mushroom houses. It can be applied as an aerosol mist but, being a liquid, is more usually formulated as a solid solution in plastic strips from which it slowly evaporates. A method for the protection of mushroom beds against adults of the phorid, *Megaselia halterata*, has been described by White (1981). The newly spawned mushroom crop was treated for the first four crucial weeks with 0.3 mg dichlorvos per cubic metre air space, applied every 24 min using an automated atomiser system. This protection is necessary to ensure that the flies do not spread the harmful fungus, *Verticillium fungicola*, during this period.

Dichlorvos is very toxic to human beings but its rapid decomposition usually enables a sprayed area to be entered with safety within 24 h. Its use has

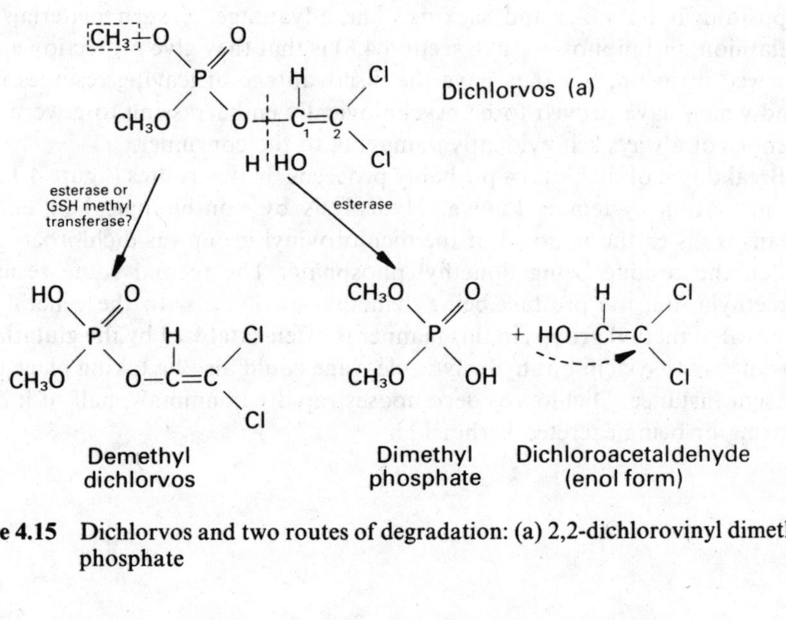

Figure 4.15   Dichlorvos and two routes of degradation: (a) 2,2-dichlorovinyl dimethyl phosphate

been reviewed by authorities in the USA since suspicion arose that it might possibly cause carcinogenic and foetotoxic effects (Gold *et al.*, 1984). These US workers studied its effect on operators who had been applying it to control cockroaches. They demonstrated that the activity of serum cholinesterase in such workers was slightly but significantly reduced and that 20 per cent of any dichlorvos that touched normal clothing was able to penetrate down to the skin. Despite the possible concerns inherent in such observations it has been extensively used in homes and hotels in many countries, particularly for the control of flies and mosquitoes.

The relatively high volatility of dichlorvos has led to its use for the protection of food in closed storage areas. In the battle against food loss during storage, the suitable design of warehouses is the first line of defence (and it should be remembered that in some parts of the world a loss of 30 per cent of all harvested food is not uncommon). The warehouse should be constructed so that insects cannot gain easy access and it should be well ventilated with cool, dry air to reduce the spread of fungi. Nevertheless, chemical treatment, especially of stored grain, is often imperative, and then there are two methods of attack. Fumigants such as dichlorvos represent one of these approaches, for such materials diffuse readily around the warehouse (compare section 2.5). Dichlorvos kills free-living insects and can also reach most beetles living within the kernels of grain (Desmarchelier *et al.*, 1977). Other common fumigants, past or present, include methyl bromide, ethylene dibromide and phosphine. Some fumigants are both highly toxic to man and absorbed into food products, so treated foods should always be cooked before use. The second method of attack includes the admixing of a relatively non-toxic and non-volatile insecticide with food material, usually grain, or depositing it on walls and sacking. The advantage of such materials (e.g. malathion, pirimiphos-methyl; section 4.8) is that they give protection against renewed invasion, but they have the disadvantage of leaving residues in the food which have proved to be psychologically embarrassing to governments even if not always self-evidently damaging to the consumer.

Breakdown of dichlorvos probably proceeds by two routes (figure 4.15) but no activation system is known. Hydrolysis by non-biological or enzymic means leads to the removal of the dichlorovinyl group (as dichloroacetaldehyde), the residue being dimethyl phosphate. The second route results in demethylation, the product being demethyl dichlorvos. In the general case, removal of methyl groups in this manner is often catalysed by the glutathione-*S*-transferase system but hydrolytic cleavage could also be taking place in the present instance. Dichlorvos decomposes rapidly in animals, half of it disappearing or being excreted within 12 h.

4.11 ORGANOPHOSPHORUS COMPOUNDS USED AGAINST SOIL ORGANISMS (subgroup 5)

Several organophosphorus compounds have been applied to soil, usually to control organisms such as the carrot root fly larvae which live in the soil or hatch from eggs laid on the soil surface and migrate to nearby crop plants. Usually, but not always, special granular formulations are made for this purpose; it will be recalled (section 2.6) that granules are often safer, cheaper and more pleasant to apply than are surface-broadcast sprays or dusts and, very frequently, last longer in the soil than do surface-applied formulations that are later tined into the soil. In earlier sections, reference has occasionally been made to soil applications when considering the active ingredient but a few extra examples will now be considered.

Chlorfenvinphos (figure 4.16a) contains a vinyl group and is distantly related to dichlorvos. It has been formulated as granules to protect brassicas against cabbage root fly larvae, carrots against carrot fly larvae and sweet corn against fruit fly larvae, respectively. It is also added to mushroom compost to control mushroom flies.

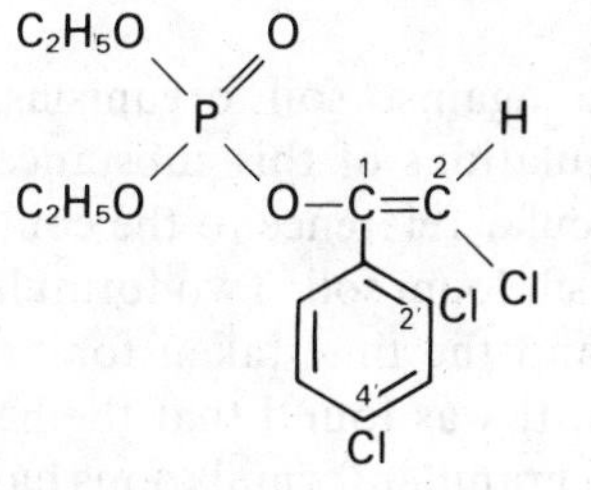

(a) Chlorfenvinphos

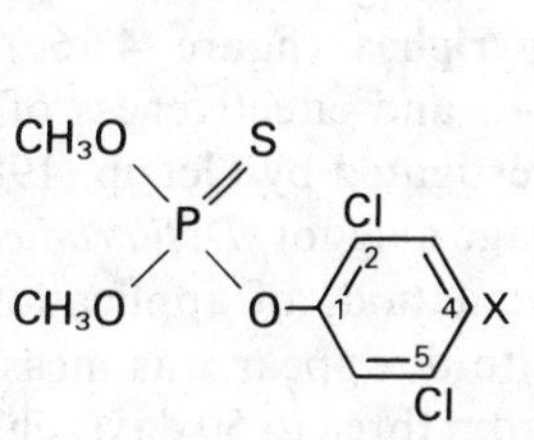

(b) Bromophos (X = Br)
Fenchlorphos (X = Cl)

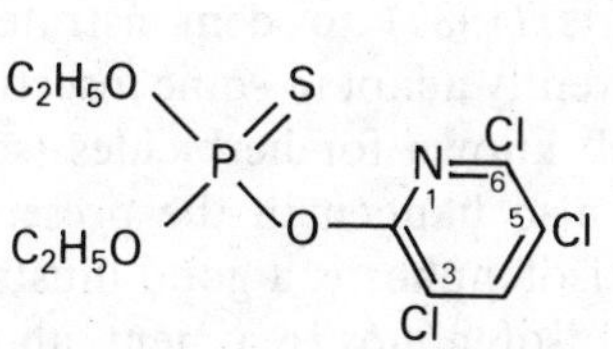

(c) Chlorpyriphos

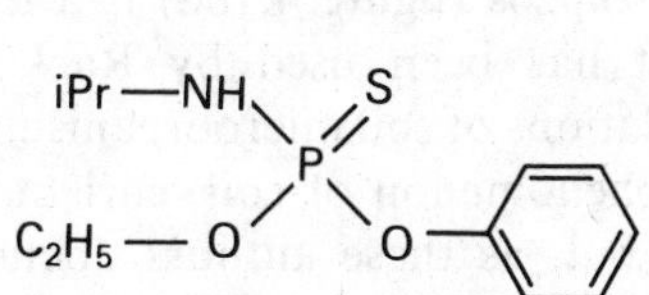

(d) Isofenphos

Figure 4.16   Some organophosphorus compounds used against soil organisms: (a) 2-chloro-1-(2′,4′-dichlorophenyl)vinyl diethyl phosphate; (b) 4-bromo-2,5-dichlorophenyl dimethyl phosphorothionate; (c) diethyl 3,5,6-trichloro-2-pyridyl thionphosphate; (d) isopropyl salicylate ester of *O*-ethyl *N*-isopropyl thionphosphoramidate

Diazinon (figure 4.11) and **disulfoton** (figure 4.12) are two organophosphorus compounds that are both used for foliage application and reformulated as granules for application to soil. In the latter case they are used for similar purposes as chlorfenvinphos.

Phorate (figure 4.12) and disulfoton are among several systemic compounds that can be applied near to the roots of seedling plants to give protection against aphids and the virus diseases that they transmit. In addition they are used by potato growers to limit wireworm damage.

Bromophos (figure 4.16b) granules are available to the home gardener in Britain because it has a much higher LD_{50} than most other organophosphorus compounds. Hence, especially when in granular form, it is very safe to use. It is extensively used by the home gardener to protect carrots and parsnips against root fly larvae; it is placed near the seedling crop plants before the tap root starts to swell. Once a larva has reached the tap root, protection measures are pointless. Bromophos is also placed on soil to protect brassicas and worked into the soil to control wireworms, cutworms and chafer grubs. Elsewhere, it has been used for the control of cinch bugs in lawns. Bromophos is somewhat phytotoxic so that its use on foliage is limited; it has, however, been used for seed treatment and as smoke formulations for greenhouses. It is of interest that it is closely related to **fenchlorphos**, which, under the name of ronnel in the USA, is used against animal parasites.

Chlorpyriphos (figure 4.16c) is also used against soil organisms. The persistence and effectiveness of various formulations of this substance have been investigated by Getzin (1985) with particular reference to the control of the cabbage maggot, *Delia radicum*, in Sultan silt loam soil. Two formulations and two methods of application were used and the time taken for half the material to disappear was measured for each. It was found that the half-life ranged from three to 50 days, chlorpyriphos in granular formulations having a longer half-life than an equal quantity in the form of a spray formulation, whether the comparison was made for incorporated chlorpyrifos or for surface-placed applications.

Isofenphos (figure 4.16d) is a less common organophosphorus compound but it has been used by Racke and Coats (1987) to demonstrate that populations of soil microorganisms can apparently adapt to some insecticides. The phenomenon of soil 'enrichment' is well known for herbicides (section 13.5) but, as these authors document, can also happen in the presence of fungicides and insecticides. Their work with isofenphos is a good illustration of what can occur. In soils with no history of isofenphos treatment, about 70 per cent of a 5 ppm treatment remained in the soil after four weeks. In contrast, in soils that had been treated with isofenphos in earlier years, only 13 to 42 per cent of a similar preparation remained after four weeks and a strain of *Pseudomonas* was isolated that enhanced the breakdown of this substance. Enrichment is thus caused by increase in numbers of soil organisms capable of attacking a pesticide, or by alteration of the species balance of such organisms in favour of those which can attack it. In some cases organisms can even thrive in the presence of a pesticide by using it as a carbon source.

REFERENCES

Abalis, I. M., Eldefrawi, M. E. and Eldefrawi, A. T. (1983). *Pestic. Biochem. Physiol.*, **20**, 39

Abou-Donia, M. B. (1981). *Annu. Rev. Pharmacol. Toxicol.*, **21**, 511

Akhtar, M. H. (1982). *J. Agric. Fd Chem.*, **30**, 551

Armstrong, D. J. and Fukuto, T. R. (1987). *J. Agric. Fd Chem.*, **35**, 500

Badawi, A. and Faragalla, A. A. (1986). *Trop. Pest Managem.*, **32**, 130

Baker, S. R., McGilliard, A. D. and Dahm, P. A. (1979). *Pestic. Biochem. Physiol.*, **11**, 20

Bignami, G., Rosic, N., Michalek, H., Milosevic, M. and Gatti, G. L. (1975). *Behavioral Toxicity of Anticholinesterase Agents: Methodology, Neurochemistry and Neurophysiology.* Plenum, New York

British Crop Protection Council (1979). *The Pesticide Manual: A World Compendium*, 6th edn, ed. C. R. Worthing. BCPC Publications, 144–150 London Road, Croydon CR0 2TB, UK

Carson, R. (1963). *Silent Spring.* Hamish Hamilton, London

Danka, R. G., Collison, C. H. and Hull, L. A. (1985). *J. Econ. Entomol.*, **78**, 1042

Dauterman, W. C. and Matsumura, F. (1962). *Science (NY)* **138**, 694

Desmarchelier, J. M., Banks, H. J., Williams, P. and Minett, W. (1977). *J. Stored Prod. Res.*, **13**, 1

DHSS (undated). *Pesticide Poisoning: Notes for Guidance of Medical Practitioners*, Dept of Health and Social Security. HMSO, London

Dulout, F. N., Oliveno, O. A., Guradze, H. V. and Pastori, M. C. (1982). *Mutation Res.*, **105**, 413

Ecobichon, D. J. and Joy, R. M. (1982). *Pesticides and Neurological Diseases.* CRC Press, Boca Raton, FL

Edson, E. F., Sanderson, D. M. and Noakes, D. N. (1966). *Wld Rev. Pest Control*, **5**, 143

Edwards, C. A. (1973). *Persistent Pesticides in the Environment*, p. 74. CRC Press, Cleveland, OH

El-Oshar, M. A., Motoyama, N. and Dauterman, W. C. (1987). *J. Agric. Fd Chem.*, **35**, 138

Fukami, J. and Shishido, T. (1966). *J. Econ. Entomol.*, **59**, 1338

Getzin, L. W. (1985). *J. Econ. Entomol.*, **78**, 412

Gold, R. E., Holcslaw, T., Tupy, D. and Ballard, J. B. (1984). *J. Econ. Entomol.*, **77**, 430

Grue, C. E., Powell, G. V. N. and McChesney, M. J. (1982). *J. Appl. Ecol.*, **19**, 327

Hollingshaus, J. G., Armstrong, D. J., Toia, R. F., McCloud, L. and Fukuto, T. R. (1981). *J. Toxicol. Environ. Hlth*, **8**, 619

Howell, J. F. and George, D. A. (1984). *J. Econ. Entomol.*, **77**, 534

ICI (1970). *ICI Technical Data Sheet*, May

Imamura, T. and Hasegawa, L. (1984). *Pestic. Biochem. Physiol.*, **22**, 312

Kao, L. R., Motoyama, N. and Dauterman, W. C. (1985). *Pestic. Biochem. Physiol.*, **23**, 66

Kravitz, E. A., Beltz, B., Glusman, S., Goy, M., Harris-Warrick, R., Johnston, M., Livingstone, M. and Schwarz, T. (1984). *Pestic. Biochem. Physiol.*, **22**, 133

Laskowski, D. A., Swann, R. L., McCall, P. J. and Bidlack, H. D. (1982). *Res. Rev.*, **85**, 139

Leake, L. D. and Walker, R. J. (1980). *Invertebrate Neuropharmacology*. Wiley, New York

Levin, H. S. and Rodnitzky, R. L. (1976). *Clin. Toxicol.*, **9**, 391

Levin, H. S., Rodnitzky, R. L. and Mick, D. L. (1975). *Arch. Environ. Hlth*, **30**, 98

Lin, P. T., Main, A. R., Motoyama, N. and Dauterman, W. C. (1984a). *Pestic. Biochem. Physiol.*, **22**, 110

Lin, P. T., Main, A. R., Tucker, W. P., Motoyama, N. and Dauterman, W. C. (1984b). *Pestic. Biochem. Physiol.*, **21**, 223

Lund, A. E. (1985). In *Comprehensive Insect Physiology, Biochemistry and Pharmacology*, vol. 12, *Insect Control*, eds G. A. Kerkut and L. I. Gilbert, p. 9. Pergamon, Oxford

Matsumura, F. (1975). *Toxicology of Insecticides*. Plenum, New York

Mitchell, J. W., Smale, B. C. and Metcalf, R. L. (1960). *Adv. Pest Control Res.*, **3**, 359

Morelli, M. A. and Nakatsugawa, T. (1979). *Pestic. Biochem. Physiol.*, **10**, 243

Motoyama, N., Dauterman, W. C. and Plapp, F. W., Jr (1977). *Pestic. Biochem. Physiol.*, **7**, 443

Natarajan, G. M. (1984). *Pestic. Biochem. Physiol.*, **21**, 194

Noble, A. (1985). *Pestic. Sci.*, **16**, 349

Oppenoorth, F. J., van der Pas, L. J. T. and Houx, N. W. H. (1979). *Pestic. Biochem. Physiol.*, **11**, 176

Pednekar, M. D., Gandhi, S. R. and Netrawali, M. S. (1987). *Bull. Environ. Contam. Toxicol.*, **38**, 925

Price Jones, D. and Edgar, E. C. (1961). *Outl. Agric.*, **3**, 123

Racke, K. D. and Coats, J. R. (1987). *J. Agric. Fd Chem.*, **35**, 94

Reinert, J. A. and Portier, K. M. (1983). *J. Econ. Entomol.*, **76**, 1187

Riskallah, M. R., Dauterman, W. C. and Hodgson, E. (1986). *Pestic. Biochem. Physiol.*, **25**, 233

Ryan, D. L. and Fukuto, T. R. (1985). *Pestic. Biochem. Physiol.*, **23**, 413

Samson, P. R., Bengston, M., Parker, R. J. and Keating, J. A. (1987). *Pestic. Sci.*, **19**, 135

Sastry, K. V. and Sharma, K. (1981). *Ecotoxicol. Environ. Safety*, **5**, 329

Skidmore, M. and Tegala, B. (1986). *Proc. Br. Crop Prot. Conf., Pests and Diseases*, p. 843

Spiller, D. (1961). *Adv. Pest Control Res.*, **4**, 249

Stewart, J. G. and Philogène, B. J. R. (1983). *Entomol. Exp. Appl.*, **33**, 315

Sultatos, L. G. and Minor, L. D. (1986). *Drug Metab. Dispn.*, **14**, 214

Thompson, C. M. and Fukuto, T. R. (1982). *J. Agric. Fd Chem.*, **30**, 282

Townend, M. G. and Busvine, J. R. (1969). *Entomol. Exp. Appl.*, **12**, 243

Ugaki, M., Shono, T. and Fukami, J.-I. (1985). *Pestic. Biochem. Physiol.*, **23**, 33

Usui, K., Fukami, J. and Shishido, T. (1977). *Pestic. Biochem. Physiol.*, **7**, 249

Van Bao, T., Szabo, I., Ruzicska, P. and Czeizel, C. (1974). *Humangenetik*, **24**, 33

Vilanova, E., Johnson, M. K. and Vicedo, J. L. (1987). *Pestic. Biochem. Physiol.*, **30**, 37

White, D. H., King, K. A., Mitchell, C. A., Hill, E. F. and Lamont, T. G. (1979). *Bull. Environ. Contam. Toxicol.*, **23**, 281

White, P. F. (1981). *Plant Pathol.*, **30**, 37

WHO (1986). *International Programme on Chemical Safety; Organophosphorus Insecticides: A General Introduction*. WHO, Geneva

Yadav, A. S., Vashishat, R. K. and Kakar, S. N. (1982). *Mutation Res.*, **105**, 403

Yu, S. J. (1985). *Pestic. Biochem. Physiol.*, **23**, 273

5 Carbamate insecticides, molluscicides and nematicides

5.1 INTRODUCTION

Physostigmine is a naturally occurring carbamate possessing powerful anti-cholinesterase activity. It is present in the calabar bean (*Physostigma benenosum*), which was used in West Africa in witchcraft trials by ordeal. The accused was made to drink a suspension in water of macerated bean seeds. The survival of the accused can be attributed more to his ability to vomit than to the extent of guilt—if he was not sick the physostigmine entered his body, inhibiting acetylcholinesterase, so that he died of an excess of his own acetylcholine (section 4.6). The local name for the calabar bean is esere, which accounts for an alternative name, eserine, often used for physostigmine.

Physostigmine is one of many medically important carbamates. It is not very toxic to insects even though *in vitro* it is a powerful inhibitor of insect nerve cholinesterase. Its low *in vivo* toxicity is a consequence of its high degree of ionisation at pH 7 because it has difficulty in penetrating insect cuticle and reaching the nervous system. Insecticidal carbamates originated from attempts to retain the supposedly toxic *N*-methylcarbamate part of the molecule but to attach to it a more lipophilic group. This, it was argued, would enable the molecule to penetrate to its site of action and, in appropriate cases, would confer the right level of chemical stability yet allow the molecule to retain adequate affinity for the enzyme. Some thousands of carbamates have probably been screened for insecticidal potential, but less than 20 are currently marketed in commercially significant amounts. Some of these are listed in table 5.1, together with their aqueous solubilities and other properties.

5.2 STRUCTURAL DIVERSITY OF CARBAMATE INSECTICIDES

Carbamates with insecticidal (and related) properties possess the general structure:

Table 5.1   Physicochemical and biological characteristics of some carbamate insecticides

Substance (subgroup)	Route of systemic action	Oral LD_{50} toxicity to rats[a] (mg/kg)	Vapour pressure at 25–30°C (mmHg)	Uses, other than as an insecticide	Solubility in water at 25–30°C[a] (ppm)
Carbaryl (1)	None	700	3×10^{-3}	Earthworm killer; fruit thinning	40
Propoxur (1)	None	90	–	–	1 000
Methiocarb (1)	None	130	–	Molluscicide	–
Carbofuran (2)	By root uptake	11	1×10^{-5}	(Nematicidal at high dosage)	700
Pirimicarb (2)	By leaves or roots but persistence very low	~ 100	3×10^{-5}	–	2 700
Aldicarb (3)	By root uptake	1	1×10^{-4}	Nematicide	6 000
Oxamyl (3)	By root uptake	5	–	Nematicide; millipede killer	–
Methomyl (3)	By leaf uptake	21	5×10^{-5}	–	58 000

[a] Data from commercial literature, from Kuhr and Dorough (1976) and from Matsumura (1975).

There are three major subgroups.

Subgroup 1. Comprises aryl *N*-methylcarbamate esters of phenols—that is, compounds with a hydroxyl group attached directly to a phenyl or naphthyl ring*. Three members of the subgroup are listed in table 5.1, and the formula of **carbaryl**, as type example, is given in figure 5.1.

Subgroup 2. Similarly comprises *N*-methyl- and *N*-dimethylcarbamate esters of heterocyclic phenols, and **carbofuran** (figure 5.1) is an example.

Subgroup 3. Contains oxime derivatives of aldehydes (e.g. **aldicarb**, figure 5.1) and the closely related thiohydroximidates. In the oximes, the OH group has been carbamylated.

Compounds in subgroup 3 illustrate most clearly the way in which carbamates were designed specifically to resemble acetylcholine and yet to remain sufficiently lipophilic to penetrate to their site of action in insects. This similarity of structure to that of acetylcholine probably helps to explain the very high toxicity of aldicarb to both mammals and insects.

The structure of compounds in subgroups 1 and 2 can hardly be regarded as

---

* Carbamic acid (HOOC.NH$_2$) is aminoformic acid; *N*-methylcarbamic acid is therefore HOOC.NH.CH$_3$. Carbamic acid should not be confused with the amide of formic acid, NH$_2$OC.H.

resembling that of acetylcholine. On the other hand, such superficial dissimilarity may obscure similarities in certain interatomic distances or of electronic distribution, which may be quite vital in regard to how well the molecule fits the active of acetylcholinesterase. In practice, the ring structures confer on the molecules a balance of properties compatible with insecticidal action. These include sufficient penetration of lipid cuticle; transport in the haemolymph without too rapid decomposition; sufficiently good fitment to cholinesterase to enable an enzyme–carbamate complex to be formed at low carbamate concentration; and carbamylation of the enzyme at an adequate rate (sections 4.5 and 5.4).

Carbamates hydrolyse slowly in neutral and mildly acidic aqueous surroundings, but, in the presence of alkali, decomposition occurs rapidly. The half-life of carbaryl, for example, is about 10 days in aqueous suspension at pH 7 but is only a few minutes at pH 11. Enzymic hydrolysis is often rapid and is brought about by enzymes of two kinds, namely esterases and amidases. Esterases attack the bond on the side of the carbonyl group attached to the oxygen atom, whereas amidases attack the bond on the side attached to the nitrogen atom.

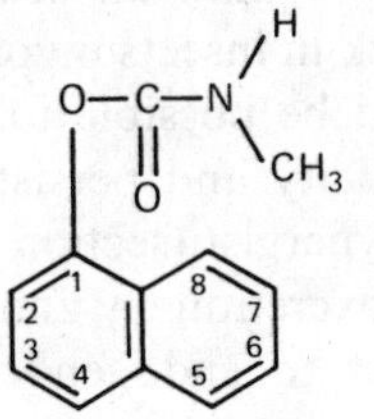

Carbaryl — (1-Naphthyl-*N*-methylcarbamate)

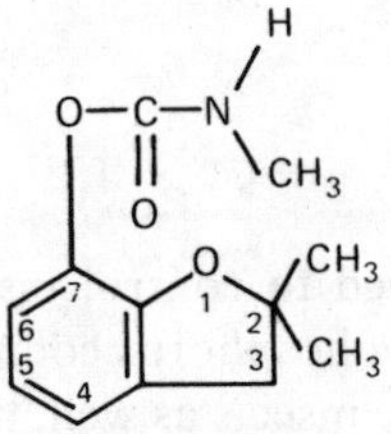

Carbofuran — (2,3-Dihydro-2,2-dimethyl-benzofuran-7-yl-*N*-methylcarbamate)

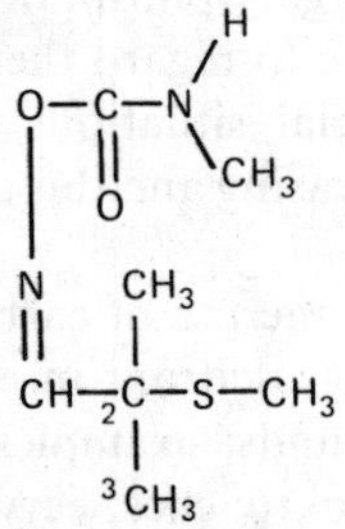

Aldicarb — (2-Methyl-2(methylthio)-propionaldehyde *O*-(methylcarbamoyl) oxime)

Figure 5.1 One important member of each of the carbamate insecticide subgroups

Esterase-catalysed hydrolysis is probably less important for carbamates than it is for organophosphorus compounds, although the extent to which hydrolysis occurs depends on both the carbamate and the organism concerned. For example, hydrolysis of carbaryl occurs quite readily in the rat, sheep and human but it is much slower in the monkey and the pig. Conversely, for one species, the rat, carbofuran and propoxur hydrolyse at only half the speed of carbaryl (Schlagbauer and Schlagbauer, 1972). The methylcarbamic acid formed when most carbamates hydrolyse is itself unstable and breaks up to give methylamine and carbon dioxide. The formation of $^{14}CO_2$ from carbonyl-labelled carbamate has consequently been used as a simple indicator that hydrolysis has occurred (although not necessarily as the first reaction in a sequence). For most species it seems unlikely that initial breakdown involves amidase-catalysed hydrolysis.

In fact, initial hydrolysis of carbamates by either esterases or amidases is probably rarer than was once thought, at least for substances in subgroups 1 and 2. Evidence discussed elsewhere (section 5.5) suggests that, in most animals, the primary attack on most carbamates involves oxidative *N*-demethylation or ring hydroxylation. Such attacks weaken the molecule and enable enzyme-catalysed hydrolytic changes to occur much more rapidly as secondary events. This distinction is much more than an academic nicety because it means that; whenever the initial attack in insects involves a rapidly proceeding mono-oxygenase reaction, it should be possible to decrease the rate of detoxication (and thus to increase toxicity and persistence) by the simultaneous use of a methylene dioxyphenol synergist (section 3.4). Finally, whatever the means of primary metabolism, excretion in animals is often facilitated by the conjugation of the products to endogenous substances (section 3.6).

5.3 PRACTICAL USES OF CARBAMATES

Carbamate insecticides are frequently employed to control insects that, for some reason, do not readily respond to organophosphorus compounds. They will, of course, usually control more susceptible insects as well, but since most of them are more expensive than common organophosphorus compounds, their higher cost is usually a sufficient incentive to regard them as essentially 'heavy-duty' insecticides, to be used in special situations or when other pesticides fail. Their production is steadily increasing and this could well lower the price differential.

There are two common circumstances when the use of carbamates may be appropriate. The first is to control tough or recalcitrant insects that do not readily respond to organophosphorus compounds; examples are whiteflies, leaf miners, ants, mealy bugs, scale insects, cockroaches, earwigs and wasps. The second is to control aphids and other pests that have developed resistance to organophosphorus insecticides, for it has been found that, despite a somewhat similar mode of action, cross-resistance (section 9.7) to compounds in these two groups does not necessarily occur.

Some carbamates are sufficiently stable for them to be able to fill needs where the pesticide armoury is weak. Some, for example, can be used in soil to control such pests as wireworms, leatherjackets and millipedes, which used to be controlled using organochlorine compounds. Moreover, several carbamates are not only insecticides but are able to kill or incapacitate phytophagous nematodes as well, albeit usually at a level of dosage greater than that at which they are insecticidal. Others are molluscicidal, i.e. are able to control slugs and snails (and, in another context, to control the water snail that is the alternate host of the organism responsible for the debilitating disease of bilharzia).

Some common agricultural uses of carbamates are shown in table 5.2. Since few insecticides have nematicidal properties at practicable concentrations, the use of carbamates for this purpose is worth particular mention. An example is provided by the work of Whitehead *et al.* (1979) on the stem nematode of onion, *Ditylenchus dipsaci*. They showed that a fair control could be obtained by the application of granules of aldicarb or oxamyl over seed furrows during sowing. Similarly, Drinkwater *et al.* (1979) found that carbofuran granules applied to planting furrows gave satisfactory control of maize streak virus. Kimpinski *et al.* (1987) investigated the use of aldicarb to control root lesion nematodes of cereals and reported that increased cereal yields of up to 15 per cent had been obtained.

It was briefly mentioned elsewhere (section 4.9) that the use of pesticides could sometimes lead to the vicarious control of virus diseases. Some plant viruses are transmitted from plant to plant by phytophagous insects. Aphids, bugs and leafhoppers are common vectors of viruses or promoters of opportunistic fungal infections. Systemic insecticides, applied to roots, are particularly useful for the control of sucking insects that can be vectors of viruses. The main requirement is that the substance must kill (or at least disable) the insect quickly. If this does not happen, the virus could well be transmitted before feeding stops. The last proviso is illustrated by a report by Satapathy and Anjaneyulu (1986) concerning the control of the rice tungro virus by attacking its leafhopper vector by adding carbofuran granules to paddy water. Carbofuran had a major advantage over a dozen other substances tested in that the insects were incapacitated sufficiently rapidly to prevent effective feeding within 15 min of application.

Another way in which carbamates are used is as root dips, often to control nematodes. Thus, Venkata Rao *et al.* (1987) dipped the soil-free roots of brinjal seedlings into 500–1000 ppm carbosulfan for 30 min and demonstrated that, under potted plant conditions, very high protection was afforded against a deliberate inoculum of the nematode, *Meloidogyne incognita*. The purpose of the work was to develop a technique to prevent the spread of nematodes from

Table 5.2 Some uses of carbamate pesticides for crop protection

Crop	Pest	Chemicals
Alfalfa	Alfalfa weevil	Methomyl
Apples and other top fruit	Codling and tortrix moths Mites on apples	Carbaryl, methiocarb, oxamyl
Bananas	Various pests	Carbaryl
Beans	Organophosphorus-resistant aphids	Pirimicarb
Brassicas	Cabbage root fly Organophosphorus-resistant aphids	Carbofuran Pirimicarb
Citrus	Mites Fruit flies	Oxamyl Methiocarb
Coffee	American bollworm	Carbaryl, carbofuran
Cotton	American bollworm	Aldicarb, carbaryl, methiocarb
Hops	Aphids	Methomyl, aldicarb, methiocarb, propoxur
Maize and sweet corn	Corn rootworm Corn earworm Various pests	Carbofuran Methomyl Metalkamate
Onions	Stem nematode	Aldicarb
Peas	Pea moth, pea aphid	Carbaryl, carbofuran, pirimicarb
Peanuts	Various soil pests	Aldicarb
Pineapple	Various pests	Metalkamate
Potatoes	Colorado beetle Potato cystworms	Oxamyl Aldicarb, pirimicarb
Rice	Army worm, stem borer, water weevil	Metalkamate, carbofuran
Sugar beet	Docking disorder, leaf miners, millipedes Organophosphorus-resistant aphids	Aldicarb, carbofuran Pirimicarb
Sugar cane	Cane borer	Carbaryl, carbofuran, aldicarb
Tobacco	Tobacco hornworm Root-knot nematode	Methomyl Oxamyl
Vegetables, esp. carrots, onions	Various pests Slugs, snails	Carbaryl, methomyl Methiocarb

nursery beds to the main field. Rather similarly, Muthukrishnan *et al.* (1977) observed that a carbofuran root dip decreased the population of the rice root nematode, *Hirschmanniella oryzae*.

5.4 MODE OF ACTION AND SIDE-EFFECTS OF CARBAMATE INSECTICIDES

The biological role of (acetyl)cholinesterase was outlined in section 4.5. In particular an account was given of the way its active site reacts with acetylcholine, organophosphorus insecticides and with carbamates. It will be recalled that whereas organophosphorus compounds appear to act by phosphorylating the enzyme, the carbamates seem experimentally to compete with acetylcholine for its active site. The reason for this difference will now be further examined.

The superficial difference between the action of organophosphorus and carbamate insecticides arises from differences in the relative magnitudes of the four rate constants in the expression (see equation (4.2)):

$$E + IX \underset{k_2}{\overset{k_1}{\rightleftharpoons}} E.IX \underset{X}{\overset{k_3}{\rightarrow}} EI \underset{H_2O}{\overset{k_4}{\rightarrow}} E + IH \qquad (5.1)$$

Here the first (reversible) reaction represents formation of transient enzyme–inhibitor complex; the second represents carbamylation of the enzyme; and the third represents decarbamylation of the enzyme. This equation is considered more fully in section 4.5, where the meanings of the symbols are explained.

Of these four rate constants, the two of most interest in relation to the mode of action of carbamates are k_3, which determines how rapidly the enzyme becomes blocked by carbamylation, and k_4, which determines how rapidly the blocked enzyme becomes unblocked by hydrolytic decarbamylation. In contrast to organophosphorus compounds, the rate constant k_3 is rather low, so that the complex, E.IX (in which the enzyme and carbamate are physically aligned but not chemically bound), tends to accumulate. In consequence, the back-reaction, governed by rate constant k_2, can, by the law of mass action, proceed at a finite speed. For the carbamates, this reaction (usually negligible for organophosphorus compounds since the concentration of the reactant is low) provides one mechanism for unbound, functional enzyme (E) to be regenerated.

Moreover, the hydrolysis, governed by rate constant k_4, occurs much more readily than the corresponding reaction involving organophosphorus compounds (although, of course, it is still very slow compared with the hydrolytic removal of acetyl groups during the normal functioning of the enzyme). In consequence, decarbamylation is rapid compared with dephosphorylation; it therefore provides a second route whereby the functional free enzyme is regenerated. Comparative figures for the rates of hydrolysis of acetylated and phosphorylated acetylcholinesterase are given in section 4.5. The time for the hydrolysis of carbamylated enzyme to be 50 per cent complete is about 20 min. The outcome of these interacting effects is that the relationship between carbamate and acetylcholine, when they compete for the active sites of acetylcholinesterase, is rather similar to that between malonate and succinate in the competitive inhibition of succinate dehydrogenase (Edwards and Hassall, 1980).

Severe carbamate poisoning causes symptoms similar to those mentioned for organophosphorus compounds. These include constriction of the pupils of the eyes, muscular weakness or spasms, respiratory failure, lowered blood pressure and cardiac arrest. Convulsions can be tonic, leading to rigid limbs, or clonic, leading to rapid, uncontrolled movements.

At sublethal dosage, humans suffer headaches, vomiting and diarrhoea. A study by Morse *et al.* (1979) of occupationally acquired disease by workers at a pesticide plant showed that almost half the packaging workers exposed to methomyl had suffered blurred vision or pupillary constriction. Indeed, at this plant where 11 per cent of the 102 workers had entered hospital for illnesses relating to some kind of chemical exposure, methomyl was the commonest cause of occupational medical problems.

Mild carbamate poisoning, like mild poisoning by organophosphorus insecticides, can affect behavioural patterns, reducing mental concentration and slowing the ability to learn. Experiments with rats have suggested that this reduced learning ability is greatly accentuated if poisoned animals are simultaneously denied adequate amounts of protein. Intramuscular injection of carbaryl into monkeys at a level of 15 mg/kg apparently reduced their capacity to learn (Anger and Setzer, 1979).

Atropine can reverse the toxic effects of carbamates, but in view of the mode of action proposed above, it is of interest that pralidoxime, an important antidote for poisoning by organophosphorus compounds, is often rather ineffective at reversing the toxic effects of carbamates. Pralidoxime is the methiodide of pyridine-2-aldoxime. The oxime hydroxyl group is a much more powerful nucleophilic reagent than is the hydroxyl group of water (i.e. it attacks positively charged atoms more readily) and the stable phosphorylated enzyme therefore hydrolyses more rapidly to yield active enzyme when pralidoxime is present. The reduced effectiveness of pralidoxime in relation to carbamate poisoning is presumably a reflection of the fact that the carbamylated enzyme hydrolyses quite rapidly even when only water is present. Perhaps for this same reason, certain carbamates partly reverse the action of organophosphates, but only if they reach the surface of the enzyme before the organophosphorus compound.

In view of the capability of some organophosphorus compounds to cause delayed neurotoxicity (section 4.6), Fisher and Metcalf (1983) investigated many carbamates and thiocarbamates (including some commercial insecticides and fungicides) to evaluate the extent to which they caused delayed neurotoxic symptoms in hens. Some thiocarbamates did cause typical delayed neurotoxicity, including ataxia (loss of mobility), often associated with ascending paralysis and with nerve demyelination. However, for the two carbamate insecticides tested (carbaryl and propoxur), the oral doses required to produce ataxia were very large. The authors concluded that it seemed to be necessary to administer carbamates repeatedly, and often in much larger doses than those typical of organophosphorus insecticides, to induce neuropathy; moreover, the effects of such treatment were often ephemeral.

Evidence for the existence of chronic toxic effects of carbamates has been reviewed by Ecobichon (1982). In essence, quite large doses are needed to produce effects such as an alteration in the oestrous cycle or the impairment of fertility. However, teratogenic effects have been observed in rabbits fed carbaryl from days 6 to 18 of gestation and increased numbers of abortions have been observed on administration to pregnant monkeys. Methomyl, in one study lasting 22 months, caused a decrease in haemoglobin in female rats when fed at a dietary level of 400 ppm. Using *Puntius*, an Indian freshwater fish, Pant and Singh (1983) found that 0.3 ppm carbaryl in the water caused a depletion of glycogen in both brain and liver but that liver cholesterol levels increased.

5.5 ARYL METHYLCARBAMATES (subgroup 1)

The formulae of four important members of this family of carbamates are shown in figure 5.2. They all possess one or more aromatic carbocyclic ring structures and all are monomethylcarbamates.

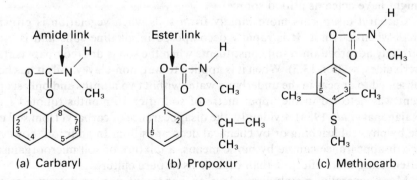

Figure 5.2 Subgroup 1, aryl methylcarbamates: (a) 1-naphthyl *N*-methylcarbamate; (b) 2-isopropoxyphenyl *N*-methylcarbamate; (c) 3,5-dimethyl-4-methyl-thiophenyl *N*-methylcarbamate

Carbaryl is the carbamate insecticide that is used in greatest amount. It has been employed against at least 150 major pests of crops, usually at an application rate of between 0.6 and 4.5 kg/ha. In the USA it is, or has been, registered for use on about 90 crops, although some 40 per cent of its total USA usage is on cotton. Other major uses are on maize and soybeans; of local importance is its use for pest control on pineapple, coffee, rice and sugar cane (table 5.2). Care has to be taken when it is being applied to foliage for as little as 1.5 µg per insect is lethal to bees. It has also been used to control earthworms, although this may be a mixed blessing. For example, Sharpley *et al.* (1979) observed that the volume of surface run-off water doubled when a permanent pasture was treated with carbaryl. They attributed this to a three-fold reduction in infiltration caused by an accumulation of litter at the soil surface in the absence of surface casting.

The American legal tolerance figures for carbaryl are often quite high, enabling it to be used on some crops up to near the time of harvesting. This high tolerance is in part a reflection of the large oral LD_{50} to vertebrates compared with the LD_{50} values of most other carbamates (table 5.1) and, indeed, of many frequently used organophosphorus and organochlorine compounds. On the other hand, it has only a moderate residual action, the half-life in soil being about 9 days. At normal levels for spray application it only persists for a few days in plant leaves.

The use of carbaryl in soils has been reviewed by Rajagopal *et al.* (1984). Soil bacteria that are able to break down cellulose are affected by concentrations of this carbamate as low as 24 ppm, and *Nitrobacter* have also been reported to be readily inhibited. On the other hand, it is not clear whether it seriously affects root nodule bacteria at normal concentrations. More generally, it has been reported to reduce the populations of some soil organisms but to stimulate the growth of others (although it should be added that the possibility also exists that in some cases where commercial formulations were used, supplementary substances present in the commercial products might have acted as a food source).

Carbaryl disappears more rapidly from soils when vegetation is growing than when it is not. It is rapidly decomposed in alkaline soils and is more strongly adsorbed onto soil constituents when the soil is dry (compare certain herbicides, section 13.5). When it is applied to wet, non-clayey soils it has been observed to appear in the underlying water within two months and only six per cent was detected in the upper metre of soil after 16 months (quoted from Rajagopal *et al.*, 1984). Evidently, the disappearance of carbaryl from soil can be by physical leaching or by chemical decomposition. In addition, however, the disappearance can be by biotic means, a mixture of soil microorganisms often being more effective than organisms in pure cultures.

More generally, metabolism plays an important part in determining the time that a carbamate persists, not only in soil and polluted water, but also in target invertebrates and in non-targeted higher animals. Degree of persistence, in turn, determines how large the external concentration (e.g. the LD_{50}) must be to maintain a given toxic concentration at the site of action. On the other hand, it plays little or no part in determining inhibitory concentrations of enzymes acting in short *in vitro* experiments on enzyme blocking. Thus comparison of these two types of data for a series of related compounds can often give useful information about the extent to which the overall toxicity of individual compounds is influenced by the intervention of metabolism.

This is well illustrated for carbaryl and other carbamates by the work of Fukuto *et al.* (1962). These workers in the USA determined the doses (I_{50} values) of carbamates needed to reduce the activity of housefly head acetyl-cholinesterase to half its control level. These values were then compared with the corresponding LD_{50} values. They found that, when carbamate solutions were applied to the cuticles of houseflies, the LD_{50} values were not closely correlated with I_{50} values for acetylcholinesterase inhibition. Significantly, however, the methylene dioxyphenols (e.g. piperonyl butoxide), which are specific inhibitors of the cytochrome P_{450} mono-oxygenase system, significantly lowered the LD_{50} values of some carbamates when mixed with them before they were applied to the insect. When a substance of low toxicity greatly increases the toxicity of an active ingredient, it is referred to as a **synergist** and the synergistic ratio is defined as being the LD_{50} for the carbamate applied alone divided by the LD_{50} observed when the carbamate is mixed with the synergist before applying it in the same way. In the present example (table 5.3), where the synergistic ratio was found to be high, it provides strong evidence that metabolism materially reduced the effective toxicity *in vivo* of the carbamates concerned. It also shows that, for such substances, the main degradative route involves one or more oxidative steps.

The principles outlined above can be applied to insect resistance to provide strong evidence that this serious problem is sometimes caused by increased metabolic activity. A good example is provided by the work of McCord and Yu (1987) on the fall armyworm, *Spodoptera frugiperda*. A strain (R) of this

Table 5.3   **Synergistic ratios of some dimethylphenyl carbamates when synergised with piperonyl butoxide (after Fukuto *et al.*, 1962)**

Substituent positions	I_{50} (mol/l) cholinesterase	LD_{50} (µg/g) unsynergised	LD_{50} (µg/g) synergised	Synergistic ratio
2,6-Dimethyl	1.0×10^{-2}	500	500	1.0
2,4-Dimethyl	1.3×10^{-4}	260	100	2.2
3,4-Dimethyl	2.6×10^{-5}	120	29	4.2
2,5-Dimethyl	9.0×10^{-6}	320	30	10.6
2,3-Dimethyl	8.1×10^{-6}	190	38	5.0
3,5-Dimethyl	6.0×10^{-6}	60	17	3.5

organism had developed a 90-fold resistance to carbaryl compared with a susceptible strain (S). However, when carbaryl and piperonyl butoxide were administered together to armyworms of resistant and susceptible strains, the ratio of the LD_{50} values (the R/S ratio) decreased to 3. Such results clearly demonstrate that, in this case, a great increase had occurred in the capacity of the mono-oxygenase system in the resistant strain.

Hydrolysis appears to play a less important initial role in metabolism of carbamates than it does for organophosphorus compounds, although it should be recalled that many degradative reactions of organophosphorus compounds once regarded as hydrolytic are now believed to be either oxidative or glutathione-dependent. The extent of hydrolysis varies from one species to another; a considerable proportion of a dose of carbaryl, for example, is hydrolysed by the rat and by the German cockroach but not by the pig or by the American cockroach (Kuhr, 1971). Plants do not appear to hydrolyse it significantly. Some species of bacteria tend to metabolise it predominantly by oxidation while others appear to do so largely by hydrolysis. The relative importance of hydrolysis also varies with the chemical structure of the carbamate.

Very little work has been done for three decades on the hydrolases that attack carbamate insecticides, and the present state of knowledge cannot be regarded as satisfactory. However, as was said earlier (section 5.2), oxidation can weaken a molecule and the oxidative metabolites of carbamates are often more vulnerable to the action of hydrolases than are the parent carbamates.

The principal routes of initial metabolism of carbaryl are summarised in figure 5.3. Oxidative routes lead to 4-hydroxy and 5-hydroxy derivatives of carbaryl. In addition, epoxidation and N-hydroxymethylcarbaryl formation are characteristic of reactions normally catalysed by NADPH-dependent mono-oxygenases. Hydrolysis of carbaryl epoxide by an epoxide hydrolase (section 3.3) leads to the formation of a diol. Since hydrolysis of the carbamyl ester linkage (to expose the l-naphthyl hydroxyl group) may occur more readily after initial oxidation in ring positions 4 and 5, the isolation of 1,4- or 1,5-dihydroxynaphthols (and of their conjugation products) does not necessarily imply that the initial attack on the molecule is hydrolytic.

The relative order in which oxidation and hydrolysis occur in the metabolic sequence of carbamate insecticides is of more than academic interest. If, for example, hydrolysis is slow unless oxidation precedes it, substances such as piperonyl butoxide can indirectly reduce loss by hydrolysis by retarding the initial oxidative step and in consequence act as synergists in carbamate formulations.

Microsomal mono-oxygenases activate many organophosphorus insecticides but in the case of carbamates the effect of oxidative metabolism depends on which carbamate is involved. 5-Hydroxycarbaryl is about twice as active against cholinesterase as is carbaryl itself, so mild activation can indeed occur *in vitro*. However, since hydroxylation may initiate rapid hydrolysis and so

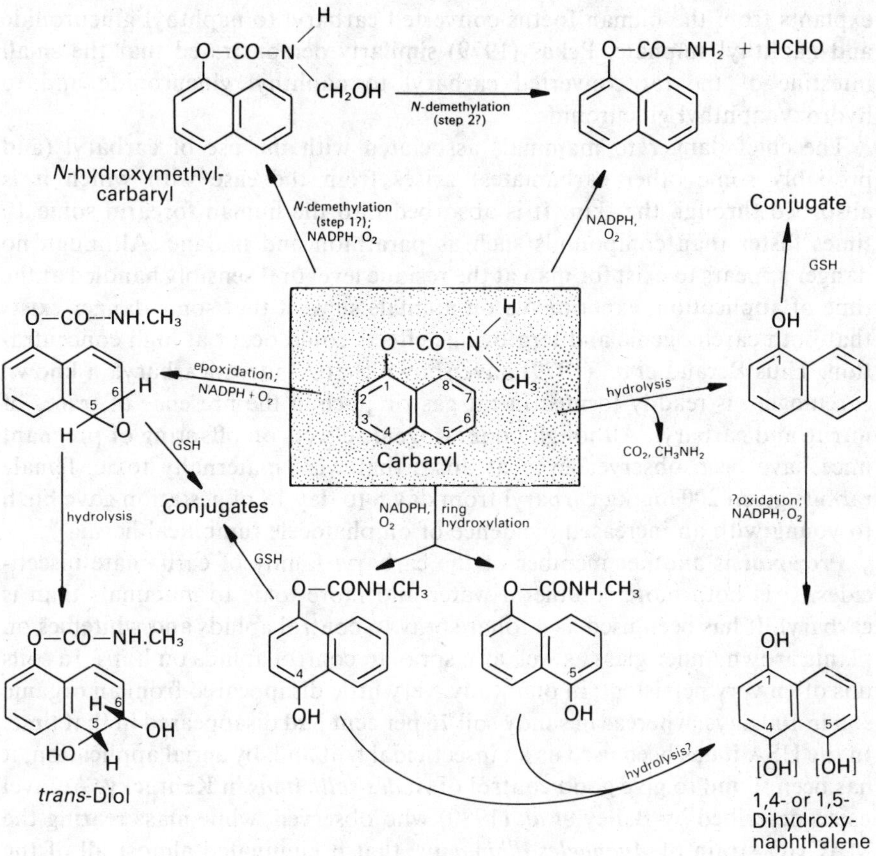

Figure 5.3   Metabolism of carbaryl

decrease persistence, the net effect of these opposing tendencies may not be predictable *in vivo*.

Many of the hydroxy compounds, whether formed by oxidation or by hydrolysis, can be conjugated in a secondary stage, which always results in detoxication. As expected (chapter 3), inter-species variation exists in the types of conjugates formed: in plants, glucosides usually predominate; in many higher animals, glucuronides and sulphates are most evident; in insects, glucosides, sulphates or phosphates are often major conjugation products.

The best compendium of information on the metabolism of carbaryl has been produced by Menzie (1969; 1974; 1978; 1980). Chin *et al.* (1979b), working with explanted livers of five species of fish, showed that the most significant common metabolite in all of these species was the glucuronide of 5,6-dihydrodihydroxycarbaryl, perhaps formed by hydrolysis of a transient epoxide (figure 5.3). The same workers (Chin *et al.*, 1979a) showed that kidney explants from the human foetus converted carbaryl to naphthyl glucuronide and naphthyl sulphate. Pekas (1979) similarly demonstrated that the small intestine of the rat converted carbaryl to naphthyl glucuronide and to hydroxynaphthyl glucuronide.

The chief danger to mammals associated with the use of carbaryl (and probably some other carbamates) arises from the ease with which it is absorbed through the skin. It is absorbed into the human forearm some 10 times faster than compounds such as parathion and lindane. Although no danger appears to exist for man at the residue level or if sensibly handled at the time of application, experiments on animals suggest that some danger exists that both carcinogenic and teratogenic effects could occur at high concentration. Thus Beraud *et al.* (1979) have shown that *N*-nitrosocarbaryl, a known carcinogen, is readily formed in rat gastric juice in the presence of traces of nitrite and carbaryl. Although no teratogenic effects on offspring of pregnant mice have been observed even at doses that were maternally toxic, female rabbits given 200 mg/kg carbaryl from day 6 to day 18 of gestation gave birth to young with an increased incidence of omphalocele (umbilical hernia).

Propoxur is another member of the carbaryl family of carbamate insecticides. It is both more soluble in water and more toxic to mammals than is carbaryl. It has been used as a foliar spray to control aphids and whiteflies on plants grown under glass as well as a spray to control aphids on hops. In soils it is often very persistent; in one study, very little disappeared from an organic soil in 100 days, whereas in sandy soil 75 per cent had disappeared in that time. In the USA it has been used as an insecticidal bait and, by aerial application, it has been found to give good control of *Aedes sollicitans* in Kentucky. A novel use is described by Bailey *et al.* (1980) who observed, while mass rearing the MACHO strain of *Anopheles albimanus*, that it eliminated almost all of the females at the egg stage so that 99.9 per cent of the pupae hatched to give males.

It is reported to have had no effect on soil organisms at 5 ppm but at 500 ppm it depressed the activity of some microorganisms for up to 16 days. On the other hand, a strain of *Pseudomonas* isolated from soil was able to utilise propoxur as the sole source of carbon (quoted from Rajagopal *et al.*, 1984). Stimulation of growth for a similar reason has been observed from time to time with soil-acting herbicides, and, in some of these cases, it would appear that metabolism leads to the detachment from the molecule of a side-group that can be readily used as a source of carbon or nitrogen. In the present instance it is possible that isopropanol or a close relative of it is the carbon source.

The isopropoxy group of propoxur is the main feature of the molecule (figure 5.2). A certain similarity with the heterocyclic ring structure of carbofuran can be detected (figure 5.1). The molecule appears to fit the surface of acetylcholinesterase more snugly than does the molecule of carbaryl, for the dissociation constant, K_D, of the enzyme–propoxur complex (E.IX) is far smaller than that for the enzyme–carbaryl complex, a difference that implies a high affinity of inhibitor and enzyme. On the other hand, k_3 is not particularly large, so carbamylation of the enzyme occurs rather slowly (sections 4.5 and 5.4).

The isopropoxy group introduces a new metabolic feature into the molecule, for its removal exposes the hydroxyl group of 2-hydroxyphenyl *N*-methylcarbamate. This hydrolytic dealkylation probably occurs in bean plants. The major routes of metabolism in most organisms are, however, hydroxylation in position 5 of the ring (figure 5.2) and hydroxylation of the *N*-methyl group. The product of the latter process is five times as active against cholinesterase as is propoxur itself. 5-Hydroxypropoxur is a major product both in houseflies and in rat liver preparations, although Hama *et al.* (1979) detected the *N*-hydroxymethyl metabolite in both a susceptible and a resistant strain of the green rice leaf hopper, *Nephotettix cincticeps*.

Methiocarb was introduced as an insecticide in 1965 and it has been used on cotton, vegetables and hops for the control of fruit flies, codling moth, leaf hoppers and mites. It has also been used in the form of a seed treatment to act as a bird repellant. Of major importance, however, is the fact that it has been found to possess useful molluscicidal properties, and for this purpose it can be applied in several ways. Pelleted baits are often broadcast on the soil surface or pellets can be placed beside seeds in rows on drilling. Alternatively, and especially for grain, it can be used as a seed treatment. Winter-sown wheat in Britain is particularly vulnerable to slugs (*Deroceras reticulatum*), which hollow the stems of newly sown seeds or sever the shoots at or below ground level. In one study (Scott *et al.*, 1984) seed treatments with methiocarb were more effective than those with any other substance tested and were also better than pelleted methiocarb formulations. The seeds were coated with 0.1 per cent methiocarb, the dressing being held in place using methylcellulose as an adhering agent. An instance was reported where this treatment increased yields by 50 per cent.

As can be seen from figure 5.2, the feature of the methiocarb molecule that distinguishes it most clearly from other members of subgroup 1 is the methylthio group in position 4. In this respect it should be compared with aldicarb and methomyl (see figure 5.7), with organophosphorus insecticides possessing an alkylthio group (figure 4.12), and with the acaricide, chlorbenside (figure 8.6), which contains a substituted methylthio group. As with these other compounds, metabolism can lead to the oxidation of the sulphide sulphur to give sulphoxide or sulphone. This is brought about by microsomal mono-oxygenases in the presence of NADPH. Whether there is a net activating effect is uncertain, but it is undoubtedly a major factor contributing to the low half-life of methiocarb in animals (it is often less than two days). In soil, it is more persistent, the half-life normally varying from one to five weeks according to soil type.

5.6 HETEROCYCLIC MONOMETHYL- AND DIMETHYLCARBAMATES (subgroup 2)

The two best-known members of this subgroup are **carbofuran** and **pirimicarb** (figure 5.4). The similarity between the structures of carbofuran and propoxur has already been noted, and a second feature of interest is that pirimicarb is one of the few examples of an insecticidal *N*-dimethylcarbamate.

Carbofuran has an LD_{50} of about 11 mg/kg body weight and so is some 50 times more poisonous to vertebrates than is carbaryl. It must therefore be handled with care, although its dermal toxicity is reported to be low. In the USA it has been used extensively, in 1971 being second only to carbaryl in terms of tonnage manufactured there. It has been used in various parts of the world for pests of sugar cane, sugar beet, maize, rice and coffee (table 5.2). In the case of rice, it has been added to paddy water to control the leafhopper, *Nephotettix virescens*. It has a rapid action and kills both adults and nymphs within 20 min of application. This rapid action gives it an advantage over some other toxic substances for one important purpose, namely to control rice tungro virus, of which the leafhopper is the vector. In Britain the use of

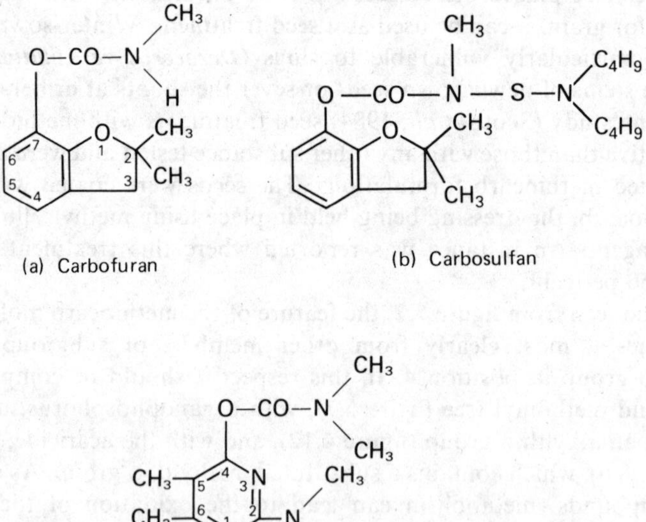

(a) Carbofuran

(b) Carbosulfan

(c) Pirimicarb

Figure 5.4   Subgroup 2, heterocyclic carbamates: (a) 2,3-dihydro-2,2-dimethylbenzo-furan-7-yl *N*-methylcarbamate; (b) 2,3-dihydro-2,2-dimethylbenzofuran-7-yl   dibutylaminothio-*N*-methylcarbamate; (c) 2-dimethylamino-5,6-dimethylpyrimidin-4-yl *N*-dimethylcarbamate

carbofuran is restricted to uptake from soil by plant roots and it is marketed as a granular formulation principally for the control of cabbage root fly larvae. It has been used to protect seed (which must then always be planted and never eaten), and Chundurwar and Karanjkar (1979) reported that sorghum seed treated with carbofuran and stored for 180 days germinated normally when sown.

In addition to these insecticidal uses, carbofuran can kill nematodes, although often at higher application levels than those at which it is normally used to control insects in soil. Under laboratory conditions it is one of the more effective non-volatile nematicides, but *in vitro* tests often flatter its actual performance in the field. However, at appropriate field concentrations, it has been observed to reduce the rate of invasion of plant roots by nematodes of the genera *Globodera* and *Ditylenchus*, and it also prevents the laying of eggs (Hague *et al.*, 1983). As well as being incorporated into soil it is sometimes applied to the soil surface in the form of granules. For example, several nematodes attack bananas, delaying the production cycle and lowering crop yield. Oman *et al.* (1987) treated each banana plant with 2 g AI carbofuran in the form of granules spread in a circle 50 cm wide around each. These Egyptian workers reported an increase in yield of 15 tonnes per hectare, a shortening of the production cycle by 24 days and a 75 per cent decrease in the number of root nematodes, in each case compared with untreated plants.

Carbofuran is applied to soil at 5–50 ppm, the higher amount being required when nematicidal action is desired. It persists for 12 to 50 weeks in acidic soils but disappears up to 10 times faster from alkaline soils. In sandy loams it may cause a decrease in bacterial populations but the soil ecosystem is often modified in favour of fungi such as *Fusarium* and *Penicillium* (quoted from Rajagopal *et al.*, 1984).

When carbofuran is applied to a sample of soil for the first time, an initial lag phase is evident before decomposition occurs (Felsot *et al.*, 1985), but this lag phase is shortened when carbofuran is applied annually for several years to the same soil. Suett (1986) reported similar results but also observed that if the soil was treated annually with both the soil sterilant, dazomet, and with carbofuran, the latter persisted in the soil for a long time (figure 5.5).

In both of these cases the differences were caused by changes in the populations of soil organisms. Some of the reported variability of performance of carbofuran in the field could be explained by this phenomenon of 'enrichment'; for example, in order to control the nematode, *Diabrotica virgifera*, it is essential that carbofuran should not be extensively degraded between the time of planting (and application) and the time the pest emerges some 30 days later. However, 'enrichment' can lead to carbofuran having a half-life of less than 20 days (Felsot *et al.*, 1985), especially if the soil is moist. After one 'enrichment' experiment, Karns *et al.* (1986) isolated from soil a strain of *Achromobacter* that could utilise carbofuran (or a derivative of it) as a sole source of nitrogen.

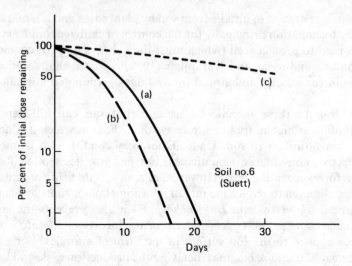

Figure 5.5   Persistence of carbofuran in soil (5 mg/kg): (a) with no previous history of carbofuran treatment; (b) after two or more years of previous treatment; (c) after pretreatment with carbofuran + dazomet (from Suett, 1986)

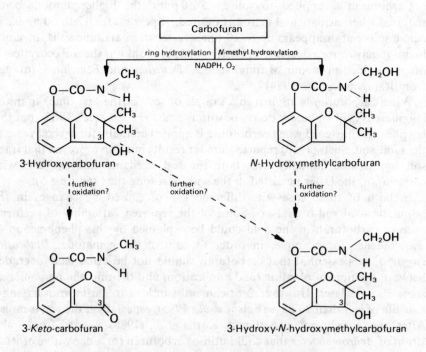

Figure 5.6   Oxidative metabolites of carbofuran

Metabolism of carbofuran is predominantly oxidative at least when done by microsomal preparations from the livers of higher animals, but once it is modified, conjugation or hydrolysis (or both) can occur *in vivo*. Four common metabolites are shown in figure 5.6. In rat liver preparations, 3-hydroxycarbofuran is formed about three times as abundantly as is the *N*-hydroxymethyl oxidation product. A small amount of the doubly hydroxylated 3-hydroxy-*N*-hydroxymethylcarbofuran is also formed. Using an injected dose of ^{14}C-labelled carbofuran, Marshall and Dorough (1979) showed that up to 45 per cent passed into rat bile. Since up to 70 per cent of the ^{14}C eventually appeared in the urine and only 3 per cent in the faeces, this implies that much of the metabolite excreted in the bile must re-enter the body (probably after hydrolysis in the gut) and so recirculate. In the present instance there is some evidence that 3-hydroxycarbofuran glucuronide is present in the bile and that this is hydrolysed to the aglycone before adsorption. Since the aglycone is quite toxic, **biliary excretion** followed by **enterohepatic circulation** is not necessarily in the animal's best interest.

The major products produced by living houseflies are 3-hydroxycarbofuran and its glucoside. Other products include *N*-hydroxymethylcarbofuran and 3-*keto*-carbofuran.

Insect resistance to carbofuran, as well as to other insecticides, is often (but not always) associated with increased rate of metabolism of the pesticide. This is illustrated by the work of Rose and Brindley (1985) on houseflies and Colorado beetles, both of which developed resistant strains. In the case of the houseflies, the simultaneous application of piperonyl butoxide and carbofuran to resistant flies almost eliminates the resistance (i.e. the LD_{50} was little greater than that for susceptible houseflies under similar conditions). In the case of the Colorado beetles, the LD_{50} for the resistant strain was 490 ppm and that for the susceptible strain was 0.6 ppm. On applying a mixture of carbofuran and piperonyl butoxide the LD_{50} fell to 80 ppm. This very considerable decrease indicates that mono-oxygenases probably play an important role in the mechanism of resistance, but the difference between 80 ppm and 0.6 ppm indicates that other factors also are clearly of importance.

The National Research Council of Canada has issued a report that considers the criteria for interpreting the effects of the use of carbofuran on environmental quality (NRC Canada, 1979). Carbofuran is discussed in this report with respect to its toxicity, possible mutogenicity, teratogenicity and carcinogenicity. The report also describes its effects on plants, invertebrates, birds, mammals and microorganisms.

Carbosulfan (figure 5.4b) is a sulphenylated derivative of carbofuran that is of particular value in the control of soil organisms, including some nematodes, although it also has foliar uses. It has been recommended for use against wireworms, millipedes, flea beetles (sugar beet) and root fly (brassicas). Drinkwater (1987) concluded that it was superior to several other compounds for the control of *Heteronychus arator*, the black beetle of maize, and

Marwaha *et al.* (1985) treated maize seed with it to reduce dead heart formation caused by the shoot fly complex, *Atherigona soccata*.

Granules are usually the favoured formulation for soil treatment and these are frequently applied to furrows with seed in a one-pass operation. For example, Clements *et al.* (1986) studied the use of carbosulfan to protect newly sown Italian ryegrass (*Lolium multiflorum*) from insect pests, and particularly from the larvae of the frit fly, *Oscinella* spp.; coulter-applied granules were found to be preferable to broadcast treatments in that one-pass treatment was cheaper, more efficacious, used less carbosulfan per hectare and killed fewer earthworms. Similarly, Winder and Dunning (1986) applied carbosulfan granules by row application at the time of sowing beet seed to control the beet leaf miner, *Pegomya betae*; this procedure decreased crop injury more than did a band spray along the row. A granular formulation of carbosulfan has also effectively controlled the sugar beet weevil, *Bothynoderes punctiventris* (Radin, 1986). It should, however, be added that in soil repeatedly treated with carbosulfan (but not carbofuran), a significant reduction has been observed in the soil biomass (Duah-Yentumi and Johnson, 1986).

Umetsu (1986) synthesised several sulphenylated carbamates and studied the metabolism of carbosulfan in various species. The high selective toxicity of this compound was attributed to the existence of more than one pathway of metabolism, for in houseflies it was mainly converted to (toxic) carbofuran whereas in rats it was degraded to innocuous phenolic products.

Pirimicarb (figure 5.4c) is the least persistent of the common insecticidal carbamates. It was marketed in 1969 as a fast-acting aphicide and it kills by fumigant as well as by contact action. When sprayed on foliage there is a rapid translaminar movement, but systemic action is only achieved by uptake through crop plant roots following soil application. Spray formulations include wettable powders and dispersible granules, and these are mainly intended for use against strains of aphids that have developed resistance to organophosphorus compounds. In Britain, it is also marketed in smoke generators to control aphids on greenhouse crops.

5.7 *N*-METHYLCARBAMATE DERIVATIVES OF OXIMES (subgroup 3)

The three most important members of this group are aldicarb, methomyl and oxamyl. All three are very toxic to higher animals (table 5.1). Their structures are shown in figure 5.7.

Aldicarb is a true oxime derivative, as is the less common **thiofanox**. Closely related to oxime derivatives are thiohydroximidates such as **methomyl** and **oxamyl**, which can be regarded as derived from the imine form of an acid thioamide. It is necessary to make this distinction because true oximes, in common with compounds in subgroups 1 and 2, normally undergo oxidation

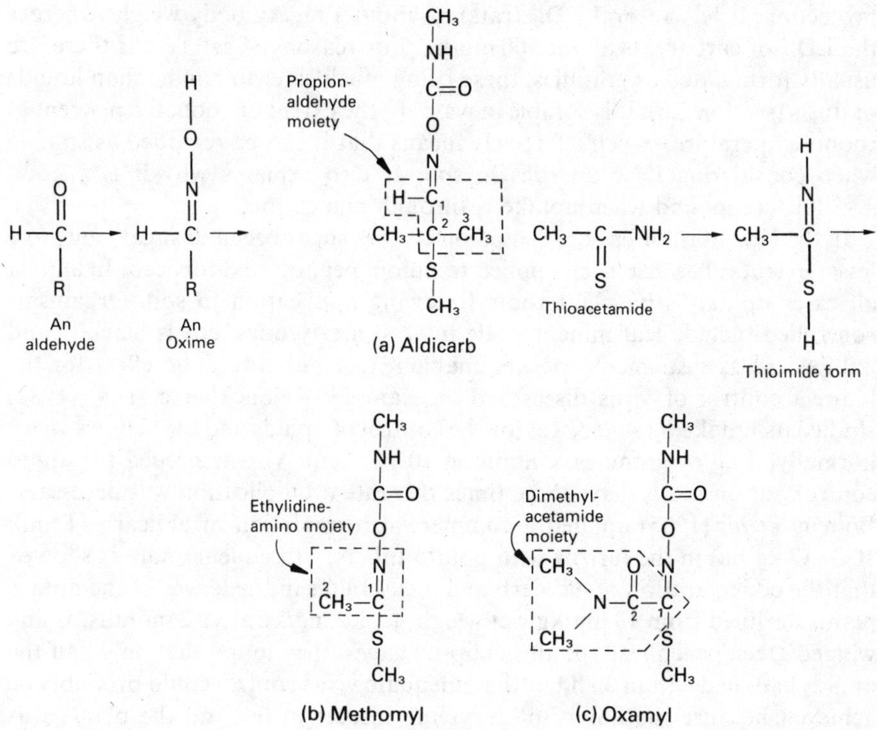

Figure 5.7   Subgroup 3, *N*-methylcarbamates of oximes: (a) 2-methyl-2-(methylthio)-propionaldehyde *O*-methylcarbamoyl oxime; (b) 1-(methylthio)ethyl-idineamino *N*-methylcarbamate; (c) *S*-methyl *N*-[(methylcarbamoyl)oxy]1-thioacetimidate

as the first step in their metabolism (after which hydrolysis is one option for further degradation). The initial step in the metabolism of thiohydroximi-dates, on the other hand, appears to be hydrolysis (Magee, 1982).

Aldicarb may be thought of as an ester-like compound formed between the carboxyl group of methylcarbamic acid and the hydroxyl group of an oxime derived from an appropriate aldehyde:

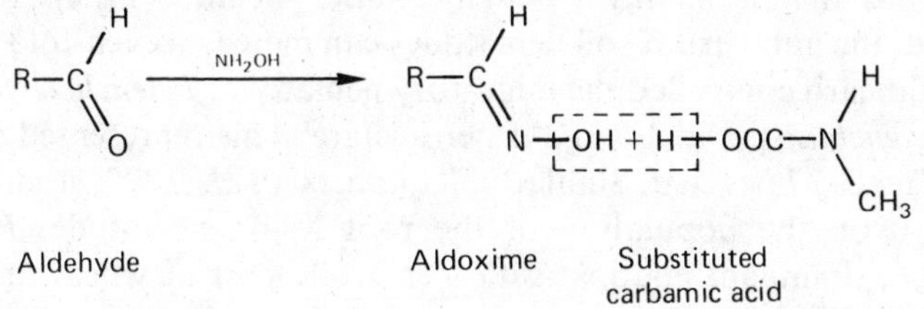

(5.2)

Aldicarb is one of the most potentially toxic substances currently used in crop protection; it has an oral LD_{50} (rats) of about 1 mg/kg body weight whereas the LD_{50} of carbaryl is about 500 mg/kg. For reasons of safety it is therefore usually formulated as granules, these being much safer to handle than liquids or dusts (section 2.6). It is soluble in water to the extent of about 0.6 per cent at room temperature, which effectively means that it can be regarded as soluble when considering its properties in soil. It also explains why it is a good systemic compound when uptake is through plant roots.

In the USA it is, or has been, used on cotton, sugar beet and sugar cane; to a lesser extent it has also been applied to onion, peanuts and tobacco. In almost all cases uptake is by plant roots following application to soil. Organisms controlled include leaf miners, scale insects, mealy bugs, citrus blackfly and millipedes. Its systemic properties enable it to be used to good effect for the indirect control of virus diseases. For example, Dejonckheere *et al.* (1982) studied its uptake by sugar beet for the control of aphids and the yellows virus; normally, 1 kg of granules containing 10 per cent AI was needed for aphid control but on heavy clays three times this rate of application was necessary. Boiteau *et al.* (1985) applied a commercial formulation of aldicarb (Temik 10G, 17 kg/ha) in the furrow with potato tubers; subsequent analysis showed that the concentration of aldicarb and metabolites in the leaves of the potato plants declined from 13 mg/kg wet weight to 1.2 mg/kg after 2 months. Using winged green peach leaf aphids in clip-on cages, they found that only half the aphids had died within 30 h but that adequate virus control could probably be achieved because the ability of surviving insects to feed on the plants was greatly diminished soon after treatment began.

Aldicarb has, however, another important use: namely it can control phytophagous nematodes. It is this property which largely explains why so toxic a substance is permitted to be used in agriculture. For this purpose it is sometimes almost as effective as the expensive volatile organohalogen compounds such as dichloropropane and 'D-D' mixture. It is therefore desirable to quote a few instances of its nematicidal use.

Nematodes can be damaging to cereals, especially in a light soil. As well as the obvious immediate damage, nematodes may facilitate the entry of fungi or they may carry virus diseases. Rhoades (1979) reported that the yield of field corn was increased in the first year of treatment with aldicarb, and greatly increased in the second year, in consequence of the partial control of *Belonolaimus longicaudatus*. Williams and Beane (1984) found that, unchecked, the numbers of soil nematodes can increase seven-fold in a season, but that aldicarb controlled the migratory nematode, *Tylenchorhychus dubius*, and *Pratylenchus* spp. at 1.7 kg AI per hectare. This represented a yield–cost benefit of up to 37 per cent. Similarly, Kimpinski *et al.* (1987) studied the effect of aldicarb on the population of the root lesion nematode, *Pratylenchus penetrans*, a dominant endoparasitic nematode pest of wheat and barley in east Canada. They found that it reduced population levels in soil and in roots of cereals in all three years studied.

Nematodes have also been reported to have adverse effects on the yields of various vegetables. Boag (1979) found that aldicarb increased carrot yield by 17 per cent on farms that were heavily infested with the nematode, *Rotylenchus robustus*. Whitehead and Tite (1987) found that high rates of application of aldicarb almost eliminated stem injury of field beans caused by *Ditylenchus dipsaci*. It was better for this purpose (and for reducing the numbers of nematodes present in the harvested seed) than any other substance tested, when applied as a single yearly dose. Whitehead *et al.* (1985) reported that aldicarb controlled the root-knot nematode, *Meloidogyne incognita*, on potatoes and tomatoes, reducing the galls on tomato roots for 13 weeks. For sugar beet the nematicidal efficacy of aldicarb granules is influenced by the precise method of application: soil incorporation proved more economical in the control of the beet cyst nematode, *Heterodera schactii*, than spreading granules around the seedlings. Whitehead *et al.* (1987) investigated several methods of soil incorporation, including rotary cultivation and band application. Their results led to the recommendation that incorporation to a depth of 15 cm should be done by band treatment using a vertical reciprocating harrow.

However, some caution should be exercised when interpreting the possible advantages of nematode control. Apart from the costs involved, a reduction in the numbers of nematodes does not necessarily lead to a marked increase in crop yield. Nor is total eradication of endoparasitic nematodes always feasible (and for some seed crops this could be important). For example, workers at Wageningen, Holland, inoculated some rows of narcissus bulbs but not others with nematodes and then applied aldicarb at different concentrations in an attempt to eradicate the infection. They concluded that this was, in fact, impracticable in field conditions, some 5 per cent infection still being present after quite a heavy application (Windrich, 1986).

The half-life (t_{50}) of aldicarb in soils appears to be very variable, depending on both the applied dosage and the nature of the soil. Read (1987) reported a greatly accelerated microbial degradation of an applied dose of aldicarb in cases where the soil employed had previously been treated with two annual subsurface applications of aldicarb. Results are shown in figure 5.8. For rates of up to about 800 ppm in soil, breakdown was almost complete in 1–14 days. However, above about 1000 ppm, the growth of microorganisms was retarded for weeks and residues persisted for months. This suggests that even strains of microorganisms favoured by 'enrichment' are affected if the concentration of the newly applied aldicarb exceeds some threshold level.

Allowing for variation of techniques and of soil type, other workers have reported similar results. Malik and Yadar (1979) found that the disappearance of aldicarb, when it was used as a side-dressing in cotton furrows, followed the course of a first-order reaction, the t_{50} being about 20 days (in the absence of 'enrichment'). Maitlen and Powell (1982) quote a case where aldicarb was applied to potato fields at 3.4 kg AI per hectare and, according to soil type, the

t_{50} varied from 17 to 30 days. The disappearance is accounted for by evaporation, by leaching, by chemical decomposition and by biotic intervention, although to varying degrees in different soils.

Bromilow *et al.* (1986) investigated the fate of aldicarb, *inter alia*, in anaerobic subsoils and cautioned that the rates at which metabolic reactions take place in aerobic circumstances could give a misleading picture concerning the stability of aldicarb and its sulphoxide in solutions that had leached through the soil. If the anaerobic subsoil contained high levels of ferrous iron, breakdown was more rapid than in aerobic topsoil from the same site; however, when the iron in the subsoil was less than 1 ppm, members of the oxime family were comparatively stable.

Interactions between soil organisms and aldicarb can be complex. Immediately after application, an initial fall in the numbers of soil organisms often occurs but thereafter the numbers of aerobic bacteria and actinomycetes usually rise again. At 220 ppm, the t_{50} in various soils varies from 7 to 12 days, persistence being increased when the water content of the soil is low (quoted from Rajagopal *et al.*, 1984). Use of ^{14}C has shown that up to 8 per cent may sometimes be unextractable from organic soils. At 50 ppm, the proportion of nitrifying soil organisms may fall for the first month. On the other hand, according to Sekar and Balasubramanian (1979), at 2 ppm it enhances the growth of *Rhizobium* spp. in the cowpea.

Metabolism in aerobic surroundings appears to be similar in animals and in soil. In animal liver preparations, the principal primary metabolite is the sulphoxide. A small proportion of the latter is normally further oxidised to the

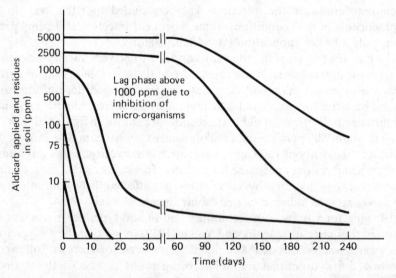

Figure 5.8 Relationship between the persistence of aldicarb and the amount added to soil that had *previously* been treated twice with aldicarb (after Read, 1987)

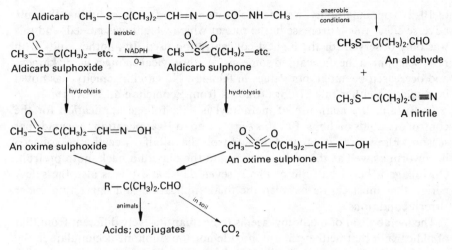

Figure 5.9 Principal metabolites of aldicarb

sulphone, although conversion of the amide moiety of the sulphoxide to a sulphoxide nitrile (figure 5.9) has also been reported. In consequence, the bulk of the identified metabolites often comprise the sulphoxide, its hydrolysis products, and the hydrolysis products of the sulphoxide nitrile (Kuhr and Dorough, 1976).

In anaerobic soil containing ferrous iron, aldicarb is normally degraded within a few hours to give a nitrile and an aldehyde (Bromilow *et al.*, 1986).

In common with other carbamates, aldicarb is a potent inhibitor of cholinesterase. It can apparently cross the placental barrier, for Cambon *et al.* (1979) found that as little as 0.01 mg/kg given by gastric intubation to pregnant rats decreased the activity of the enzyme in both maternal and foetal blood and brain.

Methomyl is a contact and systemic insecticide that is often applied to foliage. It is less toxic by mouth than is aldicarb (table 5.1) and its dermal LD_{50} is unexpectedly high (500 mg/kg for rabbits). However, for substances with oral toxicities as high as that of methomyl, constant care is essential, as is evidenced by a report by Liddle *et al.* (1979). These workers report three fatalities from accidental ingestion of methomyl stored in an unlabelled tin[*] when it was used to make an Indian dish called roti. Post-mortem studies suggested that the lethal dose of methomyl to these human beings was of the order of 12–15 mg/kg human body weight.

The longer-term toxic effects of methomyl have been studied in several experiments on rats, rabbits and dogs. In a 90-day feeding trial, dietary levels

---

[*] As Marlene Dietrich would no doubt have observed had she been singing of poisons rather than flowers, 'Wann wird man je verstehen?'—'Won't they ever learn?'

of 10–250 ppm methomyl were fed to growing rats. It was found that the only adverse effect was a decrease in the rate at which weight was gained, and this was only observed for the highest concentration used. In another study with rats, 400 ppm in the diet caused some histopathological changes in the kidneys and decreased haemoglobin values in females. No carcinogenicity was noted in studies on either rats or dogs (quoted from Ecobichon and Joy, 1982).

In Britain, the main use of methomyl is as a foliage application for the control of aphids on hops. For this purpose up to 10 applications are made per season. Elsewhere, it is used to control the alfalfa weevil, the tobacco hornworm as well as the codling moth and the diamond back moth on fruit. On foliage it has a half-life of about seven days, and this is also the safety period that must elapse between the final application and harvesting under British conditions.

The metabolism of methomyl seems to be quantitatively different from that of aldicarb in that neither the sulphoxide nor the sulphone accumulate in the animals and plants so far investigated. Instead, if they are formed at all, they rapidly break down to give volatile and water-soluble components; the former include carbon dioxide (exhaled by animals) and methyl cyanide, while most of the water-soluble compounds have not been identified. Metabolism in anaerobic soil in the presence of ferrous iron is similar to that described for aldicarb.

Oxamyl is a broad-spectrum insecticide with marked nematicidal properties. It has been used against the sugar beet leaf miner and also to control mites on apples and on citrus fruit. In the USA it has been applied to foliage to control tobacco root-knot nematode, for oxamyl has the somewhat unusual property of being able to move downwards after leaf application. Similarly, in Britain it has been applied to foliage to control the potato cyst nematode and Docking disorder of beet (the latter being caused by root damage arising from attack by nematodes). More often, however, it is applied to soil and it is normally formulated as granules. Although less poisonous than aldicarb, it must nevertheless be handled with care.

Whitehead *et al.* (1987) studied the effect of oxamyl on two potato cyst nematodes in 35 soils in which potatoes were growing. It reduced the increase in numbers of *Globodera rostochiensis* but had a smaller effect on *G. pallida* (possible because the latter takes longer to hatch and by that time the oxamyl concentration had fallen). Some effects of oxamyl on the potato cyst nematode, *G. rostochiensis*, have been described by Hague (1979). Oxamyl delayed emergence from cysts, disoriented second-stage larvae in the soil and delayed their invasion of roots. There was also a reduction in the number of eggs and a marked reduction in the final population of cysts. Yeates and Barker (1986) studied the effect of oxamyl on a mixed population of nematodes beneath ryegrass on yellow-brown loam. At 0.48 kg/ha the nematode population decreased to 55 per cent of that in untreated plots, species of *Heterodera* and *Meloidogyne* being among the more susceptible.

Van Driesche *et al.* (1985) studied the control of the apple blotch leaf miner and found oxamyl the most satisfactory substance tested. This was because it was the one which did the least damage to the natural parasite of the leaf miner, namely *Sympiesis marylandensis*. Van Driesche *et al.* use their data to make the general point that it is not necessarily the most toxic chemical that is the best one to use, for pest status is only reached when potential pests escape the controlling influence of the parasites, and a non-selective pesticide can actually make the situation worse.

A number of crops can be grown in conditions involving drip irrigation; amongst these are bell peppers and cantaloupe. The possibility of exploiting drip irrigation as a mechanism for applying oxamyl has been studied by Royer *et al.* (1988) and compared with results obtained by direct foliar application. It was concluded that insect control by drip-applied oxamyl was largely confined to phloem-feeding insects; drip application was cheaper than foliar application but effective action was slower than it was when oxamyl was applied directly to leaves.

The half-life of oxamyl in soil varies both with the soil type and with its moisture content. Rajagopal *et al.* (1984) have reviewed the literature on the relation of persistence with soil type. In loam soils the best results are obtained by deep incorporation, but in sand it leaches out readily. At a moisture content above the wilting point, the half-life was 13 days in clay loam but 39 days in humic loamy soil. In another study the amount present in soil decreased to 4 per cent of the original level in 42 days. It is weakly sorbed onto most soils and thus is usually quite mobile.

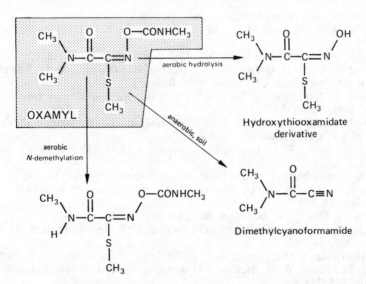

Figure 5.10 Some metabolic products of oxamyl

Oxamyl is degraded aerobically by hydrolysis to non-toxic oximino compounds (figure 5.10) but, unexpectedly, does not seem readily to oxidize to sulphoxides or sulphones. Bromilow *et al.* (1986) studied the degradation of oxamyl in anaerobic subsoils containing ferrous iron. In the presence of 27 ppm ferrous iron, oxamyl had a t_{50} of only a few hours at 10°C, a main breakdown product being *N,N*-dimethyl-1-cyanoformamide; another is thiomethanol. This rate of decomposition is about 100 times the rate of metabolism in aerobic topsoil.

REFERENCES

Anger, W. K. and Setzer, J. V. (1979). *J. Toxicol. Environ. Hlth*, **5**, 793

Bailey, D. L., Lowe, R. E., Dame, D. A. and Seawright, J. A. (1980). *Am. J. Trop. Med. Hyg.*, **29**, 141

Beraud, M., Pipy, B., Derache, R. and Gaillard, D. (1979). *Fd Cosmet. Toxicol.*, **17**, 579

Boag, B. (1979). *Ann. Appl. Biol.*, **93**, 199

Boiteau, G., King, R. R. and Levesque, D. (1985). *J. Econ. Entomol.*, **78**, 41

Bromilow, R. H., Briggs, G. G., Williams, M. R., Smelt, J. H., Tuinstra, L. G. M. and Traag, W. A. (1986). *Pestic. Sci.*, **17**, 535

Cambon, C., Declume, C. and Derache, R. (1979). *Toxicol. Appl. Pharmacol.*, **49**, 203

Chin, B. H., Sullivan, L. J. and Eldridge, J. E. (1979a). *J. Agric. Fd Chem.*, **27**, 1395

Chin, B. H., Sullivan, L. J., Eldridge, J. E. and Tallant, M. J. (1979b). *Clin. Toxicol.*, **14**, 489

Chundurwar, R. D. and Karanjkar, R. R. (1979). *Seed Res. (New Delhi)*, **7**, 34

Clements, R. O., Bentley, B. R. and Jackson, C. A. (1986). *Crop Prot.*, **5**, 389

Dejonckheere, W., Melkebeke, G., Steurbaut, W. and Kips, R. H. (1982). *Pestic. Sci.*, **13**, 341

Drinkwater, T. W. (1987). *Phytophylactica*, **19**, 275

Drinkwater, T. W., Walters, M. C. and Van Rensburg, J. B. J. (1979). *Phytophylactica*, **11**, 5

Duah-Yentumi, S. and Johnson, D. B. (1986). *Soil Biol. Biochem.*, **18**, 629

Ecobichon, D. J. (1982). In *Pesticides and Neurological Diseases*, eds D. J. Ecobichon and R. M. Joy, p. 205. CRC Press, Boca Raton, FL

Ecobichon, D. J. and Joy, R. M. (1982). *Pesticides and Neurological Diseases*. CRC Press, Boca Raton, FL

Edwards, N. A. and Hassall, K. A. (1980). *Biochemistry and Physiology of the Cell*, 2nd edn. McGraw-Hill, Maidenhead

Felsot, A. S., Steffey, K. L., Levine, E. and Wilson, J. G. (1985). *J. Econ. Entomol.*, **78**, 45

Fisher, S. W. and Metcalf, R. L. (1983). *Pestic. Biochem. Physiol.*, **19**, 243

Fukuto, T. R., Metcalf, R. L., Winton, M. Y. and Roberts, P. A. (1962). *J. Econ. Entomol.*, **55**, 341

Hague, N. G. M. (1979). *Ann. Appl. Biol.*, **93**, 205

Hague, N. G. M., Damadzadeh, M., Garabedian, S. K. and Radwan, K. H. (1983). *Pestic. Sci.*, **14**, 587

Hama, H., Iwata, T. and Tomizawa, C. (1979). *Appl. Entomol. Zool.*, **14**, 333

Karns, J. S., Mulbry, W. W., Nelson, J. O. and Kearney, P. C. (1986). *Pestic. Biochem. Physiol.*, **25**, 211

Kimpinski, J., Johnston, H. W. and Martin, R. A. (1987). *Plant Pathol.*, **36**, 333

Kuhr, R. J. (1971). *Pure Appl. Chem.*, Suppl., p. 199
Kuhr, R. J. and Dorough, H. W. (1976). *Carbamate Insecticides: Chemistry, Biochemistry and Toxicology.* CRC Press, Cleveland, OH
Liddle, J. A., Kimbrough, R. D., Needham, L. L., Cline, R. E., Smrek, A. L., Yert, L. W., Bayse, D. D., Ellington, A. C. and Dennis, P. A. (1979). *Clin. Toxicol.*, **15**, 159
McCord, E., Jr and Yu, S. J. (1987). *Pestic. Biochem. Physiol.*, **27**, 114
Magee, T. A. (1982). In *Insecticide Mode of Action*, ed. J. R. Coats, chap. 4. Academic Press, New York
Maitlen, J. C. and Powell, D. M. (1982). *J. Agric. Fd Chem.*, **30**, 589
Malik, S. K. and Yadar, P. R. (1979). *Indian J. Agric. Sci.*, **49**, 745
Marshall, T. C. and Dorough, H. W. (1979). *Pestic. Biochem. Physiol.*, **11**, 56
Marwaha, K. K., Siddiqui, K. H. and Prakash, S. (1985). *J. Entomol. Res. (New Delhi)*, **9**, 100 (abstract)
Matsumura, F. (1975). *Toxicology of Insecticides.* Plenum, New York
Menzie, C. M. (1969). *Metabolism of Pesticides*, United States Department of the Interior: Fish and Wildlife Service; Bureau of Sport Fisheries and Wildlife, Division of Pesticides Registration. Special Scientific Report, Wildlife No. 127, Washington, DC
Menzie, C. M. (1974). *Metabolism of Pesticides: An Update*, United States Department of the Interior: Fish and Wildlife Service; Office of Environmental Assistance. Special Scientific Report, Wildlife No. 184, Washington, DC
Menzie, C. M. (1978). *Metabolism of Pesticides: Update II*, United States Department of the Interior: Fish and Wildlife Service. Special Scientific Report, Wildlife No. 212, Washington, DC
Menzie, C.M. (1980). *Metabolism of Pesticides: Update III*, United States Department of the Interior: Fish and Wildlife Service; Special Scientific Report, Wildlife No. 232, Washington, DC
Morse, D. L., Baker, E. L., Kimbrough, R. D. and Wisseman, C. L. (1979). *Clin. Toxicol.*, **15**, 13
Muthukrishnan, T. S., Rajendran, G., Ramamurthy, V. V. and Chandrasekaran, J. (1977). *Indian J. Nemat.*, **7**, 8
NRC Canada (1979). *Carbofuran: Criteria for Interpreting the Effects of its use on Environmental Quality.* National Research Council of Canada, Associate Committee on Scientific Criteria for Environmental Quality
Oman, S., Kinawy, M. M., Hammouda, A. M., Hussein, M. H. and Abdel-Muhsin, F. (1987). *Trop. Pest Managem.*, **33**, 119
Pant, J. C. and Singh, T. (1983). *Pestic. Biochem. Physiol.*, **20**, 294
Pekas, J. C. (1979). *Pestic. Biochem. Physiol.*, **11**, 166
Radin, Z. (1986). *Zast Bilja*, **37**, 117 (abstract)
Rajagopal, B. S., Brahmaprakash, G. P., Reddy, B. R., Singh, U. D. and Sethunathan, N. (1984). *Res. Rev.*, **93**, 1–199
Read, D. C. (1987). *J. Econ. Entomol.*, **80**, 156
Rhoades, H. L. (1979). *Nematropica*, **9**, 43
Rose, R. L. and Brindley, W. A. (1985). *Pestic. Biochem. Physiol.*, **23**, 74
Royer, T. A., Edelson, J. V., Bogle, C. R. and McCrate, S. (1989). *Pestic. Sci.*, **25**, 231
Satapathy, M. K. and Anjaneyulu, A. (1986). *Ann. Appl. Biol.*, **108**, 503
Schlagbauer, B. G. L. and Schlagbauer, A. W. J. (1972). *Res. Rev.*, **42**, 35
Scott, G. C., Pickett, J. A., Smith, M. C., Woodcock, C. M., Harris, P. G. W., Hammon, R. P. and Koetecha, H. D. (1984). *Proc. Br. Crop Prot. Conf., Pests and Diseases*, p. 133
Sekar, T. and Balasubramanian, A. (1979). *Plants Soil*, **51**, 355
Sharpley, A. N., Syers, J. K. and Springett, J. A. (1979). *Soil Biol. Biochem.*, **11**, 459
Suett, D. L. (1986). *Crop Prot.*, **5**, 165

Umetsu, N. (1986). *J. Pest. Sci.*, **11**, 493

Van Driesche, R. G., Clark, J. M., Brooks, M. W. and Drummond, F. J. (1985). *J. Econ. Entomol.*, **78**, 926

Venkata Rao, C. H., Mani, A. and Kameswara Rao, P. (1987). *Trop. Pest Managem.*, **33**, 137

Whitehead, A. G., Bromilow, R. H., Fraser, J. E. and Nichols, A. J. F. (1985). *Ann. Appl. Biol.*, **106**, 489

Whitehead, A. G. and Tite, D. J. (1987). *Ann. Appl. Biol.*, **110**, 341

Whitehead, A. G., Tite, D. J., Fraser, J. E. and French, E. M. (1979). *Ann. Appl. Biol.*, **93**, 213

Whitehead, A. G., Tite, D. J., Fraser, J. E. and Nichols, A. J. F. (1987). *Ann. Appl. Biol.*, **110**, 127

Williams, J. D. and Beane, J. (1984). *Ann. Appl. Biol.*, **105**, 245

Winder, G. H. and Dunning, R. A. (1986). *Crop Prot.*, **5**, 109

Windrich, W. A. (1986). *Crop Prot.*, **5**, 266

Yeates, G. W. and Barker, G. M. (1986). *NZ J. Agric. Res.*, **29**, 501

6 Organochlorine insecticides

6.1 INTRODUCTION

The insecticidal potential of certain organochlorine (chlorinated hydrocarbon) insecticides was discovered during the Second World War. DDT and γ-HCH (hexachlorocyclohexane)* were at first praised as almost perfect insecticides, being relatively cheap to manufacture, strikingly effective against numerous insect pests and yet apparently safe to man and other warm-blooded animals. With the benefit of hindsight, it is easy to make accusations of complacency, but death came to many millions in more self-evident forms at that time. Furthermore, there was ample scientific evidence that acute toxicity of many members of the group was acceptably low (table 1.2). For example, occupying armies are neither renowned for their overconsiderate treatment of civilian populations nor for their scientific training in pest control, yet over a million Neapolitans were deloused by the US army with no reported untoward effects. In consequence, a typhus epidemic was brought under control, and many lives probably saved.

Since that time, several billions of people have been exposed to DDT, yet outside the range of industrial accidents or attempted suicides, one has to search assiduously for even disputed evidence of serious medical side-effects from this compound. Conversely, probably no chemical made by man—not even penicillin, streptomycin and the sulphonamides—has saved so many lives as has DDT. The reason for this is that it was, for a time, outstandingly successful in controlling the vectors of organisms responsible for such mortal and debilitating diseases as malaria, typhus, river blindness and yellow fever.

It is therefore ironic that organochlorine compounds have possibly been the target of more emotional criticism as well as learned controversy than almost any other biological discovery. Some are notoriously persistent in the environment and so can be a real hazard to wildlife and, many believe, a potential hazard to man. In addition, their use has led to the indiscriminate killing of beneficial as well as harmful insects and, increasingly, to the development of **insect resistance** (Carson, 1963). The latter reason, in itself, is sufficient justification for restricting the use of organochlorine compounds to only those purposes or occasions where no substitute is sufficiently effective. For crop protection purposes organophosphorus, carbamate and pyrethroid insecticides have replaced them in most countries.

* Formerly γ-BHC (benzene hexachloride).

6.2 STRUCTURAL DIVERSITY AND PROPERTIES OF ORGANOCHLORINE INSECTICIDES

The organochlorine insecticides are usually divided into three main families, comprising respectively compounds related to DDT, γ-HCH and compounds related to aldrin (figure 6.1). Some members of the first and third families contain elements other than carbon, hydrogen and chlorine (e.g. oxygen or sulphur, or both). Structurally, one of the few features members of the three families have in common is that the molecules contain one or more chlorinated carbocyclic rings.

Members of the different families do, however, have important physico-chemical characteristics in common. The chemical stability of many members of the group (or of their immediate and often toxic metabolites) is high because their molecules are constructed, entirely or largely, from C–C, C–H and C–Cl bonds, all of which tend to be chemically rather inactive under normal environmental conditions. In consequence, traces of organochlorine compounds are to be found in air and water throughout the world. Kenaga (1972) quoted data assembled by Edwards (1970) indicating that rain water contained (at that time) approximately 2×10^{-4} ppm, air contained about 4×10^{-6} ppm and sea water contained 1×10^{-6} ppm.

A second physicochemical feature of great importance is the low solubility in water of most members of the group. This, coupled with their strongly lipophilic character, means that they possess partition coefficients that strongly favour accumulation in biolipids. In effect, the bodies of animals and plants behave like molecular lobster traps—lipophilic molecules often enter more or less readily but, once inside, have difficulty in escaping. Thus, unless the organism's defence mechanisms can degrade them to excretable products at a rate that is sufficiently rapid to outmatch the rate of entry, accumulation in body lipids will take place. Kenaga (1972) lists typical concentrations of DDT and its derivatives in various organisms—for example, 3×10^{-4} ppm in plankton, 1×10^{-3} ppm in aqueous invertebrates and 5×10^{-1} ppm in marine fish. These figures, incidentally, illustrate the so-called food-chain effect (section 6.8). Similarly, vegetables contained 2×10^{-2} ppm, meat contained

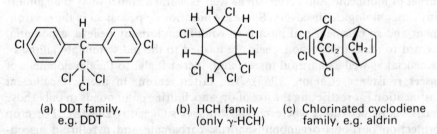

(a) DDT family, e.g. DDT   (b) HCH family (only γ-HCH)   (c) Chlorinated cyclodiene family, e.g. aldrin

Figure 6.1   The three families of organochlorine insecticides (projection formulae)

2×10^{-1} ppm and human adipose tissue contained 6 ppm. (It is interesting to observe that, at the time of maximal use of DDT, Americans were ingesting about 0.184 mg DDT per day and had 12 ppm (plus about 12 ppm DDE) in their body fat. Some humorist pointed out that, according to laws of the USA governing residue tolerances, flesh from Americans was unfit for human consumption!)

Most organochlorine insecticides are waxy solids at room temperature. Their vapour pressures are low but not negligible, for, as was implied above, their volatilisation leads to atmospheric contamination, while the volatility of such compounds as aldrin and γ-HCH enables them to be used as soil fumigants (section 6.3).

Acute oral toxicities of organochlorine insecticides are variable but mostly of intermediate magnitudes (table 1.2). The approximate LD_{50} of DDT to rats is 200–300 mg/kg body weight. If the lower figure is roughly applicable to man, then a 70 kg man would need to eat some 14 g to have a 50 per cent chance of dying.

6.3 PRODUCTION FIGURES AND PRACTICAL USES OF ORGANOCHLORINE INSECTICIDES

Uncertainty about the long-term environmental effects of highly persistent insecticides, as well as political pressures arising as a response to public concern about contaminated food, have led to voluntary or compulsory control of the use of organochlorine insecticides in most countries. In the USA, for example, large quantities were used on cotton up to about 1968; in Britain, use of lindane was still allowed for closely defined purposes in 1985 (MAFF, 1985, p. 170). Moreover, some countries continued to manufacture organochlorine compounds for export long after they were restricted or banned for home market use (such exports being intended primarily for the control of malaria and other vector-borne diseases).

It has been the experience of the author that various organochlorine compounds are still available in many developing countries usually for use for designated purposes (it cannot be stressed too much that no pesticide should ever be 'registered for use'; it should only be 'registered for use for a named and specific purpose'). Unfortunately, in some cases, and in defiance of regulations, local officials have been known to take no action to prevent farmers using organochlorine compounds on non-designated crops. There may be a temptation for farmers to do this since organochlorine compounds may be competitively priced compared with organophosphorus and other newer insecticides.

In addition to reasons arising from aspects of environment and safety referred to above, organochlorine compounds have been restricted or pro-scribed because they are known to encourage the development of insect resistance and thus to become less effective. It is nevertheless instructive to look at some of the uses to which they have been put because it shows how wide the biological spectrum of some members of the group can be. The best approach is, in fact, to draw attention to the ways in which one organochlorine insecticide is better or worse than another, and this is done in table 6.1.

Table 6.1   Biological spectrum of some organochlorine insecticides[a] (the uses of these compounds are so numerous that it is easier to say what each is *not* used for and a short list covering individual crops is not possible)

DDT	*Poor*—when there is heavy sclerotinisation; when the life cycle is rapid; for soil organisms: for organisms living in crevices. Examples: larger *Hemiptera*; aphids; boll weevils: most soil pests and root-attacking insects; white flies; mites *Medium*—cutworms; froghoppers, leaf miners, fruit flies, weevils *Good*—Most *Hymenoptera*; most *Lepidoptera*; blossom weevils; codling moths; European corn borers; gipsy moths; hoppers; plant bugs
Methoxychlor	*Good*—Colorado beetles; elm bark beetles; flea beetles
HCH	*Useful* where fumigant action, stomach poisoning or high speed of action required *Better than DDT*—cotton boll weevils (penetrates bolls); house mosquitoes (does not excite insects to leave deposit rapidly); some mites on man and livestock; tsetse fly larvae *Special uses*—seed dressings; apple sawflies; armyworms; blowflies on sheep; cockroaches; crickets; grain weevils; grasshoppers; leatherjackets; wireworms
Aldrin	*Useful* for short non-persistent foliage action; for use in soils *Good*—boll and other weevils; cutworms; dipterous larvae that eat roots; Japanese beetle larvae; mealy bugs; Mediterranean fruit fly; millipedes; scale insects; stalk borers; white grubs; wireworms; also termite control
Dieldrin	*Useful* for surface treatment of soil; for seed dressings; for root dipping; for bran baits; for sheep dips *Poor*—caterpillars; sucking insects *Good*—cabbage and similar root fly larvae; crickets; cutworms; grasshoppers; leatherjackets. (In public health: cockroaches; fleas; some locusts; mosquito larvae; scorpions; tsetse flies; also termite control)
Endrin	*Good*—sucking and boring insects of many tropical crops
Endosulfan	*Good*—ants; beetles; grasshoppers; many lepidopteran larvae; pod midges; tsetse flies; wasps
Toxaphene	*Good*—boll weevils and other species on cotton
Chlordane	*Better than DDT*—aphids; Colorado beetle larvae; grasshoppers *Special uses*—ants; beetle larvae; chafer larvae; earthworms; earwigs; household insects; moth larvae; soil insects; termites; wireworms

[a] Sources of information: Brooks (1974); Martin and Worthing (1976).

Whether compounds should be used in any of these ways now is, of course, a different matter, to be decided by individual governments and their advisers. A property common to all organochlorine insecticides is that they have negligible systemic properties in plants. Another point to bear in mind is that all of them are very toxic to bees and to fish, and appropriate safeguards are essential.

DDT is effective against a wide variety of pests, but it is relatively ineffective against aphids and spider mites. In the case of aphids, part of the problem is that the stationary colonies may escape spray droplets of DDT whereas their mobile predators can move into the contaminated area. In consequence, DDT treatment can sometimes result in a final situation worse than that which originally existed. Mites are inherently less susceptible to DDT than are insects, although the DDT analogue, dicofol, has been used to control them.

A characteristic aspect of the insecticidal action of DDT is that, if an insect receives a dose of DDT of marginal toxicity it becomes more badly affected as the temperature is lowered and recovers as the temperature is raised. A similar negative temperature coefficient is observed with most pyrethroids but not with organochlorine compounds of the cyclodiene group. Most workers have reported a positive temperature coefficient for the toxic action of γ-HCH, but Fisher and Wadleigh (1985) observed a small negative coefficient when it was applied to the midge, *Chironomus*.

The vapour pressure of γ-HCH is about 50 times as great as that of DDT. This substance is therefore preferable to DDT where a fumigant action is desirable and it is usually less persistent on a crop. The relatively high vapour pressure contributes to its usefulness for the control of soil organisms, especially in warmer climates. Certain members of the cyclodiene family possess both a strong action and a long persistence. Aldrin has a relatively high vapour pressure and is therefore useful where a fumigant action in the soil is required, e.g. for wireworm control in potatoes. Dieldrin is a very effective insecticide for the control of certain insect parasites on animals, including lice, blowfly larvae and ticks. Unfortunately, the effluent from sheep dips once contributed significantly to total environmental pollution by chlorinated hydrocarbons. In Britain, its principal use in crop protection was as a dip for roots of cabbages at the time of transplanting and, under clearly specified conditions, for the treatment of seed of sugar beet, onions, beans and spinach. All the organochlorine insecticides are phytotoxic to members of the cucumber family. In addition, DDT is toxic to some, but not to all, varieties of barley.

6.4 MECHANISM OF NORMAL AXONIC TRANSMISSION

The toxic effects of members of the three families of organochlorine compounds differ in detail but all are **neurotoxic** substances. One major difference is that the initial effect of DDT is mostly upon the peripheral nervous system, whereas γ-HCH and aldrin appear to attack the central nervous system. At the physiological level, the effect of DDT on nerve–muscle systems has been investigated intensively, the action of the other two groups rather less so. Despite some differences, the general effect of all of them is to destabilise neural activity and this is manifested by a hyperexcitability of nerves and muscles. Before describing these abnormal effects it is necessary to consider briefly the conduction along normal non-myelinated nerve axons.

A nerve axon can be regarded as a cable of aqueous fluid insulated from the extracellular fluid by a lipoprotein membrane, the plasmalemma of the nerve cell. The fluid inside is richer in potassium ions than is the fluid outside, indicating that the membrane is relatively impermeable to ions when the nerve is resting. The inside of the membrane is normally some 80 mV negative relative to the outside, a figure that can be predicted from the **Nernst equation**:

$$E_{(mV)} = \frac{1000RT}{F} \ln \frac{[K^+]_{external}}{[K^+]_{internal}} \tag{6.1}$$

if it is assumed that this resting potential is a function of the difference between the potassium ion concentrations on the inside and the outside of the membrane. In this equation E is the potential across the membrane expressed in millivolts, R is the gas constant (8.3 J/°C mol), T is the absolute temperature and F is the Faraday in coulombs/g equiv.

The passage of an impulse along a non-myelinated axon is a rapid wave of depolarisation moving at some 1–20 m/s. As the impulse passes any particular position along the axon, the inside of the plasmalemma at that point rapidly changes from being negatively charged compared with the outside of the membrane to being positively charged instead. This is caused by a rapid influx of sodium ions. Thereafter, the potential inside the membrane rapidly returns to normal for two reasons. These are that the membrane's normally low permeability to sodium ions is restored and because there is an efflux of potassium ions.

The reversal of electrical charge across the nerve membrane can be studied by amplifying the signal so that it drives the pen of a chart recorder, whereupon the alteration is recorded as a pen movement or 'spike'. The **depolarisation** that occurs when a stimulus arrives, and the subsequent restoration of the resting potential, are illustrated in figure 6.2a. Over a longer timescale the slow depletion of internal potassium ions is prevented by the operation of the 'sodium–potassium pump'. Calcium ions are also important for the correct functioning of axons, apparently because some sort of surface recalcification is a prerequisite for the restoration of a stable resting potential.

When a nerve receives a stimulus, an action potential arises as a result of changes in the permeability of the nerve membrane to sodium, potassium and

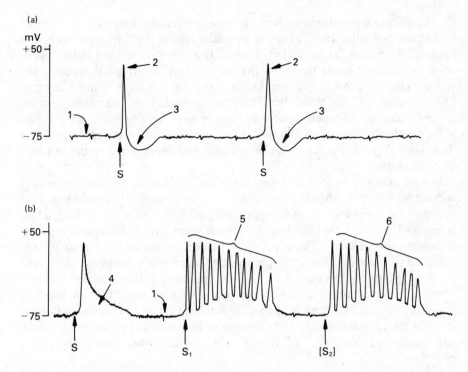

Figure 6.2 Discharges in (a) a normal nerve and (b) a DDT-poisoned nerve. (a) Electrical stimulation (S) of an unpoisoned nerve converts the resting potential (1) to a single action potential 'spike' (2), which is followed by a short afterpotential of *hyper*polarisation. (b) After DDT poisoning there may be a single spike followed by a prolonged afterpotential (4). In addition, a train of repetitive discharges (5) may occur after a single impulse (S_1 or S_2). At high DDT concentration, a train of trains (5, 6) may follow a single shock (S_1) (i.e. S_2 is unnecessary)

calcium ions. It is believed that these changes are mediated by 'gates' or channels in the membrane, which can be 'open' or 'closed' to specified ions. These channels are probably proteins, which bind, very specifically, to ions and alter their shape when stimulated, as long as an energy supply is available (Patlak and Horn, 1982).

One version of this theory, based on voltage clamp experiments, has been reviewed by Lund (1984). It proposes that the 'gate' that acts as a sodium ion channel comprises a transmembrane glycoprotein, which exists in at least three conformations, two of which are 'closed' to sodium ions:

$$
\begin{array}{ccc}
\text{Resting} & \xrightleftharpoons[]{\text{activation}} & \text{Open} & \xrightleftharpoons[]{\text{inactivation}} & \text{Inactivated} \\
\text{conformation} & & \text{conformation} & & \text{conformation} \\
\text{(closed)} & & & & \text{(closed)}
\end{array} \quad (6.2)
$$

The equilibrium constants governing these transitions vary with the transmembrane potential and, at resting potential (about $-80\,mV$) are such that the equilibrium lies far to the left. Thus only a few channels are in the 'open' conformation (in some forms of the theory, this is termed the subsidiary sodium channel). When the membrane is depolarised to $-60\,mV$ the equilibrium shifts to the right; the kinetics are such that, transiently, more channels are in the 'open' conformation, before the *slower-adjusting* right-hand equilibrium is re-established. After the membrane is repolarised the 'inactivated' conformation changes, without reopening, back to the 'resting' conformation.

For an action potential to arise, the main sodium channel opens so that sodium ions flow in, thus depolarising the nearby nerve cell membrane. This accounts for the rising line of the spike in figure 6.2a. The adjacent falling line is believed to be due to the closing of the sodium gate and the opening of a potassium ion channel. The precise mechanism by which these changes are achieved is uncertain, but ionic pumps, dependent on a supply of ATP, are involved. Many models exist for a Na^+-K^+ pump (e.g. Edwards and Hassall, 1980, p. 370) and other ion-exchange processes also exist. One of these, a Na^+-Ca^{2+} pump, has been proposed by Rashatware and Matsumura (1986). It is illustrated in figure 6.3. The existence of linked mechanisms for the input and output of Na^+-H^+, of K^+-H^+ and of K^+-Mg^{2+} have also been postulated.

It has been known for many years that membrane-bound enzymes exist which, *in vitro*, appear to split ATP to give ADP and inorganic phosphate. *In vivo*, such splitting is probably an overall effect, the reactants and products really representing fuel of, and waste from, reactions that drive vital mechanical processes. Thus ATPases are probably associated with muscular activity, mitochondrial processes and solute movement through tonoplast and plasmalemma as well as with the activities of nerve cell membranes. It now seems probable that several different ATPases are associated with the activities of nerve cells. One of these ATPases is dependent on the presence of sodium and potassium ions and is part of the mechanism of the sodium pump. Another is dependent on the presence of calcium ions and a third type requires the presence of magnesium ions. These ATPases are not necessarily all located in the axonic membrane itself; there is evidence that some could be associated with the mitochondria, which provide energy for the pump, or with the calcium-dependent release of neurotransmitter from presynaptic vesicles.

The Na^+-Ca^{2+} exchange process referred to in figure 6.3 both illustrates the principle of counter-movement of ions and explains how the energy of ATP may be linked to conformational changes in proteins which lead to the opening and closing of ion channels. According to Rashatware and Matsumura (1986), protein is phosphorylated at the expense of ATP, the catalyst being a protein kinase. For this particular pump a substance, calmodulin, also appears to be involved. It assists external calcium ions to become attached to

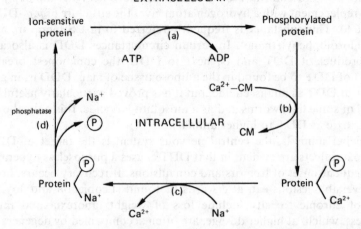

Figure 6.3 Proposed mechanism of a Na^+–Ca^{2+} pump (after Rashatware and Matsumura, 1986). CM, calmodulin. (a) Protein kinase reaction. (b) Calmodulin carries Ca^{2+} to phosphorylated protein. (c) Ion exchange deposits Ca^{2+} outside the cell. (d) Phosphatase liberates Na^+ into the cell

the phosphorylated protein of the channel. Later, sodium replaces calcium in this complex, and when this complex is hydrolysed by phosphatase the 'ATPase' activity is completed.

It will be shown in later sections that there is evidence that organochlorine and pyrethroid insecticides interfere with the opening and closing of these ion channels and that this interference goes a long way to explain why such insecticides have a neurotoxic action.

6.5 DDT AND ITS ANALOGUES

The remarkable insecticidal properties of **p,p'-DDT** (figure 6.4) were recognised in 1939 and the Swiss firm of Geigy patented it for this purpose in 1942. It proved its worth in public hygiene and was soon to become of vital importance in the control of malaria and other diseases carried by insect vectors. Technical DDT is a white waxy solid which has a characteristic sickly sweet smell. The pure p,p'-isomer melts at 110°C and has a vapour pressure of 3×10^{-7} mmHg at 25°C. It is so insoluble in water that accurate values have been difficult to determine. Biggar *et al.* (1967) used a centrifugation technique to avoid spuriously high results and concluded that the most likely value was about 1.7 ppb. It is moderately soluble in many organic solvents, including natural oils and body lipids, although solubility is generally higher in olefinic and aromatic hydrocarbons than it is in saturated aliphatic hydrocarbons.

Removal of one chlorine atom from the trichloromethyl group of *p,p'*-DDT and its replacement with a hydrogen atom gives the structure of *p,p'*-DDD (see figure 6.6). This substance is frequently referred to in US literature as TDE (tetrachlorodiphenylethane). In certain circumstances DDD is also a metabolic product of DDT and is, next to DDE, the commonest breakdown product of DDT to be found in the adipose tissue of man. DDD is, in general, inferior to DDT as an insecticide, but it has proved particularly useful for the control of some hornworms and as a mosquito larvicide. It is only about one-fifth as toxic as DDT to higher animals.

In higher animals, the central nervous system is the target of DDT. Its neurotoxic effects are evident in that DDT causes a purposeless hyperactivity, with frequent onset of tremors and convulsions. If recovery occurs, however, no irreversible lesions can afterwards be found (Ecobichon and Joy, 1982). Signs of chronic toxicity include loss of weight, anorexia and muscular weakness, which, at higher dosage, are often accompanied by degeneration of the liver and kidneys.

When DDT is acting as an insecticide its effects are on peripheral sensory fibres and motor units as well as on the central nervous system. It is these peripheral effects which usually predominate and, in the intact organism, the whole reflex arc (figure 6.5) appears to be involved in the transmission of the multiple discharges that are characteristic of its action (figure 6.2b). At higher concentrations, multiple discharges follow the application of a single stimulus; moreover, succeeding trains of impulses often occur without any further stimulation (i.e. in figure 6.2b, no S_2 is necessary).

In contrast to these symptomatic and physiological responses, the mode of

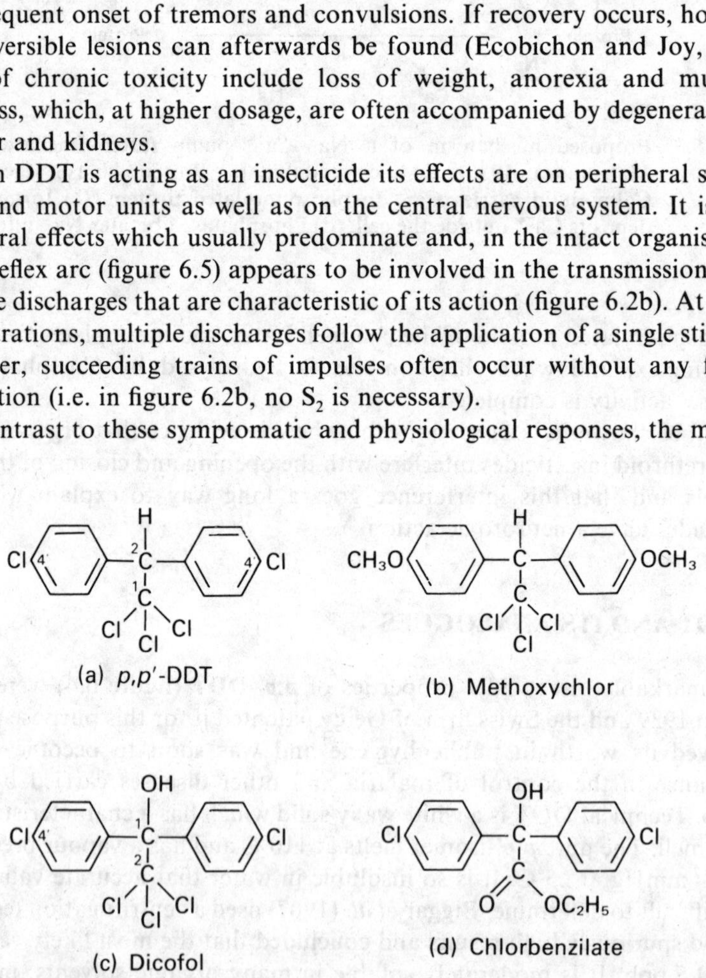

(a) *p,p'*-DDT

(b) Methoxychlor

(c) Dicofol

(d) Chlorbenzilate

Figure 6.4   DDT and its analogues. The full name for DDT is 1,1,1-trichloro-2,2-bis (4'-chlorophenyl)ethane

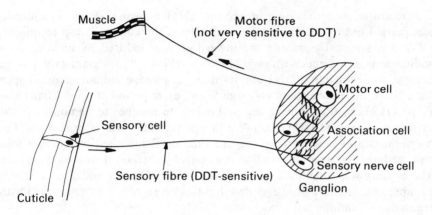

Figure 6.5 Diagram of a reflex arc

action of DDT at the mechanical or biochemical level remains unclear. Since the action of DDT (but not of other organochlorine insecticides) resembles that of the pyrethroids, the following information can be supplemented by reference to work on those compounds (chapter 7).

The effect of DDT on axonic membranes, or on the ATPases that are presumed to be involved in ion transfer across such membranes, has been the subject of most investigation. Variants of this approach do, however, exist. For example, its most damaging action could be near to presynaptic membranes of neuron-to-neuron or neuron-to-muscle contacts; were this to be so, Ca^{2+} ATPase, rather than Na^+–K^+ ATPase, might be the target of its primary action (compare pyrethroids, section 7.3). Since calcium ions are involved in transmitter release, DDT might well be indirectly affecting synaptic transmission. Another variant is that the action of DDT might not be directly on the nerve membrane at all, but rather on mitochondrial membranes responsible for supplying the energy (ATP) essential for transmembrane conduction.

A common theory of action of DDT suggests that it somehow impairs the closing of sodium ion channels after a discharge has occurred. In terms of equation (6.2), this concept implies that the duration of the 'open' conformation of the glycoprotein is prolonged by the presence of DDT (and pyrethroids). When this occurs, a depolarising afterpotential (4, figure 6.2b; also figure 7.10a) builds up and multiple discharges occur. If the 'open' conformation is even more prolonged, the membrane becomes depolarised and transmission is blocked. The latter seems to occur with appropriate concentrations of some other organochlorine compounds and some pyrethroids. Two things should however be stressed; first, dramatic neurotoxic effects probably follow the modification of a very small percentage of all sodium ion channels and, secondly, as equation (6.2) shows, some sodium channels are in the 'open' conformation even at the voltage of the resting potential.

A recent study providing evidence that DDT acts on sodium ion channels was carried out by Pichon *et al.* (1985). Using the voltage clamp technique, DDT was shown to prolong the inward current induced by movement of sodium ions. Lund and Narahashi (1983), working with the giant axons of the crayfish, concluded that DDT and its analogues wedge sodium channels open for a short, but nevertheless very significant, extra period of time. Chang and Plapp (1983a,b) used drug–receptor binding techniques to demonstrate the existence of specific DDT receptors in brain membranes of houseflies. The membranes also bind pyrethroids; the binding is inhibited by calcium ions and, perhaps significantly, binding is negatively correlated with temperature. The binding was quantified as 17 picomoles of DDT per milligram of brain membrane protein. It was suggested that these receptors were concerned with regulation of sodium ion flux.

As an example of a (possibly) alternative mode of action, it was shown as early as 1969 that a magnesium-dependent ATPase was more readily inhibited by DDT than was the Na^+–K^+ ATPase presumed to be part of the mechanism of the sodium pump. One form of such a Mg^{2+} ATPase is located in mitochondria and plays a part in the production of ATP by oxidative phosphorylation. At less than $10\,\mu M$, DDT suppresses the activity of this fraction of the total Mg^{2+}-dependent ATPase of nerve cell preparations. This led Cutkomp *et al.* (1982) to conclude that the primary effect of organochlorine insecticides is to cut off the energy supply of the Na^+–K^+ pump, rather than to attack the axonic (plasmalemma) membrane directly.

Again, at least one, and possibly several, ATPases exist which are dependent on the presence of calcium ions. Mullins and Brinley (1975) reported that a calcium-dependent ATPase is located on the outer surface of axons and is much more susceptible to DDT than is the ATPase associated with the working of the Na^+–K^+ pump. This enzyme, ecto-ATPase, appears to regulate the binding of calcium ions to the surface of the membranes. If there is a shortage of calcium ions, axonic excitation occurs which closely resembles DDT poisoning. Moreover, the neurotoxic symptoms of DDT poisoning are enhanced if the calcium ion concentration is reduced below $20\,mM$ (Matsumura and Narahashi, 1971). Some aspects of this work have, however, been criticised by Cutkomp *et al.* (1982). As was mentioned earlier, calcium ions, and therefore probably calcium-dependent ATPases, play an important role near presynaptic membranes; these enzymes could be targets for DDT.

In a wider context, DDT does not only affect membranes of axons. Attention has frequently been drawn to the fact that the mere presence of lipophilic molecules near lipoprotein membranes can distort such activities as photosynthesis, oxidative phosphorylation, active transport and nuclear division, as well as interfering with axonic transmission. Chefurka *et al.* (1987) have referred more recently to such events in the modern context of studies on synthetic membranes.

A mechanical model to illustrate what may be happening would be a series of intermeshed cog wheels attached to a thick rubber band. Upon distortion of the rubber (e.g. by putting it into solvent) the cog wheels might no longer intermesh correctly. Carriers in chloroplasts and mitochondria, as well as ion pump proteins, are the biological equivalent of the cog wheels.

With such an analogy in mind, it is appropriate to draw attention to little quoted publications by Gavaudan *et al.* (1945, 1946). These authors were originally concerned with the mechanism of the reversible process of narcosis and their approach was quasi-thermodynamic. They were probably among the first to equate the site of action (the 'biophase') with lipoprotein membranes and to attempt to explain certain (initially reversible) toxic effects by an alteration in the state of the membrane. Whatever the unique property of the membrane may be, it is likely to be very vulnerable to disturbance (Hassall, 1961). Such a concept is in no way incompatible with the fact that individual enzymes or conduction channels may appear to be very specific targets of narcotics, organochlorine insecticides, etc. The concept of 'physical toxicity' was reapplied by Mullins (1955) to the neurospecific effects of DDT and HCH and has been greatly refined in later years. Essentially, he suggested the superposition, onto the background effect of the 'presence' of a lipophilic poison, of the constraint of 'fitment' into inter-membrane spaces. In the present instance the thermodynamic concentration at the membrane (the thermodynamic activity) determines the likelihood of membrane distortion near to an ion gate or of a conformational change in a membrane-bound enzyme system, and such changes could be expected to lead to highly specific neurotoxic responses.

The three major pathways by which DDT is degraded are shown in figure 6.6. One involves dehydrochlorination to DDE, a second proceeds via reductive dechlorination to DDD and a third is oxidative and leads to dicofol.

DDE is the major DDT-derived residue normally found in autopsy or biopsy samples of animal tissues (Robinson, 1969). The enzyme catalysing its formation has been termed DDT dehydrochlorinase or DDTase. Its nature has been something of an enigma because the removal of the elements of hydrogen chloride from a molecule does not seem to fit comfortably into the metabolic pattern (oxidation, reduction, hydrolysis and conjugation) outlined in chapter 3. The reaction is dependent on the presence of glutathione and, at least in houseflies, it is brought about by a glutathione-*S*-transferase (Clark and Shamaan, 1984). Several glutathione-*S*-transferases have now been isolated from houseflies and it has been shown that DDTase activity is associated with those with isoelectric points at about pH 7.1 (Clark *et al.*, 1986). Moreover, these workers found that the ability of the enzymes to dehydrochlorinate DDT paralleled their ability to form classical glutathione conjugates with other types of insecticides. The matter is, however, not completely resolved, for multiple genes are involved in the production of housefly glutathione-*S*-transferases and the possibility cannot be ruled out that DDTase is a modified gene product related to, but not identical with, a

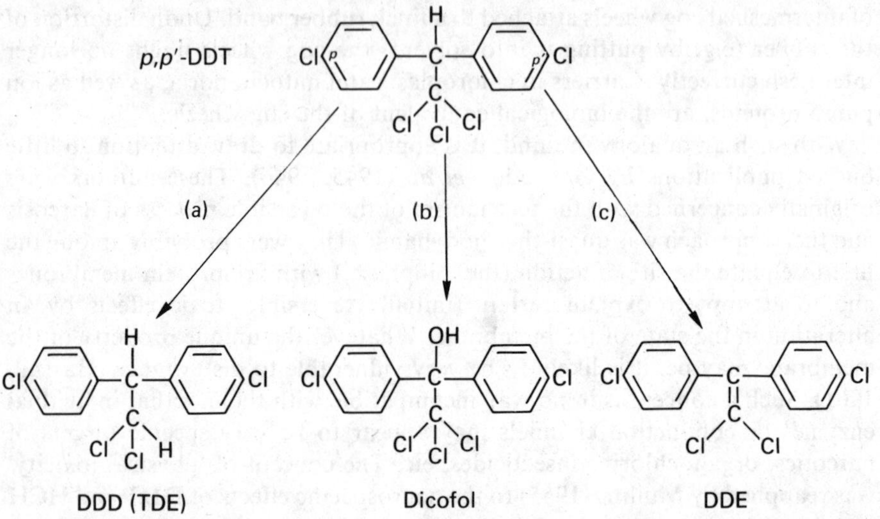

Figure 6.6   Metabolism of DDT. (a) Reductive dechlorination: by anaerobic liver + NADPH, by dead tissues and by some microorganisms. (b) Oxidation: by some insects, e.g. *Drosophila*. (c) Dehydrochlorination: by most insects, birds and mammals (the three pathways are not mutually exclusive)

glutathione-*S*-transferase (compare with the possible modification of carboxylesterase in resistant organisms (chapter 3)). It is yet to be confirmed that DDTase in other organisms is related to glutathione-*S*-transferase.

The development of resistance to DDT in some species of houseflies and mosquitoes is closely correlated with the greater capacity of resistant organisms to convert DDT to the less insecticidal DDE. Some insect species have an inherent resistance to DDT when it is administered orally but not when it is injected, a difference that can be attributed to the presence of a dehydrochlorinase in the cells of the alimentary canal, which destroy DDT before it can get to the (otherwise susceptible) nervous system. DDE is particularly effective at inducing microsomal enzymes in mammalian liver. This is not necessarily a harmful effect, but does alter the body's capacity to metabolise many types of foreign compounds, including pollutants and medical drugs.

A few insects metabolise DDT by a predominantly oxidative route, which results in the formation of dicofol. The route seems to be a typical NADPH-dependent microsomal oxidation (section 3.3). This aliphatic hydroxylation occurs in *Drosophila* and perhaps in resistant strains of the cockroach.

Reductive dechlorination of DDT occurs widely in nature and DDD is an almost ubiquitous residue in animal fat (Robinson, 1969). However, the bulk of this residue may not be formed under normal conditions by enzymes located in vertebrate liver for DDD can be readily produced by bacteria living anaerobically in the gut. Several workers, including Walker (1969), have shown that NADPH-supplemented liver preparations convert DDT to DDD under anaerobic conditions.

Hassall (1972) synthesised several DDT analogues and showed that, in anaerobic surroundings, all were reductively dehalogenated by 12 000 $g \times$ 30 min pigeon liver supernatant fraction. Moreover, the addition of exogenous NADPH was not essential, although it was when liver microsomes were used. Additional work (which, incidentally, shows that suitable controls are not only good science but sometimes yield unexpected dividends) demonstrated that while heated liver supernatant fluid did not produce DDD, the same heated preparation, when supplemented with riboflavin and NAD(P)H, actually converted DDT to DDD faster than did preparations that were similar in every way except that they contained undestroyed liver enzymes (table 6.2). It was also shown that the system was inhibited by carbon monoxide, whether or not the supernatant had been heated. These observations imply that reduction is brought about by a catalytic but non-enzymic reaction involving the participation of a haem compound, riboflavin and a reduced nucleotide. Anaerobic conditions at the bottom of ponds could lead to DDD production by similar non-enzymic means.

Further or secondary metabolism of DDT probably takes place in many species, for water-soluble metabolites occur in both insects and higher animals. In mammals, the most important of these is DDA, an acid substance formed by the replacement of the $-CCl_3$ part of the DDT molecule by $-COOH$. This acid may be excreted in free or conjugated form, in faeces or in bile, according to the species. Rather surprisingly, it is still not clear by what route or routes DDA is formed; in particular it is not clear whether DDD is an obligatory intermediate or whether it can be formed via DDE.

Methoxychlor (figure 6.4) has a lower tendency than has DDT to accumulate in animal fat. It also possesses a much lower acute oral toxicity than DDT to higher animals and is therefore sometimes used for veterinary treatment on

Table 6.2 The reductive dechlorination of DDT in anaerobic surroundings, by unheated and by heated 12 000 g supernatant made from pigeon liver

Pre-incubation treatment of 12 000 $g \times$ 30 min supernatant	Cofactors added	Conversion (%) to DDD in 2.5 h
4°C for 20 min	None	76
	NADPH + Rfl	79
	Riboflavin (Rfl)	73
75°C for 20 min	None	1
	NAD(P)H	< 3
	NAD(P)H + Rfl	100
	Riboflavin	18

or near livestock. Its biological spectrum is rather similar to that of DDT, but rather more of it is usually needed to achieve a given level of control. This, together with its greater manufacturing cost, has limited its use in crop protection. This is unfortunate, for the methoxy groups, unlike the *p,p'*-Cl groups of DDT, provide a point of attack which dramatically changes the pattern of its persistence and accumulation compared with DDT. In addition, the methoxy groups render the molecule somewhat more water-soluble than DDT and such differences can have a crucial bearing on biological magnification. This is well illustrated by the work of Kapoor *et al.* (1970) using a model ecosystem. For DDT, a concentration of 0.22 ppb in water led to a concentration of 54 ppm in *Gambusia*, a magnification of 10^5. The corresponding figures for methoxychlor were 0.11 ppb, 0.17 ppm and 10^3 respectively.

The primary metabolism of methoxychlor (figure 6.7) is probably brought about by microsomal *O*-demethylation reactions, one or both of the methyl groups being removed. Kapoor *et al.* (1970) have shown that the methoxychlor analogue of DDE is also produced in many organisms, but it seldom appears to be the predominant metabolite.

Dicofol (figure 6.4) is another interesting member of the DDT family, for it is a metabolic product of DDT in some species of insects and yet it has been marketed to control certain ticks and mites (i.e. as an acaricide). For example, it has been used against the agriculturally important red spider mite and against the medically important vector of scrub typhus (*Trombiculid* spp.), which can infest clothing under poor hygienic conditions.

Chlorbenzilate (figure 6.4) is another substance that can perhaps be regarded as a relative of DDT. It was marketed in 1956 as an acaricide. It is not very toxic to insects and of much lower mammalian toxicity than DDT. The rapid life cycle of phytophagous mites and the moderate persistence of

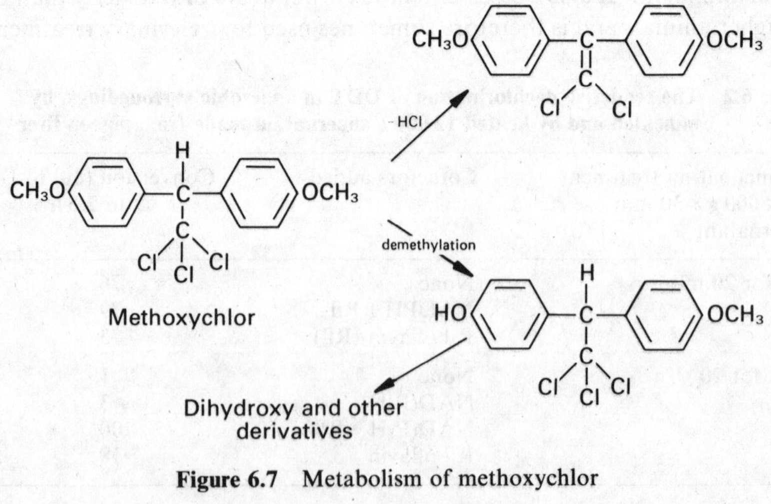

Figure 6.7   Metabolism of methoxychlor

chlorbenzilate (and of many other acaricides) provide conditions that favour the development of resistance.

6.6 HEXACHLOROCYCLOHEXANE (HCH, formerly BHC)

There is only one member of this subgroup, namely the gamma (γ) isomer of hexachlorocyclohexane (HCH). The ring that forms the framework of HCH is not planar (as is an unsaturated benzene ring) but chair-shaped, and it is possible by constructing models to show that eight forms of HCH can exist. Of these isomers, only the γ isomer is highly toxic to insects, being for various insects from 50 to several thousand times as toxic as the α or δ isomers. The β and ε isomers are usually almost inert. The purified γ isomer is often called **lindane**, a tribute to Van der Linden, who discovered some of the HCH isomers.

The cyclohexane ring is shown in figure 6.8; in figure 6.8a it is represented as it appears after making a molecular model, and in figure 6.8b it is portrayed in the conventional 'chair' form. Normally, hydrogen atoms and their valency bonds are not shown in cyclic formulae, but in figure 6.8b arrows are inserted to show the direction in which they point, the bonds a, e being occupied by chlorine atoms.

It will be observed that three carbon atoms (marked C-1, C-3, C-5) each have a bond directed upwards out of the plane of the ring. The three carbon atoms alternating with them (C-2, C-4, C-6) each have a corresponding bond directed downwards. Such bonds, whether directed up or down, are termed *axial* (a) bonds. The remaining bonds (one per carbon atom) project almost, but not quite, sideways out of the ring, and are termed *equatorial* (e) bonds. To construct a model of the γ isomer, proceed around the ring putting chlorine atoms in the following positions, a, a, a, e, e, e. Note that, if the first axial chlorine is 'up', the second must be 'down'.

Before purification, the technical material contains about 13 per cent of the γ isomer, some 68 per cent of two α stereoisomers and small quantities only of the β and δ isomers. From this mixture, lindane can be concentrated by exploiting differences in the solubility of the isomers in various solvents. Such purification is desirable, especially for treatment of crops with tap roots or storage organs, because impure γ-HCH tends to have an unpleasant musty smell and to taint foodstuffs. Lindane, however, is an almost odourless white solid, slightly soluble in water (10 ppm), moderately soluble in kerosene (2 per cent) and very soluble in acetone (43 per cent). It has a vapour pressure of about 10^{-5} mmHg at 20°C and is stable to heat and light. It is not known why only one of the eight isomers of HCH is outstandingly insecticidal; there is no obvious correlation of toxicity with either physical properties or chemical reactivity, for the vapour pressure, the solubility in oil and the chemical reactivity of the γ isomer all lie between those of various inactive isomers.

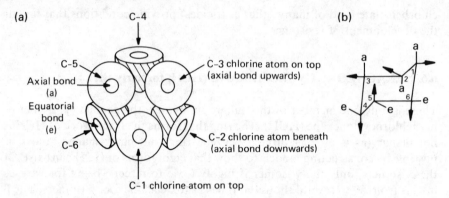

(a)   C-4   (b)

C-5   C-3 chlorine atom on top
                                       (axial bond upwards)
Axial bond
(a)
Equatorial
bond
(e)
C-6   C-2 chlorine atom beneath
                                       (axial bond downwards)

C-1 chlorine atom on top

C–4, C–5 and C–6 have chlorine atoms projecting (almost) laterally

Figure 6.8   Structure of γ-HCH (hexachlorocyclohexane). (a) Molecular model representation of γ-HCH. (b) Conventional 'chair' representation of γ-HCH (formerly γ-BHC)

Reference to the inter-membrane space theory was made in section 6.5.

The insecticidal action of lindane is somewhat similar to that of DDT in that the insect starts to tremble, with telescopic movements of the abdomen. With passage of time, hyperexcitation increases and movements become increasingly uncoordinated. At higher dosage, the insect falls onto its back and eventually suffers paralysis. As with other organochlorine insecticides, poisoning causes a pronounced increase in respiratory rate. The overall effect on the nervous system also resembles that of DDT (section 6.4) but the primary site of action in both insects and mammals is the central nervous system (CNS). This can be shown by the fact that, if insect nerves are isolated from the CNS so that only sensory impulses can arise spontaneously, it takes some time before multiple discharges appear unless the concentration of lindane is high (Ecobichon and Joy, 1982, p. 123).

Precisely what effect lindane has on the CNS remains uncertain. Sloley *et al.* (1985) found that lindane led to an increase in the levels of dopamine and of *N*-acetyldopamine in the cerebral ganglion of the cockroach. On the other hand, Abalis *et al.* (1985) concluded that, in mammalian brain, receptors for γ-aminobutyric acid (GABA) were a primary target for lindane. GABA is an inhibitory neurotransmitter, present in the CNS of vertebrates. It is also present in invertebrates, both in the nervous system and in the skeletal muscles. It was postulated that the GABA receptor is a single protein with three sites of activity. One of these binds to GABA, a second controls an ion channel and the third is the site of attachment of certain toxicants. It was concluded that lindane and cyclodienes inhibit GABA-induced chloride ion uptake, with the effect that the inhibitory neurotransmitter action of GABA is blocked, leading to CNS excitation and convulsions. Figure 6.9 shows that a fair correlation exists between the GABA receptor affinity of various organochlorine compounds (e.g., lindane, dieldrin, endosulfan) and the LD_{50}s of these compounds when fed to the rat.

It is noteworthy that in several respects there is a greater similarity between the mode of action of lindane and the cyclodienes than there is between the mode of action of lindane and that of DDT. As stated above, the actions of lindane and cyclodienes are mostly on the CNS where they probably block similar receptors. DDT, on the other hand, probably acts peripherally. These or other differences lead to rather different observed toxic effects on insects, because lindane and the cyclodienes cause convulsions to develop, with a characteristic attitude of the wings and the loss in flying insects of the ability to fly. Lindane also resembles cyclodienes and differs from DDT in that the dosage–response relationship usually shows a positive temperature coefficient (but see Fisher and Wadleigh, 1985). In addition, insect resistance to lindane is often linked to resistance to cyclodienes rather than resistance to DDT.

It is probable that both mono-oxygenases and glutathione-S-transferases are involved in the metabolism of γ-HCH but the process is complex, incompletely understood, and apparently occurs by somewhat different routes in different species. Altogether, more than 70 metabolites have been identified in birds and mammals and yet others have been detected in insects and plants.

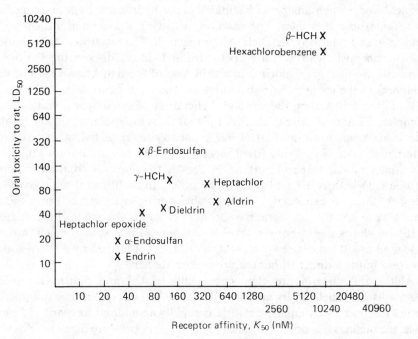

Figure 6.9   Relation between oral toxicity of organochlorine compounds to rat and their affinity to GABA receptors (from data of Abalis *et al.*, 1985)

The extensive literature on the subject has been reviewed by Macholz and Kujawa (1985); the entry for lindane in the metabolic maps of Aizawa (1982) is also useful.

It is still not clear whether isomerisation can occur enzymically (e.g. whether the γ isomer can be converted to the α isomer). This has been reported to occur in plants and microorganisms but probably does not occur in mammals. Instead, what usually happens is that a series of reactions occur in which double bonds or hydroxyl groups are inserted into the molecule and chlorine atoms (with or without accompanying hydrogen atoms) are removed. Such reactions probably involve glutathione-*S*-transferases (sometimes acting in a way analogous to their DDTase role) in combination with other enzymic and non-enzymic reactions. The outcome is the formation of a variety of penta-, tetra- and trichlorinated cyclohexane, cyclohexene and chlorinated phenolic derivatives. Glutathione conjugates have also been identified. It is probably from such compounds that the mercapturic acid and thiochlorophenols, identified in some insects, have been derived.

6.7 THE CHLORINATED CYCLODIENE FAMILY

Numerous organochlorine compounds can be made by condensing hexachlorocyclopentadiene with suitable cyclic hydrocarbons containing five or seven atoms of carbon. The reaction, involving a diene and a dienophile ('diene-liker') is termed the Diels–Alder reaction. The reaction is named after the two chemists who won a Nobel Prize in 1950 for discovering the diene synthesis. So also are dieldrin and aldrin, two of the best-known insecticidal members of the group. Their structures are shown in figure 6.10.

As figure 6.10 shows, the structural chemistry of cyclodiene insecticides is complex, because the molecule is not planar. The molecular geometry recalls the 'chair' configuration of HCH but here two such rings (which can exist in alternative 'boat' forms) are fused together, and the fusion can occur in more than one way with respect to (a) the 'bridges' in the rings and (b) the curvature of one ring with respect to that of the other. In addition, if an epoxide is present, this too can occupy two possible positions in space. For a more detailed account the monograph of Brooks (1974) should be consulted. Figure 6.10 also shows the rather remarkable structure of **mirex**, a stomach insecticide used to kill ants, wireworms and snails. It is not formed by a Diels–Alder reaction but is a dimer of hexachlorocyclopentadiene.

Aldrin and **dieldrin** are stereochemically related and aldrin is rapidly metabolised to dieldrin by an NADPH-dependent enzyme in hepatic microsomes (section 3.4). Similarly, **isodrin** is rapidly epoxidised to **endrin**. In each case, the olefin is less polar and has a higher vapour pressure than the epoxide. This difference accounts for the use of aldrin as a soil fumigant to control wireworms and the larvae of root flies whereas dieldrin has been more often employed as a root dip and as a seed dressing. Dieldrin has also been of great importance in locust control and is very effective against animal ectoparasites such as blowflies and lice; the problem is to know how to dispose of the spent liquid from sheep and cattle dips without contaminating watercourses.

The first step in the metabolism of the olefinic cyclodienes, aldrin, isodrin and heptachlor, involves oxidation by microsomal oxidases to the corresponding epoxides. These epoxides are relatively stable, especially in insects, although slow metabolism to a variety of products occurs. In the case of dieldrin, for example, a secondary alcohol group can be formed on the unchlorinated bridge by the action of mono-oxygenases present in the livers of higher animals, whereas hydrolysis of the oxirane ring by epoxide hydrolase (section 3.3) usually leads to the formation of a *trans*-diol (figure 6.11). Another characteristic product, 2-*keto*-dieldrin, is formed by oxidation, dechlorination and molecular rearrangement. In many species this substance is the metabolite present in largest amount in the urine. Despite these changes, the general picture is nevertheless, in most organisms, one of slow metabolism of epoxide cyclodienes; hence residues of these substances are almost ubiquitous in animal fats.

In mud below fresh water, where the surroundings are anaerobic, dieldrin is metabolised by several microorganisms. The reaction involves removal of one

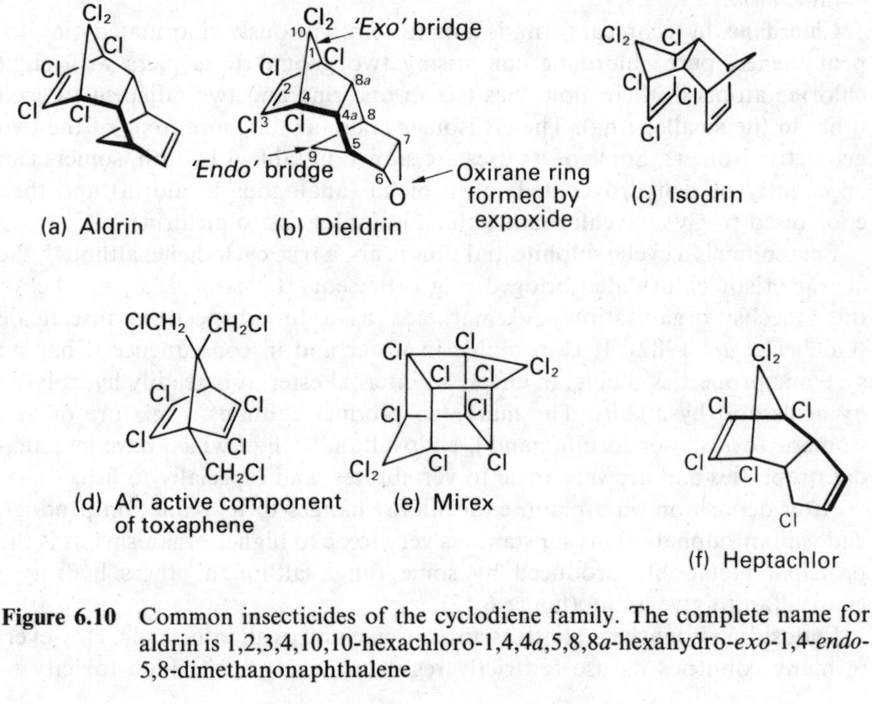

Figure 6.10   Common insecticides of the cyclodiene family. The complete name for aldrin is 1,2,3,4,10,10-hexachloro-1,4,4a,5,8,8a-hexahydro-*exo*-1,4-*endo*-5,8-dimethanonaphthalene

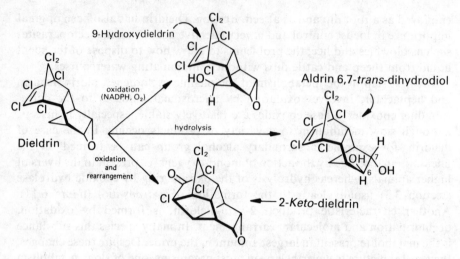

Figure 6.11   Three metabolites of dieldrin

of the two chlorine atoms from the methylene 'exo' bridge (figure 6.10). The reaction is quite slow but a mixture of 10 types of anaerobes present in mud metabolise it more rapidly than did any one of these acting in pure culture (Maule *et al.*, 1987).

Chlordane, in technical form, is a mixture of variously chlorinated dicyclo-pentadienes, pure chlordane comprising two geometric isomers with eight chlorine atoms in their molecules (six in one ring and two adjacent to each other in the smaller ring). The *cis* isomer is by far the more toxic of the two geometric isomers. Some of its uses are shown in table 6.1. Both isomers can apparently be dehydrogenated to an olefin (analogous to aldrin) and then epoxidised to give oxychlordane (which is analogous to dieldrin).

Endosulfan is a cyclic sulphite and thus is not a true cyclodiene, although the characteristic chlorinated bridged ring is present. It was made by Goebel of the Hoechst organisation and marketed as a broad-spectrum insecticide (Goebel *et al.*, 1982). It is insoluble in water and in consequence it has no systemic properties. Being, in effect, an internal ester, it is readily hydrolysed by acids and by alkalis. The marketed product contains a mixture of two isomeric forms, α-endosulfan and β-endosulfan, both of which have insecticidal properties and are very toxic to vertebrates, and especially to fish.

After deposition on a plant, endosulfan changes to its oxidation product, endosulfan sulphate. This substance is very toxic to higher organisms. It is the principal metabolite produced by some fungi, although others hydrolyse endosulfan to give a diol (figure 6.12).

Endosulfan is marketed both as an acaricide and as an insecticide. However, in many countries its use is strictly regulated owing to its high toxicity to livestock and its extreme danger to fish should it enter watercourses. It controls the gall mite that causes 'big bud' of blackcurrants (and any capsids or aphids that are present at the time of spraying) as well as the mites of strawberry and blackberry.

Chlorinated cyclodiene insecticides are among the most toxic and persistent of all pesticides and their use for most agricultural purposes is banned or restricted in most countries. In Britain, as early as 1964, the Cook Report recommended that, wherever possible, DDT, γ-HCH or organophosphorus compounds should be used instead of them. Their use in seed treatments was regarded as undesirable (even though very effective) because of their high toxicity to birds. The use of aldrin and dieldrin was, from about 1980, restricted to root dips to protect crops from larvae of the cabbage root fly and, in the case of aldrin, as a dust for the control of wireworms and leatherjackets in designated crops.

Many similarities exist between the neurotoxic effects of the cyclodienes and lindane (section 6.6). In particular, and unlike DDT, the primary site of action is in the CNS. Flying insects show a characteristic fanning of the wings but, at an early stage of poisoning, lose the ability to fly. Again, in contrast to the toxic effect of DDT, response of an insect to a given dose of a cyclodiene becomes more intense with increase in ambient temperature.

Cyclodienes are not axonic poisons. When insect nerves have been isolated from the CNS, spontaneous discharges do not occur readily and then only after a considerable lapse of time. This implies that, unlike the action of DDT, sensory receptors are not particularly sensitive and that, in the intact insect, a complete reflex arc is needed for the full toxic effect of cyclodienes to be realised. When such an arc is present, dieldrin appears to augment synaptic transmission by enhancing the release of acetylcholine from presynaptic terminals. It will be recalled (figure 4.2) that many presynaptic contacts may exist between neurons and it has been suggested that the presence of cyclodienes leads to an 'avalanching' effect as more and more presynaptic elements become involved. In the case of **heptachlor epoxide** there is evidence

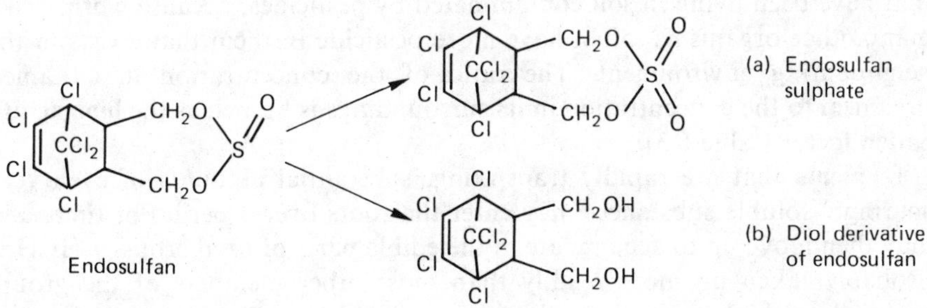

Figure 6.12 Endosulfan and metabolites: (a) endosulfan sulphate; (b) endosulfan diol

that Ca^{2+}/Mg^{2+}-dependent ATPase may be inhibited, with the result that there is an increase in uptake of calcium ions from the external medium (Matsumura and Clark, 1982). This could account for the observed increase in release of neurotransmitter but the mode of action remains unclear. Post-synaptic action has also been reported; aldrin *trans*-diol, for example, may diminish the sensitivity of the postsynaptic membrane to acetylcholine. It has also been suggested that it may block the opening of chloride ion channels at GABA-mediated postsynaptic sites (Osborne, 1985).

6.8 SECONDARY AND ENVIRONMENTAL EFFECTS OF ORGANOCHLORINE INSECTICIDES

In **soil**, most organochlorine compounds persist for months or even years. This is especially so when high doses are applied to clay soils or to soils rich in organic matter. Volatility may limit the persistence of lindane in light soils, but for aldrin the situation may be more complex. Kushwaha *et al.* (1978) found that this substance persisted for a shorter time in sandy loam at 25°C than it did at 35°C (half-lives 49 and 177 days, respectively, at 6 ppm). The probable explanation for this observation is that soil organisms probably convert aldrin to the less volatile dieldrin more rapidly at the higher tempera-ture.

There is little evidence that a long-term effect on soil fungi or bacteria takes place when organochlorine compounds are applied at normal concentration. However, there may be temporary disturbance in the equilibrium existing between the various species of soil micro-arthropods. When soil is treated with DDT, the number of Collembola (a group of insects which feed on organic matter) suffers a sharp initial decline but then increases again to a higher steady-state level, apparently because of the destruction of soil mites and other predators. Earthworms, which account for a biomass of some 500 g/m² of soil surface in pastures, are not greatly affected except perhaps by chlordane.

Indirect problems may also arise from the presence of persistent substances in or on soil. Predators may be threatened indirectly if they eat earthworms that have been living in soil contaminated by pesticides, because worms, like many other organisms, often have more pesticide in them than exists in the neighbouring environment. The ratio of the concentration in a named organism to the concentration in its surroundings is known as the **biomagnifi-cation factor** (table 6.3).

In **plants** that are rapidly transpiring, substantial amounts of even very sparingly soluble substances may enter the roots over a period of time, and may then move up to accumulate in the edible parts of food crops. γ-HCH is probably taken up more readily than most other members of the group, especially at high rates of application, and tainting of root crops has often followed the use of technical HCH. It can also cause abnormal nuclear

Table 6.3   Biomagnification of DDT and its metabolites (from Kenaga, 1972)

Environment	Organism	Maximum observed biomagnification[a]
Soil	Roots of crops	0.1
	Slugs	4
	Earthworms	73
Water	Algae	33
	Crabs	144
	Shrimps	2 800
	Clams	70 000
	Fish	829 300

[a] Biomagnification is a concentration factor, representing the concentration within the organism compared with that in the immediate soil or water environment in which the analysed organisms lived. Figures extracted, with permission, from Kenaga (1972, table 2, p. 201), which in turn contained data collated by Edwards (1970).

division in meristematic tissue. On the other hand, Lichtenstein and Schulz (1960) could not detect any translocation of DDT from roots to the aerial parts of pea plants.

Residues in water have been locally high, due to factory effluent, animal dips and run-off from agricultural land. Drainage water from treated fields is almost free from organochlorine contamination because of the high adsorption onto soil particles. Of possibly greater long-term concern (because no national government can control world-wide contamination) is the flowing of contaminated rivers into the oceans of the world and general wash-down from the air in rain water. Intermediate between these is the urgent shorter-term problem of inflow of contaminated rivers into lakes and into inland or nearly landlocked water (e.g. the Great Lakes, the Rift Valley and the Baltic, Black, Caspian and Mediterranean Seas). Some figures for the concentrations of organochlorine compounds in various stretches of water during the period 1964–70 are given by Matsumura (1972). In the case of DDT and its persistent metabolites, 112 parts were found in 10^{12} parts of water in the Mississippi Delta, 10 parts per 10^{12} in US river basins and 1.6 parts per 10^{12} in British rivers. Figures for contamination by other organochlorine compounds were in general lower than those for DDT, an exception being a much higher figure (18.7 parts per 10^{12}) for γ-HCH in British rivers.

Now that serious attempts are being made in many countries to restrict the use of organochlorine insecticides (and especially their use in crop protection), the widespread contamination problems outlined above should gradually diminish. The stability of these substances is, however, so great and their distribution so widespread that this will take a long time; environmentalists have drawn attention to the fact that organochlorine compounds have even been found several feet down in the ice of the polar ice cap.

Work on the possible chronic effects of DDT on **animals** has been reviewed by Matsumura (1975). In almost all cases where side-effects were reported the dosage applied was unrealistically high compared with the exposure of the normal human population. President Kennedy's Scientific Advisory Committee in 1963 stated that the level of DDT in American body fat was about 12 ppm in 1951 and the daily ingestion at that time was about 0.18 mg per person per day. The latter figure corresponds to some 0.003 mg/kg human body weight (the amount ingested has greatly diminished since then). Experiments conducted by Shabad *et al.* (1972) obtained evidence of hyperplasia in mice with a daily dose of 0.020 mg/kg. Spindler (1983) reviewed investigations into possible chronic toxic effects of DDT. In mice, high doses of DDT did increase the incidence of non-malignant tumours; embryotoxic (but not teratogenic) effects have also been observed. However, in rats, hamsters, dogs and monkeys several investigations failed to reveal any carcinogenic response, even when DDT was administered at 100 ppm in the diet. Nor did the Ames test reveal any increased tendency for microorganisms to mutate in the presence of DDT, whether or not metabolic activation systems (section 1.5) were added. The only observed effect on reproduction in dogs was that females chronically exposed to DDT had their first oestrus two or three months earlier than expected.

Some evidence exists that chronic exposure to DDT can cause behavioural changes in animals which could, in the wild, prove disadvantageous. For example, chronic application of doses of 25 mg/kg body weight increased the open-fields exploratory behaviour of mice. In addition, the offspring of female mice that, after mating, had been given 200 ppm DDT in their diet often made more mistakes than did control mice when put into an experimental maze and their performance did not improve with time (Ecobichon and Joy, 1982, p. 109).

Exposure of higher animals to appropriate doses of organochlorine insecticides, polychlorinated biphenyls, phenobarbital and many other lipid-soluble substances can cause the **induction** of liver enzymes that metabolise potential poisons. Whether this effect, and the enlargement of the liver that often accompanies it, is beneficial or harmful probably depends on the circumstances—it can result in quicker metabolism of pesticide residues, for example, but also may interfere with medication. Induction may, however, be associated with cytological abnormalities, for De la Pena de Torres (1978) observed not only that DDT caused a proliferation of the smooth endoplasmic reticulum (the site of enzyme induction) but also that the nuclei of liver cells of mice contained large intranuclear cytoplasmic invaginations and an increase in the number of nucleoli.

The level of contamination of **meat**, **milk** and **eggs** with organochlorine compounds is of importance to man. In particular, the reliance of the young upon cow's milk places this food in a very special category. Zweig *et al.* (1961) observed that, when DDT was fed to dairy cows, the concentration of DDT in the milk came within a fortnight into steady state with the amount in the diet. When the cows were taken off the diet, the concentration in the milk fell rapidly. More recently, Indian workers have made somewhat similar observations in relation to milk produced by Indian buffaloes (Kalra *et al.*, 1986). After feeding 20, 100 and 400 mg in the daily rations, the DDT in milk fat rose rapidly to a plateau level. Once feeding ceased, the rate of decline of DDT residues in milk was such that the concentration in milk fat had fallen to half in about six days. Similar results were obtained when application was to the skin rather than by mouth; the only major difference was that after oral application much DDD was to be found in the milk (presumably because of the action of rumen organisms) whereas after dermal application the milk contained DDT itself.

Several surveys have been made of organochlorine levels in human milk, and most of them indicate that the levels are higher than in cow's milk. Moreover, placental transfer seems to favour higher amounts (0.07 ppm) in the milk than in the maternal blood. Matsumura (1975) has pointed out that if, as is probable, infants are more susceptible to organochlorine toxicity than are adults, they are probably exposed to an insult some 50 times greater than that suffered by a normal adult (on the assumption that the normal adult now only takes in about 0.005 mg/kg per day of DDT). Spindler (1983) provided comprehensive data based on studies that evaluated residues of organochlorine insecticides in human milk in many countries. Values in 1978 ranged from 0.8 ppm in Germany to 15.6 ppm in Africa.

Another aspect of the consequence of high stability and lipid solubility is often called the **food-chain effect**. When organisms are dependent on one another in a biological sequence, many members of a species of one trophic level may be eaten by one organism of the next higher trophic level. If, then, a small quantity of a stable lipid-soluble pesticide should be present in each of the lowlier organisms, the possibility exists that lipid concentration may rise with the trophic level of the organisms (figure 6.13).

The most notorious example of a chain operating in this way is one terminating in *fish-eating birds*. An illustration is provided by Robinson *et al.* (1967), who sampled marine organisms off the Northumberland coast for their content of dieldrin and of DDT. Samples of the seaweeds *Fucus serratus* and *Laminaria digitata* (trophic level 1) contained only 0.001 ppm of dieldrin, whereas *Echinus esculentis* and *Mytilus edulis* (trophic level 2) contained 0.027 and 0.023 ppm respectively. Herrings (*Clupea harengus*) in trophic level 3 contained 0.057 ppm and some fish-eating birds (trophic level 4) contained 0.5 ppm. Other examples from data collated by Edwards (1970) are provided in table 6.3. The harm to avian species arising from this effect has, however, sometimes been overstated, for the operation of a food-chain effect requires either that a closed system exists such that the fish-eating birds have no

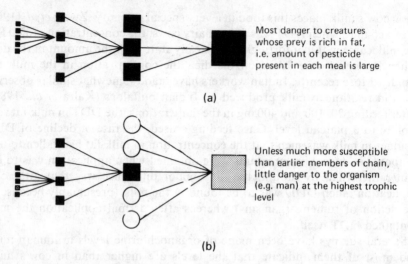

Most danger to creatures
whose prey is rich in fat,
i.e. amount of pesticide
present in each meal is large

(a)

Unless much more susceptible
than earlier members of chain,
little danger to the organism
(e.g. man) at the highest trophic
level

(b)

Figure 6.13   The food chain as it operates (a) in a closed community and (b) when a
less specific feeder participates

alternative source of food or that the whole local environment is equally
contaminated. Man is an omnivorous species that eats foods originating from
different parts of the world and is therefore less at risk than a species that has
an obligatory requirement for one or a few kinds of foods obtained from a
highly localised source.

Birds are frequently more susceptible to organochlorine compounds than
are mammals. In addition, some species select one type of seed for their main
diet, and should that seed be the farmer's newly sown seed-treated cereal, the
birds may well pay dearly for their predations. Eggs laid by birds that have
eaten sublethal amounts of organochlorine compounds frequently have thin
shells. Experiments have shown that at realistic intake levels of organochlorine compounds the thickness may decrease by 10 per cent, but whether this is,
in nature, a cause of declining populations is debatable. Organochlorine
residues in birds or their eggs also seem sometimes to cause decreased egg
production, lower fertility and lower hatchability of eggs. A delay in ovulation
caused by DDT may be of practical importance, for large sublethal doses in
adult birds may so delay egg-laying that double-brooding birds produce a late
brood just as the food supply is failing.

REFERENCES

Abalis, I. M., Eldefrawi, M. E. and Eldefrawi, A. T. (1985). *Pestic. Biochem. Physiol.*,
   24, 95
Aizawa, H. (1982). *Metabolic Maps of Pesticides*. Academic Press, New York

Biggar, J. W., Dutt, G. R. and Riggs, R. L. (1967). *Bull. Environ. Contam. Toxicol.*, **2**, 90

Brooks, G. T. (1974). *Chlorinated Insecticides*, vol. 1, *Technology and Applications*. CRC Press, Cleveland, OH

Carson, R. (1963). *Silent Spring*. Hamish Hamilton, London

Chang, C. P. and Plapp, F. W., Jr (1983a). *J. Econ. Entomol.*, **76**, 1206

Chang, C. P. and Plapp, F. W., Jr (1983b). *Pestic. Biochem. Physiol.*, **20**, 76 and 86

Chefurka, W., McLeod, H. L. and Steele, J. E. (1987). *Pestic. Biochem. Physiol.*, **28**, 93

Clark, A. G. and Shamaan, N. A. (1984). *Pestic. Biochem. Physiol.*, **22**, 249

Clark, A. G., Shamaan, N. A., Sinclair, M. D. and Dauterman, W. C. (1986). *Pestic. Biochem. Physiol.*, **25**, 169

Cutkomp, L. K., Koch, R. B. and Desaiah, D. (1982). In *Insecticide Mode of Action*, ed. J. R. Coats, p. 45. Academic Press, New York

De la Pena de Torres (1978). *Archos. Farmacol. Toxicol.*, **4**, 339

Ecobichon, D. J. and Joy, R. M. (1982). In *Pesticides and Neurological Diseases*, eds D. J. Ecobichon and R. M. Joy. CRC Press, Boca Raton, FL

Edwards, C. A. (1970). *Critical Reviews in Environmental Control*, vol.1. CRC Press, Cleveland, OH

Edwards, N. A. and Hassall, K. A. (1980). *Biochemistry and Physiology of the Cell*, 2nd edn. McGraw-Hill, Maidenhead

Fisher, S. W. and Wadleigh, R. W. (1985). *J. Econ. Entomol.*, **78**, 1222

Gavaudan, P., Dode, M. and Poussel, H. (1945). *Mem. Serv. Chim. État*, **32**, 388

Gavaudan, P., Dode, M. and Poussel, H. (1946). *C.R. Acad. Sci., Paris*, **223**, 407, 521, 591

Goebel, H., Gorbach, S., Knauf, W., Rimpau, R. H. and Hüttenbach, H. (1982). *Res. Rev.*, **83**, 1

Hassall, K. A. (1961). *J. Exp. Bot.*, **12**, 47

Hassall, K. A. (1972). *Pestic. Biochem. Physiol.*, **2**, 331

Kalra, R. L., Chawla, R. P., Joia, B. S. and Tiwina, M. S. (1986). *Pestic. Sci.*, **17**, 128

Kapoor, I. P., Metcalf, R. L., Nystrom, R. F. and Sangha, G. K. (1970). *J. Agric. Fd Chem.*, **18**, 1145

Kenaga, E. E. (1972). In *Environmental Toxicology of Pesticides*, eds F. Matsumura, G. M. Bousch and T. Misato. Academic Press, New York

Kushwaha, K. S., Gupta, H. C. L. and Kavadia, V. S. (1978). *Ann. Arid Zone*, **17**, 200

Lichtenstein, E. P. and Schulz, K. R. (1960). *J. Agric. Fd Chem.*, **8**, 452

Lund, A. E. (1984). *Pestic. Biochem. Physiol.*, **22**, 161

Lund, A. E. and Narahashi, T. (1983). *Pestic. Biochem. Physiol.*, **20**, 203

Macholz, R. M. and Kujawa, M. (1985). *Res. Rev.*, **94**, 119

MAFF (1985). *Agricultural Chemicals Approval Scheme:Approved Products for Farmers and Growers*. HMSO, London

Martin, H. and Worthing, C. R. (1976). *Insecticide and Fungicide Handbook*. Blackwell, Oxford

Matsumura, F. (1972). In *Environmental Toxicology of Pesticides*, eds F. Matsumura, G. M. Bousch and T. Misato, p. 33. Academic Press, New York

Matsumura, F. (1975). *Toxicology of Insecticides*. Plenum, New York

Matsumura, F. and Clark, J. M. (1982). *Prog. Neurobiol.*, **18**, 231

Matsumura, F. and Narahashi, T. (1971). *Biochem. Pharmacol.*, **20**, 825

Maule, A., Plyte, S. and Quirk, A. V. (1987). *Pestic. Biochem. Physiol.*, **27**, 229

Mullins, L. J. (1955). *Science (NY)*, **122**, 118

Mullins, L. J. and Brinley, F. J., Jr (1975). *J. Gen. Physiol.*, **65**, 135

Osborne, M. P. (1985). In *Comprehensive Insect Physiology, Biochemistry and Pharmacology*, vol. 12, *Insect Control*, eds G. A. Kerkut and L. I. Gilbert, p. 131. Pergamon, Oxford

Patlak, J. and Horn, R. (1982). *J. Gen. Physiol.*, **79**, 333
Pichon, Y., Guillet, J.-C., Heilig, U. and Pelhate, M. (1985). *Pestic. Sci.*, **16**, 627
Rashatware, S. S. and Matsumura, F. (1986). *Pestic. Biochem. Physiol.*, **26**, 90
Robinson, J. (1969). *Can. Med. Assoc. J.*, **100**, 180
Robinson, J., Richardson, A., Crabtree, A. N., Coulson, J. C. and Potts, G. R. (1967). *Nature (Lond.)*, **214**, 1307
Shabad, L. M., Kolesnichenko, T. S. and Nikonova, T. V. (1972). *Int. J. Cancer*, **9**, 365
Sloley, B. D., Bailey, B. A. and Downer, R. G. H. (1985). *Pestic. Biochem. Physiol.*, **24**, 213
Spindler, M. (1983). *Res. Rev.*, **90**, 1
Walker, C. H. (1969). *Life Sci.*, **8**, 1111
Zweig, G., Smith, L. M., Peoples, S. A. and Cox, R. (1961). *J. Agric. Fd Chem.*, **9**, 481

7 Natural and synthetic pyrethroids

7.1 NATURAL PYRETHROIDS

At least six closely related compounds occur (1–2 per cent w/w) in the dried inflorescences of *Chrysanthemum cinerariaefolium*, a plant that is grown commercially as a source of these insecticides in Kenya, Tanzania and, to a lesser extent, in several other countries (figure 7.1). Characterised by a remarkable 'knock-down' effect on flying insects, the natural pyrethroids have long been used as active ingredients in domestic sprays employed against flies and mosquitoes. This spectacular knock-down effect, coupled with their extremely low toxicity to warm-blooded animals, renders them ideal for this purpose. Knock-down, however, does not necessarily imply eventual death and many a user's jubilation would have been premature but for the

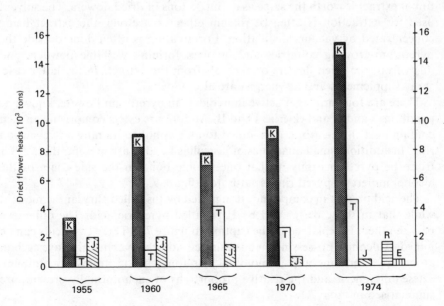

Figure 7.1 Production of dried pyrethrum flowers, 1955–74 (K, Kenya; T, Tanzania; J, Japan; R, Rwanda; E, Ecuador); figures for last two only plotted for 1974 (drawn using values from ITC, 1976, table 1)

customary presence of a second poison, usually an organophosphorus or organochlorine compound with a slower but more reliably lethal action.

Historical aspects of **natural pyrethrum** production have been described in an International Trade Centre publication (ITC, 1976). *C. cinerariaefolium* probably originated in Persia (now Iran) but by the mid-nineteenth century was grown and processed in Yugoslavia. By 1914, some 1500 tons of dried flowers were sold to the USA. Between the two world wars, Japan became the world's main producer, some 1400 tons of dried flowers being produced each year before trade was halted by the Second World War. Japanese production is now being phased out, for the yield of flowers per acre in the Kenyan highlands is such as to make Japanese production uneconomic. Tanzania, Zaire and Rwanda followed Kenya's example and started to grow pyrethrum, although production in Zaire has been disappointingly low since independence. Tanzanian production, however, is now 25 per cent of that of Kenya (figure 7.1).

Pyrethrum plants when grown on volcanic ash at altitudes of 1500–3500 m in tropical zones give larger overall yields of pyrethrin than do plants at low altitudes. The use of fertilisers, irrigation, herbicides—and insecticides—is often essential. Harvesting is usually done by hand, the flowers being frequently, but not always, dried in the sun. Nowadays the dried flowers (about 350 kg/ha) are processed in the producing countries. In terms of tonnage, extracts represent about 12 per cent of total pyrethrin exports, but a ton of extract is worth the same as about 35 tons of dried flowers. The solvent used for extraction is often petroleum ether or acetone, the extract being concentrated by vacuum distillation. Formulation is often done outside the pyrethrum-growing countries and involves forming wettable powders and dusts from the dried flowers or aerosols from the extract. In the latter case, spray supplements and a synergist are also added.

There are four principal active ingredients in pyrethrum flowers, known as **pyrethrins I** and **II** and **cinerins I** and **II**. All four are esters comprising an acid containing a three-carbon ring joined to an alcohol containing a five-carbon ring. In addition, small quantities of **jasmolins I** and **II** are present; these differ from the pyrethrins only in that one double bond in the side-chain of the alcohol moiety of pyrethrins is saturated (figure 7.2).

The acid present in compounds designated by I is called chrysanthemic acid while that in those designated by II is called pyrethric acid. The difference between them is explained in the caption to figure 7.2. These two acids can be joined to alcohols possessing an unsaturated side-chain containing five carbon atoms (pyrethrolone and jasmololone) or four carbon atoms (cinerolone). These differences, and the relative proportions of each normally present, are summarised in table 7.1.

The acid component of natural pyrethroids is capable of existing in *cis* and *trans* forms, and each of these could exist as optical enantiomers. The naturally occurring acid is, in fact, the *trans* (dextrorotatory) form and its

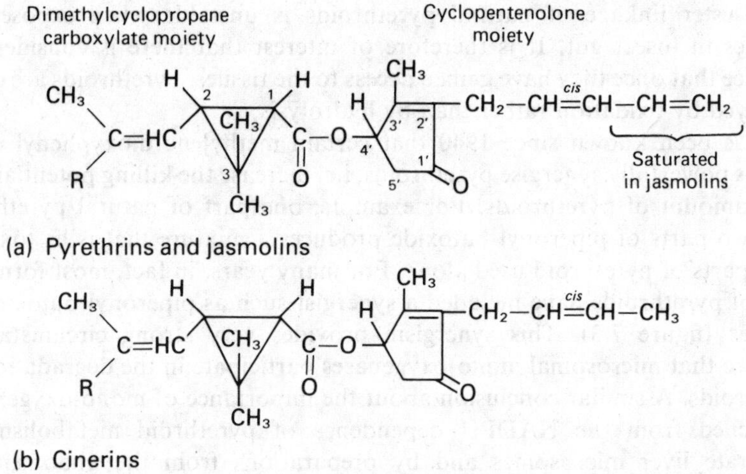

Dimethylcyclopropane carboxylate moiety   Cyclopentenolone moiety

(a) Pyrethrins and jasmolins

(b) Cinerins

Figure 7.2 Natural pyrethroids: (a) pyrethrin I, $R = CH_3$; pyrethrin II, $R = COOCH_3$ (jasmolins I and II resemble the corresponding pyrethrins but the side-chain is saturated as indicated); (b) cinerin I, $R = CH_3$; cinerin II, $R = COOCH_3$

esters are more toxic than those formed from the three other stereoisomers produced synthetically.

Similarly, each of the alcohols can be made as *cis* and *trans* forms, and each of these as two optical isomers. Of these, only the *cis* (dextrorotatory) isomer occurs naturally. The geometrical isomerism occurs at the double bond marked in the formulae (figure 7.2), while the asymmetric carbon atom is the one carrying the hydroxyl group when the alcohol is uncombined.

The pyrethroid esters are oily liquids soluble in alcohol, acetone and petroleum but insoluble in water. The esters are unstable, even in the dust from the dried flower heads (there is about 20 per cent loss of activity per year on storage), but can be protected by anti-oxidants as long as light and water are excluded. In water they are hydrolysed, the reaction being both acid- and base-catalysed. In consequence they are unable to kill insects as stomach poisons and are also very ephemeral contact poisons.

Table 7.1 Proportions of the six active ingredients in a typical pyrethrum product

	Acid present	
Alcohol present	Chrysanthemic	Pyrethric
Pyrethrolone	Pyrethrin I (35%)	Pyrethrin II (32%)
Cinerolone	Cinerin I (10%)	Cinerin II (14%)
Jasmololone	Jasmolin I (5%)	Jasmolin II (4%)

The ester linkage of natural pyrethroids is unstable when exposed to enzymes in insect gut. It is therefore of interest that there is considerable evidence that once they have gained access to the tissues, pyrethroids are often destroyed by oxidation rather than by hydrolysis.

It has been known since 1940 that certain methylene dioxyphenyl compounds powerfully synergise pyrethroids, i.e. increase the killing potential of a given amount of pyrethroids. For example, one part of natural pyrethroid with two parts of piperonyl butoxide produces a mixture that is as toxic as seven parts of pyrethroid used alone. For many years, in fact, most formulations of pyrethroids have included a synergist such as piperonyl butoxide or sesamex (figure 7.3). This synergism provides very strong circumstantial evidence that microsomal mono-oxygenases participate in the degradation of pyrethroids. A similar conclusion about the importance of mono-oxygenases is reached from the NADPH dependence of pyrethroid metabolism by vertebrate liver microsomes and by preparations from the abdomens of houseflies (section 3.4).

The metabolism of pyrethrin appears to occur without initial hydrolysis, i.e. the ester linkage remains intact. Instead, to form the major oxidation product of pyrethrin I, the asterisked methyl group (figure 7.4) in the isobutenyl side-chain of the acid moiety is oxidised to a hydroxymethyl group in a NADPH-dependent reaction. The primary alcohol group formed in this way from pyrethrin I is readily converted to a carboxylic acid group. A major metabolite of pyrethrin II is identical to that formed from pyrethrin I. In this case, O-demethylation, another typical mono-oxygenase reaction, appears to occur (figure 7.4). Oxidative changes can also take place in the five-carbon side-chain of the alcohol moiety, and altogether some 10 oxidative metabolites of the pyrethrins have been recognised.

Natural pyrethroids have proved of great value for use indoors for public hygiene, medicine and animal health. Uses include the control of lice and fleas in the home and in public buildings, and the control of houseflies, mosquitoes

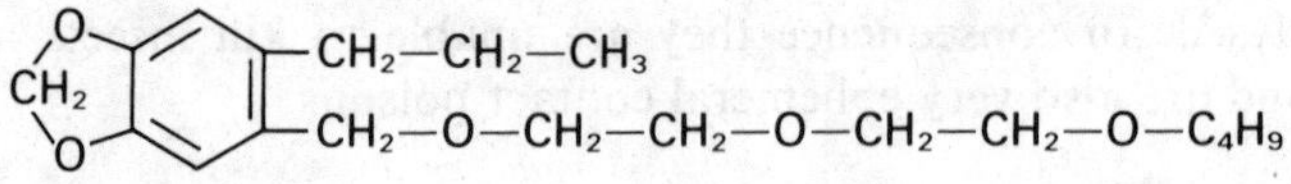

CH_2
$-CH_2-CH_2-CH_3$
$-CH_2-O-CH_2-CH_2-O-CH_2-CH_2-O-C_4H_9$

(a) Piperonyl butoxide

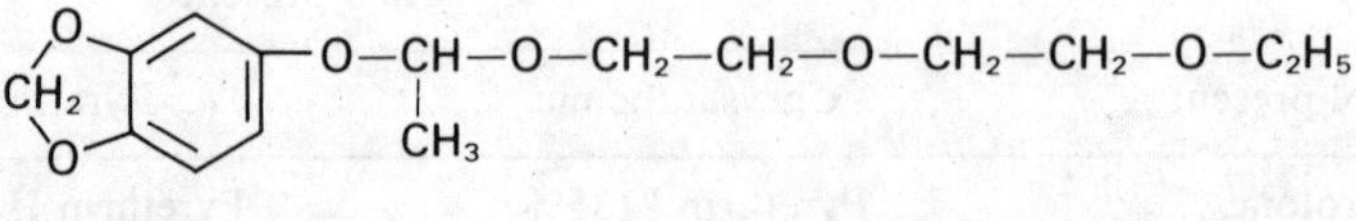

CH_2
$-O-CH-O-CH_2-CH_2-O-CH_2-CH_2-O-C_2H_5$
CH_3

(b) Sesamex

Figure 7.3 Structures of two methylene dioxyphenyl synergists

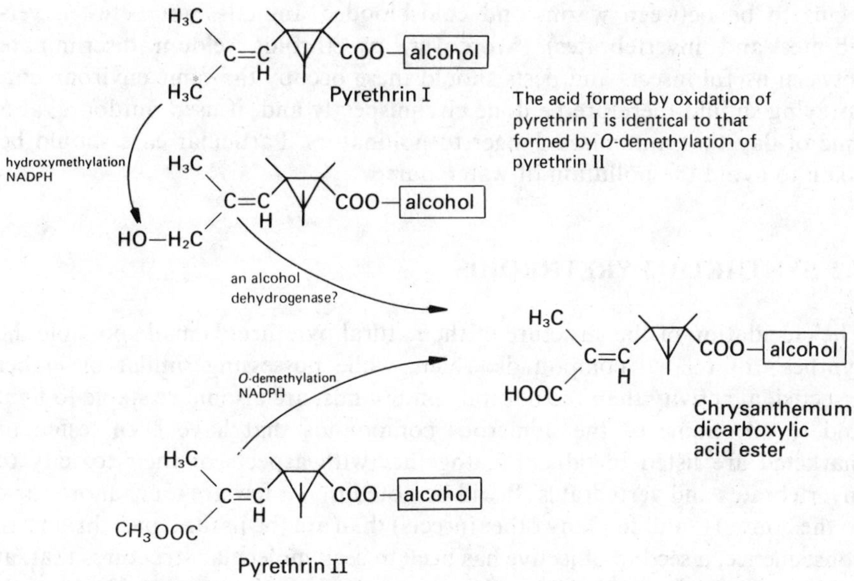

Figure 7.4 Probable oxidative metabolism of the acid moiety of pyrethrins I and II

and other insects that spread diseases of animals and humans. In the USA, some 20 per cent of all insecticides are sold for such purposes. Pyrethroids are ideal for many of these uses because they are of low toxicity to man and other warm-blooded animals. Moreover, they are readily destroyed by cooking or by digestive juices should traces get into food, onto the fingers of children or onto the feet of domestic animals. The principal factor limiting their use is, in fact, cost, for they are several times more expensive than equally effective (but perhaps more dangerous) substitutes, even after the contribution of synergists has been discounted.

Their use outdoors is, however, severely restricted. The reason for this is that they are rapidly decomposed by light (Ruzo, 1982). To overcome the problem of photodecomposition, a variety of additives have been tried over the decades, usually with limited success. Indeed, some of the anti-oxidants and ultra-violet screens that have been investigated have turned out to be themselves environmentally contaminating. A recent approach has been to attach an organic 'chromophore' to montmorillonite and to bind a light-sensitive pyrethroid to this (Margulies *et al.*, 1987). These workers in Israel found both methyl green and naphthylammonium cations to be effective chromophores and enabled the pyrethroid to control *Tribolium castaneum* for up to five days in sunlight.

Although safe to higher animals, it should be remembered that pyrethroids, both natural and synthetic, are toxic to fish (the natural toxicological division seems to be between warm- and cold-blooded animals, not between vertebrates and invertebrates). Moreover, pyrethroids seldom discriminate between useful insects and pests should these occupy the same environment. Spraying should therefore be done circumspectly and, if used outdoors, at a time of day that minimises danger to pollinators. Particular care should be taken to avoid the pollution of watercourses.

7.2 SYNTHETIC PYRETHROIDS

The elucidation of the structure of the natural pyrethroids made possible the synthesis of related compounds which, while possessing similar or higher insecticidal activity than the natural compounds, are also more stable to light and to air. Some of the numerous compounds that have been tested or marketed are listed in table 7.2, together with aspects of their toxicity to invertebrates and vertebrates. It will be noted that a few are much more toxic to the housefly (and to many other insects) than are the natural pyrethroids; in consequence, a second objective has been to seek molecular structures that, at field concentrations, could be cheaper to make, or more specific in their action, than are the natural compounds.

The first pyrethrin analogue (or pyrethroid) to be synthesised was **allethrin** (Schechter *et al.*, 1949) which comprised a synthetic alcohol attached to a racemic *cis–trans* mixture of chrysanthemic acid. The resulting mixture of isomers had a somewhat similar toxicity to the natural pyrethrins but possessed a much weaker knock-down effect. The performance of the allethrins improves when synergists are added, although not to the same extent as usually is observed for the natural substances.

Among the early workers were Barthel in the USA and Elliott and colleagues in Britain. The latter, working at Rothamsted Experimental Station, synthesised **bioresmethrin** (figure 7.5a) in 1966. This is about 100 times as toxic to houseflies as are the natural esters. The most significant aspect of this success is that the synthesis is based less upon an attempt to mimic the chemical structure of natural pyrethrin than upon a copying of its molecular geometry. This was elegantly illustrated by Elliott (1967) by the diagrammatic superposition of pyrethrin I and the synthetic substance (figure 7.6).

Up to this stage the work had concentrated on the synthesis of a variety of alcohols, each of which was then attached to the cyclopropanecarboxylic acid derivative that is present in the natural pyrethrins (figure 7.2). In 1972 the same workers observed that, if appropriate alcohols were attached to dichlorovinyl analogues of this acid, the ester that was formed is much more stable to light and to oxygen than are the natural pyrethroids. One such substance is **permethrin** (figure 7.5b), the discovery of which proved to be a turning point in pyrethroid chemistry. It has rather poor knock-down potential (section 7.1) but its high toxicity to some insects and its stability to

Table 7.2   Comparison of some properties of natural and synthetic pyrethroids

Compound	Knock-down propensity[a]	Relative toxicity to houseflies[b]	Toxicity to vertebrates[c]	Relative cost[a]
Pyrethrin	Good	2	Moderate	100
Bioallethrin	Good	6	Moderate	100
Allethrin	Fair	3	Moderate	60
Resmethrin	Poor	42	Low	155
Bioresmethrin	Fair	100	Very low	215
Tetramethrin	Good	2	Very low	65
Permethrin	Poor	60	Moderate	>100
Deltamethrin	Poor	1900	Very high	>100
Fenvalerate	Fair	38	High	>100

[a] Mostly from ITC (1976).
[b] After Elliott *et al.* (1978); these authors warn that their figures are for general comparison only.
[c] Pyrethrins are variously reported to have LD_{50} values of the order of 570–1100 mg/kg. This range of LD_{50} values is referred to as representing moderate toxicity. 'Low' implies that the LD_{50} is above this range and 'High' that it is below it.

light has led to its continued use in agriculture. It will be considered in more detail later.

Meanwhile, Japanese workers successfully prepared pyrethroid-like esters in which, for the first time, the three-membered carbon ring of cyclopropane-carboxylic acid is absent. **Fenvalerate** (figure 7.5d) has remained a highly successful pesticide. The presence of the α-cyano group in the 3-phenoxyben-zyl alcohol moiety is also noteworthy, for two other important light-stable pyrethroids, **cypermethrin** and **deltamethrin**, also contain this α-cyano group in their molecules.

It is of interest that the presence of the α-cyano group in the molecule of a pyrethroid appears to alter in a small but significant way some of the toxicological responses of both vertebrates and invertebrates to pyrethroids. Gammon *et al.* (1981) divided pyrethroids into two classes, namely:

(a) type I pyrethroids, which elicit a tremor syndrome accompanied with prostration—this group includes natural pyrethroids and those synthetics which do not possess an α-cyano group; and
(b) type II pyrethroids, which elicit a writhing syndrome in rodents, as well as copious salivation.

Some workers have speculated that these differences in response might indicate that type I and type II pyrethroids act at different sites in the nervous system. Others, however, remain unconvinced (e.g. Staatz and Hosko, 1985). Some illustrations, mostly drawn from recent work, will now be given of the stereochemistry, metabolism and use of a few important type I and type II pyrethroids.

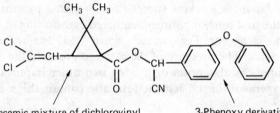

(a) Bioresmethrin

Separated (1R)-*trans*-isomer
of chrysanthemic acid

5-Benzyl derivative of
furyl-3-methanol

(b) Permethrin

Racemic mixture of dichlorovinyl
chrysanthemic acids

3-Phenoxy derivative
of benzyl alcohol

(c) Cypermethrin

Racemic mixture of dichlorovinyl
chrysanthemic acids

3-Phenoxy derivative
of substituted benzyl
alcohol

(d) Fenvalerate

An aryl-substituted
fatty acid

Alcohol moiety resembles
cypermethrin

Figure 7.5 Some synthetic pyrethroids. For details of absolute configuration see Elliott *et al.* (1974) and Leahey (1985). Examples are (c) cypermethrin, (*RS*)-α-cyano-3-phenoxybenzyl-(1*RS*)-*cis,trans*-(2,2-dichlorovinyl)-2,2-dimethylcyclopropane carboxylate and (d) fenvalerate, (*RS*)-α-cyano-3-phenoxybenzyl-(*RS*)-2-methyl-3-(4-chlorophenyl) butyrate

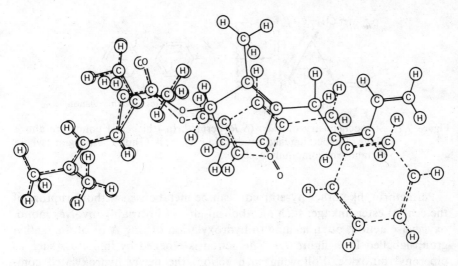

Figure 7.6   Superposition of pyrethrin I (full lines) and a synthetic pyrethroid (broken lines) of higher toxicity to flies than the natural material (from Elliott 1967)

(a) Permethrin

This substance is a non-systemic and moderately persistent insecticide that has proved to be very effective against a wide range of phytophagous insects, but especially against larvae of Lepidoptera and Coleoptera. It has also found uses in domestic hygiene and veterinary medicine (e.g. against *Stomoxys* and similar biting flies) and for the control of mosquitoes. It is usually marketed as an approximately 40:60 mixture of *cis:trans* isomers. It is nonvolatile, of low solubility in water (1 ppm) but soluble in acetone and ethanol.

Permethrin consists of a mixture of isomers, related *cis* and *trans* with respect to the spatial arrangement of the ester linkage and the dichlorovinyl linkage (the cyclopropane ring restricts rotation in the same way as does a double bond). This is most readily followed by observing the relative position of the corresponding two hydrogen atoms (figure 7.7). Both the *cis* and *trans* forms in turn comprise a mixture of stereoisomers. The isomeric mixture can give rise to a large number of metabolites but, for present purposes, a relatively simple metabolic pattern can nevertheless be recognised. First, most of the initial changes involve hydrolysis or oxidation. Secondly, *trans*-permethrin is usually metabolised more rapidly than is *cis*-permethrin. Thirdly, initial attack in most organisms is on readily specified parts of the molecule; and fourthly, many of the 50 or more isolated metabolites are conjugates formed by secondary metabolism.

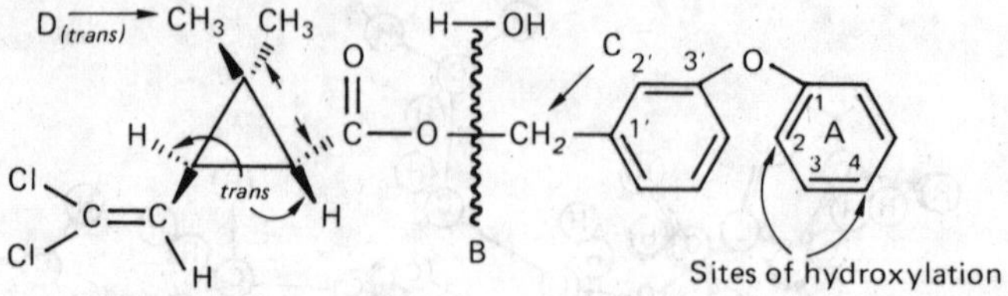

Figure 7.7   Stereochemistry of *trans*-(*S*,*R*)-permethrin (thickened bonds are above plane of paper; hatched bonds below it). A, B, C and D are regions where metabolism commonly occurs

Permethrin, like other pyrethroids, can be metabolised without rupture of the central ester linkage; such metabolism almost invariably involves mono-oxygenase action, often leading to hydroxylation of ring A or of the methyl group labelled D in figure 7.7. The action is blocked by inhibitors such as piperonyl butoxide. Following such action, the newly hydroxylated compound may be conjugated with various exogenous compounds or possibly hydrolysed by esterases. However, in higher animals, and probably also in most plants and most insects, the major route of degradation involves early cleavage of the ester linkage. This cleavage has caused much debate for, while it often occurs hydrolytically, especially when *trans* isomers are being metabolised, for *cis* isomers much, or even all, of the cleavage may be catalysed by oxidative enzymes. On the other hand, Dowd and Sparks (1987a,b,c), working with two species of insects, regarded the metabolic changes they were studying as being by hydrolysis, for both the *cis* and *trans* isomers of permethrin. Why, then, should doubt be possible in cases where the metabolic systems have been less rigorously studied?

The problem arises in part because it is not always easy to place oxidative and hydrolytic reactions in sequence and partly from observations arising from work using inhibitors presumed to be specific for particular reactions. It has been observed, for example, that addition of NADPH or other reagents that support the mono-oxygenase system can sometimes lead to increased cleavage of the ester linkage. From this, it can be argued that the cleavage is an oxidative event. However, if increased mono-oxygenase activity were, say, to hydroxylate a pyrethroid in such a way as to make it more vulnerable to attack by esterases also present in the *in vitro* system under study, then clearly NADPH could, vicariously, accelerate the action of an esterase. Again, ester cleavage is sometimes inhibited by piperonyl butoxide, which is usually taken to be a specific inhibitor of mono-oxygenases, and sometimes by certain organophosphorus compounds, which are known to block esterases. A further complication is that it has been shown, in metabolic systems made from housefly tissue, that an organophosphorus compound and piperonyl butoxide acting together have the same inhibitory effect as when they are used separately; from this it can be concluded that the organophosphorus compound also inhibits certain piperonyl butoxide-sensitive degradative steps, although it does not follow that this is the only possible explanation.

A few selected examples of metabolism in vertebrates, plants and insects follow; for more detailed treatment the accounts of Leahey (1985) or of Soderlund *et al.* (1983) are recommended. Where the original authors referred to cleavage as hydrolysis this will be indicated.

Soderlund and Casida (1977) demonstrated that mouse hepatic microsomes metabolised *trans*-permethrin four times as rapidly as *cis*-permethrin and concluded that the difference was largely due to the fact that the *trans* isomer was hydrolysed by esterase whereas the *cis* isomer was probably cleaved by an oxidase. In studies with plant preparations, Ohkawa *et al.* (1977) observed that the (uncleaved) molecule of permethrin was hydroxylated in positions 2 or 4 of the alcohol moiety (ring A, figure 7.7). However, the major route of degradation was by cleavage of the ester linkage at B to give 3'-phenoxybenzyl alcohol and a chlorovinyl derivative of cyclopropanecarboxylic acid. One of the methyl groups, D, of the latter could then oxidise to $-CH_2OH$ and then to a carboxyl group. Any of these substances may then undergo conjugation, usually with glucose.

For insects, an example of a difference in the rates of metabolism of *cis* and *trans* isomers of permethrin is provided by the work of Bigley and Plapp (1978) on cabbage looper larvae, where metabolism of the *trans* isomer occurred very much more rapidly than did that of the *cis* isomer. Nicholson and Sawicki (1982) made a similar observation in relation to the metabolism of permethrin by houseflies, although Holden (1979) found that the two isomers were metabolised at similar rates by larvae of the cotton leafworm.

More recently, the rates of hydrolysis of permethrin isomers and fenvalerate have been studied in the soybean looper and the tobacco budworm (Dowd and Sparks, 1987a). It was found that *trans*-permethrin was hydrolysed more rapidly by both insects than was fenvalerate, and that this was hydrolysed faster than was *cis*-permethrin. The same authors (Dowd and Sparks, 1987b), using the same insect species, have shown that the rate of hydrolysis for all three pyrethroids increased from the egg stage to the last larval instar and then decreased again. For example, the rate of hydrolysis of *trans*-permethrin in the third instar of *Pseudoplusia includens* (soybean looper) was 94 pmol/min per larva but rose to 594 pmol/min in the last instar; the corresponding figures for *cis*-permethrin were only 3.5 and 27 pmol/min.

It is of interest, in view of the comments made earlier about specificity of inhibitors, that Dowd and Sparks (1987c) found that the metabolism of permethrin by *Pseudoplusia includens* was inhibited by low concentrations of certain organophosphorus compounds. This could mean that, in the species being investigated, a hydrolytic step is normally rate-limiting in permethrin metabolism, inhibition occurring because organophosphorus compounds block certain esterases (section 3.3). The most effective organophosphorus compounds were found to be those that are relatively non-polar because they contain rather large alkyl substituents. An outstanding example was found to be *S,S,S*-tri-butyl phosphorotrithiolate. Similarly, Nicholson and Sawicki (1982) found that an organophosphorus compound, NIA 16388, reduced metabolism of permethrin more than did piperonyl butoxide in both resistant and sensitive strains of the housefly. NIA 16388 is prop-2-ynyl phenyl phosphonate.

$$\text{Ph}-\overset{\overset{\displaystyle O}{\|}}{\underset{\underset{\displaystyle C_3H_7O}{|}}{P}}-O-CH_2-C\equiv CH$$

Prop-2-ynyl phenyl phosphonate

This supports the view that metabolism of permethrin is primarily hydrolytic, but Miyamoto and Suzuki (1973) are among those who have suggested that NIA 16388 may inhibit oxidases as well as hydrolases. While studying the toxicity of tetramethrin to houseflies, they found that co-application of piperonyl butoxide with this pyrethroid did not stop the cleavage of the ester bond but that NIA 16388 was inhibitory. Gaughan *et al.* (1980) have described the interactive effects of organophosphorus pesticides on the metabolism, toxicity and persistence of pyrethroids. The picture is evidently confused, but the probability appears to be that the cleavage of the ester link in *trans* isomers is predominantly hydrolytic but that an oxidative step may sometimes precede and accelerate the action of esterase.

Permethrin, like most pyrethroids, becomes more toxic to insects as the temperature is lowered (contrast the work on nerve–muscle preparations discussed in section 7.3 and illustrated in figure 7.10). Consequently, field effectiveness may be greater on cooler days. It is also of interest that, when resistance exists, the level of tolerance may vary with temperature. Thus Brown (1987) observed that the difference in toxicity of permethrin to a resistant and to a susceptible strain of the tobacco budworm, *Heliothis virescens*, largely disappeared as the temperature was lowered.

(b) Cypermethrin

This substance is structurally similar to permethrin except that it possesses an α-cyano group (and hence a new chiral centre) at position C of figure 7.7. This insertion improves photostability and leads to a powerful and rapid debilitating effect on insects; it also greatly increases the number of possible metabolic products. It exists as a mixture of *cis* and *trans* isomers. It has been found that many birds possess a tolerance of it; this may be because it passes rapidly through the intestines or because they metabolise it rapidly. There is also some evidence that their nervous system is relatively insensitive to it.

It has a wide biological spectrum and has consequently been used on numerous crops against biting and sucking insects. Its use against insect-borne virus diseases has been advocated by several investigators. Atiri *et al.* (1987) found it to be efficacious in the control of the cowpea mosaic virus, an infection that can cause complete loss of the crop. The virus belongs to the troublesome 'non-persistent' group; these can be passed on by the vector (in this case *Aphis craccivora*) within a few minutes of starting to feed on the plant, and hence for any insecticide to be useful it must have a very rapid action. Cypermethrin may, in fact, take hours to kill the vector but its rapid debilitating effect, mentioned above, reduces the duration of the first probe and the insect desists from eating. Parallel conclusions were reached by Antignus *et al.* (1987) in respect to the maize rough dwarf virus (vector, the planthopper *Laodelphax striatellus*) and by Gibson and Rice (1986) who worked on the 'non-persistent' potato virus and the 'semi-persistent' beet yellows virus (vector, the aphid *Myzus persicae*).

De Jersey *et al.* (1985) separated from the cattle tick several enzymes that were capable of hydrolysing pyrethroids. Although some of these appeared to have general esterase activity, one, with an isoelectric point at pH 4.6, was able to hydrolyse *trans*-cypermethrin, a type II pyrethroid, but did not attack the closely related *trans*-permethrin, a type I pyrethroid.

Since cypermethrin is used on or near animals and their food, a knowledge of how it is taken up, metabolised and excreted is of importance. Croucher *et al.* (1985) used ^{14}C-labelled cypermethrin to study its secretion in lactating cows. After applying 0.2 to 10 ppm in food, less than 1 per cent was eliminated in milk, mostly in the form of unchanged cypermethrin. Equilibrium between uptake in diet and output in milk was reached within four days of the commencement of feeding; at 10 ppm in food the milk content was 0.1 ppm. References to similar studies in cows and other animals are quoted by Hutson and Stoydin (1987).

When ^{14}C-labelled cypermethrin was fed to domestic hens, most of the retained radioactivity was found in the liver, either in the form of cypermethrin or as highly polar metabolites. Radioactivity in eggs rose for about 8 days and was largely confined to the yolk (Hutson and Stoydin, 1987).

The degradation of cypermethrin appears in most species to be initiated by cleavage at bond B (figure 7.7) or by hydroxylation in positions 2 or 4 of ring A. Often, on cleavage, the alcohol loses at some stage the elements of HCN, to give 3-phenoxybenzaldehyde and then 3-phenoxybenzoic acid.

Ishaaya *et al.* (1987) concluded that the tolerance to cypermethrin shown by some strains of whitefly (*Bemisia tabaci*) could probably be attributed to the presence in the resistant strain of large amounts of an esterase that is able to destroy the pyrethroid. Using monocrotophos, an organophosphorus compound that inhibits many esterases, they observed a synergistic ratio of 38 or more when monocrotophos was applied with cypermethrin under greenhouse conditions (i.e. the isotoxic dose of cypermethrin was at least 38 times as great in the absence of monocrotophos from the spray mixture than it was in its presence). It will be recalled that a similar synergistic effect is obtained using mixtures of permethrin and tri-*n*-butyl phosphorotrithiolate.

(c) Fenvalerate

This substance is another pyrethroid with an α-cyano group in the molecule (figure 7.8). As was mentioned earlier, it was discovered by the Japanese and was the first pyrethroid not to contain a cyclopropane ring in the acid part of the molecule.

It is a broad-spectrum insecticide and is of particular use against insects that do not respond readily to cheaper insecticides; examples are the boll weevil, tobacco budworm, leafrollers and the pink bollworm. It is also of value against species that have developed tolerance of organophosphorus compounds. However, a broad spectrum of action also has its disadvantages; Hull (1985) found that it gave good control of the tufted budworm in apple orchards but that it also killed a predator of red spider mites, requiring more money to be expended to control the latter than was needed in unsprayed areas. In veterinary work it has been used in the form of ear tags to protect cattle from horn fly and face fly attack (Akhtar, 1983).

By adding doubly labelled fenvalerate to chicken liver enzyme preparations, Akhtar (1983) demonstrated that, in these preparations, the main metabolic route commenced by cleavage of the ester linkage, B (figure 7.8). Identified products included chlorophenoxy-3-methylbutyric acid (formed from the acid moiety) and 3-phenoxybenzaldehyde. The latter is formed by decomposition, with loss of carbon and nitrogen from an unstable cyanhydrin, the latter being derived from the alcohol part of the molecule. The metabolism of fenvalerate

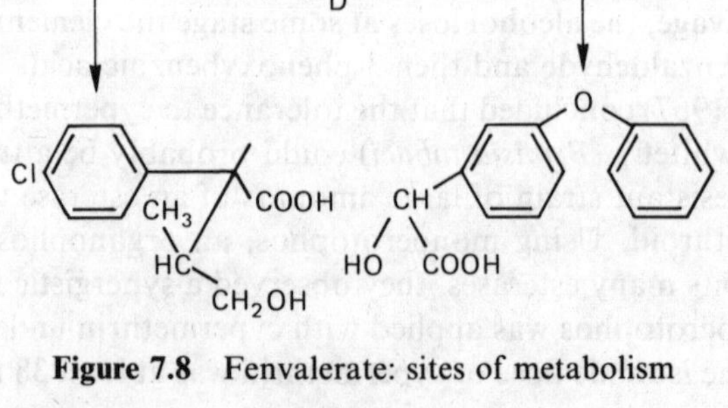

Figure 7.8   Fenvalerate: sites of metabolism

was studied in plants by Mikami *et al.* (1985). Again, it was found that the principal metabolic route involved the cleavage of the bond B, with or without hydroxylation of the ring A. After such cleavage (whether by hydrolysis or otherwise), the cyano group on carbon atom C is probably hydrolysed to carboxyl and, after loss of carbon dioxide, eventually forms 3-phenoxybenzoic acid (which often then conjugates with glucose).

The work of Soderlund *et al.* (1987) is representative of investigations into metabolism in insects. Using a resistant strain of the Colorado potato beetle, *Leptinotarsa decemlineata*, it was concluded that the first step in the process was oxidative. The evidence was that the LD_{50} of the resistant strain is some 39-fold greater than that of sensitive controls, yet half this difference is annulled by co-application of piperonyl butoxide. This oxidative capability may be relevant to the mechanism whereby resistance develops but does not necessarily give guidance as to the balance of metabolic routes in sensitive organisms. Using labelled fenvalerate, Soderlund *et al.* (1987) isolated 10 metabolites from the resistant beetles; as expected, cleavage occurs at B (figure 7.8), hydroxymethylation occurs at D and (after hydrolysis) loss of carbon occurs at C. Less typically, the diphenyl ether linkage at E is ruptured and little hydroxylation can be detected in position 4' of ring A of fenvalerate or of its decomposition products. Silcox *et al.* (1985) observed a synergistic ratio of 2–4 for the Colorado potato beetle, *L. decemlineata*, when treated with fenvalerate in the presence and absence of piperonyl butoxide.

As was mentioned earlier, the rate of metabolism of fenvalerate and of permethrin by insects increases from egg to fourth instar and then decreases in pupae and adults (Dowd and Sparks, 1987b). For fenvalerate, an increase from 2.3 to 33 pmol/min per larva of the soybean looper, *Pseudoplusia includens*, was observed.

(d) Deltamethrin

Originally called decamethrin, this substance resembles cypermethrin in that it possesses a cyclopropane ring and an α-cyano group in its molecule, but differs in that it has two bromine atoms in the vinyl side-chain. It is also the most insecticidal of eight chiral isomers. It is almost insoluble in water but is moderately soluble (> 1000 ppm) in many common organic solvents. It is of medium or low toxicity to most mammals and birds yet kills insects at very low dosage both by contact action and by ingestion. It has a rapid disabling effect on feeding insects (compare cypermethrin) and for this reason there is hope that it may be useful to control the vectors of 'non-persistent' viruses (section 7.2(b)). Although a broad-spectrum insecticide, it nevertheless appears to possess some specificity of action, and some attempts have been made to exploit its use to achieve integrated control. For example, Mani and Krishna-moorthy (1984) found that it had little harmful effect on *Apanteles plutellae*, a parasite of the diamond back moth in India.

The initial step in metabolism in most organisms appears to be by hydrolysis, leading to the formation of dibromovinyldimethylcyclopropane-carboxylic acid and phenoxybenzyl cyanhydrin. The cyanhydrin is unstable and breaks down as described for fenvalerate. All of these compounds, together with varying amounts of hydroxylated derivatives formed by the mono-oxygenase system, can then undergo conjugation in ways that vary with the species (section 3.6). Deltamethrin is a *cis* isomer and an extra feature of its metabolism is that it undergoes slow conversion after spraying to the less toxic *trans* isomer.

(e) Tefluthrin

This substance was discovered at Jealott's Hill, Bracknell, UK, a research station of ICI. It is the first pyrethroid designed specifically as a soil insecticide and is a broad-spectrum compound, active against many members of the Coleoptera, Lepidoptera and Diptera (ICI, 1986). A feature of the molecule is the presence of seven covalently bound fluorine atoms (figure 7.9). These, no doubt, partly explain its volatility and moderate stability in soil, properties that ensure that it can provide good residual control of soil pests.

It can be applied as a band of granules on the soil surface above the seeds or applied in the seed furrows. The former is best for the control of insects that attack the plant from the soil surface whereas the latter (or a modification, T-band application) is usually better for soil organisms that live deeper in the soil and often attack roots or young stems (e.g. symphilids, cutworms and wireworms). Tefluthrin is normally applied at between 25 and 125 g AI per hectare, an application rate that is often only a fifth or a tenth of that of other substances used for similar purposes. Toxicological studies have indicated that it has a low oral and dermal toxicity to mammals and birds and that it has little effect on earthworms. Its half-life in soil varies from a few weeks to several months.

Heath and Leahey (1989) carried out metabolic studies on tefluthrin to determine its fate in lactating goats. Radioactive tefluthrin was fed to goats on four occasions and the appearance of radioactivity in milk, urine and faeces was observed. It was found that 70 per cent of the radioactivity was excreted within 16 h in urine or faeces and was mainly in the form of metabolites; these

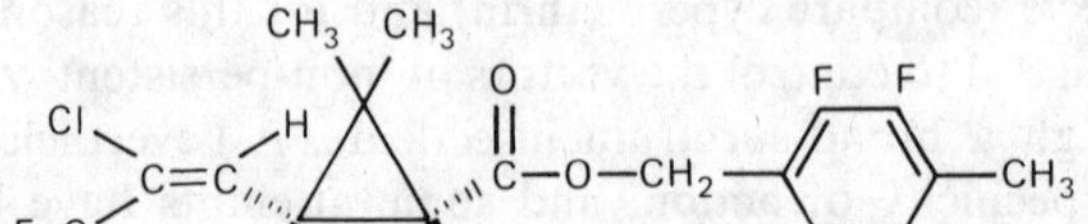

Figure 7.9   Tefluthrin: a soil-acting pyrethroid

metabolites appeared to have been formed both by ester cleavage and by several kinds of oxidation. In contrast, relatively little radioactivity was detected in the milk and that which was detected was mostly in the form of unmetabolised tefluthrin.

7.3 MODE OF ACTION AND SIDE-EFFECTS

The rapid knock-down effect on flying insects possessed by all natural and some synthetic pyrethroids strongly suggests that these insecticides have a neurotoxic action. In many respects, the behavioural and physiological manifestations of poisoning superficially resemble those caused by DDT (section 6.5). In particular, an initial period of sensory hyperexcitability leads successively to loss of co-ordination, ataxia, prostration, convulsions and death. Nevertheless, considerable quantitative differences have been noted, not only between the effects of DDT and the pyrethroids, but even also between the toxic manifestations of type I and of type II pyrethroids. It is also of interest that the toxic action of natural pyrethroids can, for a while, be reversed by washing excised preparations free from pyrethroid, a possibility which implies that the toxic action does not initially involve a strong chemical attachment of the poison to a neural receptor.

Physiological investigations into the mechanism of this toxic action have been of several kinds; in the account which follows, examples will be given, first, of work carried out on neuromotor preparations and then of that done using isolated axons or synaptic junctions (it is not always possible to distinguish between the two).

The work of Adams and Miller (1979) illustrates well the effect of pyrethroids on nerve–muscle preparations. Using **tetramethrin** as toxicant to flight motor units of the housefly, they confirmed earlier work which showed that trains of impulses occurred in poisoned preparations and concluded that motor unit discharges originate in peripheral motor nerve endings. Typical traces before and 10 min after poisoning are shown in figure 7.10a. Upon lowering the temperature of the nerve–muscle preparation, the muscle potentials evoked by giving shocks to poisoned nerve endings are as shown in figure 7.10b. It will be seen that the duration of the discharge increases with decreasing temperature but the number of spikes in a discharge remains almost unaltered. Below about 19°C, similarly poisoned preparations show only a single firing upon receiving a single stimulus. Moreover, if the frequency of stimulation is increased from about 0.5 Hz to about 2 Hz, multiple discharges are replaced by single spikes at temperatures above 20°C.

Experiments on isolated axons using the voltage clamp technique demonstrate that not all pyrethroids lead to the propagation of trains of impulses by poisoned nerves. In particular, type II pyrethroids such as deltamethrin cause a gradual depolarisation of the membrane and reduction in amplitude of the

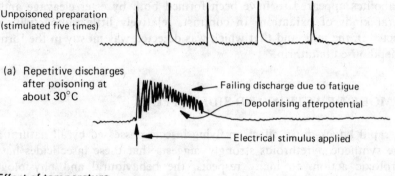

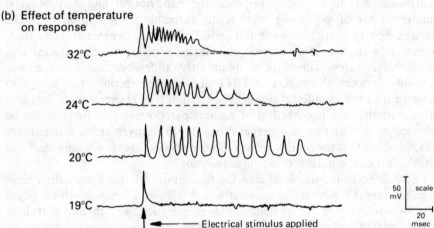

Figure 7.10   Effect of a pyrethroid on flight motor activity of houseflies (idealised diagrams based on the work of Adams and Miller, 1979). (a) The top recording shows flight motor activity before poisoning, the lower one is the response 10 min after applying the LD_{50} dose of tetramethrin. Stimulus applied by shocking. (b) Four recordings showing the muscle potentials evoked in a tetramethrin-poisoned fly at different temperatures. Above about 20°C, the number of repetitive discharges in a train is roughly constant, but the frequency increases and duration decreases with increasing temperature. Below about 19.5°C a poisoned nerve–muscle system gives only a single muscular discharge on shocking.

action potential. Figure 7.11 is based on the work of Laufer *et al.* (1985) using the giant axon of the cockroach. After deltamethrin treatment, each stimulation resulted in a summation of the depolarising after-potentials because the decay of the tailing sodium current occurs very slowly (whereas, for type I pyrethroids it usually decays in less than 400 ms). Such a summation progressively depolarises the axon, leading to an irreversible block and absence of action potential.

Experiments of the type just described provide a reasonably clear picture of the effect of different pyrethroids on various types of nerve preparations from various organisms. Essentially, natural and type I pyrethroids cause multiple responses to a stimulus, whereas α-cyano pyrethroids tend to *block* conduction. Such differences may reflect real differences in the mode of action, perhaps at different sites of attack, or, as argued by Laufer *et al.* (1985), they may only signal reaction with different states of the sodium channel (equation 6.2). There seems little doubt that both types of pyrethroid interfere with the *trans*-membrane movement of sodium ions, although the production of the characteristic depolarising after-potential is unlikely to involve the 'wedging open' of more than a very small percentage of the total number of sodium ion channels at any one time. The nature of voltage-dependent sodium ion channels and the effect on them of DDT and pyrethroids has been mentioned elsewhere (sections 6.4 and 6.5). Precisely where the most sensitive of such channels are located is, however, uncertain, for it may be such channels in the vicinity of synapses which are especially vulnerable.

The more work that has been done, the more possibilities have emerged as to the primary mode of action of pyrethroids. In particular, even if sodium channels are the primary site of action, it does not follow that those that are most readily affected are the ones present along the whole length of the axon. It appears possible that the primary effect of pyrethroids, at least at low concentrations, is in the vicinity of the pre-synaptic membrane (it is generally agreed that pyrethroids do not have a direct effect on post-synaptic membranes either in insects or in mammals).

Increasingly, then, emphasis has been placed upon the possible effect of pyrethroids upon ion channels in the neighbourhood of the pre-synaptic membrane. Such effects may be, but not necessarily are, upon sodium

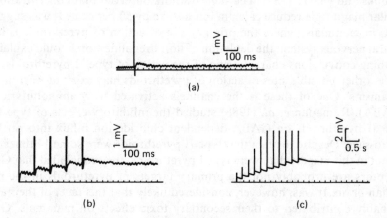

(a)

(b)　　　　　　　　　　(c)

Figure 7.11　Effect of deltamethrin on the resting potential of the cockroach giant axon: (a) 5 min after applying 2 μM deltamethrin; (b), (c) bursts of stimulation lead to summation of depolarising afterpotentials, which only decay slowly (after Laufer *et al.*, 1985)

channels of the types described above. Other possibilities include calcium ion channels and chloride ion channels.

Interneuronal communication is by synaptic contact (figure 4.2). Such contact may involve the interdigitation of numerous nerve cells. In consequence, activity, both normal and abnormal, at such junctions can amplify the transmission of signals. Thus, when an impulse reaches a synapse, it evokes an inward flux of calcium ions and it is this which triggers the release of neurotransmitter from the end-foot vesicles. If this argument is correct, the **calcium ion uptake system** (one version of which is shown in figure 6.3) is an obvious potential target for some neurotoxicants and is, indeed, known to be sensitive to DDT and to pyrethroids (Doherty *et al.*, 1986). Salgado *et al.* (1983) observed that nanomolar concentrations of deltamethrin and fenvalerate blocked neuromuscular transmission in housefly larvae and that this effect could be reversed by removal of calcium ions from the saline. Also using these larvae, Schouest *et al.* (1986) found that synaptic transmission was blocked within an hour by micromolar amounts of tetramethrin; moreover, microscopic examination revealed a lack of end-foot vesicles, suggesting that pyrethroid-enforced depletion of these vesicles could have caused synaptic failure and hence led to a block in conduction.

Work using preparations from higher animals has supported the observations made on insects. For example, sensory nerve fibres are much more sensitive to pyrethroids than are motor fibres, although, as in insects (figure 7.10), motor axons very near to motor synaptic membranes can respond to pyrethroids by the induction of repetitive discharges (Ruigt, 1985). Moreover, nanomolar concentrations of pyrethroids with an α-cyano group enhance calcium-dependent release of noradrenaline by rat brain synaptosomes (Brooks and Clark, 1987). The same authors observed that concentrations of similar magnitude reduce calcium ion uptake by 50 per cent. It was suggested that, in mammals, where the primary site of action of pyrethroids is in the central nervous system, the depletion of noradrenaline stores could explain the writhing convulsions characteristic of the action of type II pyrethroids.

Yet other possible sites of action of pyrethroids may exist, at least in some organisms. One of these is the channels activated by γ-aminobutyric acid (GABA). Ramadan *et al.* (1988) studied the inhibitory effects of type I and type II pyrethroids on GABA-dependent chloride ion influx into rat brain micro-sacs. Despite the fact that type II pyrethroids were some 14 times more potent in this respect than were type I pyrethroids, they concluded that GABA receptors are probably not the primary targets of pyrethroids in the mammalian brain. It was, however, considered likely that this facet of their action probably contributed to their secondary toxic effects on mammals. GABA receptors are present in post-synaptic membranes and are allosterically linked to chloride ion channels, such that activation with GABA increases permeability to chloride ions.

It will be evident from the foregoing discussion that while the action of

Table 7.3 Some recent publications reporting work on negative temperature coefficients (from these, references to earlier work are readily obtained)

Substance	Genus	Reference
Fenvalerate	*Heliothis*	Brown (1987)
Permethrin, fenvalerate	*Tricoplusia*	Sparks (1982)
Deltamethrin, permethrin, fenvalerate	*Heliothis*	Sparks (1983)
Cyfluthrin	Stored product insects	Subramanyam (1987)
Permethrin	Colorado beetle	Grafius (1986)
Cypermethrin	*Sitophilus*	Thaung (1986)
Permethrin	Housefly	Scott (1984)
Cypermethrin, DDT		Chang (1983)
HCH[a]	*Chironomus*	Fisher (1985)

[a] Atypical for this substance.

pyrethroids is understood at the physiological level, there is still considerable doubt about the precise molecular basis underlying these physiological effects. Pyrethroids possess potent neurotoxic activity on several types of ion channels, including chloride ion channels that are activated by GABA, voltage sensitive sodium channels and calcium channels. In addition, they appear to affect membrane pumps that involve Ca^{2+}-dependent ATPase and Ca^{2+}/Mg^{2+}-dependent ATPase. In different biological contexts, it is possible that different receptors, channels or enzymes may be targeted and a similar complexity has been demonstrated for DDT (section 6.5) and γ-HCH (section 6.6). As Seabrook *et al.* (1988) have pointed out, in each context it is the site that responds at the lowest concentration that is the most likely primary target.

Finally, there is a need to recommend caution in relation to the attribution of the lethal paralysis that leads to the death of insects to the intense convulsions that are induced by pyrethroids. The reason is that almost all of the physiological events just described have a positive temperature coefficient (compare figure 7.10) whereas numerous experiments have demonstrated that insecticidal effectiveness of both DDT and pyrethroids usually increases as the temperature falls (table 7.3). For this reason some authors have attempted to correlate the ability of some pyrethroids to produce repetitive discharges with their knock-down effect, whereas the ability to increase rates of neurotransmitter release is negatively related to temperature and may therefore be a more direct cause of lethal convulsions.

REFERENCES

Adams, M. E. and Miller, T. A. (1979). *Pestic. Biochem. Physiol.*, **11**, 218
Akhtar, M. H. (1983). *J. Agric. Fd Chem.*, **31**, 1080

Antignus, Y., Klein, M. and Ovadia, S. (1987). *Ann. Appl. Biol.*, **110**, 557
Atiri, G. I., Thottappilly, G. and Ligan, D. (1987). *Ann. Appl. Biol.*, **110**, 455
Bigley, W. S. and Plapp, F. W., Jr (1978). *J. Agric. Fd Chem.*, **26**, 1128
Brooks, M. W. and Clark, J. M. (1987). *Pestic. Biochem. Physiol.*, **28**, 127
Brown, M. A. (1987). *J. Econ. Entomol.*, **80**, 330
Chadwick, P. R. (1963). *Pyrethrum Post*, **7**, 25
Chang, C. P. (1983). *Pestic. Biochem. Physiol.*, **20**, 76, 86
Croucher, A., Hutson, D. H. and Stoydin, G. (1985). *Pestic. Sci.*, **16**, 287
De Jersey, J., Nolan, J., Davey, P. A. and Riddles, P. W. (1985). *Pestic. Biochem. Physiol.*, **23**, 349
Doherty, J. D., Nishimura, K., Kurihara, N. and Fujita, T. (1986). *Pestic. Biochem. Physiol.*, **25**, 295
Dowd, P. F. and Sparks, T. C. (1987a). *Pestic. Biochem. Physiol.*, **27**, 123
Dowd, P. F. and Sparks, T. C. (1987b). *Pestic. Biochem Physiol.*, **27**, 309
Dowd, P. F. and Sparks, T. C. (1987c). *Pestic. Biochem. Physiol.*, **27**, 237
Elliott, M. (1967). *Sci. J.*, **3**(3), 61
Elliott, M., Elliot, R. L., Janes, N. F., Khambay, B. P. S. and Pulman, D. A. (1986). *Pestic. Sci.*, **37**, 691
Elliott, M., Janes, N. F. and Potter, C. (1978). *Annu. Rev. Entomol.*, **23**, 443
Elliot, M., Janes, N. F. and Pulman, D. A. (1974). *J. Chem. Soc., Perkin Trans. I*, 2470
Fisher, S. W. (1985). *J. Econ. Entomol.*, **78**, 1222
Gammon, D. W., Brown, M. A. and Casida, J. E. (1981). *Pestic. Biochem. Physiol.*, **15**, 181
Gaughan, L. C., Engel, J. L. and Casida, J. E. (1980). *Pestic. Biochem. Physiol.*, **14**, 81
Gibson, R. W. and Rice, D. (1986). *Ann. Appl. Biol.*, **109**, 465
Grafius, E. (1986). *J. Econ. Entomol.*, **79**, 588
Heath, J. and Leahey, J. P. (1989). *Pestic. Sci.*, **25**, 375
Holden, J. S. (1979). *Pestic. Sci.*, **10**, 295
Hull, L. A. (1985). *J. Econ. Entomol.*, **78**, 163
Hutson, D. H. and Stoydin, G. (1987). *Pestic. Sci.*, **18**, 157
ICI (1986). *Technical Bulletin: Pyrethroid Soil Insecticide*. Jealott's Hill Research Station, Bracknell, UK
Ishaaya, I., Mendelson, Z., Ascher, K. R. S. and Casida, J. E. (1987). *Pestic. Biochem. Physiol.*, **28**, 155
ITC (1976). *Pyrethrum: A Natural Insecticide with Growth Potential*. International Trade Centre, UNCTAD/GATT, United Nations, Geneva
Laufer, J., Pelhate, M. and Sattelle, D. B. (1985). *Pestic. Sci.*, **16**, 651
Leahey, J. P. (ed.) (1985). *The Pyrethroid Insecticides*. Taylor and Francis, London
Mani, M. and Krishnamoorthy, A. (1984). *Trop. Pest. Managem.*, **30**, 130
Margulies, L., Cohen, E. and Rozen, H. (1987). *Pestic. Sci.*, **18**, 79
Mikami, N., Wakabayashi, N., Yamada, H. and Miyamoto, J. (1985). *Pestic. Sci.*, **16**, 46
Miyamoto, J. and Suzuki, T. (1973). *Pestic. Biochem. Physiol.*, **3**, 30
Nicholson, R. A. and Sawicki, R. M. (1982). *Pestic. Sci.*, **13**, 357
Ohkawa, H., Kaneko, H. and Miyamoto, J. (1977). *J. Pestic. Sci.*, **2**, 67
Ramadan, A. A., Bakru, N. M., Marei, A. S. M., Eldefrawi, A. T. and Eldefrawi, M. E. (1988). *Pestic. Biochem. Physiol.*, **32**, 97
Ruigt, G. S. F. (1985). In *Comprehensive Insect Physiology, Biochemistry and Pharmacology*, vol. 12, *Insect Control*, eds G. A. Kerkut and L. I. Gilbert, p. 183. Pergamon, Oxford
Ruzo, L. O. (1982). In *Progress in Pesticide Biochemistry*, vol. 2, eds D. H. Hutson and T. R. Roberts, pp. 1–33. Wiley, New York
Salgado, V. L., Irving, S. N. and Miller, T. A. (1983). *Pestic. Biochem. Physiol.*, **20**, 100

Schechter, M. S., Green, N. and La Forge, F. B. (1949). *J. Am. Chem. Soc.*, **71**, 3165
Schouest, L. P., Jr, Salgado, V. L. and Miller, T. A. (1986). *Pestic. Biochem. Physiol.*, **25**, 381
Scott, J. G. and Georghiou, G. P. (1984). *Pestic. Biochem. Physiol.*, **21**, 53
Seabrook, G. R., Duce, I. R. and Irving, S. N. (1988). *Pestic. Biochem. Physiol.*, **32**, 232
Silcox, C. A., Ghidiu, G. M. and Forgash, A. J. (1985). *J. Econ. Entomol.*, **78**, 1399
Soderlund, D. M. and Casida, J. E. (1977). *Pestic. Biochem. Physiol.*, **7**, 391
Soderlund, D. M., Hessey, C. W. and Jiang, M. (1987). *J. Agric. Fd Chem.*, **35**, 100
Soderlund, D. M., Sanborn, J. R. and Lee, P. W. (1983). In *Progress in Pesticide Biochemistry and Toxicology*, vol. 3, eds D. H. Hutson and T. R. Roberts, p. 401. Wiley, Chichester
Sparks, T. C. (1982). *J. Econ. Entomol.*, **75**, 643
Sparks, T. C. (1983). *J. Econ. Entomol.*, **76**, 243
Staatz, C. G. and Hosko, M. J. (1985). *Pestic. Biochem. Physiol.*, **24**, 231
Subramanyam, B. H. (1987). *J. Econ. Entomol.*, **80**, 9
Thaung, M. and Collins, P. J. (1986). *J. Econ. Entomol.*, **79**, 909

8 Other insecticides and similar compounds

Acylureas (benzoylphenylureas)

8.1 SPECIAL FEATURES AND FIELD USES

Members of this group have some unusual characteristics, which offer hope that they might be suitable for incorporation into integrated pest management schemes. This hope is based on the fact that one of their toxic effects is to disrupt the synthesis of chitin, a polysaccharide of particular importance to arthropods. Since it is the synthesis that is disrupted, the major effect of members of this group is upon those periods of the life cycle where chitin is being formed and where its incorrect or insufficient production can lead to malformation of later stages of the life cycle. Because of this apparently very specific effect on an event of vital importance to insects but one that has no counterpart in higher animals, it would be expected that they could possess a high margin of safety for vertebrates (so long, of course, as no quite different adverse effects occur). In fact, most are of low acute toxicity to mammals. In addition, however, it has been widely accepted that they are primarily stomach poisons, their main route of entry being by ingestion with food. Whether they do, or do not, enter readily through insect cuticle is a matter of crucial importance; if an acylurea is to be useful in integrated pest management, beneficial insects must survive contact action, and this is made more likely in the absence of rapid cuticular uptake.

In practice, the situation is probably more complex, because it has been shown that diflubenzuron, the best-known member of the group, readily gains access to cotton leafworm, *Spodoptera littoralis*, through the cuticle. Granett *et al.* (1983) similarly showed that *Spodoptera exigua*, the beet armyworm, was also vulnerable to cuticular uptake. Moreover, these authors studied the toxicity of several members of the group closely related to *S. exigua* and demonstrated that different analogues varied some 40-fold in topical toxicity. Presumably the same variation of response could occur among beneficial insects, although Granett *et al.* (1983) remarked that the genus *Spodoptera* might be in some way unique in its cuticular properties.

Diflubenzuron (figure 8.1a) was introduced in 1973 and initially registered in

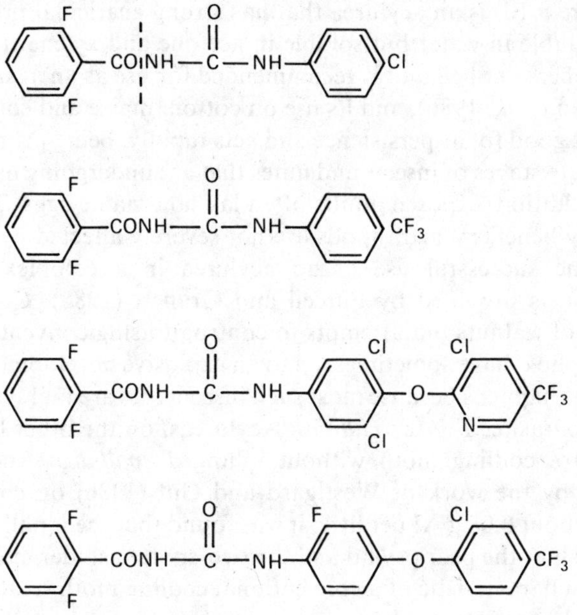

Figure 8.1 Structures of diflubenzuron and related compounds

the USA for the control of the cotton boll weevil, *Anthonomus grandis*. The acylureas are particularly useful for the control of Lepidoptera, Coleoptera and Diptera. For example, **chlorfluazuron** (figure 8.1c) effectively controls lepidopteran pests of cotton (e.g. *Heliothis* spp. and *S. littoralis*). Since the mode of action of the acylureas is very different from the neurotoxic actions characteristic of most other groups of insecticides, they have attracted attention as a possible means of dealing with the problem of resistance caused by neurotoxic poisons.

Diflubenzuron has also been used against the codling moth, the gypsy moth, the soybean looper and the rice water weevil, the latter being a major pest of rice in the USA and Japan. Smith *et al.* (1985) reported that diflubenzuron, employed at about 0.28 kg/ha just after ovipositing, significantly reduced the number of immature organisms present but did not deter egg-laying. Haynes (1987) successfully applied diflubenzuron analogues to boll weevils by both dipping and feeding. It has also been employed successfully against a number of pests in stored products*, and especially against pests in stored grain (where its apparent safety to higher animals is clearly of importance). At 1–10 ppm it effectively controls *Rhyzopertha dominica* and *Sitophilus oryzae* for a period in excess of a year (Mian and Mulla, 1983).

* Refer to footnote in section 4.8(b); diflubenzuron is not currently registered for such purposes in several countries.

Flufenoxuron (figure 8.1d) is an acylurea that has strong acaricidal properties. It is almost insoluble in water but soluble in acetone and xylene. It was
discovered by researchers at Shell and is recommended for use as an acaricide
on top fruit (Anderson *et al.*, 1986), and its use on cotton, maize and coffee is
being explored. It has good foliar persistence and acts rapidly, being primarily
active against immature stages of insects and mites that are undergoing moults
between instars. In addition, exposed adults often lay non-viable eggs. There
are reports that many beneficial arthropods are not severely affected by it.

An example of the successful use of an acylurea in a complex pest
management situation is provided by Purcell and Granett (1985). Codling
moth is a major pest of walnuts but attempts to control it using conventional
insecticides (e.g. azinphos) have sometimes led to an explosive development of
the walnut aphid. This happens because most such insecticides are highly toxic
to the walnut aphid parasite, *Trioxys pallidus*. Acylureas, on the other hand,
were found to control codling moth without killing *T. pallidus*. Another
example is provided by the work of Westigard and Gut (1986) on codling
moth in Oregon. At about 0.08 g AI per litre, it was found that the numbers of
non-target species such as the pear psyllid and the two-spotted spider mite did
not increase in a way characteristic of a conventional codling moth treatment
with an organophosphorus insecticide.

An illustration of the possible value of benzoylphenylureas in relation to the
control of resistant strains of insects is provided by the work of Perng and Sun
(1987). In Taiwan very considerable resistance of the diamond back moth to
conventional insecticides has developed; resistance factors (or ratios)

$$RF = \frac{LC_{50} \text{ for a strain being studied}}{LC_{50} \text{ for the susceptible control}}$$

of between 100 and 10 000 are usual. After collecting field specimens of
Plutella xylostella they fed third instar larvae with chlorfluazuron (figure 8.1c)
and teflubenzuron. Resistance factors did not exceed 3.5, providing evidence
that cross-resistance between the acylureas and conventional insecticides
(DDT, organophosphorus compounds and pyrethroids) was on this occasion
very low.

8.2 MODE OF ACTION OF ACYLUREAS

Most of the varied insecticidal effects of compounds such as diflubenzuron
appear to be manifestations of an interference with the way chitin is formed
and deposited in the cuticle. Life cycles of insects are complex, involving the
laying of eggs, hatching of larvae, moulting (ecdysis) of successive larval
stages as enlargement occurs, pupation of the last instar, followed by
emergence of the adult form or imago. These events are largely requirements

arising from the presence of an exoskeleton, which is cast off and re-formed at each ecdysis. The synthesis and deposition of chitin, an important component of cuticle, is controlled by the secretion of several substances that regulate growth.

Chitin is important because it provides the cuticle with strength and a certain degree of flexibility. Furthermore, with wax and sclerotised protein, it protects insects against the entry of harmful substances and the exit of useful ones (notably water). Not surprisingly, the formation and decomposition of chitin are therefore carefully controlled at each stage of the life cycle and, if this finely tuned control mechanism is disturbed, developmental abnormalities can occur. Several groups of toxic substances are known that act as (abnormal) insect growth regulators and, of these, the acylureas are an important example. Therefore, before describing the effects of diflubenzuron, some aspects of the structure and synthesis of chitin will be outlined. For greater detail, reference should be made to reviews by Kramer *et al.* (1985) and by Cohen (1987).

The structure of the insect cuticle is considered in section 2.3. Chitin is a polysaccharide-like substance comprising units of *N*-acetylglucosamine joined together in the 1,4 positions by β-linkages (figure 8.2a). Such polysaccharides are built up by the addition of an appropriate monomeric (monosaccharide-like) unit to a pre-existing primer molecule. Before it can be attached to the primer, the monomeric unit is activated by forming part of a nucleoside diphosphate–monomer complex. The latter is formed at the expense of the energy of the corresponding nucleoside triphosphate (the base in such triphosphates acting as a 'code' determining which polysaccharide is formed from a particular monomer). In the case of chitin, uridine triphosphate (UTP) reacts with the 1-phosphate of *N*-acetylglucosamine to give the UDP–acetylglucosamine complex (figure 8.2b). The final step of chitin synthesis, catalysed by chitin synthetase, thus involves the transfer of an *N*-acetylglucosamine unit from this complex to a pre-existing poly(*N*-acetylglucosamine) primer.

Enzymic reactions that have to undergo periodic changes in activity clearly need to be switched on and off. This is often achieved by a device whereby the enzyme is actually formed initially in an inactive 'zymogen' form (compare the conversion of pepsinogen to active pepsin in the gut). The inactive form often differs from the active form by having extra amino acids at the end of a polypeptide chain; these blocking units have to be removed from more zymogen molecules when greater activity is required. The activating factor (presumably a protease) is produced endogenously at the right moment in the life cycle of the insect and is probably carried to the site of chitin synthesis by lysosome-like vesicles. There is evidence that the activity of chitin synthetase is controlled by at least two endogenous insect growth hormones, which are secreted at critical periods of morphogenesis. In particular, synthesis of cuticular constituents is induced by moulting hormone and the formation of

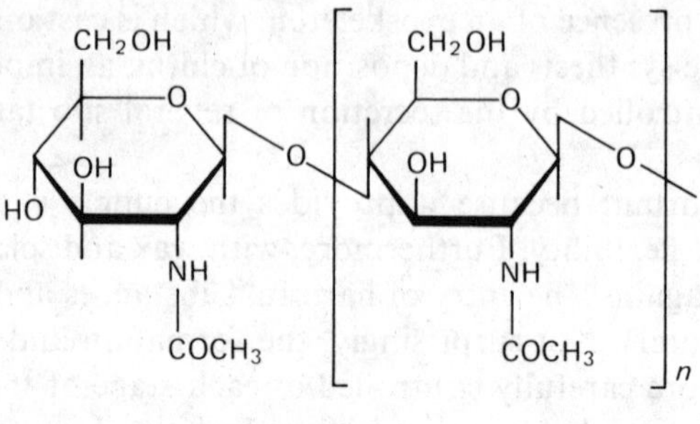

(a) Chitin

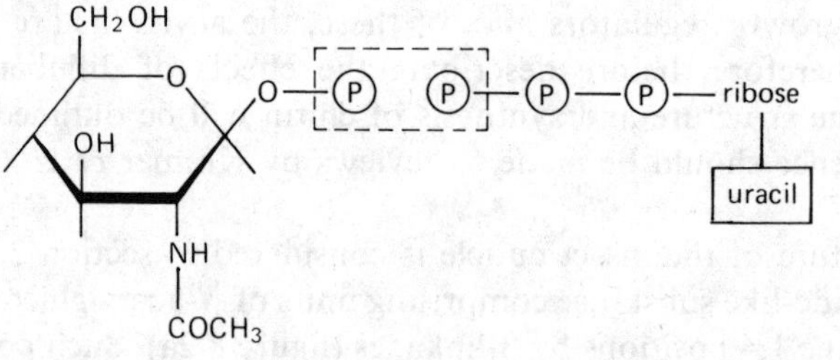

(b) Synthesis of UDP-*N*-acetylglucosamine

Figure 8.2   Chitin. (a) A chain of *N*-acetylglucosamine residues. (b) 'Activated' *N*-acetylglucosamine, i.e. uridine diphosphate–acetylglucosamine formed from UTP and *N*-acetylglucosamine phosphate. The 'active' *N*-acetylglucosamine deposits a new monomeric unit on to the chitin primer

larval cuticle is dependent on the presence of juvenile hormone and a steroid (ecdysteroid).

In different organisms, different substances appear to interfere with chitin metabolism in different ways. For example, polyoxins (which are structurally similar to UDP–acetylglucosamine) are competitive inhibitors of chitin synthetase in fungi but not in insects (Misato *et al.*, 1979). Similarly, the acylureas rather specifically affect chitin formation in insects. How they do this remains uncertain, but very low concentrations inhibit the formation of chitin. For example, Hajjar and Casida (1979), using an abdominal preparation made from the milkweed bug, *Oncopeltus fasciatus*, observed a 50 per cent reduction in the rate of chitin formation in the presence of a diflubenzuron concentration of only 0.5 µM.

Several explanations for this inhibition have been proposed. One is that acylureas prevent the activation of a precursor of chitin synthetase (Leighton *et al.*, 1981), although the evidence for this remains inconclusive. Nor does the action seem to be a direct attack on the chitin synthetase itself, for in *in vitro* systems capable of chitin synthesis, the enzyme functions in the presence of these insecticides (Cohen and Casida, 1982). Another possibility is that an active metabolite is the effective toxicant. However, diflubenzuron affects chitin synthesis very rapidly and in any case no such metabolite has yet been identified (Deul *et al.*, 1978). Another unconfirmed suggestion is that insecticides of this group may prevent the movement of UDP–acetylglucosamine across lipoprotein membranes. Finally, acylureas could accelerate chitin destruction rather than retard its formation, but most workers discount this possibility. It is of interest that chitin synthetase systems in fungi are not particularly sensitive to acylureas; this appears to imply that the primary target of these substances is some reaction or control mechanism of particular relevance to insects.

A wide range of behavioural and chemical manifestations of impairment of chitin synthesis in insects has been reported, as some specific examples will illustrate. Characteristically (and no doubt significantly), the inhibition of chitin formation during one stage of development leads to malfunction at a later stage. For example, treatment of female adults often causes egg development to fail in its later stages; contact with early instars may affect later instars; and treatment of the last instar may affect the emergence of adults from pupae.

In now classic work, Bull and Ivie (1980) showed that the embryonic development of eggs of treated female boll weevils apparently proceeds normally at first, but things go wrong just before development is complete. Smith *et al.* (1985), working with the rice water weevil, treated water containing submerged rice stems immediately after oviposition. It was observed that the number of eggs placed on plants in treated water was the same as on plants in untreated water but that treatment greatly reduced the number of immature insects present later on. Rup and Chopra (1985) found that the fertility of the eggs of banana fruit fly decreased from 86 to 20 per cent when laid within one day of treatment of adult females with an acylurea. However, these Indian workers also reported that the effectiveness of the treatment declined as the time between the treatment and the laying of the eggs increased.

Parallel results have been obtained with events occurring later in the life cycle. Guyer and Neumann (1988) injected varying amounts of diflubenzuron into larvae of *Spodoptera littoralis* and *Heliothis zea*. At high doses there was a failure to ecdyse; at low doses, however, the moulting was apparently normal but the larvae, after ecdysis, did not develop properly and eventually starved to death. The effect of diflubenzuron on pupae was studied by Soltani *et al.* (1983). The insecticide was applied in three different ways to the pupae of *Tenebrio molitor* and, in each case, it was observed that the death of the beetles took place at the time of adult ecdysis. As with eggs, it was found that the effectiveness of treatment decreased as the pupae aged, an effect that was ascribed to an age-related decrease in the ease with which pesticide entered the pupae. Later, Soltani *et al.* (1984), working in France on the same test material, reported that several types of abnormalities can occur. These included blocked pupae and partly ecdysed adults. These workers also observed that the treatment led to cuticles of reduced thickness and with modified architecture. They concluded that treatment of pupae resulted in the cuticle of the adult being imperfectly formed at the pupal stage. According to Leopold *et al.* (1985), if pupae of the cotton boll weevil are treated with a mixture of juvenile hormone and diflubenzuron, there is a synergistic response that causes a seven-fold increase in failure at ecdysis.

8.3 METABOLISM AND PERSISTENCE OF ACYLUREAS

The degradation of diflubenzuron by soil microorganisms was studied by Seuferer *et al.* (1979) using species of *Fusarium, Cephalosporium, Penicillium* and *Rhodotorula.* Identified metabolic products included difluorobenzoic acid, chlorophenylurea and chloroaniline. It is therefore very likely that the principal metabolic route in soil organisms is hydrolytic, hydrolysis occurring principally in the position shown in figure 8.1a. For chloroaniline to be formed it is probable that hydrolysis of the amide linkage occurs adjacent to the chlorinated ring. More recently, similar conclusions were reached by Nimmo *et al.* (1984, 1986). Using an applied dose of 1 mg per kg soil of ^{14}C-diflubenzuron it was found that the time for half of this to disappear varied from 2 days to 5 weeks in different soils. They, too, found that the main products were 4-chlorophenylurea and 2,6-difluorobenzoic acid. In addition, with increasing time in the soil, the amount that could not be readily extracted increased. These soil-bound metabolites were, however, apparently not available for root uptake and translocation. In one set of experiments the maximal concentration of chlorophenylurea was attained in 4 days, whereupon decomposition occurred with the formation of carbon dioxide. In an anaerobic hydrosol a half-life of 16 weeks was recorded. In all of these cases the products are consistent with a predominant metabolic role for hydrolysis.

When applied to plants a similar pattern emerges except that some workers have reported that the disappearance curve is bimodal. For example, Lauren *et al.* (1984) applied 20–100 g/ha to growing lucerne. The lowest of these rates represented a deposit of about 2 mg/kg of plant material. These workers in New Zealand found that the time taken for half the deposit to disappear was about 3.5 days. The same was true for half of the remainder to disappear, but thereafter the rate of disappearance slowed down and 0.3 mg/kg could still be detected 22 days after application. In stored grain the persistence is much greater; Mian and Mulla (1983) found that residues of between 1 and 10 ppm declined by 40–50 per cent in 23 months of post-treatment storage. As mentioned earlier, diflubenzuron has in consequence been considered for use for the post-harvest control of *Rhyzopertha dominica* and *Sitophilus oryzae* in stored wheat, although it is not yet registered for this purpose in Britain.

Penetration of diflubenzuron into pupae of *Tenebrio molitor* after topical application is rapid and it appears not to be degraded during pupal life (Soltani *et al.*, 1983). Younger instar larvae are often more susceptible than older ones, although this is not always so (Granett *et al.*, 1983). However, when such differences exist they are usually attributed to differences in patterns of uptake, metabolism or excretion, or in terms of differences of the target at the site of action. Evidence as to which of these factors is most important in individual cases can be obtained in a variety of ways. One way is to compare the toxicities of closely related compounds with the relative rates at which these substances are degraded by a given species. Clearly, if metabolism plays an important role in determining differences in susceptibility, tolerant instars should metabolise the substance faster than more susceptible ones. Another approach is to determine both the toxicity and the rate of metabolism of a substance in first the presence and then the absence of substances believed to be specific inhibitors of particular enzymic processes. These methods apply equally to investigations concerned with tolerances of different stages of the life cycle of one insect species, those concerned with the causes of insect resistance and those relating to why different species have different natural tolerances.

The first method above is illustrated by the work of Guyer and Neumann (1988) using larvae of *Spodoptera littoralis*. When injected, **chlorfluazuron** was found to be 100-fold more toxic than **diflubenzuron**; when, however, their t_{50} values were measured (these are the times taken for 50 per cent of the pesticide to disappear), these were found to be 50 h and 5 h, respectively. In conjunction with other data, results such as these are often interpreted as evidence that relative longevity of effective concentrations is a major factor determining relative toxicity. In this case such a view is strengthened by the fact that both ureas inhibited chitin synthesis *in vivo* in only 2 h but the duration of the inhibition was much longer for the chlorfluazuron than for the diflubenzuron.

An example of the use of inhibitors to demonstrate the toxicological significance of metabolism is provided by the work of Granett and Hejazi (1983) on the beet armyworm, *Spodoptera exigua*, and on the leafroller, *Platynota stultana*. They demonstrated that the beet armyworm was highly susceptible to acylureas (the oral LC_{50} of diflubenzuron was about 1.1 ppm) but that the leafroller required a dietary dose several thousand times greater than this to kill it. When, however, tri-n-butyl phosphorotrithioate (section 7.2) was present, most of this difference disappeared. This synergistic effect strongly suggests that hydrolytic metabolism plays a major part in determining the natural tolerance of this species to diflubenzuron.

Similarly, piperonyl butoxide and sesamex (figure 7.3) are powerful inhibitors of the mono-oxygenase system (section 3.4), and they have often been used to provide clues as to the contribution of oxidative metabolism in regard both to natural *tolerance* and to the *resistance* sometimes developed by insect populations that have been exposed to insecticides. The use of sesamex by

Pimprikar and Georghiou (1982) illustrates this; a 20-fold difference in LD_{50} values of diflubenzuron existed between larvae of two strains of the housefly, *Musca domestica*, but, in the presence of sesamex, this difference largely disappeared. Moreover, the amount of unmetabolised internal diflubenzuron recovered from larvae of the resistant strain was 10–30 times greater when the insecticide was applied with sesamex than when it was applied alone.

Insect growth regulators

8.4 JUVENILE HORMONE AND METHOPRENE

The complex nature of the insect life cycle, with metamorphosis and ecdysis, requires the presence of a variety of natural growth regulators. The action of any of these can theoretically be disrupted, with disastrous results to the insect. Insect growth regulators (IGRs) may be either natural or artificial, helpful or disastrous, agonistic or antagonistic. In the future, it is likely that insect control will increasingly involve the use of such substances that mimic or antagonise those natural processes that are an essential part of insect development.

The acylureas considered in the preceding sections are insect growth regulators, acting, as has been seen, by disruption of the action of chitin synthetase. Another group of growth regulators are mimics of insect juvenile hormone(s); the latter are several closely related substances essential for successful progression from egg, through instar stages, to pupa and imago. The structure of juvenile hormone isolated from several insect species is shown in figure 8.3a. Once its structure was known, analogues were synthesised and several have been exploited commercially, mostly for medical and veterinary, rather than for crop protection, purposes. Of juvenile hormone mimics, or juvenoids, the best known are methoprene and hydroprene; the structure of **methoprene** is shown in figure 8.3b. Hammock and Quistad (1981) have pointed out that a difficulty relating to the marketing of juvenoids and similar substances is that such substances have a highly directionalised action, often on a narrow range of possible pests. In consequence, a major disincentive to the introduction of these (potentially safe) chemicals based on natural hormones is the cost of registration *vis-à-vis* the market return of substances likely to have a limited market in the field of crop protection. Thus regulations introduced to increase safety may well be slowing the progress towards precisely that end. For the moment, except perhaps for such insects as the cotton boll weevil, the major use of juvenoids has been to control the vectors of mammalian disease.

Juvenoids, pheromone analogues and growth regulators are likely to be the

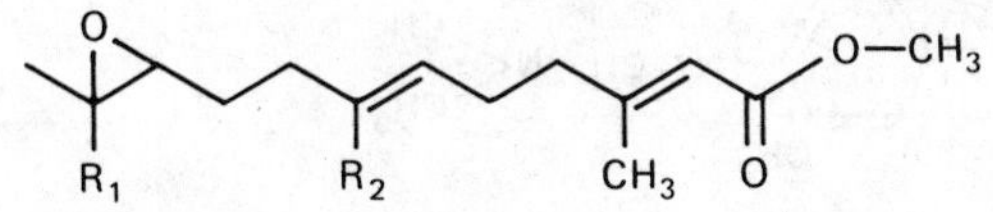

(a) Juvenile hormone

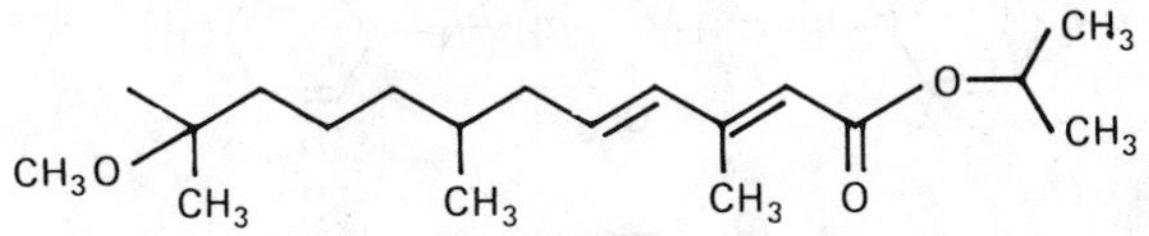

(b) Methoprene

Figure 8.3 (a) Juvenile hormone; in JHIII R_1 and $R_2 = CH_3$. (b) Methoprene, an agonist of JH

subjects of much investigation in the future. Textbooks dealing exclusively with this interface between chemical and biological control can be expected to multiply during the course of the next decade.

Formamidine insecticides and acaricides

8.5 BEHAVIOURAL CHARACTERISTICS, CHEMISTRY AND USES

The two commonest members of this group are **chlordimeform** and **amitraz** (figure 8.4). The formamidines are characterised by their ability to evoke a variety of behavioural and other effects in a limited range of insects and, importantly, in acarines (including phytophagous mites). The LD_{50}s of formamidines can, of course, be determined, but they are imperfect indices of the field-effectiveness of these substances. The reason for this is that, at much lower concentrations, they bring about changes in behaviour of target organisms that ultimately prove to be disastrous. Some examples will illustrate this.

They have been described as having a repellent action, yet an affected organism will not feed even if provided with insecticide-free food. Appetite is suppressed, and this anorexic action leads to death by starvation and by desiccation (Beeman, 1982). The organisms can suffer an increased excitability that can lead to ineffectual probing of the food source, attempts to fly or

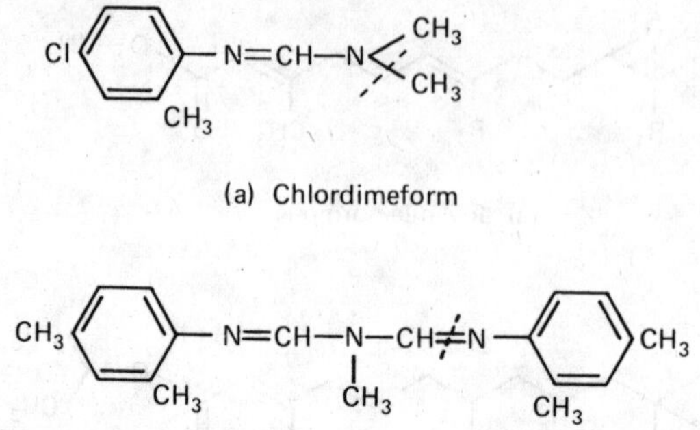

(a) Chlordimeform

(b) Amitraz

Figure 8.4   The structures of two formamidines. The broken lines indicate common loci for metabolism

aimless walking. Spider mites may fall off the plant or detach themselves on a thread. Adult whitefly, *Bemisia tabaci*, may respond by mass emigration from cotton plants when chlordimeform is applied to the foliage (Uk and Dittrich, 1986). Rice borers leave rice plants and enter the paddy water, where they soon drown since their swimming capability is impaired.

Disruption of behavioural patterns essential to mating and reproduction are also common. The sensitivity of male moths to sex pheromones may alter, with strange flight performance and hypersensitivity to olfactory signals (Linn and Roelofs, 1985). Sometimes, affected moths fly by day instead of by night. On other occasions the sexes cannot separate after mating. The number of eggs laid tends to be lower than usual and the viability poor (Hollingworth and Lund, 1982). The formamidines do not have a genuine ovicidal effect but, on hatching, the larvae may not detach themselves cleanly from the eggshell and their development is often restricted.

In relation to insect control, the value of existing amidines is largely confined to the control of Lepidoptera and some Hemiptera. Two particularly important examples are the genera *Heliothis* and *Spodoptera*. Formamidines are also extremely useful for use against insects that have become resistant to other insecticides. For example, during the use of dimethoate in the Gezira cotton-growing project, Uk and Dittrich (1986) observed that whiteflies had developed a 240-fold resistance to it, but nevertheless responded to chlordimeform. Whiteflies are very difficult to control because of their rapid reproduction and abaxial lifestyle, and Uk and Dittrich have suggested that it could well play a part in an integrated pest management programme. Chlordimeform has also been used to control cotton pests and to increase cotton yields, although multiple applications may be necessary (Benedict *et al.*, 1986; Cathey and Bailey, 1987).

The possibility of employing formamidines to control phytophagous mites has assumed considerable importance, especially in those countries where cyhexatin has been withdrawn from use on grounds of safety. Amitraz is often applied to fruit trees to control mites on top fruit, although it does not appear to be as effective as cyhexatin against some species when the temperature is low (Aveyard, 1988). In some cases it is applied jointly with clofentezine, especially to control spider mites (*Tetranychus urticae*) and rust mites (*Aculus schlechtendali*).

The susceptibility of many acarines to the formamidines is of major importance in view of the problems that have arisen in relation to explosive reproduction of spider mites following the use of classical pesticides. *T. urticae*, one of the commonest of the spider mites, is apparently controlled by perturbation of the processes of egg hatching and of larval development rather than by an inhibition of reproduction (Ibrahim and Knowles, 1986). The use of formamidines for mite control in the context of integrated pest management was advocated by these authors on the grounds that formamidines could limit the predations of the mites during the early, most susceptible, stages of crop growth, whether or not full economic control could be achieved.

8.6 MODE OF ACTION OF FORMAMIDINES

The behavioural aberrations described in section 8.5 are probably caused, at least in part, by interference with the functioning of bioactive amines in the insect nervous system. In invertebrates, some of these amines have roles that differ from those that they have in vertebrates.

Both neurotransmitters and neurohormones participate in neural activity. The role of transmitters has already been considered (section 4.4). Neurohormones, on the other hand, are messengers acting within a local region of the nervous system and their message can affect several postsynaptic cells (compare figures 4.2 and 4.3). In insects, neurohormones are probably more important than they are in vertebrates. One type of neurohormone is a **neuromodulator**; it is a hormone that functions by changing the *quality* of information passing through a synapse.

Adrenaline (epinephrine) and noradrenaline (norepinephrine) have a restricted distribution in most groups of invertebrates but the closely related octopamine is present. It possesses some of the functional characteristics of vertebrate catecholamines, being a neurohormone with some sympathomimetic qualities. It increases the rate at which metabolism occurs in insect nerve and fat body tissues and the concentration in the haemolymph rises severalfold during the initial stages of flight (compare the role of adrenaline in 'fight and flight' in vertebrates). These effects are possibly consequent upon the stimulation of the production of cyclic AMP and the mobilisation of diacylglycerol (Goldsworthy, 1983). It also increases the activity of glycogen phosphorylase and stimulates glycogenolysis in nerve cord. All of these activities suggest that it could form part of an arousal system; octopamine receptors occur *inter alia* in lepidopteran wing muscles, in firefly lanterns (Hollingworth and Murdock, 1980) and in the fat body of the cockroach. It should, however, be noted that no octopaminergic action has yet been identified in acarines (see below).

Matsumura and Beeman (1982) and Linn and Roelofs (1985) support the theory that the formamidines, at least when acting as insecticides, interfere with octopamine activity. This interference could take the form of occupation of octopamine receptors in a way that leads to an agonistic response (i.e. the occupation leads, not to a blocking of octopamine activity, but to sustained and abnormal octopamine-like stimulation).

A variant of this proposal is that formamidines interact with octopamine-sensitive adenylate cyclase, the enzyme that catalyses the production of cyclic AMP (Downer *et al.*, 1985). These workers suggest that the behavioural changes following formamidine poisoning could be a reflection of the cumulative effects of a continuous octopamine-like action. Similarly, Davenport *et al.* (1985), working with the locust, *Schistocerca gregaria*, found that chlordimeform and amitraz mimicked the action of octopamine both by increasing the amplitude and relaxation rate of motor neuron tension and by altering the levels of cyclic AMP.

Not all workers support the theory of octopamine agonism; other sympathomimetic amines have been implicated in the action of the formamidines, as have their possible effects on monoamine oxidase and their possible interference with ion transport across nerve membranes (Hollingworth and Lund, 1982). At least two important objections appear to exist to a single comprehensive theory advanced to explain all the effects of formamidines on invertebrates in terms of octopamine. The first of these is that many of the effects of chlordimeform in insects are central nervous system effects whereas the octopamine receptors that have so far been studied involve peripheral action. A second, and apparently telling, objection is that the formamidines are of great practical value because they control acarines as well as some important lepidopterans, and the excitation, anorexia and behavioural perturbation characteristic of formamidines are remarkably similar in mites and moths. Yet, not only is there little evidence for the existence of octopamine receptors in mites but octopamine appears to play a similar role in formamidine-sensitive lepidopterans and in other orders of insects for which the formamidines are of no commercial significance.

In vertebrates, relatively high concentrations of formamidines have a local anaesthetic effect, which is about two-thirds that of procaine (Hollingworth and Yim, 1980). It should be added that, at high concentrations, similar local anaesthetic effects have also been noted in insects, where the neurotransmitter is glutamate. Thus, even though many of the low-concentration effects of formamidines on the behaviour of insects may be partly attributable to interaction with some part of the octopamine-sensitive system, nevertheless, at high concentrations, both in vertebrates and in invertebrates, they can, like well known local anaesthetics, depress the activity of excitable membranes irrespective of the chemical mediator. This may be because it affects ion channel conductance (Hollingworth and Lund, 1982, p. 204). Finally, some effects in vertebrates contrast sharply with those evoked in insects; in particular, while the anorexic effect in insects is a major factor in determining their usefulness in pest control, in vertebrates their effect is exactly the opposite, for they powerfully stimulate appetite.

8.7 METABOLISM OF FORMAMIDINES

Chlordimeform undergoes N-demethylation in the position shown in figure 8.4a, giving (mono)-demethyl chlordimeform, and there is evidence that, for at least some behavioural disturbances, it is more potent than the dimethylated parent compound. For example, Knowles and Roulston (1972, 1973) observed that demethyl chlordimeform was 700-fold more effective than was chlordimeform itself in stimulating tick detachment from host plants. If piperonyl butoxide is mixed with chlordimeform it reduces its toxicity, whereas if it is added to demethyl chlordimeform before this is applied as an acaricide the toxicity of the mono-N-methyl compound is enhanced. These results are unlikely to have been idiosyncratic for chlordimeform because, in the later of their two papers, these authors observed similar relationships for several other di-N-methyl and mono-N-methyl analogues. The observation that piperonyl butoxide prevents the less toxic dimethylated compounds from undergoing N-demethylation incidentally demonstrates the participation of mono-oxygenase in this stage of metabolism; similarly, the fact that piperonyl butoxide accentuates the toxicity of the mono-N-methyl compounds demonstrates that these, too, are N-demethylated by the action of mono-oxygenases (section 3.4).

Further evidence to support the view that demethyl chlordimeform may be more toxic than the parent chlordimeform is provided by an observation of Hollingworth and Murdock (1980). The stimulation of octopamine receptors in the light-producing organs of fireflies, *Photinus pyralis*, leads to a strong intensification of glow. Application of octopamine causes this to happen and, to a lesser extent, so does application of chlordimeform, but only after a lag phase. Demethyl chlordimeform, on the other hand, produces a response immediately it is applied. From these and other observations it seems quite possible that it is demethyl formamidine that is the actual toxicant at the site of action.

Knowles and Gayen (1983) describe the breakdown of amitraz in the corn borer, *Diatraea grandiosella*. A major initial reaction is for the molecule to split in the position shown in figure 8.4b. The product is the dimethyl analogue of demethyl chlordimeform and resembles the latter in that it is more toxic to insects than is the parent insecticide. This is then further degraded to 2,4-dimethylformanilide and 2,4-dimethylaniline. In further reactions the methyl groups in the benzene rings of these substances undergo slow oxidation to carboxyl. The chlordimeform equivalent of 2,4-dimethylaniline, 2-methyl-4-chloroaniline, has been shown by Hill *et al.* (1979) to be potentially carcinogenic, causing sarcomas when administered to rats in their diet. For this reason the use of chlordimeform has been restricted in some countries and it does not appear in the list of pesticides approved under the UK Control of Pesticides Regulations, 1986.

Some other insecticides of plant origin

8.8 NICOTINE, ROTENONE AND THEIR DERIVATIVES

As well as the natural pyrethroids, several other insecticides originate from plants. **Nicotine** and its near-relatives *nornicotine* and **anabasine** (figure 8.5) are all viscous liquids. Nicotine darkens on exposure to light and should be stored in the dark. It boils at 247°C, has a vapour pressure of about 0.04 mmHg at 25°C and is miscible with water. It is a weak base ($pK_a = 8$), and forms salts with acids. The free base has been employed as a contact spray, and it is possible that much of it enters insects through the spiracles, possibly then acting in the vapour phase. The salts have also been used as insecticides. In earlier years a suitable balance between short- and long-term action (i.e. of fumigation as against persistence of a deposit) was obtained by formulating it as the salt of an acid of appropriate solubility and hydrolysability. For example, nicotine tannate is insoluble, and was used to achieve a stomach poison action.

Nicotine and nornicotine occur in certain members of the Solanaceae and especially in species of the genus *Nicotiana*. Anabasine occurs in *Anabasis aphylla*, a member of the Chenopodiaceae. Not much nicotine is used commercially now, for it, and its analogues, are unpleasant toxic liquids, and organophosphorus compounds are usually equally effective, especially for the control of aphids. Insofar as nicotine is needed (about 500 tons per year are used in the USA), it is extracted by steam distillation from the leaves and roots of the tobacco plant. In tobacco leaves it occurs at a concentration of 2–5 per cent, usually as a salt of Krebs cycle acids (e.g. citric acid, malic acid).

Natural nicotine is the laevorotatory isomer; the dextrorotatory isomer, prepared chemically, is of relatively low toxicity. Natural nicotine appears to possess a structure of the right dimensions and of the right basicity to enable it to bind on to acetylcholine receptors in the nervous system. It has been suggested, for example, that the distance between the two nitrogen atoms,

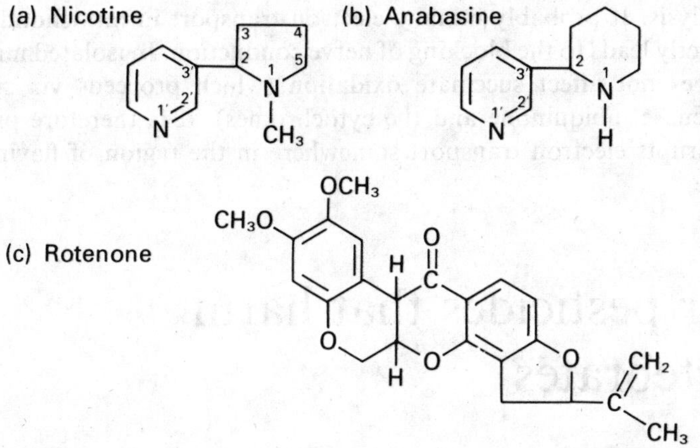

(a) Nicotine   (b) Anabasine

(c) Rotenone

Figure 8.5 Nicotine, anabasine and rotenone: (a) (*S*)-1-methyl-2-(3'-pyridyl)pyrroli-
dine; (b) (*S*)-2-(3'-pyridyl)piperidine; (c) (*R*)-1-(4-chlorophenyl)-3-(2',6'-
difluorobenzyl)urea

namely 0.42 nm, mimics acetylcholine in that the esteratic oxygen atom and
the positively charged nitrogen atom of acetylcholine are about 0.4 nm apart.
The receptor that it attacks may be in the neuromuscular junctions of
mammals but in synaptic ganglia of insects.

In both insects and vertebrates **cotinine**, a 5-*keto* derivative of nicotine, is
usually the major metabolic product. It is probably formed by a NADPH-
dependent hydroxylation reaction, the 5-hydroxynicotine then being converted to cotinine by further dehydrogenation.

Rotenoids form another group of plant-derived insecticides, which play a
small but useful role in pest control in the home garden and the market garden
and to control ectoparasites on animals. The insecticides are present in the
roots of certain genera of the Leguminosae, especially *Derris* spp. in the Far
East and *Lonchocarpus* in South America. Long before they were first used as
insecticides (about 1914), their toxic effect was exploited by local fishermen,
who used to macerate the plants and throw them into water to paralyse fish,
which then floated to the surface.

The active principles of **derris** (of which there are about six, rotenone being
the most active) can be extracted from the dried, ground-up roots by organic
solvents. Alternatively, the still-popular 'derris dust' is made by mixing the
ground roots with a clay diluent. **Rotenone** itself forms yellow laevorotatory
crystals, which dissolve in many organic solvents but are insoluble in water. Its
structure is shown in figure 8.5c. It is of low but variable toxicity to mammals
when given by mouth but it is extremely toxic to fish. It is destroyed by light
and so is of limited persistence in the garden.

Rotenone does not appear to be a nerve poison but instead it brings about a slow paralysis. It probably inhibits electron transport in mitochondria, and this indirectly leads to the blocking of nerve conduction. In isolated mitochondria it does not affect succinate oxidation (which proceeds via succinate dehydrogenase, ubiquinone and the cytochromes). It is therefore presumed that it disrupts electron transport somewhere in the region of flavin mononucleotide.

Other pesticides that harm invertebrates

8.9 ACARICIDES

Mites are of considerable commercial importance as pests of fruit trees and of some vegetable crops. In addition they affect larders, barns and animal houses, as well as stored food. Different genera of red mites attack fruit trees and greenhouse crops, while white mites often thrive in places where grain is stored.

When first introduced, organic insecticides led in some districts to an alarming increase in the number of red spider mites after early-season foliage applications to fruit trees. This was partly a consequence of the insect predators of red spider mites being killed more readily than the mites themselves. Taken in conjunction with the very rapid life cycle of the red spider mites, this removal of biological control enabled the few surviving mites to generate an enormous population within a few weeks of applying a spray aimed at insect pests. The more recent introduction of formamidines, tetrazines, organotin compounds and a new generation of pyrethroids has helped to reduce these difficulties; indeed, integrated pest management trials now commonly involve the use of acaricides in programmes relating to top fruit cultivation (Brooker *et al.*, 1987).

From about 1945, **azobenzene** (figure 8.6a) was in use in glasshouses for the control of glasshouse red spider mites. It is unsuitable for outdoor use, but workers at East Malling Research Station, UK, showed that the central moiety, the azo group, could be replaced by a variety of other bridging groups and that chlorination of the phenyl rings often enhanced toxicity.

An early discovery was **tetradifon**, a tetrachlorinated derivative of phenylsulphone (figure 8.6c). It found considerable commercial application, the chlorine atoms conferring persistence as well as high lipid solubility and chemical stability. Unfortunately, resistance rapidly developed and limited its use. Tetradifon acts against the eggs and nymphal stages of mites and it also makes the females sterile. In common with many other acaricides, it is not

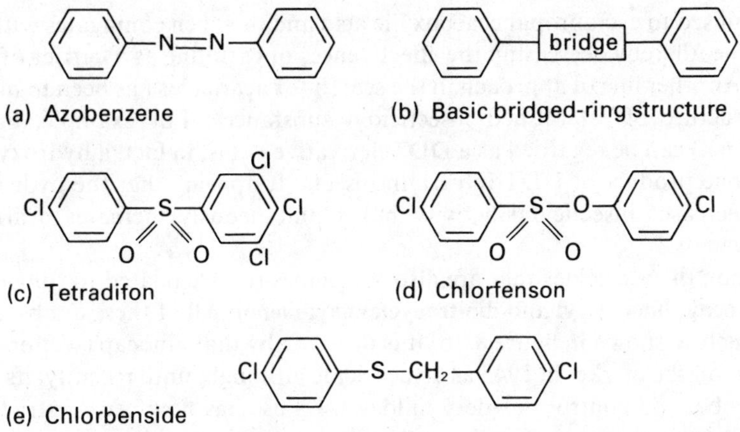

(a) Azobenzene

(b) Basic bridged-ring structure

(c) Tetradifon

(d) Chlorfenson

(e) Chlorbenside

Figure 8.6 Bridged-ring acaricides; (c) 4-chlorophenyl-2,4,5-trichlorophenylsulphone; (d) 4-chlorophenyl-4-chlorobenzenesulphonate; (e) 4-chlorophenyl-4-chlorobenzyl sulphide

systemic because it is too insoluble in water but it is able to kill mites on both surfaces of a sprayed leaf. It is phytotoxic to cucumbers, but is used to control red spider mites on a variety of fruit trees and bushes and also on ornamental plants. McBride (1959) showed that it persisted for two or three months in the peel of citrus fruits but that little of it was present in the pulp or juices.

Another possible bridge between phenyl or chlorinated phenyl rings is the sulphonate linkage. **Chlorfenson** (figure 8.6d) has been used commercially, but phytotoxic effects have been reported, including cracking of the epidermis of fruit and scorching of leaves. As with tetradifon, this compound is toxic to the hatching eggs and nymphal stages but is less effective against adult mites. Chlorfenson is of low mammalian toxicity (oral LD_{50} about 2000 mg/kg).

Chlorbenside has a sulphur atom in the bridging group (figure 8.6e) and was for many years a successful acaricide. Like the other acaricides mentioned above, it is a water-insoluble solid. It oxidises, after spraying, to the sulphoxide and the sulphone; this may ensure a longer persistence when the oxidation occurs after the substance has penetrated the leaf.

Cycloprate is another substance that shows promise for use against phytophagous mites. It is the hexadecyl ester of cyclopropanecarboxylic acid (figure 8.7a). It appears to be rather specifically acaricidal and ovicidal, for eggs of insects, and motile stages of both mites and insects, are less sensitive to it than are the eggs of mites (Quistad *et al.*, 1979). Cycloprate may cause a lethal disruption of lipid metabolism, arising from interference with the transfer of fatty acids into mitochondria by the blocking of the normal fatty acid carrier, carnitine. There appears to be less carnitine in mite eggs than in adult mites and less free carnitine in mites than in insects. Cycloprate is probably first metabolised to cyclopropanecarboxylic acid and this then conjugates with free carnitine, thereby decreasing the effectiveness of carnitine as a carrier of fatty acids. Another line of approach in the search for acaricides has been to modify the structure of established insecticidal substances. For example, dicofol (figure 6.4) can be regarded as a DDT derivative—it is, in fact, a hydroxylated metabolic product of DDT in certain insects. It appears that the hydroxylation decreases insecticidal activity but simultaneously increases acaricidal effectiveness.

Among the acaricides that are also fungicides (or are related to fungicides) are **dinocap**, **binapacryl** and **dinitrocyclohexylphenol**. All of these are based on the structure shown in figure 8.7b. It is noteworthy that dinocap (section 11.5) was put on the market in 1945 as an acaricide although, until recently, its main use has been to control powdery mildews. Its use has now been restricted in some countries because of evidence that its use could possibly endanger higher animals.

A group of compounds with selectively acaricidal properties has been investigated by workers at Chesterford Park Research Station, UK. Several 1*a*,2,4,5-tetrazines proved to be good ovicides for mites in the laboratory and one, **clofentezine** (figure 8.7c) has been marketed for mite control on top fruit. It is specifically ovicidal, having little contact action on mobile forms of *Tetranychus urticae* and *T. cinnabarinus*, spider mites that are major pests of crops in greenhouses and outdoors. It is less effective at 22°C than at 16°C (Neal *et al.*, 1986).

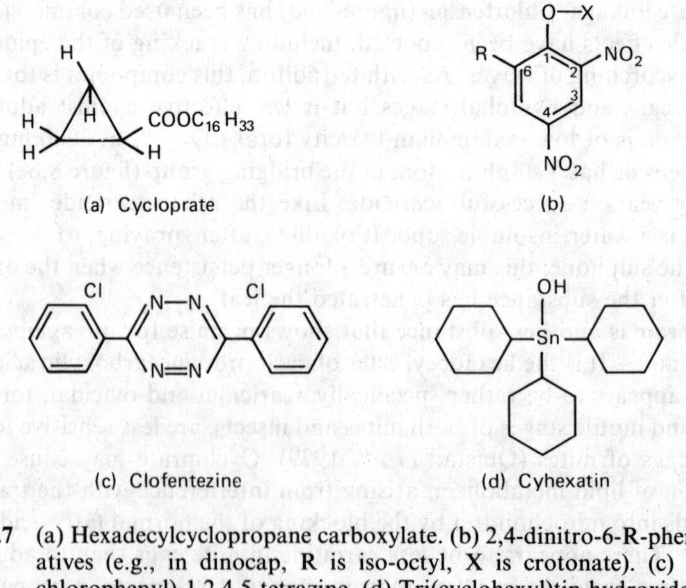

(a) Cycloprate

(b)

(c) Clofentezine

(d) Cyhexatin

Figure 8.7   (a) Hexadecylcyclopropane carboxylate. (b) 2,4-dinitro-6-R-phenol derivatives (e.g., in dinocap, R is iso-octyl, X is crotonate). (c) 3,6-bis(2-
chlorophenyl)-1,2,4,5-tetrazine. (d) Tri(cyclohexyl)tin hydroxide

Of the two or three organotin compounds used as acaricides, **cyhexatin** is probably the best known. It is tri(cyclohexyl)tin hydroxide (figure 8.7d), and was introduced in 1968 for use against phytophagous mites on apples, plums and raspberries. Most workers agree that only low levels of resistance have developed in the field so far and that even selection pressure in the laboratory has not led to rapid development of resistance. Chapman and Penman (1982) collected spider mites from two areas of New Zealand; one of these areas had a history of cyhexatin application whereas the other area had never been sprayed. No significant difference in sensitivity to cyhexatin was detected between organisms from the two areas. Croft *et al.* (1984) reported that *T. urticae* collected from strawberries and pears in the USA had LD_{50} values that differed no more than 17-fold; while Edge and James (1986) reported a 15-fold variation in LD_{50} values for females of *T. urticae* collected from apple and pear orchards in Australia. Such (relatively small) differences in sensitivities at the LD_{50} level to organotin compounds have been attributed to what has been termed vigour tolerance—i.e. that mites living in good surroundings can withstand more of the poison than others living in poorer environments.

Under field conditions, for only 50 per cent of a pest infestation to be controlled would normally be inadequate. For this reason, LD_{50} values are, by themselves, an insufficient index of whether resistance is present or not. A further requirement is that the slopes of the dosage–response curves for susceptible and tolerant strains must be similar (section 1.5). This, in effect, means that the two populations of organisms being compared must have the same spread of tolerances around the mean. Bearing this in mind, it is noteworthy that Croft *et al.* (1984) observed that at the LD_{95} level the resistance factor was 171 (at the LD_{50} level, it was 17). A somewhat similar observation was made by Hoyt *et al.* (1985); these investigators found that the LD_{50} values of two strains of spider mites were fairly similar but that, at the LD_{95} level, the resistance factor was nearly 2000.

This apparently low tendency on the part of organotin compounds to cause resistance to develop has led to their use in integrated pest management schemes. Nevertheless, care must be exercised, for resistance has occasionally been reported. For example, Carbonaro *et al.* (1986) studied the uptake and metabolism of organotin compounds in two strains of *T. urticae* that differed 100-fold in susceptibility to these compounds. Very little metabolism was observed in either strain and differences in the rate or route of metabolism are therefore unlikely to explain levels of tolerance in this case. Kimmel *et al.* (1980) ascribed the difference in sensitivities to modification at the site of action. In mammalian feeding experiments metabolism of organotin compounds was quite low, although several monohydroxylated derivatives of cyhexatin have been detected in faeces of rats, mice and rabbits.

In view of the low tendency of cyhexatin to cause resistance in acarines it is particularly unfortunate that recent work with female rats and rabbits has indicated the possibility that it could, in some circumstances, have teratogenic effects. A press release (MAFF, 1987) by the British authorities confirmed that safe levels for human female operators could not be established and, in consequence, approval for pesticide products containing cyhexatin was to be withdrawn.

8.10 NEMATICIDES

There are numerous species of phytophagous **nematodes**; some live as ectoparasites on the roots of plants and others live within plants. In either case their feeding can result in stunted plant growth, poor yields and virus infection. There are few reliable estimates of how seriously nematodes affect crop yields. One estimate of cereal damage in the UK was as low as 1 per cent, whereas Prasad *et al.* (1987) quoted estimates that put damage by the rice root nematode as sometimes exceeding 40 per cent. The same authors quote rice losses caused by the root-knot nematode, *Meloidogyne graminicola*, as exceeding 20 per cent and those caused by the stem nematode, *Ditylenchus angustus*, as being as high as 30 per cent in some states in India. Most annual crops can suffer nematode damage; in Britain, the potato root nematode may cause losses of up to 5 tons per hectare in badly infected land. Other examples will be found in the introductions to papers quoted in sections 5.5, 5.6 and 5.7.

It is usually necessary to integrate cultural, physical and chemical methods to achieve adequate nematode control. In addition, it is highly desirable to be familiar with the life cycles and habits of the principal nematode species. For example, many species seasonally migrate to different depths in the soil, and effective control is more likely to be achieved by treatment during the phase of shallow occupation of the soil. Again, many eggs are covered by cysts impermeable to pesticides and some eggs only hatch when stimulated by substances secreted by the roots of the host plant species.

Many **nematicides** have a fumigant action. Such compounds are usually applied to the soil by injection or by sprinkling, the application often being followed by rotary cultivation. They are volatile liquids which quickly volatilise to fill the soil air spaces. Others are relatively non-volatile solids. **1,3-Dichloropropene** (figure 8.8a) and **D-D mixture** (table 8.1) are used to control potato root and root-knot nematodes; for best results the soil temperature should not be too low. Dichloropropene is normally applied to soil at a depth of 20–30 cm. **1,2-Dibromo-3-chloropropane** has been used for soil treatment in citrus groves. Moje (1960) discussed the physicochemical characteristics likely to favour nematicidal activity.

Some compounds, such as formaldehyde, carbon disulphide, chloropicrin and metham sodium, can best be described as soil sterilants. They not only control nematodes, but a variety of soil insects and fungi as well. **Metham-sodium** is applied to the soil as a drench and then breaks down to the volatile methyl isothiocyanate (section 11.2). **Thionazin** (figure 8.8b) is an organophos-

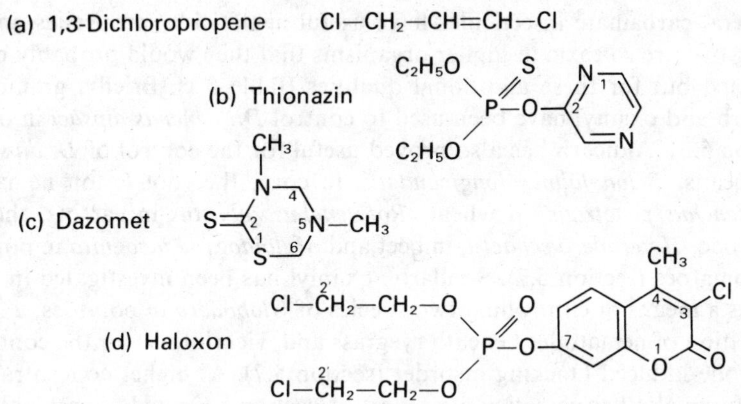

(a) 1,3-Dichloropropene $Cl—CH_2—CH{=}CH—Cl$

(b) Thionazin

(c) Dazomet

(d) Haloxon

Figure 8.8 Some common nematicides: (b) diethyl pyrazin-2-yl phosphorothionate; (c) tetrahydro-3,5-dimethyl-1,3,5-thiadiazine-2-thione; (d) di(2'-chloro-ethyl)-3-chloro-4-methylcoumarin-7-yl phosphate

phorus compound that is often hand-applied to the furrow for potato nematode control. It is also used to control the bulb and stem nematodes of tulip and narcissus and the bud nematode of chrysanthemum. Other organophosphorus compounds employed to control stem, bulb and root nematodes include parathion and demeton-*S*-methyl. **Dazomet** (figure 8.8c) is of interest in that, after soil incorporation, it, too, breaks down to give methyl isothiocyanate. The latter may well be the actual toxicant when both metham-sodium and dazomet are used.

Table 8.1 Some nematicides used in agriculture

Type	Substance
Volatile liquids or gases (with halogen)	Methyl bromide Ethylene dibromide D-D mixture (1,2-dichloropropane plus 1,3-dichloropropene) Chloropicrin 1,2-Dibromo-3-chloropropane
Volatile liquids or gases (without halogen)	Formaldehyde Methyl isothiocyanate Carbon disulphide
Relatively involatile solids	Metham-sodium Dazomet Thionazin Aldicarb, oxamyl, carbofuran (chapter 5) Parathion, demeton (chapter 4)

Several carbamate insecticides have useful nematicidal properties; indeed, one or two are so toxic to higher organisms that they would probably not be marketed but for these additional qualities (table 5.1). Briefly, granules of aldicarb and oxamyl have been used to control *Ditylenchus dipsaci* in onions (section 5.3). Aldicarb has also proved useful for the control of *D. dipsaci* in field beans, *Belonolaimus longicaudatus* in corn, the root lesion nematode, *Pratylenchus penetrans*, in wheat, *Rotylenchus robustus* in carrots, the cyst nematode, *Heterodera schactii*, in beet and *Meloidogyne incognita* in potatoes and tomatoes (section 5.7). Similarly, oxamyl has been investigated in many soils as a means of controlling two species of *Globodera* in potatoes, a mixed population of nematodes beneath ryegrass and, vicariously, for the control of nematode-induced Docking disorder (section 5.7). At higher concentrations, carbofuran also has nematicidal properties (section 5.6) and has been used as a root dip to decrease the population of the rice root nematode, *Hirschmanniella oryzae*.

The fumigant and soil sterilant nematicides mentioned earlier are usually applied to the soil weeks before sowing or planting. Treatments involving volatile liquids are usually expensive and some halides have come under suspicion of having undesirable side-effects. On the other hand, carbamate nematicides are usually formulated as granules and are often incorporated into the seed furrows. Nematicides have, however, agricultural uses outside crop protection and several have been investigated for the control of helminth diseases of sheep and cattle. One such veterinary nematicide is haloxon (figure 8.8d).

8.11 THE AVERMECTINS

The avermectins form a group of closely related antibiotics produced by *Streptomyces avermitilis*. They were discovered as a result of a search for naturally produced compounds possessing anthelmintic activity. It later became apparent that they were not only useful against parasites in animals but also against a wide range of insect pests of crops, and it is to these that this section is confined.

The formula is complex (Gullo *et al.*, 1983) and is shown in figure 8.9; it will not be considered in detail. Briefly, however, the avermectin group comprises two series of compounds; one type, series A, is the methoxy derivative of the other, series B. So far, compounds of series A have not proved to be so useful as those of series B. There are two subsets of compounds in series B, termed B_1 and B_2; compounds in the first of these contain a particular double bond (positions 22,23), which is hydrated in the second. In addition, a small difference exists in a side-chain attached in position 25 and, in the double-bonded subsets, dihydro derivatives (HB_1, HB_2), or ivermectins, have been

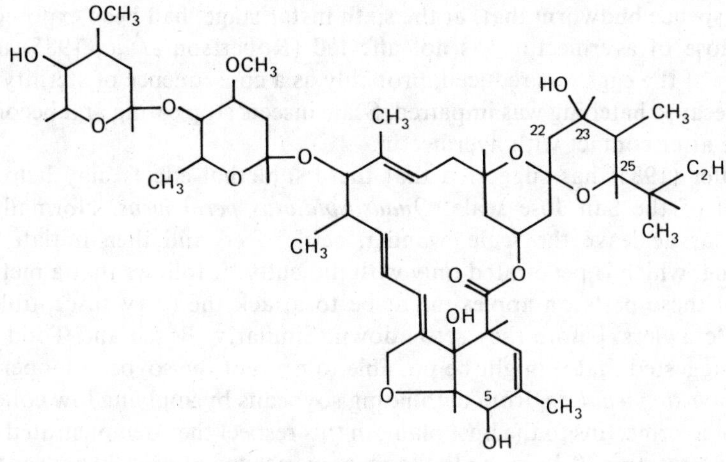

Figure 8.9 Avermectin B_2

investigated. The most used member of the group so far is probably avermectin B_1 and its dihydro derivative.

The avermectins act at low dosage against a wide range of nematodes (Campbell *et al.*, 1983) and insects (Strong and Brown, 1987). The latter workers applied avermectins to 84 species of insects in 10 orders, including some that attack animals and others that attack plants.

It is of particular interest that organisms that have become resistant to substances in one or more of the classical groups of insecticides usually respond to avermectins (e.g. Roush and Wright, 1986). Another observation of note is that neonatal stages may be more vulnerable than later instars, pupae or adults (Ishaaya *et al.*, 1986). One consequence of this is that first instars may lose their appetite, with the result that young plants may suffer little damage even though the organisms do not die immediately. In the case of the codling moth, for example, the neonate larvae are six times as susceptible as the 10-day-old larvae and are vulnerable as they search for and enter fruit (Reed *et al.*, 1985). In the case of scale insects the first instar 'crawlers' can be controlled before they settle and form a new scale (Pfeiffer, 1985). Another corollary is that the less easily affected adults of certain foraging insects (e.g. wasps) may carry lethal amounts to their nests before being affected themselves (Parrish and Roberts, 1984).

When avermectins are used to control ticks, the latter are not killed at once but their feeding habits, reproduction and moulting are disrupted (Campbell *et al.*, 1983). According to Strong and Brown (1987) high doses of avermectins may immobilise an insect and upset the water balance, while sublethal doses cause an inhibition of feeding, abnormal mating behaviour and disruption of oviposition. Death may take up to 30 days. The fecundity of surviving adults of the spruce budworm that, at the sixth instar stage, had been exposed to an LC_{50} dose of avermectin was not affected (Robertson *et al.*, 1985) but the fertility of the eggs was reduced, probably as a consequence of sterility rather than because hatching was impaired. Scale insects stop eating and become less mobile after contact with avermectin.

Pfeiffer (1985) has suggested that these sublethal effects may help in the control of the San José scale, *Quadraspidiotus perniciosus*. Normally, first instar larvae leave the scale, wander, settle, feed and then initiate a new covering, which is penetrated only with difficulty. It follows that a method to control these pests on apples might be to attack the (very susceptible) first instar 'crawlers' before they settle down. Similarly, Beach and Todd (1985) have suggested that it might be possible to prevent the soybean looper moth, *Pseudoplusia includens*, from defoliating soybeans by applying low concentrations of avermectins to the host plant; in this respect they demonstrated that at a concentration of 0.16 kg/ha the loopers oviposited at only 20 per cent of the rates of insects on untreated (cotton) plants.

Avermectins affect a wide range of insects and it is thus unlikely that much real selectivity is to be expected in favour of beneficial insects or mites. Nevertheless, there is some evidence that careful timing of application can avoid damage to some parasitoids. For example, red spider mites are attacked by a phytoseiid mite that is readily damaged by avermectin; however, if the timing of orchard spraying is such that mobile stages of red spider mites (and phytophagous insects) are present while the phytoseiids are still ascending the tree from the ground where they overwintered, a time-dependent selectivity can be achieved (Pfeiffer, 1985).

Most work to date supports the view that avermectins block signal transmission from interneurons to excitatory neurons that have GABA (γ-aminobutyric acid) as neurotransmitter. It is known that, in insects, GABA receptors exist in the peripheral nervous system (in mammals they are only in the central nervous system) and that these receptors regulate the opening of chloride channels (Campbell *et al.*, 1983). Thus, *inter alia*, avermectin could stimulate GABA release, leading to increased chloride ion conductance. The work of Tanaka and Matsumura (1985) on the leg muscles of the cockroach largely supported this opinion, except that there remained the possibility that the avermectin opened the chloride ion channels directly, rather than vicariously via GABA receptors. These authors showed that avermectin at 0.1 μM stimulated chloride ion uptake by leg muscles within 4 min.

In vertebrate brain, GABA is an inhibitory neurotransmitter which, as in invertebrates, increases the permeability of the postsynaptic membrane to chloride ions. Avermectin appears to potentiate the action of GABA in the vertebrate brain by causing its release from brain synaptosomes (Pong *et al.*, 1980).

The metabolism in soils of avermectin B_2 has been studied by Gullo *et al.* (1983). In pots of moist sandy loam it has a half-life of about three days and a

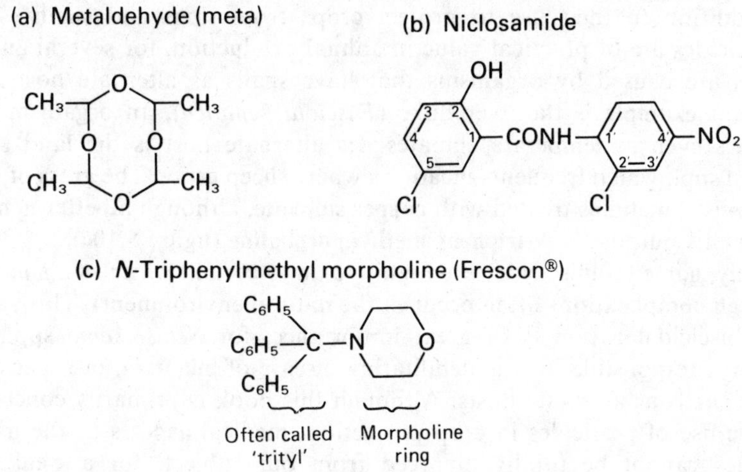
(a) Metaldehyde (meta)
(b) Niclosamide
(c) N-Triphenylmethyl morpholine (Frescon®)
Often called 'trityl'
Morpholine ring

Figure 8.10 Three molluscicides: (b) 2′,5-dichloro-4′-nitrosalicylanilide

major metabolite is formed by the oxidation of the secondary alcohol group in position 23 to a ketone. This ketone is apparently much more persistent than the parent compound and could be responsible for its month-long activity in soil against the root-knot nematode, *Meloidogyne incognita*. The metabolism of dihydroavermectin B_1 has been studied by Lee Chiu *et al.* (1984). On incubation with pig liver microsomes a metabolite was formed that proved to be an *O*-demethylation product. Other workers had previously shown that rats convert a methyl group in position 24 into a hydroxymethyl group. All of these reactions (ketone formation, *O*-demethylation and hydroxymethyl group formation) appear to be typical microsomal mono-oxygenase reactions.

8.12 MOLLUSCICIDES

The principal molluscs of importance in temperate-zone agriculture are slugs and snails, and, of the molluscicides mentioned elsewhere in this book, phorate (section 4.9) and methiocarb (section 5.5) have proved useful in crop protection. In addition, metaldehyde–bran baits are frequently used and can be very effective for small-scale use in the home garden or in the market garden. Metaldehyde is a tetramer of acetaldehyde with the structure shown in figure 8.10a. It is said to have its effect by narcotising the slug or snail so that, in the absence of shelter, it desiccates.

In addition to their use to protect crops from slugs and snails, some molluscicides are of practical value in animal production, for several animal diseases are caused by organisms that have snails as alternate hosts. An important example is the liver fluke (*Fasciola hepatica*), an organism that flourishes even in temperate climates. Its alternate host is the land snail, *Limnaea* spp., which frequents meadows where sheep graze. The grass of such pastures is sometimes treated with **copper sulphate**, although a better nematicide for this purpose is *N*-**triphenylmethylmorpholine** (figure 8.10c).

Finally, some molluscicides are highly toxic to certain water snails *in vitro* (although complications often occur in the natural environment). This aspect of molluscicidal action is of great importance, for *Schistosoma* spp., the organisms responsible for the debilitating disease of **bilharzia**, use species of aquatic snails as alternate hosts. Although this book is primarily concerned with the use of pesticides in crop protection, medical aspects of the use of pesticides cannot be totally divorced from our subject, for a weak and demoralised farmer is a bad farmer. This section therefore ends with a brief consideration of some chemical measures for the control of bilharzia (the simplest and cheapest of all control measures is not to drink from, and excrete into, the same water)*.

Copper sulphate, at 2 ppm, can be quite effective in slow-moving non-alkaline water, especially if the vegetation and fish are expendable. It is, however, adsorbed onto clay particles. **Pentachlorophenate** is also sometimes used, but it, too, is highly toxic to water plants, including algae. **Niclosamide** (figure 8.10b) is safer to handle than is pentachlorophenate and it has a less devastating effect on water plants. It has been used in bilharzia projects in several countries, including Brazil, Puerto Rico, Egypt and Iran. The control of the snails is apparently satisfactory but the cost of the successful treatment varies greatly with the geographical situation. In particular, costs rise as the volume of a habitat increases and as the distance between such habitats widens. In common with most other organic molluscicides, it is adsorbed onto organic matter, and the latter often abounds in the near-stagnant water that is the favourite habitat of the snails.

Another substance used in the control of vectors of *Schistosoma* spp. is *N*-**triphenylmethylmorpholine** (figure 8.10c). According to Brezden and Gardner (1980) it acts rather specifically on prosobranch and pulmonate aquatic snails, including *Biomphalaria glabrata*, the intermediate host of *Schistosoma* spp.

Plummer and Banna (1979), in a study of the effect of the molluscicide on the large neurons of *Archachatina*, found that some neurons were inhibited and others were excited by it. They concluded that it probably had a direct action on the nerve cells, possibly by altering the inward currents of sodium or calcium ions.

---

* Gönnert (1962) reported that even bathing in contaminated water can lead to infection since the cercarial stage can penetrate the skin.

REFERENCES

Anderson, M., Fisher, J. P., Robinson, J. and Debray, P. H. (1986). *Proc. Br. Crop Prot. Conf., Pests and Diseases*, p. 89

Aveyard, C. S. (1988). *Proc. Br. Crop Prot. Conf., Pests and Diseases*, p. 211

Beach, R. M. and Todd, J. W. (1985). *J. Econ. Entomol.*, **78**, 1125

Beeman, R. W. (1982). *Annu. Rev. Entomol.*, **27**, 253

Benedict, J. H., Walmsley, M. H., Segers, J. C. and Treacy, M. F. (1986). *J. Econ. Entomol.*, **79**, 238

Brezden, B. L. and Gardner, D. R. (1980). *Pestic. Biochem. Physiol.*, **13**, 169

Brooker, P. J., Parsons, J. H., Reid, J. and West, P. J. (1987). *Pestic. Sci.*, **18**, 179

Bull, D. L. and Ivie, G. W. (1980). *Pestic. Biochem. Physiol.*, **13**, 41

Campbell, W. C., Fisher, M. H., Stapley, E. O., Albers-Schönberg, G. and Jacob, T. A. (1983). *Science*, **221**, 823

Carbonaro, M. A., Moreland, D. E., Edge, V. E., Motoyama, N., Rock, G. C. and Dauterman, W. C. (1986). *J. Econ. Entomol.*, **79**, 576

Cathey, G. W. and Bailey, J. C. (1987). *J. Econ. Entomol.*, **80**, 670

Chapman, R. B. and Penman, D. R. (1982). *NZ J. Agric. Res.*, **25**, 119

Cohen, E. (1987). *Annu. Rev. Entomol.*,**32**, 71

Cohen, E. and Casida, J. E. (1982). *Pestic. Biochem. Physiol.*, **17**, 301

Croft, B. A., Miller, R. N., Nelson, R. D. and Westigard, P. H. (1984). *J. Econ. Entomol.*, **77**, 574

Davenport, A. P., Morton, D. B. and Evans, P. D. (1985). *Pestic. Biochem. Physiol.*, **24**, 45

Deul, D. H., de Jong, B. J. and Kortenbach, J. A. M. (1978). *Pestic. Biochem. Physiol.*, **8**, 98

Downer, R. G. H., Gole, J. W. D. and Orr, G. L. (1985). *Pestic. Sci.*, **16**, 472

Edge, V. E. and James, D. G. (1986). *J. Econ. Entomol.*, **79**, 1477

Goldsworthy, G. J. (1983). *Adv. Insect Physiol.*, **17**, 149

Gönnert, R. (1962). *Pflanzenschutz-Nachrichten-Bayer*, **15**, 1

Granett, J., Bisabri-Ershadi, B. and Hejazi, M. J. (1983). *J. Econ. Entomol.*, **76**, 399

Granett, J. and Hejazi, M. J. (1983). *J. Econ. Entomol.*, **76**, 403

Gullo, V. P., Kempf, A. J., MacConnell, J. G., Mrozik, H., Arison, B. and Putter, I. (1983). *Pestic. Sci.*, **14**, 153

Guyer, W. and Neumann, R. (1988). *Pestic. Biochem. Physiol.*, **30**, 166

Hajjar, N. P. and Casida, J. E. (1979). *Pestic. Biochem. Physiol.*, **11**, 33

Hammock, B. D. and Quistad, G. B. (1981). In *Progress in Pesticide Biochemistry*, vol. 1, eds D. H. Hutson and T. R. Roberts, p. 1. Wiley, Chichester

Haynes, J. W. (1987). *J. Econ. Entomol.*, **80**, 597

Hill, D. L., Shih, T.-W. and Struck, R. F. (1979). *Cancer Res.*, **39**, 2528

Hollingworth, R. M. and Lund, A. E. (1982). In *Insecticide Mode of Action*, ed. J. R. Coats, p. 189. Academic Press, New York

Hollingworth, R. M. and Murdock, L. L. (1980). *Science*, **208**, 74

Hollingworth, R. M. and Yim, G. K. W. (1980). *Toxicity, Interactions and Metabolism of Formamidine Pesticides in Mammals*, EPA Rep. 600/1-80-028. US Environ. Prot. Agency, CERI, Cincinnati, OH

Hoyt, S. C., Westigard, P. H. and Croft, B. A. (1985). *J. Econ. Entomol.*, **78**, 656

Ibrahim, Y. B. and Knowles, H. (1986). *Crop Prot.*, **5**, 411

Ishaaya, I., Yablonski, S., Gurevitz, E. and Renneh, S. (1986). *J. Econ. Entomol.*, **79**, 1621

Kimmel, E. C., Casida, J. E. and Fish, R. H. (1980). *J. Agric. Fd Chem.*, **28**, 117

Knowles, C. O. and Gayen, A. K. (1983). *J. Econ. Entomol.*, **76**, 410

Knowles, C. O. and Roulston, W. J. (1972). *J. Aust. Entomol. Soc.*, **11**, 349
Knowles, C. O. and Roulston, W. J. (1973). *J. Econ. Entomol.*, **66**, 1245
Kramer, K. J., Dziadik-Turner, C. and Koga, D. (1985). In *Comprehensive Insect Physiology, Biochemistry and Pharmacology*, vol. 3, eds G. A. Kerkut and L. I. Gilbert, p. 75. Pergamon, Oxford
Lauren, D. R., Agnew, M. P. and Henzell, R. F. (1984). *NZ J. Agric. Res.*, **27**, 425
Lee Chiu, S.-H., Sestokas, E., Taub, R., Smith, J. L., Arison, B. and Lu, A. Y. H. (1984). *Drug Metab. Dispn.*, **12**, 464
Leighton, T., Marks, E. and Leighton, F. (1981). *Science*, **213**, 90
Leopold, R. A., Marks, E. P., Eaton, J. K. and Knoper, J. (1985). *Pestic. Biochem. Physiol.*, **24**, 267
Linn, C., Jr and Roelofs, W. (1985). *Pestic. Sci.*, **16**, 445
McBride, J. J. (1959). *J. Agric. Fd Chem.*, **7**, 255
MAFF (1987). *UK Ministry of Agriculture, Fisheries and Food: Press Release No. 341/ 87*. Whitehall Place, London
Matsumura, F. and Beeman, R. W. (1982). In *Insecticide Mode of Action*, ed. J. R. Coats, p. 229. Academic Press, New York
Mian, L. S. and Mulla, M. S. (1983). *J. Econ. Entomol.*, **76**, 622
Misato, T., Kakiki, K. and Hori, M. (1979). In *Advances in Pesticide Science*, eds H. Geissbühler, G. T. Brooks and P. C. Kearney, p. 458. Pergamon, Oxford
Moje, W. (1960). *Adv. Pest Control Res.*, **3**, 181
Neal, J. W., McIntosh, M. S. and Gott, K. M. (1986). *J. Econ. Entomol.*, **79**, 479
Nimmo, W. B., de Wilde, P. C. and Verloop, A. (1984). *Pestic. Sci.*, **15**, 574
Nimmo, W. B., Willems, A. G. M., Joustra, K. D. and Verloop, A. (1986). *Pestic. Sci.*, **17**, 403
Parrish, M. D. and Roberts, R. B. (1984). *J. Econ. Entomol.*, **77**, 769
Perng, F. S. and Sun, C. N. (1987). *J. Econ. Entomol.*, **80**, 29
Pfeiffer, D. G. (1985). *J. Econ. Entomol.*, **78**, 1421
Pimprikar, G. D. and Georghiou, G. P. (1982). *J. Agric. Fd Chem.*, **30**, 605
Plummer, J. M. and Banna, H. B. (1979). *Comp. Biochem. Physiol. (C) Comp. Pharmacol.*, **62**, 9
Pong, S.-S., Dehaven, R. and Wang, C. C. (1980). *Soc. Neurosci. Abstr.*, **6**, 542
Prasad, J. S., Panwar, M. S. and Rao, Y. S. (1987). *Trop. Pest Managem.*, **33**, 127
Purcell, M. and Granett, J. (1985). *J. Econ. Entomol.*, **78**, 1133
Quistad, G. B., Staiger, L. E., Schooley, D. A., Sparks, T. C. and Hammock, B. D. (1979). *Pestic. Biochem. Physiol.*, **11**, 159
Reed, D. K., Tromley, N. J. and Reed, G. L. (1985). *J. Econ. Entomol.*, **78**, 1067
Robertson, J. L., Richmond, C. E. and Preisler, H. K. (1985). *J. Econ. Entomol.*, **78**, 1129
Roush, R. T. and Wright, J. E. (1986). *J. Econ. Entomol.*, **79**, 562
Rup, P. J. and Chopra, P. K. (1985). *J. Econ. Entomol.*, **78**, 1118
Seuferer, S. L., Braymer, H. D. and Dunn, J. J. (1979). *Pestic. Biochem. Physiol.*, **10**, 174
Smith, K. A., Grigarick, A. A., Lynch, J. H. and Oraze, M. J. (1985). *J. Econ. Entomol.*, **78**, 185
Soltani, N., Besson, M. T. and Delachambre, J. (1984). *Pestic. Biochem. Physiol.*, **21**, 256
Soltani, N., Delbecque, J.-P. and Delachambre, J. (1983). *Pestic. Sci.*, **14**, 615
Strong, L. and Brown, T. A. (1987). *Bull. Entomol. Res.*, **77**, 357
Tanaka, K. and Matsumura, F. (1985). *Pestic. Biochem. Physiol.*, **24**, 124
Uk, S. and Dittrich, V. (1986). *Crop Prot.*, **5**, 341
Westigard, P. H. and Gut, L. J. (1986). *J. Econ. Entomol.*, **79**, 247

9 Insect resistance to insecticides

9.1 AN OVERVIEW

Resistant strains of insects tend to develop whenever a species survives in a locality despite the use of pesticides. Some pesticides lead to the development of resistance more quickly than others, the organochlorine insecticides being notoriously bad in this respect. Usually, the more persistent the poison and the more rapid the life cycle of the insect or acarine, the greater is the risk that the development of resistance will be rapid. In field conditions the influx of non-exposed migrants dilutes the inbreeding of resistant organisms, so that isolated populations are often found to develop resistance quickly. Forgash (1984) reported that 428 different types of insects and acarines, belonging to 14 orders and 83 families, were at that time known to have developed resistance; of these about 60 per cent were organisms of agricultural importance.

In the laboratory, the breeding of insects under 'selection pressure' of an insecticide can lead rapidly to the development of resistance, even for substances to which, when used in field circumstances, resistance seldom develops. To achieve this a captive population is exposed to a dose of an insecticide sufficient to kill, say, 75 per cent of the organisms and then the survivors are mated. By this means it is quite common to achieve a resistance factor (resistance ratio) of between 50 and 1000 (the resistance factor is defined as the LD_{50} for the resistant strain divided by the LD_{50} for the susceptible strain). Roush and Wolfenbarger (1985) recorded a particularly large resistance factor ($RF > 40\ 000$) for a strain of *Heliothis virescens* exposed to methomyl. This was achieved in one generation by first exposing neonatal larvae to selection pressure using a methomyl-contaminated wheatgerm diet and then repeating this process with later instars.

An early seminal experiment demonstrated that the propensity for resistance was inherent in the genetic variation within a population (or, as someone expressively explained, 'theory requires that some mammoths must have had an innate resistance to warfarin'!). The experiment was carried out by Bennett (1960); essentially, working on female *Drosophila melanogaster*, he started with 44 pair-mating progenies and divided each into two groups, one of which was treated with DDT and one of which was not. The unsprayed siblings of the 20 groups of flies that proved to be the most resistant to DDT were then bred, divided, and the process repeated. By this means, within 5–15 generations a 30-fold increase in resistance was recorded without the organisms concerned, or any of their predecessors, having ever been exposed to DDT at all. Such experiments do not, of course, give any information about how frequently mutation occurs in the presence of particular pesticides. The latter, in turn, should be distinguished from chance mutations (believed to be about 1 in 100 000) that lead to genetic differences in a population, which allow some individuals (compare Bennett's experiment) to survive should they later come into contact with an appropriate pesticide (Muggleton, 1984).

In field conditions, the effect of a persistent pesticide is to lead to 'unnatural selection'. It kills the more susceptible pest organisms, leaving a few naturally resistant individuals to recolonise the area. Breeding rapidly in the absence of predators (unless the pesticide is very selective), these resistant organisms produce offspring that have a greater tolerance to the poison than had the earlier population.

The development of resistance has several serious consequences for mankind. At best, it leads to the need to apply more pesticide to achieve the same level of control as hitherto, with correspondingly greater risks to the environment. In many parts of the world the consequence is that the cost of application becomes prohibitive and spraying ceases, with an increase of vector-borne disease, greater crop losses and poorer-quality agricultural produce. Moreover, for everyone, there is ever present in the background the spectre that pests may develop resistance quicker than new products (or non-chemical methods of control) can be introduced.

It is now clear that there is not one single cause of resistance. For any one species the cause (or mixture of causes) of resistance to different pesticides may vary from substance to substance. Moreover, the resistance that develops to a particular substance may occur for quite different reasons in different species. Briefly, factors involved in resistance may be of a behavioural, morphological, physiological or biochemical nature.

Behavioural changes may decrease the chances of an insect coming into contact with a toxic dose of the poison. For example, flying insects may acquire the instinct not to alight on a contaminated surface. Similarly, Aliniazee (1983) demonstrated that a part of the resistance developed by field populations of filbert aphids, *Myzocallis coryli*, to repeated carbaryl sprays was due to more effective avoidance capability.

Morphological changes may result in a decrease in the amount entering the insect body in unit time compared with the amount taken up by a susceptible strain; for example, alteration of cuticular structure may reduce the rate of penetration of a topically applied poison.

Physiological changes include alteration in the pattern of uptake or in the rate of excretion of an insecticide or of its metabolites. Examples are given in the next section.

Biochemical changes are broadly of two kinds. One of these (changes in the rate or route of metabolism of a particular insecticide) determines how much may reach its site of action; the other (loss of susceptibility of the target cell, receptor or enzyme) determines how much has to reach the site of action to have a detrimental effect.

Before giving specific examples to illustrate the contribution of various factors to resistance, it is necessary to mention the further complication of **cross-resistance**. When, for instance, insects are exposed to γ-HCH (section 6.6), it is common for resistance to develop not only to this substance (to which they were exposed) but also to members of the cyclodiene family (to which they had never been exposed). On the other hand, insects resistant to γ-HCH usually develop little or no resistance to members of the DDT family. Cross-resistance is considered in more detail in section 9.7.

There is, however, another undesirable complication somewhat similar to cross-resistance; it has been called **conditioning**. It is possible for a strain of insects, already resistant to one group of insecticides, A, when exposed to another group of substances, B, to lose their susceptibility to these substances more rapidly than do insects that had not initially developed resistance to compounds in group A. For example, strains of an insect species that are resistant to a cyclodiene often tend, on exposure to DDT, to develop DDT resistance more rapidly than do other strains that have no history of exposure either to cyclodienes or to DDT. Such 'conditioning' (which is little understood) can even cross group frontiers; thus dieldrin-resistant strains of insects have been known rapidly to develop resistance to the carbamate, carbaryl. Conditioning could involve amplification of inducible enzymes capable of accelerating metabolism, but this is not always evident in relation to the types of metabolism affecting pesticides in the two groups, A and B.

9.2 IMPORTANCE OF UPTAKE AND EXCRETION

Resistance can be caused by any mechanism or barrier that reduces the amount of a pesticide reaching its site of action or that reduces the sensitivity of the site of action itself. The nature of the barrier that a toxicant has to penetrate in order to gain access to an insect is therefore the first possible variable to be considered. Alteration in the lipid composition of insect cuticle can result in a decreased rate of absorption and thus be one factor in an overall development of resistance (Patil and Guthrie, 1979). Change in the rate of uptake is, however, seldom the sole cause of resistance (Macdonald *et al.*, 1985) but may contribute a low level of resistance by which levels of resistance caused by all other factors must be multiplied. An example is provided by the work of Scott and Georghiou (1986). Working with susceptible and resistant strains of the housefly, they concluded that diminished cuticular penetration partly contributed to an observed 6000-fold increase in resistance to permethrin. Similarly, Noppun *et al.* (1989) reported that reduced cuticular penetration appeared to be an important mechanism of resistance to fenvalerate in a resistant strain of the diamondback moth, *Plutella xylostella*. Again, Golenda and Forgash (1989) found that the penetration of fenvalerate was faster into a susceptible strain of the housefly than it was into a tolerant strain, leading for a while to a doubling of the internal concentration. These workers also reported that the excretion of metabolites was not detected in the susceptible strain until 24 h had elapsed after treatment, whereas in the resistant strain metabolites were detected after 4 h. Another example is provided by Delorme *et al.* (1988) who reported that reduced penetration of deltamethrin contributed in small but significant degree to the resistance noted in a strain of *Spodoptera exigua* from Guatemala.

Nevertheless, the precise role played by differences in the ease with which a given pesticide penetrates into different strains of an insect are not always clear (Oppenoorth and Welling, 1976). In its simplest form, it can be argued that if the rate of destruction or elimination of any pesticide that has entered is commensurate with the amount penetrating in unit time, little will get to the site of action. However, for more persistent pesticides the significance of reduced rate of penetration into tolerant organisms is not so readily explained, yet Plapp and Hoyer (1968) found that both DDT and dieldrin entered more slowly into one strain of housefly, a difference that they ascribed to a mutant gene (symbol, *tin*).

Excretion can also be a factor in increased resistance. This is illustrated by the work of le Patourel and Salama (1986), who found that organisms belonging to a strain of *Sitophilus granarius* resistant to γ-HCH excreted a large proportion of a topically applied dose in the frass pellets whereas those of a susceptible strain accumulated the poison in their bodies.

Occasionally, the physiological state of the insect can alter its tolerance of an insecticide. Riordan (1987) studied the susceptibility of pregnant and non-pregnant females of the tsetse fly, *Glossina palpalis palpalis*, to various pesticides. It was found that the pregnant flies, which were about 1.3 times as heavy as non-pregnant females, were 2.5–4 times more tolerant of organochlorine insecticides than were the non-pregnant insects. This tolerance (and in this context, *tolerance* is a better description than *resistance*) was attributed to these lipophilic insecticides becoming immobilised by passing into the maternal fat body and lipid-rich larval food. A practical consequence of this could be the survival in the field of pregnant tsetse flies even though males might be killed. No increase in tolerance of organophosphorus compounds was observed.

9.3 THE ROLE OF HYDROLASES

Resistance based on altered hydrolase activity is only well documented in relation to the metabolism of organophosphorus compounds (Wood, 1981).

Resistance associated with altered hydrolase activity can arise in two ways. First, the resistant strain (R) may be able to make more molecules of an enzyme identical in structure to that present in the susceptible strain (S); or, secondly, the R strain may produce a modification of that enzyme which is able more effectively to catalyse the decomposition of the toxicant to which the R strain has become resistant. An example of the latter is the production of a mutant form of carboxylesterase, which, while poor at hydrolysing such linkages, becomes capable of hydrolysing other esters that possess no carboxylic acid groups at all.

Hydrolases of many types play a part in pesticide metabolism and so could sometimes be responsible for the development of insect resistance. Those involved in hydrolysis of organophosphorus insecticides include phosphatases, phosphorotriesterases, aliesterases, A-esterases, carboxy(l)esterases and amidases. Not all of these names are mutually exclusive; in addition, hydrolases may be named after the substrate being acted upon at the time (e.g. paraoxonase, malaoxonase). Figure 9.1 shows two ways in which a phosphotriester may be hydrolysed, possibly in reactions catalysed by different enzymes. Parallel reactions occur with varying ease with thio- and dithiophosphates, although, again, considerable enzyme specificity probably exists.

An apparently straightforward case in which resistance is related to hydrolase activity is provided by de Villar *et al.* (1983). Working with the Hirokawa strain of *Musca domestica* (which is resistant to malathion), they found that esterase activity, as assessed by the ability of extracts to hydrolyse α-naphthylacetate, was greater than in the sensitive strain. It is therefore noteworthy that the authors included in the title to their publication the words 'unusual type of malathion carboxylesterase'. The reason for this is that some malathion-resistant strains of houseflies, apparently resistant by virtue of high hydrolase activity, may actually have no greater carboxylesterase activity than is present in the sensitive strain (Oppenoorth and van Asperen, 1961).

The preceding observation is of interest, for in some circumstances it appears to lead to a paradox: a strain that is resistant to malathion as a consequence of the presence of a gene product usually designated as a carboxylesterase (because in the S strain it splits the ethyl succinate linkage, figure 4.7) is frequently also resistant to organophosphorus compounds

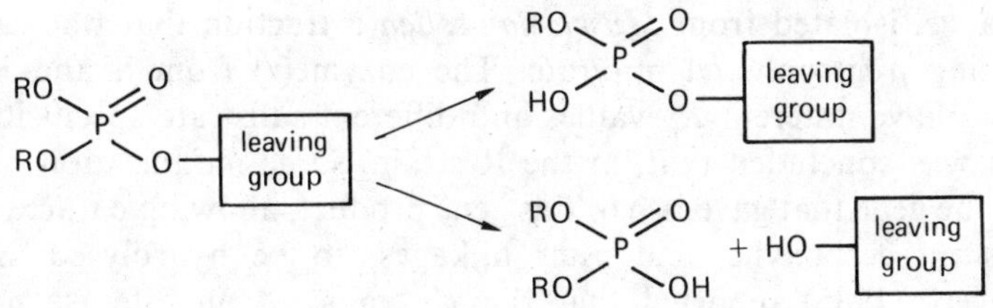

Figure 9.1 Two types of hydrolytic cleavage of organophosphates

possessing no such linkage. A good example is provided by the work of Beranek and Oppenoorth (1977) using two strains of the peach potato aphid, *Myzus persicae*, that were respectively susceptible to, and tolerant of, organophosphorus insecticides. They observed that methyl paraoxon was rapidly destroyed by a partly purified enzyme possessing the same electrophoretic characteristics as one previously shown to have carboxylesterase activity with respect to malathion. Corresponding preparations from the S strain were found to possess little carboxylesterase activity and they had little effect on methyl paraoxon. The possibility of an unknown enzyme being responsible for the methyl paraoxon breakdown was minimised by partial purification of the enzymes from the S and R strains; using these preparations it was demonstrated that the physical and electrophoretic properties of the enzymes derived from the two strains were extremely similar.

Evidence concerning the importance of the part played by hydrolases in the development of resistance is somewhat conflicting. Nolan and O'Brien (1970) studied the metabolism in susceptible and resistant houseflies of paraoxon that had been labelled on the ethyl groups. De-ethylation occurred in both S and R strains but there was little evidence that differences in phosphotriester hydrolase activity contributed greatly to the resistance. On the other hand, Oppenoorth and Voerman (1975) reported that the hydrolysis of paraoxon and malaoxon to dialkylphosphoric acids was 3–8 fold greater in resistant forms of *Myzus persicae* than it was in susceptible strains.

Villani *et al.* (1983) bioassayed 18 strains of the *Culex pipiens* complex for resistance to chlorpyrifos. They then electrophoresed extracts to separate esterases. Susceptible strains invariably had low activity bands for these enzymes whereas high esterase activity was always associated with resistance. It was pointed out, however, that the converse was not necessarily true, for R strains could possess resistance for reasons that had nothing to do with esterase activity. Yasutomi (1983) similarly concluded that the mechanism of resistance to organophosphorus insecticides in culicine mosquitoes was different from that in houseflies; resistance paralleled high esterase activity and it was furthermore concluded that inheritance was as a single factor with intermediate dominance.

One way to investigate whether hydrolysis-based resistance is due to more of the enzyme present in the S strain or to enzymic modification is to separate esterases by electrophoresis and then to do kinetic studies. Kao *et al.* (1985), for instance, isolated from *Musca domestica* a fraction that was capable of hydrolysing *p*-nitrophenyl butyrate. The enzyme(s) from S and R strains proved to have different K_m values and different substrate specificities, from which it was concluded that, in the R strain, some modification had taken place in the gene that gave rise to this gene product, allowing paraoxon, which contains no carboxylic acid ester linkages, to be hydrolysed. Similarly, Hemingway (1985) reported that the K_m value of an esterase present in malathion-resistant adult *Anopheles arabiensis* was three times that of an esterase extracted from an S strain. In both cases, the K_m value was observed for α-naphthyl acetate as substrate. It should be added, however, that there are no known 'natural substrates' for the hydrolases involved in foreign-compound metabolism, and some researchers have queried the validity of using the hydrolysis of *p*-nitrophenyl butyrate or of α-naphthyl acetate as a criterion of *in vivo* carboxylesterase activity.

Another way to investigate the mechanism by which resistance develops is by gene mapping. For example, using the sheep blowfly, *Lucilia cuprina*, Raftos and Hughes (1986) showed that resistance to malathion was associated with a gene located on a chromosome in a position spatially inseparable from the locus controlling high esterase activity.

Further studies often reveal that gene amplification has occurred, a single gene present in the S strain occurring more than once in the R strain. Precisely how gene amplification occurs in individual cases is seldom clear, but there is evidence that one method could involve mismatch of homologous chromosomes at meiosis. For example, if two such chromosomes $[A_1,H_1,B_1,C_1, \ldots; A_2,H_2,B_2,C_2, \ldots]$ were misaligned before cross-over, a gene, H, coding for a hydrolase, could become duplicated in one daughter cell $[A_2,B_1,C_1, \ldots; A_1,H_1,H_2,B_2,C_2, \ldots]$.

Devonshire and Sawicki (1979) studied several strains of *Mysus persicae* and reported that the titres of an extractable hydrolase capable of hydrolysing paraoxon were, in different strains, related roughly geometrically (1,2,4,8, ...) and that this was associated with an apparent parallel progression in the number of copies of the gene coding for the hydrolase. Similarly, Mouchès *et al.* (1986) found, by the use of an antiserum technique, that a strain of *Culex quinquefasciatus* had an esterase titre 500-fold that of the S strain. Then, by genetic engineering they made a combinant DNA to the mRNA for the esterase. By means of a nitrocellulose slot–blot technique (compare Watson *et al.*, 1983) they were able to confirm that the R strain (Tem-R) being used had 250 times as many copies of the gene as had adults of the S strain.

A third way of investigating the cause of resistance is to apply the pesticide jointly with a compound that is believed to be a specific inhibitor of a particular type of enzyme. The use of piperonyl butoxide and sesamex as specific inhibitors of the mono-oxygenase system was mentioned in section 3.4. Rather similarly, many workers believe, triphenyl phosphate, *S,S,S*-tributyl phosphorotrithioate and EPN (figure 9.2) are specific inhibitors of some hydrolases.

The use of inhibitors of hydrolases is illustrated by the work of Binns (1986) using a strain of *Tribolium castaneum* that was specifically resistant to malathion. He first determined the toxicity of malathion to these organisms and then applied it mixed with triphenyl phosphate. In the second case the resistance was largely annulled in both larvae and adults. Similarly, Payne and Brown (1984) demonstrated that a strain of the tobacco budworm, *Heliothis virescens*, that was resistant to methyl parathion (resistance factor, 375 at the

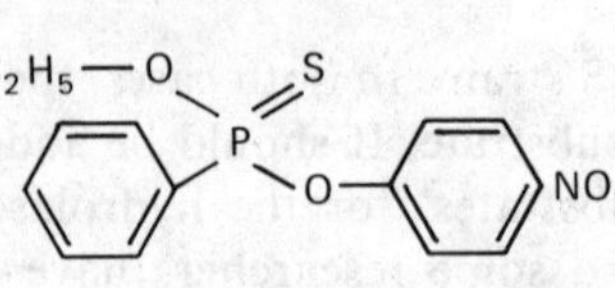

(a) EPN (*O*-ethyl *O*-(*p*-nitrophenyl)
phenyl phosphonothioate)

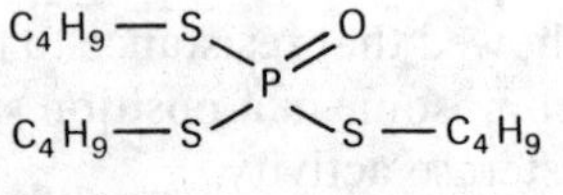

(b) *S,S,S*-Tributyl phosphorotrithioate (DEF®)

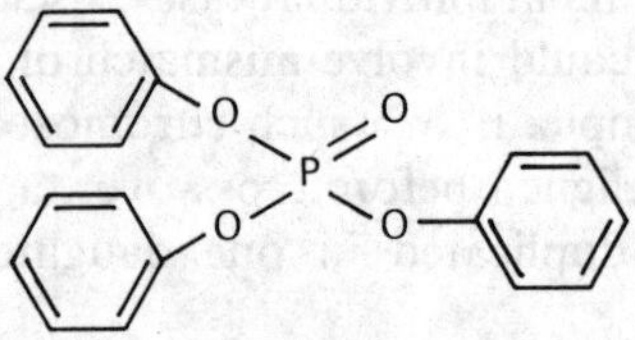

(c) Triphenyl phosphate

Figure 9.2   Some probable inhibitors of esterases

LD$_{90}$ level) lost most of the resistance (resistance factor, 10) if applied mixed with EPN or tributyl phosphorotrithioate. It is of interest that these authors raised the question of whether synergists such as EPN really were inhibitors of hydrolases or whether they acted in some unknown way. (Readers of current literature will often observe that the phrase 'ester cleavage' is used, rather than the more explicit expression 'hydrolysis of the ester linkage', especially when glutathione transferase involvement is a possibility.) Despite these doubts, it is of interest that Delorme *et al.* (1988), working with a resistant strain of *Spodoptera exigua* from Guatemala, concluded that a 100-fold increase in resistance to deltamethrin was in large measure due to enhanced metabolism for which an esterase was responsible. A 17-fold increase in the rate of degradation was observed in the resistant strain and this increase was largely annulled by *S,S,S*-tributyl phosphorotrithioate.

A final example is provided by the work of Raymond *et al.* (1986) on two chlorpyrifos-resistant strains and one susceptible strain of *Culex quinquefasciatus* from southern France. They determined the toxicity of chlorpyrifos and three carbamates to organisms from each of the three strains, first in the absence and then in the presence of synergists; they also studied the distribution of four types of enzymes. It was demonstrated that the reason why one strain (termed S54) was resistant was because it possessed large quantities of a detoxifying hydrolase, amounting to at least 6 per cent of the total protein. In a second strain (MSE), where resistance occurs for a quite different reason, esterase protein was so small a proportion of the total protein that its percentage could not be determined.

9.4 MONO-OXYGENASE ACTIVITY IN RELATION TO RESISTANCE

In view of the importance of mono-oxygenase systems to pesticide metabolism, it is to be expected that they should sometimes be involved in mechanisms leading to resistance. For carbamates and pyrethroids this expectation is realised; in the case of organophosphorus compounds the position is complicated by the fact that oxidation can sometimes lead to initial activation while often, at the same time, enabling later hydrolytic attack to occur more rapidly.

Moorefield (1960) showed that the build-up of resistance that occurred when houseflies were exposed to carbaryl (section 5.5) was largely prevented when selection was attempted using a 1:5 mixture of carbaryl and the methylene dioxyphenyl synergist, piperonyl butoxide (figure 7.3). At about the same time, Eldefrawi and colleagues came to a similar conclusion, observing that the resistance of houseflies to carbaryl could be abolished by simultaneous application of carbaryl and another methylene dioxyphenyl compound, sesamex (Eldefrawi *et al.*, 1960). More generally, whenever compounds of the methylene dioxyphenyl type are able to decrease the resistance factor (or prevent rapid build-up of resistance that occurs in their absence), such events provide strong evidence that oxidative metabolism is a major cause of resistance.

Methylene dioxyphenyl compounds were used as synergists for natural pyrethroids from about 1940 (section 7.1) and were therefore in use commercially before their mode of action was fully appreciated. Resistance to pyrethroids is now known often to be related to increased oxidative effectiveness. For example, Farnham (1973) demonstrated that sesamex-synergised natural pyrethrins decreased the resistance factor (section 8.1) observed for a resistant strain of houseflies but had little effect on pyrethrin toxicity to susceptible strains. Similarly, Golenda and Forgash (1985) found that both piperonyl butoxide and *S,S,S*-tributyl phosphorotrithioate (section 7.2) synergised the action of fenvalerate in resistant strains of houseflies but that piperonyl butoxide was by far the more effective; these investigators, like many others, found that presence of the synergist had little effect on the LD_{50} of the pyrethroid to susceptible flies. The work of Pimprikar and Georghiou (1979, 1982), also using resistant and susceptible houseflies, has shown that a 20-fold difference in LD_{50} values of diflubenzuron (section 8.1) when applied to larvae of two strains of houseflies largely disappears in the presence of sesamex. High mono-oxygenase activity may also explain some cases where resistance has developed to the juvenile hormone analogue, methoprene (section 8.4). An example of housefly resistance of this kind is provided by Hammock *et al.* (1977).

Another approach that sometimes shows whether metabolism is likely to be involved in resistance is to compare *in vitro* and *in vivo* studies with a pesticide in the presence and in the absence of a particular metabolic inhibitor. In relation to oxidation, for example, Fukuto *et al.* (1962) demonstrated that there was a large discrepancy between the dose of several carbamates that inhibited by 50 per cent the activity of isolated housefly cholinesterase and the corresponding LD_{50} values to whole flies. It was observed, however, that this discrepancy largely disappeared when the LD_{50} values of carbamates synergised with piperonyl butoxide were compared with the 50 per cent inhibitory doses for acetylcholinesterase of carbamates *in vitro*. The implication of this observation is that, if oxidative metabolism *in vivo* is prevented, the doses of the several carbamates able to reach the site of action in the organism are more closely related to the doses that inhibit the enzyme *in vitro*. Other examples have been provided by Wilkinson and Brattsten (1972). From such work it can often be concluded with reasonable certainty that, in the particular case of resistance being studied, the selection for particular forms of cytochrome P_{450} capable of rapidly oxidising the pesticide in question is likely to be a mechanism leading to the development of resistance.

Oxidation is almost certainly of importance in relation to resistance to some organophosphorus compounds. Morton and Holwerda (1985) demonstrated that this was the case for malathion resistance in a resistant strain of the housefly, where resistance was highly correlated with both glucose 6-phosphate dehydrogenase activity and mono-oxygenase activity. In general, however, for organophosphorus compounds the interpretation of experimental results may not be easy because of the interplay of several factors. First, there is the problem of oxidative activation, which complicates any attempt to relate oxidation to *loss* of activity. Secondly, as in the case of malathion, a toxic oxidation product often has a short half-life, being destroyed, *inter alia*, by hydrolytic enzymes. A third complication is that oxidation products such as malaoxon are not only more active inhibitors of acetylcholinesterase but also of carboxylesterases (and probably of other detoxifying esterases too).

It follows from the above considerations that oxon metabolic products formed from many organophosphorus compounds could have a feedback interference effect on the metabolism of the parent substance. For example, malathion can be converted to malaoxon in strains of insects rich in mono-oxygenase; the powerful inhibitory effect of this oxon upon esterases could prevent the breakdown of malathion to its mono-ester (figure 4.7). Hence a strain rich in mono-oxygenase could provide a situation in which the alternative route of hydrolytic metabolism was greatly retarded. Again, the production of highly toxic oxons would probably be expected to delay the development of resistance, but their high activity also implies that they become strongly bound to hydrolytic esterases. Not only are those esterases highly inhibited but, simultaneously, this binding prevents much of the oxon from reaching its site of action on acetylcholinesterase (Motoyama *et al.*, 1984). These two effects may be inseparable from one another, yet the first of them might be expected to delay the development of resistance while the second could be an excellent defence mechanism and hence a cause of the development of resistance.

A final difficulty in studying mono-oxygenases in relation to resistance is that it is not always clear whether oxidation is involved in certain metabolic changes; the reaction leading to *O*-dealkylation, for example, is almost always detoxifying and could lead to resistance, but it can be brought about by mono-oxygenase action, or by hydrolases or by glutathione-*S*-transferase action (chapter 3 and section 9.5).

The same two genetic possibilities postulated to explain individual cases of resistance to hydrolases (gene modification and gene amplification) have been invoked to explain the contribution of oxidases. It is found that there is frequently a higher level of cytochrome P_{450} in resistant insects than in susceptible ones, but the difference is seldom sufficient fully to account for the increase in metabolism. The simplest possibility—namely, replication of the P_{450} gene(s)—is thus an insufficient explanation. The total P_{450} system must therefore be in some way more efficient in those resistant strains where resistance is linked to an oxidative mechanism than it is in susceptible strains. Working with microsomes prepared from housefly abdomens, Ronis *et al.* (1988) found that at least four isozymes of cytochrome P_{450} were present and that some oxidative processes were actually more evident in the susceptible strain than in the particular resistant strain under investigation. They concluded that changes in the microsomal mono-oxygenase system associated with pesticide resistance can be more complex than the appearance of new forms of cytochrome P_{450} (or, indeed, of more of the old), since in this case it would appear that the development of resistance was associated with a simultaneous decrease in the quantity of a form of cytochrome P_{450} that was present at high levels in the susceptible strain.

9.5 GLUTATHIONE-*S*-TRANSFERASES AND DDT DEHYDROCHLORINASE

The glutathione-*S*-transferase complex and its role in metabolism was discussed in section 3.5. Briefly, in many (but not all) of the reactions it catalyses, a part (R) of a foreign compound RX is transferred to the thiol group of glutathione, a tripeptide comprising cysteine, glycine and glutamic acid. The hydrogen atom of the cysteine thiol group is transferred to the residue X, to give a substance HX. The latter is often a dealkylated or dearylated derivative of RX with low toxicity and is often more reactive than the original molecule, undergoing further reactions leading to conjugation and to elimination from the body. Enzymes of the glutathione-*S*-transferase complex are soluble, consisting of two subunits, each with a molecular weight of approximately 23 000. Different amounts of different forms of enzymes of this complex occur in different species of animals and plants, a fact that contributes to the variation in tolerances shown by such species when they come into contact with certain pesticides or drugs.

The extent to which glutathione-*S*-transferases contribute to insect resistance towards insecticides remains uncertain. Much of the pioneering work was done on organophosphorus compounds because of the commercial importance of these compounds and because it was soon evident that high resistance to organophosphorus compounds was sometimes associated with *low* classical esterase activity. Instead, resistance seemed, at that time, to be associated with an enzyme with phosphatase-like action. In some such cases, this action was found to be dependent on a supply of glutathione and could not, therefore, be attributed to an enzyme with altered *hydrolase* capability.

An early illustrative example is provided by Yang *et al.* (1971). These workers found that glutathione-supplemented extracts from a multi-resistant strain of housefly degraded diazinon more rapidly than did similar extracts from a susceptible strain. At about the same time Lewis and Sawicki (1971) showed that an enzyme with low classical esterase activity nevertheless acted as a 'phosphatase', splitting diazinon to give de-ethyl diazinon and diethyl phosphorothioic acid (figure 9.3). The enzyme was present in extracts made from a diazinon-resistant strain of housefly.

The work of Motoyama and Dauterman in the early 1970s illustrated particularly clearly the significance in some resistant strains of housefly of enhanced glutathione-*S*-transferase activity. They demonstrated that the rates of degradation of azinphos-methyl and of diazinon were often 4–6 times greater in the presence of enzyme preparations made from resistant strains than in those made from susceptible strains. This work has been summarised and illustrated by Dauterman (1983). More recently, Armstrong and Suckling (1988) observed that metabolism of azinphos-methyl occurred more rapidly in a resistant strain of the light brown apple moth (*Epiphyas postvittam*) than it did in a susceptible strain. Moreover, the rate of metabolism was influenced by the presence of glutathione. A kinetic study, using 2,4-dichloronitrobenzene as a substrate for glutathione transferases, led to the conclusion that the higher activity of this enzyme complex in the resistant strain was probably a consequence of the presence in these organisms, not of new and more active forms of the enzyme, but of more of the types of the enzyme to be found in the susceptible strain.

Clark *et al.* (1986) purified up to 100-fold the glutathione-*S*-transferases in different strains of the housefly. They demonstrated the presence of several such enzymes with overlapping specificities and that different strains of the

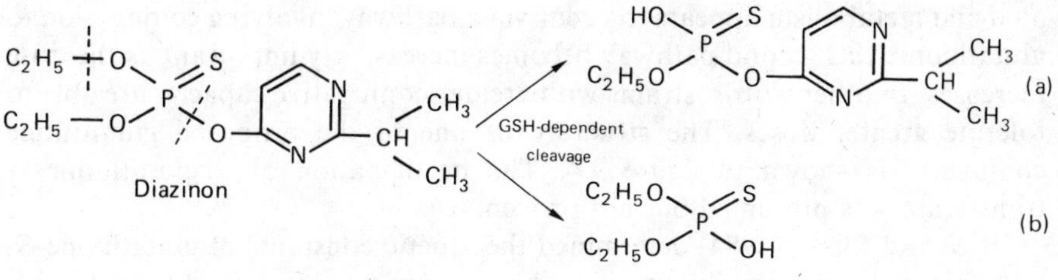

Figure 9.3 GSH-dependent cleavage of diazinon to (a) de-ethyl diazinon and (b) diethyl phosphorothioic acid

housefly had different types of these enzymes. It was concluded that differences in the quantity or type of glutathione-*S*-transferases might explain differences in tolerances of the different strains.

Oppenoorth *et al.* (1977), using a strain of housefly that was resistant to tetrachlorvinphos, found that organisms of this resistant strain contained a glutathione-dependent enzyme that could degrade various compounds, including parathion and methyl parathion, up to 120 times more rapidly than could organisms of a susceptible strain. Wells *et al.* (1986) studied the *in vivo* metabolism in houseflies of propetamphos, an organophosphorus insecticide used in public hygiene (figure 9.4). The leaving group is joined to phosphate by a P–O–vinyl linkage. At low substrate levels this linkage is broken by hydrolysis, with the formation of the isopropyl ester of acetoacetic acid. This hydrolysis is the main metabolic route in both susceptible and resistant organisms. However, at substrate levels exceeding about 25 ng per fly (i.e. in surviving resistant organisms) this enzyme system appears to become satur-

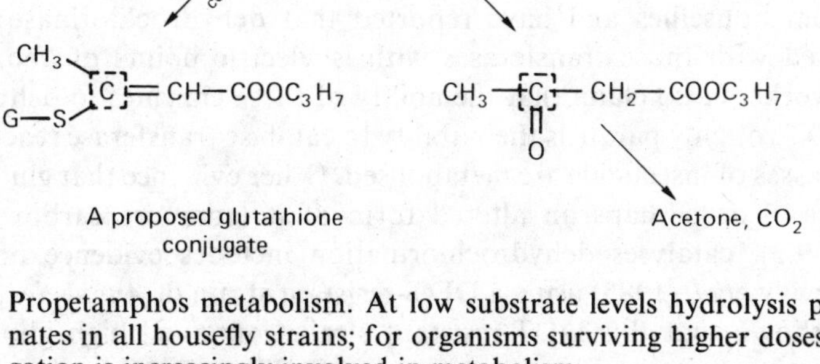

Figure 9.4 Propetamphos metabolism. At low substrate levels hydrolysis predominates in all housefly strains; for organisms surviving higher doses, conjugation is increasingly involved in metabolism

ated and metabolism appears to occur via a pathway involving conjugation to glutathione; this second pathway becomes increasingly important as the dose increases. In other words, strains with greater conjugative capacity are able to tolerate greater doses. The structure of one of the proposed glutathione conjugates is shown in figure 9.4. The participation of a glutathione-S-transferase was presumed but not proven.

Ottea and Plapp (1984) determined the kinetic constants of glutathione-S-transferases in a susceptible strain and in two resistant strains of houseflies. It was found that the Michaelis constant, K_m, of the enzyme or enzymes in the two resistant strains differed from that in the susceptible strain (compare mono-oxygenases, section 3.4). It was concluded that the resistance was attributable to metabolic differences associated with the presence of different glutathione-S-transferases in the resistant and susceptible forms, rather than to production in resistant strains of more of the type present in the susceptible organisms. They also noted that it was possible to induce enzymes in all three strains of houseflies, although the best inducing agent varied with the species; induction, like resistance, resulted in an alteration of the K_m of the enzymes, rather than a change in the V_{max} values (compare induction, section 6.8).

Many species of insects develop resistance to DDT very readily and the resistant strains are often found to contain elevated dehydrochlorinase activity (e.g. Wood, 1981). Dehydrochlorinase, formerly DDTase, is an enzyme capable of removing the elements of hydrogen chloride from the DDT molecule. As has been mentioned elsewhere (section 6.5) this reaction, important in DDT metabolism, does not fit readily into the range of metabolic reactions common to most pesticides. The enzyme was first separated by Lipke and Kearns (1960) and it was soon shown that its action depends on a supply of glutathione. However, unlike the versatile glutathione-S-alkyl and -S-aryl transferase systems, the glutathione is, according to these workers, not depleted during the course of the dehydrochlorination. Furthermore, Motoyama and Dauterman (1977) partly purified glutathione-S-transferase(s) from the soluble fraction of resistant houseflies and found that this enzyme, when provided with GSH, had no dehydrochlorinase activity although it was active in the degradation of organophosphorus compounds.

In contrast, Clark *et al.* (1986) have isolated several glutathione-S-transferases from houseflies and have reported that dehydrochlorinase activity is associated with those transferases with isoelectric points of about pH 7.1. These workers also claim that the ability of these enzymes to dehydrochlorinate DDT roughly parallels their ability to catalyse transferase reactions when other classes of insecticide are metabolised. Other evidence that glutathione-S-transferase, or perhaps an altered form of it (compare carboxylesterases, section 9.3), catalyses dehydrochlorination includes evidence provided by Hemingway *et al.* (1985) using a DDT-resistant strain of *Anopheles sacharovis*. It was shown that this DDT-resistant strain contained high glutathione-S-transferase activity and readily converted DDT to DDE in the presence of glutathione. Again, Chadwick *et al.* (1984) worked with two strains of mosquito that had already developed some resistance to both DDT and to pyrethroids. After 14 generations of selection pressure using DDT, the resistance to DDT was so high that no LC_{50} could be recorded, yet the LD_{50} of pyrethroids to the mosquitoes had hardly changed, suggesting that the cause of resistance to these two groups of insecticides was different. The very high tolerance of DDT was apparently due to the presence of a dehydrochlorinase.

9.6 MODIFICATION OF THE SITE OF ACTION

The site of action of organophosphorus and carbamate insecticides is acetyl-cholinesterase (section 4.5). In preparations made from insect heads or bodies, part of the acetylcholinesterase appears in the microsomal fraction and so appears to be membrane-bound, but both soluble and membrane-bound acetylcholinesterase are similarly inhibited by carbamates and organophosphorus insecticides (Hama, 1983). The first suspected case of resistance relating to an altered and less sensitive acetylcholinesterase was observed in *Tetranychus urticae* in 1964. Since then, many cases have been recognised in mites and insects of importance in crop protection, animal hygiene and public health. Examples have been collected by Oppenoorth and Welling (1976), by Hama (1983) and by Hemingway and Georghiou (1983).

Voss (1980) referred to cases where resistance factors (section 8.1) of between 100 and 1000 had been reported for *Tetranychus urticae*, houseflies, rice hoppers and *Spodoptera littoralis*. Other examples are provided by Hama (1983). In each case an alteration in the structure or conformation of cholinesterase appears to have occurred, leading to increased insensitivity to certain organophosphorus compounds and carbamates. The mechanism whereby this is achieved is uncertain, but the change leads to a delay in the appearance of symptoms for long enough to allow enzymic defence mechanisms to come into operation. There is, however, a difficulty; it has been pointed out that modified acetylcholinesterase is insensitive to some, but seldom to all, organophosphorus compounds and carbamates. Hemingway and Georghiou (1983) have discussed this problem and speculated on what type of mechanism could account for such discriminatory insensitivity. Differences in defence mechanisms located at the target site could theoretically account for it but there is usually little evidence to support this possibility. It seems more likely, therefore, that the structure of acetylcholinesterase has undergone change leading to different degrees of binding with anticholinesterases of different molecular conformations. Oppenoorth and Welling (1976) concluded that the modified forms of acetylcholinesterase independently evolved in different species are different from one another; a practical consequence of this is that different patterns of cross-resistance are to be expected (section 9.7).

O'Brien *et al.* (1978) demonstrated that altered acetylcholinesterase present in resistant strains of houseflies had different substrate preferences from that in susceptible strains. Essentially, these workers purified acetylcholinesterase from heads of houseflies and found that the form obtained from the resistant strain of flies bound organophosphorus compounds, carbamates (and also butyrylcholine) less firmly than did the enzyme from the susceptible strain (butyrylcholinesterase, or pseudocholinesterase, which is present in mammals, is probably absent in insects). A difference between acetylcholinesterase from resistant and susceptible strains was also observed by Devonshire and Moores (1984), although they reported a contrasting situation, where the acetylcholine from a resistant strain of houseflies had a 3.4-fold *greater* affinity for an analogue substrate, acetylthiocholine, than did the form of the enzyme derived from a susceptible strain. It must, however, be admitted that conventional means of studying differences in protein structure (e.g. gel electrophoresis) have so far failed to distinguish between forms of the enzyme present in susceptible and resistant strains of several species of insects. However, some separation using DEAE-cellulose chromatography has apparently been achieved of the forms of acetylcholinesterase in such strains of *Nephotettix cincticeps* (Hama, 1976).

Another method of approach which suggests that one form of resistance to organophosphorus compounds and to carbamates can be due to altered acetylcholinesterase is the determination of kinetic constants, and particularly the Michaelis constant, K_m. This essentially measures the affinity between an enzyme and its substrate (in this case, acetylcholine, butyrylcholine or acetylthiocholine). An example is provided by O'Brien *et al.* (1978) using butyrylcholine as the substrate for the acetylcholinesterase in susceptible and resistant houseflies. It was found that the K_m value was 25 times greater for the enzyme in the resistant strain than for that obtained from the susceptible organisms. However, differences of this magnitude were not obtained using other substrates, and it was concluded that the secondary binding site for organophosphorus compounds (or the distance between this site and the primary esteratic binding site) had undergone alteration in the type of cholinesterase present in resistant organisms.

Other recent work which probably indicates that altered acetylcholinesterase is responsible for the resistance includes that of Morton and Holwerda (1985) using *Drosophila melanogaster* (resistance towards malathion); Pree *et al.* (1986) using the leafminer, *Phyllonorycter blancardella* (towards pyrethroids); Raymond *et al.* (1986) studying the *Culex pipiens* complex (towards the oxon of chlorpyrifos); and Hemingway *et al.* (1985) working with *Anopheles sacharovi* (towards carbamates and organophosphorus compounds).

In other cases of resistance, where the predominant mode of action is neurotoxic but acetylcholinesterase is not the target, the modification could be to individual receptors or involve the structure or content of phospholipids in the membranes of neurons. In some cases, where resistance cannot be explained by any other means (e.g. by uptake, excretion or metabolism), a modification in the structure of the site of action has been presumed, not always with good experimental evidence to support the assumption.

Altered targets other than acetylcholinesterase have not been well researched. However, an exception is a form of resistance in flying insects that leads to a diminution of the knock-down effect. It is carried by the *kdr* gene in houseflies and may relate to an altered receptor or cell membrane in the nervous system (Wood, 1981). It was first reported in houseflies that had become resistant to DDT (Tsukamoto *et al.*, 1965) and was later studied in relation to pyrethroid resistance by Farnham (1977), who established that the resistance arose from a single recessive gene, *kdr* (knock-down resistance gene), sited on the housefly chromosome III. Miller and his colleagues showed that pyrethroids act predominantly near synaptic sites rather than at axons and that these sites are less sensitive in resistant strains of houseflies to both pyrethroids and to DDT than are such sites in susceptible strains. Miller *et al.* (1983) have summarised work on motor nerve terminals showing site insensitivity to permethrin and decamethrin. Chang and Plapp (1983) studied the binding of DDT and *cis*-permethrin to membrane receptors derived from the heads of susceptible and *kdr* resistant houseflies. They reported that membrane preparations from the susceptible (*sbo*) strain bound 2–3 times as much DDT as did similar preparations from the *kdr* houseflies. They concluded that target site insensitivity in the resistant strain could be due to the presence there of fewer receptors for the two insecticides. Alternatively, the diminished binding could be due to a configurational change of a protein or to a change in lipid organisation near the ion channels in the *kdr*-resistant strains. Such changes, in turn, could lead to a smaller modification of the ion channel mechanism or a smaller repetitive depolarising response than is typical of unmodified receptors. These and other possibilities have been discussed by Narahashi (1983).

The evidence for and against modification of numbers or types of ion channels is still ambiguous. For example, Rossignol (1988), working with a strain of houseflies showing *kdr* resistance to pyrethroids, concluded that fewer sodium ion channels were present in the nerve membrane, an adaptation that was considered to be a response to persistent channel activation. On the other hand, Grubs *et al.* (1988), also working with housefly head preparations, could not confirm that *kdr* resistance to DDT and pyrethroids was a consequence of the presence of a lower density of sodium ion channels in the nerve membranes. They favoured the hypothesis that the number of channels was similar in resistant and susceptible strains but that macromolecular change had reduced neuronal sensitivity to the insecticides.

Another possible difficulty is illustrated by the work of Kasbekar and Hall (1988), namely, that various workers may have been studying different things. Using a mutant form of *Drosophila melanogaster* in which the individuals apparently had a diminished number of sodium ion channels in nerve membranes, they concluded that the mutation conferring resistance to certain pyrethroids was situated at a phenotypically different locus from the *kdr* mutation in houseflies. The mutation is described as the *nap* (no action potential) mutation.

Altered cell or receptor sensitivity is probably also responsible for one of the two types of resistance reported by Chadwick *et al.* (1984) in strains of *Aedes aegypti* bred under selection pressure of DDT and of permethrin in the laboratory. Chiang and Devonshire (1982) showed that the membrane-bound acetylcholinesterase from the *kdr* resistant strain of houseflies had an activity that varied with temperature, and that a discontinuity of activity that was noted could be explained by a 6°C difference in the temperature at which the viscosity of membrane lipids changed in the susceptible and resistant strains. After phospholipase treatment, much of this tempeature difference disappeared, suggesting that altered cholinesterase activity could involve an alteration in the precise membranal environment at the site of action.

9.7 CROSS-RESISTANCE

It has long been known that insect populations exposed to certain insecticides have the ability simultaneously to acquire tolerance of other substances to which they have never been exposed. For example, insects highly resistant to γ-HCH tend also to be resistant to cyclodienes. This is illustrated by data of Le Patourel and Salama (1986), working with a strain of *Sitophilus granarius* that was 176 times more tolerant of γ-HCH than was an S strain (resistance factor, $RF = 176$). The cross-resistance was high for dieldrin ($RF = 75$) and aldrin ($RF = 67$) but low for malathion ($RF = 1.6$), permethrin ($RF = 1.2$) and DDT ($RF = 1.5$).

The last example illustrates that cross-resistance does not necessarily extend to all members of a group (in this case, the organochlorine group), nor is it necessarily confined to closely related pesticides. More important than the closeness of chemical relationship between two substances is a similarity in their mode of action or, sometimes, a similarity in the enzyme systems of importance in their degradation. As was seen in chapter 6, the mode of action of γ-HCH is similar to that of the chlorinated cyclodienes but less similar to that of DDT and methoxychlor. On the other hand, a gene in *Aedes aegyptii* confers resistance to both DDT and pyrethroids (Wood, 1981). Other examples of resistance to DDT linked with cross-resistance to pyrethroids include certain strains of ticks (Wharton and Roulston, 1970) and mosquitoes (Prasittisuk and Busvine, 1977). An instance where similarity of metabolic degradation is probably responsible for cross-resistance to some, but only some, substances of a group is provided by Beeman (1983). A strain of red flour beetle, *Tribolium castaneum*, resistant to malathion, was found to be highly cross-resistant to phenthoate ($RF = 53$) but not to several other organophosphorus compounds. It would appear that phenthoate, being an ethyl ester, is metabolised by the same mechanism as malathion (a diethylsuc-cinic acid ester).

$$CH_3O \diagdown \underset{CH_3O \diagup}{P} \diagup \overset{S}{\diagup} \underset{S-CH}{\overset{COOC_2H_5}{|}}$$

Phenthoate

Compounds within a whole group with a similar mode of action are sometimes vulnerable to the development of cross-resistance, especially if their metabolism and their target site attachment are very similar. For example, Riskallah *et al.* (1983) developed a strain of *Spodoptera littoralis* under fenvalerate selection pressure. After several generations, a 33-fold increase in tolerance to fenvalerate was achieved. Further work then showed that the new resistant strain was inherently resistant to all other pyrethroids tested (*RF* values varied from 11 to 36). Cross-resistance was also noted for DDT, probably because it has a rather similar mode of action (section 7.3), although the level of cross-resistance was lower than for the pyrethroids. Similarly, Georghiou (1980), whose work has greatly added to our knowledge about the mechanisms leading to insect resistance, reported that the mosquito, *Culex quinquefasciatus*, when exposed to permethrin selection pressure, not only developed a 450-fold tolerance of this pyrethroid but simultaneously developed a high tolerance of cypermethrin (*RF*=432) and fenvalerate (*RF*=6000). Again, Golenda and Forgash (1985) found that a strain of houseflies that was resistant to resmethrin was also highly tolerant of fenvalerate (*RF*=30).

Sometimes, cross-resistance can occur between groups. As well as the examples already given, an important example was provided by Georghiou and Calman (1969). They exposed *Culex quinquefasciatus* to selection pressure with fenitrothion (section 4.8) and found that the organisms had also developed resistance to the carbamate insecticide, propoxur (section 5.5). Again, a similarity in mode of action is probably responsible. Cross-resistance has also been reported in the leafminer, *Phyllonorycter blancardella* (Pree *et al.*, 1986). Succeeding generations were exposed in the field for five years to fenvalerate and a six-fold increase in resistance was observed; later laboratory studies showed that the population was not only resistant to all pyrethroids tested (*RF*=4–17) but was even more resistant to DDT (*RF*=39). Similarly, Scott and Georghiou (1985) demonstrated that cross-resistance is not always self-evidently associated with a similar mode of action. They described the development of a 6000-fold increase in resistance to permethrin in response to selection pressure exerted over 22 generations and reported that the resistant strain also showed considerable cross-resistance to methomyl, DDT and dichlorvos.

It is worthy of note that occasional cases have been reported of negative cross-resistance: i.e. with increasing resistance to one compound a decreasing resistance to another may occur. The importance of possible exploitation of such a phenomenon is evident. One example is described by Oppenoorth (1984); *Nephotettix cincticeps* exhibited a strong negative cross-resistance between *N*-methylcarbamate and *N*-propylcarbamate insecticide analogues. Similarly, Riskallah *et al.* (1983), in the work quoted earlier, reported that, after selecting with fenvalerate, a modest negative cross-resistance was apparent for methamidophos. Finally, Walker and Wood (1986) reported that when a DDT-tolerant strain of *Aedes aegyptii* was bred under diflubenzuron (section 8.1) selection pressure, the LC_{50} for diflubenzuron increased 3.3-fold but much of the tolerance towards DDT was lost. While negative cross-resistance has probably not yet been profitably exploited in the field, a knowledge of the mechanism leading to this phenomenon is clearly of potential practical importance.

It should be stressed that cross-resistance is not the same as multiple resistance. The latter may occur when a population of organisms comes into contact (but not necessarily at the same time) with two or more different poisons. In this case, the resistance follows exposure, whereas in cross-resistance, the tolerance is present even though exposure to the second substance has not occurred. Since multiple resistance may well involve polygenetic changes, its development can be most serious should it occur in the field.

9.8 MANAGEMENT OF RESISTANCE

Much emphasis has been placed in recent times upon the need to control pests in such a way as to limit the rate at which resistance develops. In this regard, chemicals are usually seen as being but one part of an integrated pest management programme, in which biological and cultural factors also play essential roles. The crucial question in any pest management scheme must always be 'What level of selection pressure, in the existing circumstances, can be applied to the target organisms without running the risk of causing the development of an unacceptable level of resistance?'

The life cycle and preferences of the insect pest, the relationship of the pest with local predators and competitors, as well as the inherent resistance of the crop to insect attack, are among the many biological factors that must be borne in mind when the nature and dose of an insecticide that is to exert selection pressure are under consideration. Chemical factors to be considered are the modes of action of the insecticide(s) designated for use and how these relate to those of other pesticides to which the insects may already have been exposed. A major factor in determining the level of risk of resistance developing is the time that effective residues persist in the treatment area. The method of application may also influence the rate at which selection for resistance occurs.

In a (wild-type) insect population unexposed to pesticides, genes R conferring resistance to any particular insecticide are extremely rare. Georghiou and Taylor (1977) have estimated that resistant genes in unselected wild populations occur with a frequency of less than one in a thousand. So, in the simplest case, most individuals have a genetic composition SS, a few are RS and extremely few are RR. The former can thus be regarded as a gene pool that must be preserved and which, once lost, may never be regained (compare gene banks for rare crops, etc.). If insecticides are applied at doses just sufficient to kill all the homozygous SS individuals, the balance of frequencies is displaced in favour of resistance. However, if the dose is marginally decreased so that a small (but very vital) proportion of the SS individuals survive, the risk of resistance developing rapidly is dramatically reduced. The same authors have pointed out that if, in field conditions, a small proportion of individuals survive in untreated or protected pockets of the treatment area, a similar SS gene pool is preserved. In each of these cases, survival of S genes allows a gradual dilution of RR homozygotes, as does the ingress of wild-type SS individuals from outside the treated area. The rationale for an integrated management policy is based upon these and similar considerations.

One approach to the pesticide side of a multiple intervention programme follows from the above. If S genes are to be conserved, the selection pressure must be reduced; on the assumption that R genes in a wild-type population occur with a frequency of less than 0.1 per cent, Georghiou and Taylor (1977) concluded that a dose applied at the LD_{90} level will ensure that sufficient susceptible genes are preserved to delay greatly the onset of resistance. For such a scenario to be successful in the field, any additionally required pest control must rest with the other inputs into the multiple intervention system; these inputs could include reliance on natural enemies, use of bacteria that attack insects and use of crop cultivars that are less susceptible to insect damage. The need to kill heterozygous carriers of the R gene in order to delay evolution of resistance has been studied by Mani and Wood (1984) in relation to persistence of pesticide and the frequency of its application.

A second approach is sometimes more acceptable for use on high-value crops. It is to apply the pesticide at such a high concentration that not only the SS insects but also the RS insects are wiped out. If this is done effectively, the heterozygotes do not survive to interbreed to produce RR homozygotes (it will be recalled that RR homozygotes are virtually absent in an untreated population owing to the very low frequency of the R gene). Conversely, however, saturation management is a highly undesirable procedure if the population to be treated has suffered previous exposure to insecticides, for, if this has happened, it is possible that the proportion of RR individuals is already finite before the multiple treatment begins. It is also evident that, for safety reasons, the method is most applicable for the use of pesticides that disappear rapidly or for compounds such as juvenile hormone analogues that do not possess high mammalian toxicity (Georghiou, 1983).

Another method of approach is to apply an appropriate dose of active ingredient mixed with a synergist capable of preventing the rapid destruction of the insecticide. Where resistance is exclusively caused by metabolic factors, synergists such as piperonyl butoxide, sesamex (figure 7.3) and tributyl phosphorotrithioate (figure 9.2) have in some instances greatly decreased the rate at which resistance develops in selection pressure experiments carried out in the laboratory. For example, Ranasinghe and Georghiou (1979) demonstrated that when the organophosphorus compound, temephos, was used alone, the mosquito, *Culex quinquefasciatus*, developed resistance to it, but when temephos was applied mixed with tributyl phosphorotrithioate, no resistance developed over 12 generations. This effect is distinct from the use of synergists to make a given dose of an active ingredient more effective, although these events are clearly related. It should not, however, be assumed that the presence of a synergist always delays to a significant degree the development of resistance. This is demonstrated by the work of Chen and Sun (1986), who studied the development of resistance to fenvalerate of larvae of the diamond back moth, *Plutella xylostella*. They observed that a high level of resistance developed within five generations when fenvalerate was applied alone. However, when fenvalerate and piperonyl butoxide were applied together, although the rate of development of resistance was somewhat less, a similar high level of resistance was eventually attained. They also observed that this resistance was associated with a strong cross-resistance to three other pyrethroids (permethrin, cypermethrin and deltamethrin), but with only a slight increase of resistance to some organophosphorus insecticides.

An alternative approach is to use a mixture of several insecticides with different modes of action. In these cases, the concentrations of each individual poison are so low that the S gene pools associated with each of the target sites under attack are not greatly depleted in the population as a whole, even though the cumulative damage provides a practical level of control of the insect population in the field. According to Georghiou (1983), and perhaps surprisingly, the number of reliably documented cases where the use of mixtures markedly delayed the appearance of resistance is, for insecticides, somewhat low. One reason for this is that most mixtures used in the field were employed to control mixed infestations of insects. With fungicides, however, much success has been reported (section 12.1).

The use of insecticides consecutively rather than as mixtures has also been investigated somewhat incompletely; it remains uncertain whether resistance in a crop protection context is avoided more successfully by this approach than by the use of mixtures. However, in relation to the control of the malarial vector, an interesting variant has been described by Muir (1977). A large area of land was divided into a grid and pesticides with a different mode of action were sprayed in different areas. The object was to attempt to avoid selection of the mosquito population for the same resistance mechanism in all the sprayed regions, and to leave it to the surviving mosquitoes to migrate and re-establish a genetic pool rich in S genes.

For further information on resistance management strategies the reviews by Wood (1981) and Georghiou and Saito (1983) should be consulted, as well as the review by Hollingworth (1976) and the monograph produced by the Committee on Strategies for the Management of Pesticide Resistant Pest Populations of the US National Research Council (Anon, 1986).

The last-mentioned monograph was reviewed by Oppenoorth (1987) and, to emphasise how much is still to be done on molecular aspects of insecticide resistance, it is perhaps appropriate to end this chapter with a short quotation from his review. He wrote: 'thirty years of study of resistance [in the housefly] has convinced me that we do not know the molecular genetics of a single case of insect resistance . . . ; we do not even know in most cases whether a so-called "gene" is perhaps a cluster due to amplification . . . or whether it arose by a single change or by a series of consecutive ones'. And this is an expert's opinion on the housefly, the most studied of all the thousands of economically important types of insects.

REFERENCES

Aliniazee, M. T. (1983). *J. Econ. Entomol.*, **76**, 1002
Anon (1986). *Pesticide Resistance: Strategies and Tactics for Management*, ed. Committee on Strategies for the Management of Pesticide Resistant Pest Populations, National Research Council, Washington, DC
Armstrong, K. F. and Suckling, D. M. (1988). *Pestic. Biochem. Physiol.*, **32**, 62
Beeman, R. W. (1983). *J. Econ. Entomol.*, **76**, 737
Bennett, J. (1960). *Heredity (Lond.)*, **15**, 65
Beranek, A. P. and Oppenoorth, F. J. (1977). *Pestic. Biochem. Physiol.*, **7**, 16
Binns, T. J. (1986). *J. Stored Prod. Res.*, **22**, 97
Chadwick, P. R., Slatter, R. and Bowron, M. J. (1984). *Pestic. Sci.*, **15**, 112
Chang, C. P. and Plapp, F. W., Jr (1983). *Pestic. Biochem. Physiol.*, **20**, 86
Chen, S. J. and Sun, C. N. (1986). *J. Econ. Entomol.*, **79**, 22
Chiang, C. and Devonshire, A. L. (1982). *Pestic. Sci.*, **13**, 156
Clark, A. G., Shamaan, N. A., Sinclair, M. D. and Dauterman, W. C. (1986). *Pestic. Biochem. Physiol.*, **25**, 169
Dauterman, W. C. (1983). In *Pest Resistance to Pesticides*, eds G.P. Georghiou and T. Saito, p. 229. Plenum, New York
Delorme, R., Fournier, D., Chafaux, J., Cuany, A., Bride, J. M., Auge, D. and Berge, J. B. (1988). *Pestic. Biochem. Physiol.*, **32**, 240
De Villar, M. I. P., van der Pas, L. J. T., Smissaert, H. R. and Oppenoorth, F. J. (1983). *Pestic. Biochem. Physiol.*, **19**, 60
Devonshire, A. L. and Moores, G. D. (1984). *Pestic. Biochem. Physiol.*, **21**, 336
Devonshire, A. L. and Sawicki, R. M. (1979). *Nature (Lond.)*, **280**, 140
Eldefrawi, M. E., Miskus, R. and Sutcher, V. (1960). *J. Econ. Entomol.*, **53**, 231
Farnham, A. W. (1973). *Pestic. Sci.*, **4**, 513
Farnham, A. W. (1977). *Pestic. Sci.*, **8**, 631
Forgash, A. J. (1984). *Pestic. Biochem. Physiol.*, **22**, 178
Fukuto, T. R., Metcalf, R. L., Winton, M. Y. and Roberts, P. A. (1962). *J. Econ. Entomol.*, **55**, 341
Georghiou, G. P. (1980). *Res. Rev.*, **76**, 131

Georghiou, G. P. (1983). In *Pest Resistance to Pesticides*, eds G. P. Georghiou and T. Saito, p. 769. Plenum, New York

Georghiou, G. P. and Calman, J. R. (1969). *Bull. WHO*, **40**, 97

Georghiou, G. P. and Saito, T. (eds) (1983). *Pest Resistance to Pesticides*. Plenum, New York

Georghiou, G. P. and Taylor, C. E. (1977). *J. Econ. Entomol.*, **70**, 319

Golenda, C. F. and Forgash, A. J. (1985). *J. Econ. Entomol.*, **78**, 19

Golenda, C. F. and Forgash, A. J. (1989). *Pestic. Biochem. Physiol.*, **33**, 37

Grubs, R. E., Adams, P. M. and Soderlund, D. M. (1988). *Pestic. Biochem. Physiol.*, **32**, 217

Hama, H. (1976). *Appl. Entomol. Zool.*, **11**, 239

Hama, H. (1983). In *Pest Resistance to Pesticides*, eds G. P. Georghiou and T. Saito, p. 33. Plenum, New York

Hammock, B. D., Mumby, S. M. and Lee, P. W. (1977). *Pestic. Biochem. Physiol.*, **7**, 261

Hemingway, J. (1985). *Pestic. Biochem. Physiol.*, **23**, 309

Hemingway, J. and Georghiou, G. P. (1983). *Pestic. Biochem. Physiol.*, **19**, 167

Hemingway, J., Malcolm, C. A., Kissoon, K. E., Boddington, R. G., Curtis, C. F. and Hill, N. (1985). *Pestic. Biochem. Physiol.*, **24**, 68

Hollingworth, R. (1976). In *Pesticide Biochemistry and Physiology*, ed. C. F. Wilkinson, p. 580. Plenum, New York

Kasbekar, D. P. and Hall, L. M. (1988). *Pestic. Biochem. Physiol.*, **32**, 135

Kao, L. R., Motoyama, N. and Dauterman, W. C. (1985). *Pestic. Biochem. Physiol.*, **23**, 228

Le Patourel, G. N. J. and Salama, M. A. (1986). *Pestic. Sci.*, **17**, 503

Lewis, J. B. and Sawicki, R. M. (1971). *Pestic. Biochem. Physiol.*, **1**, 275

Lipke, H. and Kearns, C. W. (1960). *Adv. Pest Control Res.*, **3**, 253

Macdonald, R. S., Solomon, K. R., Surgeoner, G. A. and Harris, C. R. (1985). *Pestic. Sci.*, **16**, 10

Mani, G. S. and Wood, R. J. (1984). *Pestic. Sci.*, **15**, 325

Miller. T. A., Salgado, V. L. and Irving, S. N. (1983). In *Pest Resistance to Pesticides*, eds G. P. Georghiou and T. Saito, p. 353. Plenum, New York

Moorefield, H. H. (1960). *Misc. Publ. Entomol. Soc. Am.*, **2**, 145

Morton, R. A. and Holwerda, B. C. (1985). *Pestic. Biochem. Physiol.*, **24**, 19

Motoyama, N. and Dauterman, W. C. (1977). *Insect Biochem.*, **7**, 361

Motoyama, N., Kao, L. R., Lin, P. T. and Dauterman, W. C. (1984). *Pestic. Biochem. Physiol.*, **21**, 139

Mouchès, C., Pasteur, N., Bergé, J. B., Hyrien, O., Raymond, M., de Saint Vincent, B. R., de Silvestri, M. and Georghiou, G. P. (1986). *Science*, **233**, 778

Muggleton, J. (1984). *Proc. Br. Crop Prot. Conf., Pests and Diseases*, p. 585

Muir, D. A. (1977). *World Health Organisation Document WHO/VBC/77.659*. WHO, Geneva

Narahashi, T. (1983). In *Pest Resistance to Pesticides*, eds G. P. Georghiou and T. Saito, p. 33. Plenum, New York

Nolan, J. and O'Brien, R. D. (1970). *J. Agric. Fd Chem.*, **18**, 802

Noppun, V., Saito, T. and Miyata, T. (1989). *Pestic. Biochem. Physiol.*, **33**, 37

O'Brien, R. D., Tripathi, R. K. and Howell, L. L. (1978). *Biochim. Biophys. Acta*, **526**, 129

Oppenoorth, F. J. (1984). *Pestic. Biochem. Physiol.*, **22**, 187

Oppenoorth, F. J. (1987). *Pestic. Biochem. Physiol.*, **27**, 350

Oppenoorth, F. J., Smissaert, H. R., Welling, W., van der Pas, L. J. T. and Hitman, K. T. (1977). *Pestic. Biochem. Physiol.*, **7**, 34

Oppenoorth, F. J. and van Asperen, K. (1961). *Entomol. Exp. Appl.*, **4**, 311

Oppenoorth, F. J. and Voerman, S. (1975). *Pestic. Biochem. Physiol.*, **5**, 431

Oppenoorth, F. J. and Welling, W. (1976). In *Insect Biochemistry and Physiology*, ed. C. F. Wilkinson, p. 507. Heyden, London

Ottea, J. A. and Plapp, F. W., Jr (1984). *Pestic. Biochem. Physiol.*, **22**, 203

Patil, V. L. and Guthrie, F. E. (1979). *Pestic. Sci.*, **10**, 399

Payne, G. T. and Brown, T. M. (1984). *J. Econ. Entomol.*, **77**, 294

Pimprikar, G. D. and Georghiou, G. P. (1979). *Pestic. Biochem. Physiol.*, **12**, 10

Pimprikar, G. D. and Georghiou, G. P. (1982). *J. Agric. Fd Chem.*, **30**, 605

Plapp, F. W., Jr and Hoyer, R. F. (1968). *J. Econ. Entomol.*, **61**, 1298

Prasittisuk, C. and Busvine, J. R. (1977). *Pestic. Sci.*, **8**, 527

Pree, D. J., Marshall, D. B. and Archibald, D. E. (1986). *J. Econ. Entomol.*, **79**, 318

Raftos, D. A. and Hughes, P. B. (1986). *J. Econ. Entomol.*, **79**, 553

Ranasinghe, L. E. and Georghiou, G. P. (1979). *Pestic. Sci.*, **10**, 502

Raymond, M., Fournier, D., Bride, J.-M., Cuany, A., Berge, J., Magnin, M. and Pasteur, N. (1986). *J. Econ. Entomol.*, **79**, 1452

Riordan, E. K. (1987). *Bull. Entomol. Res.*, **77**, 213

Riskallah, M. R., and Abd-Elghafar, S. F., Abo-Elgha, M. R. and Nassar, M. E. (1983). *Pestic. Sci.*, **14**, 85

Ronis, M. J. J., Hodgson, E. and Dauterman, W. C. (1988). *Pestic. Biochem. Physiol.*, **32**, 74

Rossignol, D. P. (1988). *Pestic. Biochem. Physiol.*, **32**, 146

Roush, R. T. and Wolfenbarger, D. A. (1985). *J. Econ. Entomol.*, **78**, 1020

Scott, J. G. and Georghiou, G. P. (1985). *J. Econ. Entomol.*, **78**, 316

Scott, J. G. and Georghiou, G. P. (1986). *Pestic. Sci.*, **17**, 195

Tsukamoto, M., Narahashi, T. and Yamasakai, T. (1965). *Botyu-Kagaku*, **30**, 128

Villani, F., White, G. B., Curtis, C. F. and Miles, S. J. (1983). *Bull. Entomol. Res.*, **73**, 153

Voss, G. (1980). *J. Econ. Entomol.*, **73**, 189

Walker, A. L. and Wood, R. J. (1986). *Pestic. Sci.*, **17**, 495

Watson, J. D., Tooze, J. and Kurtz, D. T. (1983). *Recombinant DNA: A Short Course*, Scientific American Books. Freeman, New York

Wells, D. S., Motoyama, N. and Dauterman, W. C. (1986). *Pestic. Sci.*, **17**, 631

Wharton, R. H. and Roulston, W. J. (1970). *Ann. Rev. Entomol.*, **15**, 381

Wilkinson, C. F. and Brattsten, L. B. (1972). *Drug Metab. Rev.*, **1**, 153

Wood, R. J. (1981). In *Genetic Consequences of Man Made Change*, eds J. A. Bishop and L. M. Cook, p. 53. Academic Press, New York

Yang, R. S. H., Hodgson, E. and Dauterman, W. C. (1971). *J. Agric. Fd Chem.*, **19**, 14

Yasutomi, K. (1983). In *Pest Resistance to Pesticides*, eds G. P. Georghiou and T. Saito, p. 249. Plenum, New York

10 Fungicides: general principles; inorganic and heavy-metal fungicides

10.1 FUNGI AND FUNGICIDES

Problems associated with the chemical control of fungi are in some ways different from those that arise in relation to the control of insects. In particular, fungal mycelium has an almost limitless propensity to regenerate from a few surviving hyphal strands. Consequently, a fungus that is already well established is often difficult to eradicate. Systemic fungicides have eradicant properties, but even for pathogens for which a suitable systemic compound exists, eradication may not be worth while, for a well established fungus may have set back plant growth irreparably.

A fungicide that kills on contact can check the growth of mycelium and limit the production of reproductive structures. Such action delays or prevents the disease from spreading from infected plants to healthy ones nearby, but the majority of successful non-systemic fungicides are most effective when applied prior to the arrival of the infection. Non-systemic fungicides must therefore normally possess some degree of persistence and the majority are, in fact, insoluble in water. Some fungi are ectoparasites, and these are more vulnerable to contact sprays than are endoparasites. However, even ectoparasites produce nutritive branches (haustoria), which penetrate plant cuticle and enter plant cells, where they may survive when the external mycelium is destroyed.

In addition to airborne pathogens, fungi may attack plants through the soil or be transmitted on or in the seeds. Such fungi are frequently controlled by soil or seed treatment, often by the use of fungicides specifically developed for these purposes. Clearly, a knowledge of the habits and life cycles of such fungi is an essential prerequisite for effective chemical control.

A strictly taxonomic classification of fungi in the present context is of less practical value than is an approach based upon the means by which the infection is transmitted to the plant, upon the lifestyle of the fungus and upon the types of fungicides that control it. A scheme, modified from one originally used by Barnes (1977), appears in table 10.1. In this table, pathogenic fungi are first divided according to whether the principal route of infection is via air,

Table 10.1 **A simplified classification of pathogenic fungi according to method of reaching host plants and reliance on water; examples of effective fungicides are included**

AIRBORNE INFECTIONS[a]

Group 1A. Water-dependent at infection stage—motile spores. Mostly Oomycetes (e.g. the downy mildews, *Pythium, Phytophthora, Peronospora, Bremia, Pseudoperonospora, Sclerospora*)
Fungicides: copper, dithiocarbamates, phthalimides, dichlofluanid (most systemics are ineffective)

Group 1B. Most need water to infect but spores move passively. Mycelium hydrophobic and lives under cuticle. Mostly members of Ascomycetes and Deuteromycetes (e.g. *Septoria, Venturia, Sclerotinia, Botrytis, Pseudocercosporella*)
Fungicides: phthalimides, dichlofluanid, some systemic fungicides (e.g. benzimidazoles)

Group 2. Not directly dependent on water at infection stage. Live, at least initially, under the cuticle or deeper. Includes pathogenic Ascomycetes, especially all the powdery mildews. Also rusts
Fungicides: hydroxypyrimidines, triforine, azole derivatives

SEEDBORNE INFECTIONS

Fungi belong to many different orders. Some live on seeds, others within them. Include some Basidiomycetes (e.g. *Ustilago*), some Ascomycetes (e.g. *Pyrenophora*) and some Deuteromycetes (e.g. *Septoria*)
Fungicides: dithiocarbamates, cuprous oxide, organomercury, some systemic compounds (e.g. carboxin, azoles)

SOILBORNE INFECTIONS

Fungi belong to many taxonomic groups, e.g. *Pythium* (Oomycetes), *Fusarium* (Deuteromycetes) and *Urocystis* (Basidiomycetes)
Fungicides: according to circumstances, correct choice from nabam, dichloran, chloroneb, copper, some systemic fungicides (e.g. thiophanate-methyl, thiabendazole)

[a] *Seed* or *soil* applications of systemic fungicides can sometimes control *airborne* infections.

seeds or soil. Those that are airborne vary in relation to their requirement for water. Those in group 1 enter plant cells by aqueous transmission and infection is favoured by damp conditions. Those in subgroup 1A usually depend on water to gain access because they produce free-swimming zoospores. Examples are Oomycetes, of which the downy mildews merit special mention, as does *Phytophthora infestans*, the cause of late blight of potatoes. Fungi in subgroup 1B belong to several taxonomic divisions but have one feature in common, namely that the spores, although not motile, nevertheless gain access in consequence of the movement of droplets of rain or dew in which they are suspended. Once established, the hydrophobic mycelium lives in the surface layers of the plant. An important example is *Botrytis cinerea*, which is a member of the Deuteromycetes (Fungi Imperfecti) and is the cause of grey mould on many plants. Group 2 also includes fungi responsible for a number of rot and scab diseases of great commercial importance.

The airborne fungi of group 2 (table 10.1) are different in that they prefer dry conditions at the time of infection. The mycelium grows on the leaf surface and is frequently hydrophobic, as are the conidiophores. Pathogenic Ascomycetes of the order Erysiphales include the very important powdery mildews.

The fungi that infect via the seeds also belong to several different taxonomic groups. The Basidiomycetes are represented by the smuts and bunts, some of which, because they can lay waste to cereal crops, are of fundamental importance to mankind. Some Ascomycetes, such as *Pyrenophora avenae*, an important pathogen of grasses and cereals, also infect plants via their seeds.

Soilborne infections also involve fungi from different taxonomic groups. *Pythium* is one of several genera that cause damping off; it is a member of the Oomycetes. Other soilborne fungi belong to the Basidiomycetes (e.g. the onion smut, *Urocystis cepulae*) or to the Fungi Imperfecti (e.g. *Fusarium* and *Verticillium*).

Just as a strictly taxonomic approach has not been adopted for fungi, neither is a rigorous chemical classification of fungicides adopted in table 10.2. Although many similarities will be observed between the formulae of compounds in most groups, the fungicides are predominantly grouped according to the similarity in their (probable) main mode of action. Table 10.2 is based upon a convention followed by the British Ministry of Agriculture (MAFF, 1984, p. 15) except that extra groups have been inserted, including groups of

Table 10.2   Groups of fungicides (based on MAFF, 1984, with additions)

Possibly multiple sites of action	*Site-specific*
Copper and tin compounds	Dinitrocompounds (e.g. dinocap)[a]
Mercurials	Benzimidazoles (e.g. benomyl)
Sulphur	Oxathiins (e.g. carboxin)
Dithiocarbamates (e.g., thiram, maneb)	Steroid synthesis blockers
Phthalimides (e.g. captan)	(a) Morpholines (e.g. tridemorph)[a]
Phthalonitriles (e.g. chlorothalonil)	(b) C–14 demethylation inhibitors (e.g. prochloraz, triforine, triarimol)
	Hydroxyaminopyrimidines (e.g. ethirimol)
Site(s) of action uncertain	Antibiotics (e.g. kasugamycin)
Dicarboximides (e.g. vinclozolin)	Phenylamides (e.g. metalaxyl)
	Organophosphorus compounds (e.g. pyrazophos, fosetyl)
	Others (e.g. guazatine, cymoxanil, prothiocarb)

[a] Systemic activity may be low or absent.

compounds not currently approved for use in the UK. Those appearing in the right-hand column are believed to have as their targets very specific sites or processes within the fungus, such as single receptors or enzymes; many of these fungicides are systemic in their action. Most of those in the left-hand column have low systemic and eradicant propensity and their targets appear to be rather non-specific; for example, some react with thiol groups and others disorganise lipoprotein membranes. Most of the compounds in this column are protective poisons that are deposited on the surfaces of plants (or seeds) and attack fungal spores when they germinate.

The numerous fungicides in use today are not equally effective against all pathogenic fungi and it is found that fungi from different habitats or belonging to different taxonomic divisions often respond to different types of fungicides. The pathogens of group 1A are often controlled by fungicides of the heavy-metal and dithiocarbamate families. An example is *Phytophthora infestans*, which is controlled by the use of copper fungicides*, although fentin acetate and dithiocarbamates such as zineb and maneb are now often used instead. Relatively few systemic fungicides effectively control diseases caused by Oomycetes, but the acylalanine derivative, metalaxyl, has been developed rather specifically for this purpose. In addition, phosetyl-Al is widely employed in France to control *Plasmapara viticola*, the cause of downy mildew of vine.

Group 1B fungi, such as *Botrytis* and *Venturia*, are controlled by phthalimides and dichlofluanid. Various writers, including Jacob and Neumann (1987), have described as '*loco-systemic*' compounds that sorb into leaves but do not move around the plant. One such compound is prochloraz, which is used against *Pseudocercosporella*, a fungus that causes eyespot disease of cereals. Some systemic compounds also control organisms in this group; carbendazim, for example, controls *Septoria* spp., which, *inter alia*, cause leaf spot and glume blotch of cereals.

One of the few groups of non-systemic organic fungicides capable of controlling the powdery mildews of group 2 are the dinitrophenols such as dinocap and binapacryl. The reason for this selectivity is not clear. Their use is now in decline because of suspected chronic effects on higher animals (section 11.5) and because the newer systemic fungicides also control powdery mildews. Examples of such systemic compounds are propiconazole, often used to control *Erysiphe graminis*, the cause of powdery mildew of cereals, and bupirimate, which is used against powdery mildew of roses.

Various seedborne infections are controlled by a variety of contact fungi-

* In 1842–48 the course of history was changed by the Irish potato famine brought about by potato blight. Vast numbers of people died or emigrated to the USA. Someone wrote long ago (ashamedly, I've lost the reference) that, in tragic irony, the mountains of Snowdonia, on a clear day visible in Ireland, were scarred by unsightly piles of copper slag from the copper workings there. At that time neither the cause of the disease nor its cure were, of course, known.

cides, including seed dressings containing thiram, quintozene or drazoxolon. Organomercury seed dressings are often used to protect cereal seeds but are been phased out in many countries for reasons of safety. Some systemic fungicides are also effective against fungi that cause smut diseases (*Ustilaginales*). For example, carboxin, nuarimol and triadimenol are used against loose smut of barley and wheat. They are particularly useful for the control of fungi that live in the embryo and thus cannot be reached by externally deposited poisons. In practice, many crops are open to simultaneous attack from seedborne fungi belonging to more than one taxonomic division; consequently, many seed treatments comprise a mixture of two or more fungicides, one of which is systemic.

Various soilborne infections are controlled by contact fungicides such as nabam, dichloran, quintozene, chloroneb and copper compounds. Certain systemic fungicides (e.g. thiophanate-methyl) are used to control Deuteromycetes and related pathogens. In addition soil sterilants such as methyl bromide and chloropicrin, which are used (especially in glasshouses) to control nematodes and weed seeds, also control soilborne fungi.

10.2 PENETRATION OF FUNGICIDES INTO FUNGI

Fungal cell walls are negatively charged and comprise fibres of chitin and cellulose, together with some protein, polysaccharides other than cellulose (e.g. glucans), and lipids. In the case of *Mucor*, chitosan (30 per cent) and phosphate are present and in some fungi callose and nucleic acid derivatives are also present. It is probable that most non-cationic fungicides readily pass through the cell walls of most fungi, the main barrier to entry being the lipoprotein membrane within it. The walls of some fungal spores may be less permeable and more rigid than those of the general mycelium, their lipid and callose components possibly providing a physical barrier to penetration. However, spores usually become more susceptible to fungicides at the time of emergence of the germ tube. Electron microscope studies of the conidia of *Botrytis* spp. show that the wall is double, only the outer one of which ruptures when the germ tube emerges.

Charged particles have difficulty in penetrating the lipoprotein plasmalemma, and the entry of such substances may be facilitated by their temporary conversion to non-ionic forms. Thus, weak acids and bases usually only enter in the undissociated form; weak cations may form *covalent salts* with fatty acids (which therefore act as carriers) or *metal chelates* may be formed with amino or keto acids (compare section 10.4). The relative rates of entry of closely related substances is frequently related to the sizes of the oil–water partition coefficients. Entry may, in fact, comprise a large number of steps in which the substance partitions between aqueous and lipid phases (a similar phenomenon is the basis of some forms of chromatography). Within the cell, fungicides are probably transported through cell or syncytium by protoplasmic streaming.

Internal distribution between subcellular components varies greatly with the type of fungus and fungicide. Owens and Miller (1957) demonstrated that 18–48 per cent of a dose of various metals remained attached to spore-wall components of *Aspergillus niger* but that less than 4 per cent was held back by the walls of *Neurospora sitophila*. Most of the metal that penetrated the walls of *A. niger* became attached to mitochondrial components, whereas the bulk of that which entered *N. sitophila* was present in the 12 000 g supernatant fluid (i.e. the endoplasmic reticulum plus the cytosol). In the case of dichlone (section 11.6), 75–78 per cent remained in the cytosol of the spores of both fungi. Cycloheximide binds to the ribosomes of *Saccharomyces* and this may account for its fungitoxic action.

One of the most striking aspects of the influx of many fungicides is the rapidity of the process—it sometimes leads rapidly to the virtual removal of all toxicant from a dilute circumambient solution. Superficially, such rapid entry may seem to militate against the possibility of diffusion being the main force at work, for it is not unusual for the 'concentration' in the spore (defined as the weight of fungicide per unit volume of spore) to be 10 000 times that in the surrounding aqueous phase. Moreover, entry is often 60–90 per cent complete within 1 min of exposure to the external aqueous solution (Somers, 1963).

These data do not necessarily imply that influx occurs 'against the concentration gradient', for not only may diffusion be associated with partition into lipids but, in addition, the ionic or molecular species may be different on either side of the cell membrane. The second possibility is illustrated by a simple analogy; imagine a suitable vessel divided by a membrane that allows only copper ions to pass through, and where one compartment contains copper sulphate solution and the other a dilute solution of hydrogen sulphide. Soon, almost all the copper ions would end up as insoluble copper sulphide on one side of the partition, but simple diffusion down a concentration gradient, followed by immobilisation of the diffused copper, is still the driving force.

In contrast to the rapidity with which fungicides enter fungi, any efflux is usually gradual. This efflux is, in the case of fenarimol (section 12.5), energy-dependent, and is inhibited by low temperature, by anaerobiosis and by respiratory inhibitors (de Waard and van Nistelrooy, 1980). The net effect of influx and efflux at any moment is known as the uptake of the fungicide. If uptake continues for a finite time, the fungicide will *accumulate* within the fungus.

10.3 SELECTIVITY OF FUNGICIDES

As was seen in section 10.1, many fungicides tend to be very specific with regard to the type of fungus that they control. It is perhaps ironic that the main problem with insecticides is to achieve selectivity since many insects near plants are beneficial; fungicides, on the other hand, often seem to be too specific since most fungi on plants are either harmful or neutral. However that may be (and not all the facts about species interactions are known), the fungicide chemist is faced with the task of studying up to 20 important groups of fungicides, most of which have a limited range of action. It is probably true to say that the mechanisms whereby the highly selective actions implied by such data as those shown in table 10.3 are still little understood.

Table 10.3 contains figures quoted by Lyr (1987); further details are to be found in this excellent edited treatise. Briefly, however, the table lists six fungi from several different taxonomic divisions as well as five fungicides; of the latter, three are from different systemic groups, one is poorly systemic and another, dichlofluanid, is non-systemic. It will be seen that *Phytophthora*, a member of the Oomycetes, is not readily controlled by systemic compounds, whereas *Erysiphe*, an Ascomycete, is controlled by the systemic compound, triarimol, but not by another systemic compound, carboxin. On the other hand, carboxin has a specific action on Basidiomycetes such as rusts and smuts (these fungi are not represented in table 10.3) and proves to be effective against *Rhizoctonia*, a Deuteromycete that may be an imperfect stage of an

Table 10.3   Relative toxicities of various fungicides to several fungi (after Lyr, 1987, p. 33, with permission). Figures in the table are obtained from reciprocals of ED$_{50}$ values, so highest toxicity is represented by the largest figure

Fungus (group)	Benomyl	Triarimol	Carboxin	Chloroneb	Dichlofluanid	Dicloran
Phytophthora sp. (Oomycetes)	4	2	2	100	50	1
Pythium sp. (Oomycetes)	2	2	2	20	100	1
Erysiphe sp. (Ascomycetes)	29	10 000	10	10	67	–
Verticillium sp. (Asco/Deutero-mycetes)	1000	1000	40	20	22	25
Fusarium sp. (Deutero-mycetes)	100	67	1	1	4	1
Botrytis sp. (Deutero-mycetes)	500	50	20	40	400	200
Rhizoctonia sp. (Deutero/Basidiomycetes)	40	20	40	13	67	1

Autobasidiomycete. The Deuteromycetes *Fusarium* and *Verticillium* are both readily controlled by the wide-spectrum and systemic benomyl as well as by triarimol, yet they differ greatly in their response to carboxin and chloroneb.

So far as is known, the reasons for the existence of selectivity in the action of fungicides are similar to those mentioned earlier in relation to the tolerance of insects to insecticides. For instance, it is likely that factors that influence the absorption of a particular fungicide into, or its efflux from, a fungal spore could affect selectivity. Again, metabolic factors determine how quickly a fungus can inactivate two different fungicides (or, in some cases, carry out lethal metabolism by activating a latent fungicide). Again, by analogy with receptor modification discussed in section 9.6, it is to be anticipated that different receptors (or other types of sites of action) may exist in different fungi, or that the importance of those sites differs in different fungi. An example is the sensitivity to oxathiins of succinate dehydrogenase in different types of fungi (section 12.3). Fungi of different types also differ anatomically and structurally, and such differences may have a bearing on selectivity of fungicidal action. In particular, the mycelia of Oomycetes are aseptate. Again, while ergosterol is the principal sterol produced by most fungi, the Oomycetes produce other sterols in larger amounts. It is also noteworthy that the *Pythium* family of the Oomycetes are almost devoid of sterols.

10.4 COPPER FUNGICIDES: PREPARATION, PROPERTIES AND USES

Copper ions in solution are toxic to all forms of life, so copper fungicides used on foliage are necessarily insoluble in water. A variety of copper compounds has been used for this purpose. Some, such as freshly prepared Bordeaux mixture, are gelatinous and have the advantage that the copper is thereby bound to the leaf surface. Moreover, gels dry slowly and this increases the probability of the spore being killed by the fungicide, for spores usually germinate under damp conditions. To others, such as copper oxychloride, a sticking agent such as starch is added to increase adhesion after spraying. Most copper fungicides (table 10.4) are formulated either as dusts or as wettable powders.

Copper fungicides are used to control potato blight but they are also active against a wide variety of fungi. In this respect they can be contrasted with many organic fungicides, for the latter often have a narrow biological spectrum. Copper dusts are used to control the downy mildew of hop, and copper sprays are used *inter alia* against cane and leaf spots, peach leaf curl and tomato leaf mould. In addition, a few formulations (e.g. the water-soluble Cheshunt compound) are applied to soil to control damping-off diseases. Cuprous oxide has been employed for seed treatment and it is also used as a spray, especially in the tropics. Copper derivatives of aromatic carboxylic

Table 10.4   Some copper fungicides, past and present

Substance	Approximate formula	Comments
Bordeaux mixture	$CuSO_4.3Cu(OH)_2$	Made from $CuSO_4$ and lime. Used as a spray
Copper oxychloride	$CuCl_2.3Cu(OH)_2$	Made from NH_4OH and $CuCl_2$. Used as a spray and a seed dip
Basic copper carbonate	$Cu(OH)_2.3CuCO_3$	Used as a dust
Cuprous oxide	Cu_2O	Yellow or red copper oxide. Used for seed treatment and as a spray
Copper hydroxide	$Cu(OH)_2$	Formulated as wettable powder for use as a spray
Cheshunt compound	$CuSO_4 + NH_4.HCO_3$	A soluble copper fungicide used as a soil drench against damping off. Not to be used on foliage

acids (naphthenic acids) are too toxic for foliage application but are useful for the treatment of timber in barns, fences and greenhouses.

Bordeaux mixture is an insoluble precipitate formed by adding, at room temperature, a concentrated solution of copper sulphate to a slight excess of lime suspended in the rest of the water. The precise method of preparation influences such physical properties as the fineness of the precipitate and the ease of dispersion. It also influences the speed of conversion of excess lime to carbonate after spraying, and this, in turn, affects the retention of the deposit by foliage. Similarly, the fungicidal efficiency of Bordeaux precipitate decreases on storage, probably because of changes in the extent and type of crystalline aggregation. For this reason, Bordeaux mixture is one of the few pesticides that can, with advantage, be prepared by the grower.

The main component of Bordeaux mixture is a basic copper sulphate, which is a molecular complex containing all the copper and none of the calcium:

$$4CuSO_4 + 3Ca(OH)_2 \longrightarrow CuSO_4.3Cu(OH)_2 + 3CaSO_4 \qquad (10.1)$$

After deposition on the leaf, the precipitate acts as a reservoir from which copper ions can be mobilised, while the calcium sulphate and any excess lime help to increase the binding of the precipitate to the leaf surface.

Mobilisation of the copper from the Bordeaux mixture involves the formation of complexes rather than of cupric salts. Solubilisation is mainly brought about by exudates from the germinating fungal spores themselves; in effect, the fungal spores become their own executioners. No doubt similar exudates can originate from the host plant, but fungal spores can be killed by Bordeaux precipitate on microscope slides so the presence of the host plant is not essential.

It is known that small but measurable quantities of various metabolic intermediates are exuded by germinating fungal spores. Among these are amino and keto acids, and copper readily forms chelate complexes with such substances. The amino acid, *glycine*, aminoacetic acid, is quantitatively the most important component of most exudates, and possible bidentate and tridentate ligands with copper ions are shown in figure 10.1.

Much of the pioneering work on copper fungicides was done by R. L. Wain in the 1950s. He investigated the nature of the Bordeaux precipitate and the mechanism of solubilisation of copper; in consequence he proposed the well known 'suicide theory' that was mentioned earlier. Although widely accepted, the theory nevertheless has its critics, for, it is argued, in the absence of copper, fungi only exude minute quantities of amino acids. The liberation of amino and keto acids could, therefore, be an abnormal response to the toxic effect of the copper; alternatively, the copper may disturb an equilibrium that normally lies very far to one side. The present writer favours the latter hypothesis, applied to a situation where local contact leads to cascading damage. Whether or not this is so, spore exudates provide a plausible explanation for a pH-independent mechanism capable of transporting copper from the insoluble deposit to the wall of the fungal spore or mycelium.

If, as seems highly probable, organocopper complexes are formed, the level of stability of various types of complexes is potentially important. Thus Tröger (1960) observed that some copper complexes were not toxic to spores of *Fusarium* and it would seem that the stability requirements of complexes capable of carrying copper are rather delicately poised. If the complex is of appropriate stability it will chelate copper and convey it to the fungal spore.

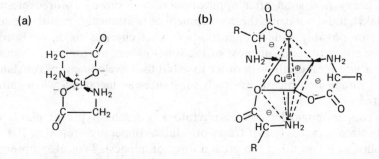

Figure 10.1   Possible chelate complexes between copper ions and glycine: (a) a bidentate ligand (electrically neutral); (b) an octahedral tridentate ligand (electrically negative)

Once there, however, it is essential that the complex loses the copper to an even more aggressive chelating agent within the wall, from where it eventually moves (by unknown means) to a vital internal component. If, however, the transporting complex is *extremely* stable it could sequester (mop up) any free copper in the vicinity and then fail to lose it to the chelating agent in the fungal wall. In this second case the complex would no longer be acting as a carrier of a lethal agent but would instead be functioning as an inactivating mechanism.

For historic reasons, Bordeaux mixture has been chosen as the example to illustrate the general chemistry of copper fungicides—its fungitoxic properties were accidentally discovered because a lime and copper sulphate mixture was applied to roadside vines to deter the wayfarer from sampling the grapes. Nowadays, **copper oxychloride** is probably the most widely employed copper fungicide. It is a basic copper chloride with a structure analogous to that of the main component of Bordeaux mixture (table 10.4). It can be purchased both as a wettable powder and as a colloidal liquid (which contains very small particles permanently suspended in a dispersing agent). **Copper hydroxide** is marketed as a wettable powder and a dust for use as a foliar spray. It is often formulated with sulphur or copper oxychloride (Thomson, 1985). **Cuprous oxide** is used both as a foliar spray and for seed treatment. It is made by the electrolytic oxidation of metallic copper.

Except on plants that are very sensitive to copper, there is often little to choose between the efficacy of these insoluble copper preparations in the field. Local variations in manufacture and local differences in climate probably explain the small differences in efficiency that have been reported. There is some evidence that copper fungicides may sometimes be more cost-effective in mixtures with other fungicides than when used alone. For example, Kingsland and Sitterly (1986), working in the Seychelles, found copper oxychloride to be more cost-effective in mixtures with chlorothalonil than when used alone against *Corynespora* leaf spot of tomatoes. Similarly, McGregor (1984) found that, at an equal-cost dose level, copper fungicides were usually as effective as metalaxyl in the control of diseases on cocoa in Papua New Guinea, except when heavy rain soon after application caused run-off. Moreover, unlike metalaxyl, it did not cause the development of resistance. A useful recommendation of possibly wider applicability is that cuprous oxide or Bordeaux mixture could be used for most of the time—when, in tropical climates, the weather was trustworthy—in order to avoid the development of resistance to organic fungicides, but to use such substances as metalaxyl when rain was expected.

All copper fungicides can be phytotoxic on some types of plants or in certain circumstances (e.g. if traces of soluble copper are present or if a spray is applied to leaves using too great a force of impact). Typical symptoms are leaf scorch and russetting, especially on fruit trees and bushes. Kairu *et al.* (1985) reported that copper fungicides caused phytotoxic symptoms on coffee bushes growing on light soil containing little organic matter, the phytotoxicity being manifest in the form of chlorotic leaves and a shortening of the internodes of young shoots.

10.5 COPPER FUNGICIDES: MODE OF ACTION

The mode of fungitoxic action of copper is uncertain, although it is initially fungistatic rather than fungicidal (i.e. it stops growth, rather than kills). This important observation is nearly as old as the chemistry of fungicides (an interesting review of this early work has been given by McBrien (1964)). At the turn of the century, Herzeberg, Tubeuf and Volkart independently observed that spores of bunt or smut fungi treated with copper sulphate do not germinate if washed and placed in water, but do germinate normally if placed on gelatin or in soil. The probable explanation is that these media contain complexing agents with a greater affinity for copper than have the binding sites within the spores. Hecke later showed that most of the copper could be washed out of poisoned spores by treatment with dilute acid and that the spores were then able to germinate normally. He also observed that spores had the ability to accumulate large amounts of copper even from external solutions of very low copper concentration. Up to some limiting value, the factor deciding the amount of copper absorbed from solutions of copper salts is not the concentration as such, but the total amount available from the medium. Rate of mixing determines the time it takes for uptake to be complete when the concentration is very low and the volume large.

Factors that influence the amount of copper taken up by fungal spores may throw some light on the mode of action of copper ions, or at least on their availability at the site of action. As could be anticipated from Hecke's results, the amount of copper absorbed becomes less as the hydrogen ion concentration of the external medium increases. Secondly, reagents that form stable complexes with copper may reduce both the uptake and the toxic effect of copper. Thus EDTA (ethylenediamine tetraacetate) reverses the inhibition of germination of *Alternaria* spores pretreated with copper. Various sulphydryl compounds, including glutathione, cysteine and British Anti-Lewisite (BAL), have a similar effect.

It will have been noted that chelate complexes have been mentioned in two related but different contexts, namely (a) the *solubilisation* of copper from an insoluble fungicidal residue and (b) the *removal* from poisoned but still viable fungal spores of copper that is already attached to some component of their walls. A picture thus seems to be emerging, not of the importance of a chelate complex *per se*, but of the relative stabilities of different complexes, present at each stage along the line from the components of a fungal exudate to the toxic complex at the ultimate site of action within the spore. This is worthy of further examination.

Many of the most fungitoxic heavy metals are transition elements (e.g. Cu,

Ag, Ni). For those that are not transition elements, those of larger atomic weight and of variable valency are often the more toxic (e.g. Zn is less toxic than Cd, which is less toxic than Hg). These general relationships, imperfect though they are, suggest that fungitoxicity (when defined in terms of the magnitude of the applied dose) is a function of the ease with which atoms gain, lose or share electrons. A physicochemical term often used to express the tendency of an atom to attract electrons is *electronegativity*. This is, in effect, a measure of the ionic character of a covalent bond*. Bond polarities greatly influence both physical and chemical properties, so, for related elements, many chemical properties roughly parallel electronegativity. Among these is the ease of formation of chelate complexes and the subsequent stability of such complexes.

The fungitoxicities of a number of metal ions were compiled by Horsfall (1956) and the relative sizes of these figures have been compared both with the electronegativity values for these ions and to Mellor and Maley's (1948) data on the relative stability of chelate complexes (table 10.5). When it is remembered how little is known about the nature of the toxic complexes formed en route to the site(s) of action, surprisingly good agreement exists between the order of fungitoxicity of different cations and the ease with which metals form covalent or coordinate bonds in chelate complexes.

It is still not clear whether copper exerts its ultimate toxic effect in the cuprous or the cupric form. The present writer found that copper absorbed onto algal cells was replaced by (univalent) silver ions almost quantitatively on an equivalent-for-equivalent basis if the copper was assumed to be divalent. This demonstrates that, in algae, the vast majority of copper ions absorbed form cupric complexes but it does not exclude the possibility that a small but important percentage could form cuprous complexes at a relatively few vital sites.

Somers (1963) observed that spores of *Neurospora* absorb 25 per cent more copper under anaerobic conditions than when air is present. Similarly, McBrien and Hassall (1967) showed that cells of *Chlorella vulgaris* exposed to copper under aerobic conditions suffer drastic respiratory collapse if, after removing excess copper, the cells are then exposed to a period of anaerobiosis. These and other data suggest that fungi, algae and some bacteria are more vulnerable to the toxic action of copper when air is excluded, but the reason for this increased susceptibility remains obscure.

Most heavy metals, including copper, are able to precipitate proteins if the effective concentration is high enough. Using Somer's (1963) data, which showed a 100-fold concentration of copper in fungal spores compared with that in the immediate environment, Corbett (1974) calculated that the internal concentration of copper could rise to 1.5 mM. This is possibly sufficient to

* The reader who needs to brush up bond chemistry is referred to a helpful little book by Brown (1961).

Table 10.5   **Partial correlation of fungitoxicity with chemical properties of metal ions and metal chelate complexes**

Fungitoxicity	Electronegativity[a]	Chelate stability[b]
Ag (highest)	Cu (highest—about 2.0)	Hg (highest)
Hg	Hg	Cu
Cu	Ag	Ni
Cd	Ni	Pb
Ni	Co	Co
Pb	Pb	Zn
Co	Zn	Cd
Zn (lowest)	Mn (lowest—about 1.4)	Mn (lowest)

[a] Haissinsky, as quoted by Somers (1961). A somewhat different plot is given by Danielli and Davies (1951).
[b] Mellor and Maley (1948).

bring about non-specific precipitation of protein. However, as was seen earlier, much of the copper is probably immobilised on insoluble cell components, and hence the value of calculations based upon the weight of copper per unit cell volume is highly dubious.

10.6 INORGANIC AND ORGANIC MERCURY COMPOUNDS

Inorganic mercury compounds are still used in some countries for clearly defined purposes but their use is rapidly declining; in the USA no residue of mercury at all is tolerated in food. One reason for this is that mercury (whether in ionic or elemental form) is potentially toxic to higher animals, including man; another is that the accumulation of mercury in soil or in living creatures represents a serious environmental hazard. It has been found that various types of microorganisms, in aerobic or sometimes in anaerobic conditions, can interconvert different forms of mercury—organic to inorganic, inorganic to organic and inorganic to elemental mercury—hence choice of a 'safer' form for application is no guarantee of longer-term environmental safety. The subject has been reviewed by Beijer and Jernelov (1979) and is mentioned again under organomercury compounds below.

Mercuric oxide, formulated as a 5 per cent paint, was marketed in Britain in

1986 as a seal for pruning cuts or injuries to bark. **Mercurous chloride** (calomel) is phytotoxic and cannot be employed as a fungicide on foliage other than grass. It is often formulated as a 4 per cent dust for soil application to control clubroot (*Plasmodiophora*) of brassicas and white rot of onions, but a suspension of it in water is sometimes used as a root dip. It has insecticidal and nematicidal properties, especially when mixed into the soil. When used as a fungicide, or against clubroot, it can give incidental suppression of cabbage root fly and onion fly. Another use of calomel is to control moss in turf.

The mode of action of inorganic mercury compounds remains uncertain, but many of the comments made in the previous section about copper are also relevent here. The toxic action of mercuric chloride when added to spores can be reversed by thiol reagents such as cysteine and it is generally believed that it reacts with thiol groups in proteins. Many dehydrogenases have active thiol groups, and Webb (1966) referred to more than 40 such enzymes that were partly inhibited by concentrations of less than $10\,\mu M$ mercuric ions.

Organomercury compounds were first used for seed treatment some 60 years ago. This use continues, but for reasons of safety they are now seldom employed as foliage sprays. The general formula is

$$R\text{--}Hg\text{--}X$$

where R nowadays is an aryl or alkoxyalkyl group and X is frequently derived from an acid. The Hg–X bond is said to be salt-like (the cation being $R.Hg^+$) but this is often obscured by the fact that acids, HX, are so chosen that the total complex is highly insoluble.

Phenylmercury chloride (PMC) was introduced in 1942 as a foliage spray for the control of *Nectria galligena* (which causes apple canker) and *Venturia inequaelis* (which causes apple scab). The acetate, PMA (figure 10.2a) has also been used against these fungi. As well as these arylmercury compounds, alkoxyalkylmercury derivatives have been used both for foliar application and as seed treatments. An example is methoxyethylmercury silicate and the corresponding acetate (figure 10.2b). Alkoxyalkyl compounds tend to hydrolyse rather more rapidly than do arylmercury compounds. Alkylmercury compounds were once used for seed treatment, but their use for any aspect of crop protection is highly undesirable because they have a virulent, traumatic

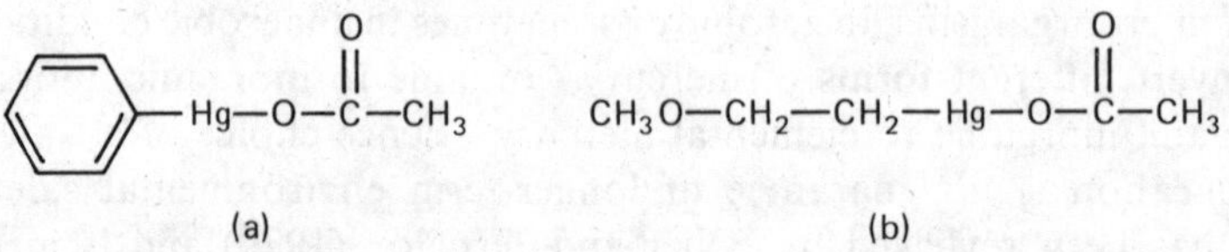

Figure 10.2   Organomercury fungicides: (a) phenylmercury acetate (PMA); (b) methoxyethylmercury acetate

Table 10.6   **Some important diseases of cereals that are controlled by organomercury seed treatment**[a]

Crop	Disease	Pathogen
Wheat	Bunt	*Tilletia caries/foetida*
	Seedling blight	*Fusarium* spp.
	Snow mould	*Fusarium nivale*
Barley	Covered smut	*Ustilago hordei*
	Leaf stripe	*Helminthosporium gramineum*
	Seedling blight	*Fusarium* spp.
Oats	Loose smut	*Ustilago avenae*
	Covered smut	*Ustilago levis*
	Leaf spot	*Helminthosporium avenae*
Maize	Leaf spot	*Helminthosporium* spp.
Sorghum	Seedling blight	*Fusarium* spp.

[a] Data from table 1 of FAO Agricultural Studies Report no. 95 (FAO, 1974)

and largely irreversible neurotoxic effect. An EEC Directive (79/117) has effectively halted the use of all types of organomercury compounds as foliar sprays in Europe and, as was mentioned earlier, these compounds are also banned in the USA. As for less advanced countries, it is not only undesirable but unethical, in the writer's view, to make mercury compounds of any kind available to peasant farmers for use in the developing world.

Seed treatments with organomercury compounds were commonly used up to about 1980, especially to protect cereal seeds from a variety of diseases (table 10.6). They have also been used to control seedborne diseases of sugar beet and of fodder beet. The mercury content of most seed treatment formulations was usually between 0.2 and 0.5 per cent.

Despite the desirability of phasing out the use of organomercury compounds for seed treatment, the need for caution in this instance should not disguise the fact that, in general, the method of seed treatment has considerable advantages over foliage application for controlling specified diseases. It is a method of use that enables an expensive poison to be applied very economically (grain treated with mercury seed dressing adds about 1 g/ha of mercury to the soil). Moreover, seed treatment in many industrialised countries is now done by the seed merchant rather than by the grower*. This is a highly desirable development, for reputable merchants have expertise, qualified staff and appropriate equipment for carrying out the operation safely. When seed treatment is possible, the grower therefore need not handle

* It will be recalled that, as a part of the harmonising of EEC Regulations, soon only certificated workers will be allowed to handle certain types of pesticides in the UK.

dangerous concentrates personally. On the other hand, *all treated grain must, of necessity, be sown; it must never be employed to prepare food for man or livestock*. Similarly, treated grain must be stored securely prior to sowing, so that it is inaccessible to children.

To reduce the risk of treated grain being consumed by accident, it is conventional to colour the seed dressing, the colour acting as both a warning and a code to indicate the nature of the fungicide or insecticide in the dressing. Unfortunately, this safety precaution has, on occasion, misfired with disastrous consequences. On more than one occasion, a starving community has deliberately washed the seed-treated grain, assuming that the removal of the colour was a demonstration that the poison had also been removed. Since serious symptoms may be delayed for weeks, a false sense of security may compound the error beyond the point of no return (FAO, 1974).

Treated grain can be a major hazard to grain-eating birds and, in springtime, when alternative food is scarce, the more voracious devourers of the farmers' newly sown seed may pay dearly for their predations. This is an unfortunate complication for it has brought into disrepute a method that, when applicable, is one of the safest and most efficient of all methods of pest and disease control. The reason for the greater safety is that a seed dressing is present on a seed below ground whereas the harvested part of many crops is above ground; that harvest, moreover, is separated by the length of a growing season from the time of application of poison. It should also be stressed that so far as mercury is concerned, serious damage to seed-eating birds and to birds of prey has always been a consequence of the consumption of seed treated with *alkyl*mercury seed dressings; aryl and alkoxyalkyl compounds are not known to have this devastating effect (FAO, 1974).

In view of the potential hazard associated with the use of organomercury seed dressings, attempts have been made to restrict the use of such compounds and wherever possible to employ alternatives. The joint FAO/WHO Meeting in Rome in March, 1974, further recommended that alkylmercury compounds should only be employed for the treatment of nuclear stocks of seed. Organomercury compounds are very effective against many important diseases of staple food crops (table 10.6) and have a broad spectrum of attack, whereas, unfortunately, many of the replacement substances have a restricted range or a limited effectiveness. In addition, some promote the development of resistance or are very expensive to employ. **Hexachlorobenzene** is effective against wheat bunt except where resistant strains occur, but it is scarcely less hazardous to man than are the organomercurials. **PCNB (quintozene)** has also been used for the treatment of various kinds of seeds in some countries. **Benomyl** and **thiabendazole** are costly and are ineffective against barley leaf stripe. **Dithiocarbamates** such as maneb and thiram are moderately broad-spectrum compounds and often prove highly successful. **Carboxin** is highly effective against diseases borne within the seed (e.g. loose smut of barley) but is very expensive for general use. More recently, Riedel and Grün (1986) investigated the toxicity to Japanese quail of three substances that are tending to replace organomercury compounds for seed treatment of cereals. These are thiram, carboxin and carbendazim. They concluded that none was less toxic than PMA to these birds; thiram, in particular, was very toxic to reproduction and a threat to grain-eating birds.

The mode of action of organomercury compounds remains obscure. Possibly, they break down to inorganic mercury at the site of action, the organic complex merely acting as a vehicle to transport toxic mercury ions into the organism (compare copper in organic complexes, section 10.5). If this is the case, the comments about thiol groups of dehydrogenases made in respect to inorganic mercury may also apply here. However, Ulfvarson (1969) concluded that compounds of the type R–Hg–X probably all broke down to give ions of the type $R-Hg^+$. These may then be toxic in their own right. This certainly seems to be the case for methylmercury ions, CH_3-Hg^+, for they are more toxic than are equal numbers of free mercuric ions.

In addition to possible effects upon thiol groups, there is some evidence that, at least in plants, organomercury compounds can affect nuclear division and lead to mitotic abnormalities. Bielecki (1977) noted mitotic abnormalities in the root tips of *Allium cepa* upon treatment with 1 ppm solution of PMA; slightly higher concentrations inhibited cytokinesis, with the formation of binucleate cells containing diploid or even tetraploid nuclei. Czuba and Mortimer (1982) similarly noted that the apical cells of the shoot of *Elodea densa* showed increased nuclear aberrations when exposed to about 1 nM solutions of methylmercury chloride.

It is, however, not always easy to be sure which ionic or molecular species is the toxicant at the site of action, except perhaps in short-term experiments, for from about 1970 several groups of workers have been able to show that organisms, and especially microorganisms, contain enzymes that are able to interconvert organic and inorganic mercury compounds and can reduce mercurous and mercuric ions to elemental mercury. As is well known, mercury vapour is extremely toxic to mammals. The formation of methylmercury ions *from* inorganic mercury in biological systems has been reported, *inter alia*, by Vallee and Ulmer (1972), and much of the early work has been reviewed by Beijer and Jernelov (1979).

A useful summary of work on the metabolism of organomercury compounds by microorganisms has been provided by Pan-Hou *et al.* (1982). For example, an organomercury hydrolase has been isolated and purified from an organomercury-resistant strain of *Escherichia coli*; the active site of this enzyme contained a thiol group. Other workers (Tezuka and Tonomura, 1978), using a mercury-resistant strain (K–62) of *Pseudomonas* spp., isolated two enzymes that sequentially attack organomercury compounds; the first converts organic mercury ions *to* inorganic mercury and the second reduces inorganic mercury ions to elemental mercury. Pan-Hou *et al.* (1982) themselves worked with a strain of *Clostridium cochlearium* containing a plasmid that mediated resistance to organomercury compounds; in this case the splitting of the C–Hg linkage was catalysed by an enzyme in the cell extract, the action of which was dependent upon the presence of glucose but not dependent on the presence of thiol compounds.

10.7 ORGANOTIN COMPOUNDS

In 1950, the Institute for Organic Chemistry in Utrecht commenced investigations into the possible agricultural use of organotin compounds. It was found that alkylated tetravalent tin compounds of the types $RSnX_3$, R_2SnX_2 and R_3SnX became more toxic to fungi as the number of alkyl groups increased to three, but that the nature of the group X (chloride, hydroxide, acetate) was less important. Compounds of the type R_4Sn were less toxic than those with the general formula R_3SnX.

Of the alkyl compounds, **bis(tri-n-butyltin) oxide** has been used to proof fabrics against rot and it and the corresponding fluoride have been used as molluscicides and as mosquito larvicides (Cardarelli, 1978). However, trialkyltin compounds are unsuitable for use on crops because they are too phytotoxic. On the other hand, certain triphenyltin derivatives are well tolerated by some plants. For example, Hatzios and Penner (1978) found that young soybean and rice plants suffered no respiratory or photosynthetic damage, nor did electron microscopy reveal any damage to cell ultrastructure, when they were treated with **triphenyltin acetate** at up to 2.2 kg/ha. Triphenyltin (fentin) acetate and triphenyltin hydroxide have been recommended for use on ornamental plants in Britain as well as for the control of potato blight. Fentin hydroxide has also been reported to be second only to sulphur in efficacy in the control of *Erysiphe betae*, the cause of powdery mildew disease of sugar beet (Byford, 1978). Triphenyltin compounds often control fungi at doses of not much more than one-tenth of those at which copper is fungitoxic.

Fentin acetate is slightly soluble in water (20 ppm) but it is readily hydrolysed to fentin hydroxide. The mode of action is uncertain. Rose and Aldridge (1972) demonstrated that it inhibited oxidative phosphorylation in mammalian mitochondria, but the work does not seem to have been extended to fungi. Mottley (1978) has shown that photophosphorylation in pea chloroplasts is inhibited as a result of interference with the chloroplastic electron transport system. He also provided indirect evidence that organotin compounds may inhibit calcium-dependent ATPase in *Chlamydomonas*. On the other hand, Leow *et al.* (1979) have shown that triphenyltin compounds inhibit adenylate cyclase activity in brain homogenates at a concentration of only 1 μM. It is possible that an attack on membrane integrity is a common denominator in these different manifestations of toxicity, but the cause of specific fungitoxic action remains obscure.

In view of the uses of trialkyltin compounds mentioned earlier, it is of interest that Seinen *et al.* (1979) have demonstrated that di-n-butyltin and related compounds have antilymphocytic properties and marked immunosuppressive action.

10.8 SULPHUR AND LIME SULPHUR

In 1971 the amount of sulphur used by farmers in the USA was 2.5 times as great as the amount of all other fungicides combined (Green *et al.*, 1977, table 7). This, of course, partly reflects the fact that it is applied at a rate of kilograms per hectare, whereas most organic fungicides are effective at less than one-hundredth of this amount. Its use is declining, but nevertheless the UK Ministry of Agriculture in 1986 still listed 44 sulphur-based fungicides as being approved under the 1986 Control of Pesticides Regulations (MAFF, 1986). Yet, despite intensive research, we are little nearer to understanding the mechanism of its fungicidal activity than was Forsyth, who, in 1803, first described the use of a sulphur spray on fruit trees. Horsfall (1956) has summarised in an amusing and scholarly way the vacillations of the views of the scientific fraternity on the mode of action of sulphur fungicides.

Briefly, it was suggested as early as 1879 that sulphur acted in the elemental state. After nearly 100 years of research (most workers had given up by about 1965!), and after the suggested involvement of nearly every combined form of the element imaginable, the majority view now is that sulphur probably acts in the elemental state. Admittedly, Mach's idea in 1879 was that the toxicity of sulphur was 'physical', the crystals acting as lenses that focused light on the fungal tissue. In contrast, the modern idea is 'chemically' based, the sulphur being thought to be an antimetabolite of oxygen. Excluding Mach, the main proponent of the *direct action* hypothesis was Sempio (1932).

On the other hand, the *oxidation* hypothesis suggested that sulphur dioxide and sulphur trioxide are the actual toxicants, but it was eventually shown that sulphur in this form is no more toxic than would be expected from the hydrogen ion concentration of their solutions in water. The *hydrolysis* theory suggested that sulphur is hydrolysed by water to active polysulphides. This hypothesis was championed by Hubert Martin, one of the pioneers of the subject of chemical crop protection. The *reduction* theory suggested that hydrogen sulphide is the actual toxicant. This possibility was apparently disproved in 1953 when it was shown that colloidal sulphur was 5–50 times more toxic than hydrogen sulphide. (This is perhaps not totally conclusive evidence, for it would be possible to imagine a cyclic catalytic effect that liberated a sulphide or polysulphide at the *site of action*; an analogy can be found in the cyclic catalytic effect of the quaternary ammonium weedkillers, section 14.1.) Earlier, Yarwood had tested the efficacy of lime sulphur against a powdery mildew with and without the addition of the powerful oxidising agent, $KMnO_4$. Unfortunately for this particular reduction theory, the permanganate prevented hydrogen sulphide production but the mildew was nevertheless controlled.

Spores of some fungi have a remarkable capacity to reduce sulphur—some spores can take up nearly 2 per cent of their own weight of sulphur and then convert most of it into hydrogen sulphide within 2 h. It thus seems likely that the biochemical processes leading to sulphide formation cannot be far removed from those implicated in the fungitoxicity of elemental sulphur. Several workers have suggested that sulphur competes with oxygen for electrons and thereby fouls the machinery of intermediary metabolism. For example, Owens (1960) considered that the S_6 molecule of sulphur is converted to a free radical that interferes with the conversion of acetate to citrate by *Neurospora*. Tweedy (1964), working with *Monilinia*, provided evidence that sulphur competes with mitochondrial cytochromes for electrons.

The trouble with all such theories, which attribute a very highly specific form of toxicity (in this case, fungitoxicity) to interference with an all but ubiquitous biochemical process, is that it is necessary to postulate that in one case the toxicant does get to its site of action and that in all the others it does not. It is virtually impossible to counter such an argument, yet scarcely ever is the evidence to support it unequivocal. Sulphur is an excellent illustration of this dilemma, because in this case it must be assumed that the factors of access and distribution are all-important, for sulphur is powerfully fungicidal yet it is apparently non-toxic to mammals—short of risking disaster by choking or constipation*. Yet, by applying radioactive sulphur to plants it was shown long ago that internal sulphur compounds rapidly become radioactive, the main labelled end-product being hydrogen sulphide (McCallan and Miller, 1957). This and similar work must surely demonstrate that elemental sulphur does indeed get into plants and does indeed entangle with the metabolic machinery, notwithstanding the fact that few plants are readily damaged by neutral sulphur preparations.

Sulphur is sometimes used as a fumigant, a colloidal smoke being made by vaporising it in lamps. In addition it is applied to plants in three formulations—as wettable powders, as colloidal sulphur and as lime sulphur. **Wettable powders** in Britain contain not less than 70 per cent w/w of sulphur and the particle size range is also officially specified. Not less than 40 per cent of the sulphur should be in particles of 6 μm or less in diameter. In practice, most of the particles are within the range 1–10 μm. A dispersing agent and a diluent such as kaolin or zinc oxide are usually also present and these account for the remaining 30 per cent of the wettable powder preparation.

The composition of **colloidal sulphur** liquid formulations (suspension con-

---

* My mother, who died during the preparation of the last chapter, used, long ago, to put a lump of rock sulphur in the dog's drinking bowl to 'purify the water', as she put it. It occurs to me that we still don't know much more about the curative value of sulphur than she did. The dog died of old age when he was 16.

centrates) is similarly subject to official specification in Britain. A suspension concentrate must contain 40 per cent or more of sulphur and not less than 90 per cent of the particles should be less than 6 μm diameter. In practice, most of the particles are within the range of 0.3–3.0 μm.

Lime sulphur is an orange-coloured liquid which should contain at least 24 per cent w/v of polysulphide sulphur. It is made by boiling a suspension of lime with an excess of flowers of sulphur. In effect, alkali-catalysed hydrolysis of sulphur occurs, the calcium salts of hydrogen sulphide and hydrogen sulphite being formed. Excess sulphur then reacts with each of these to give calcium polysulphide and calcium thiosulphate. Experience has shown that it is the **polysulphide sulphur** content of lime sulphur, rather than the total sulphur, that provides the best index of fungicidal efficiency in the field.

Compared with organic fungicides, a very high rate of application of inorganic sulphur fungicides is necessary. On the other hand, sulphur has the great advantage of being cheap and does not present a hazard to man. A further advantage is that it has a fairly wide biological spectrum—in sharp contrast to the insecticide situation, selective control of different fungi present on plants is seldom necessary or desirable.

Sulphur sprays are used against apple scab, for which a full spray programme in the UK classically required the successive application of four sprays: an early one of higher concentration at the 'green cluster' stage of growth; a second, less concentrated, at the 'pink bud' stage; a third, dilute, at petal fall; and a fourth at the fruitlet stage. One or more of the later applications may be replaced by sprays containing organic fungicides such as captan or dodine (especially on *sulphur-shy* varieties). Other uses of sulphur sprays include the control of peach leaf curl and of powdery mildews. For example, Byford (1978) found that two sprays of sulphur, the first applied at the onset of the attack, suppressed severe infections of sugar beet by the powdery mildew, *Erysiphe betae*, and increased the yield of sugar by 13 per cent. Sulphur sprays are also used against the gall mite, which causes 'big bud' of blackcurrants; this is an instance of an interesting occurrence that will be encountered elsewhere, namely that those fungicides that are particularly effective against the Erysiphales are also very often quite useful acaricides as well.

Certain varieties of fruit trees and bushes suffer damage from sulphur sprays and are said to be 'sulphur-shy'. Examples are the apple cultivars Cox's Orange Pippin, Newton Wonder and Beauty of Bath and the gooseberry varieties Leveller and Careless. Acute damage is visible as marginal burns on the leaves; chronic damage includes the formation of premature abscission layers leading to early drop of leaves and fruit. Overspraying with sulphur (especially lime sulphur) on warm days (above 26°C) is particularly liable to cause problems.

When sulphur is deposited on leaves it probably undergoes a cyclic series of weathering changes, which result in the particles of sulphur becoming smaller and more firmly bound to the leaf surface. Such changes increase both distribution and persistence of the fungicidal deposit and are therefore advantageous. Weathering changes include hydrolysis to give sulphides and sulphites; these two types of products dissolve more sulphur to give polysulphides and thiosulphates respectively. Polysulphides can be hydrolysed or can react with carbonic acid, in both cases to reprecipitate sulphur in nearcolloidal form. Thiosulphates can be oxidised to sulphur and insoluble sulphates, the latter then helping to bind the sulphur to the leaf surface. During the course of these changes some part of the sulphur is converted to hydrogen sulphide, which may contribute to the fungitoxic action, as may hydrogen polysulphides.

REFERENCES

Barnes, G. (1977). In *Herbicides and Fungicides; Factors Affecting their Activity*, ed. N. R. McFarlane, Chem. Soc. Spec. Publ. no. 29, p. 35. Chemical Society, London

Beijer, K. and Jernelov, A. (1979). In *Topics in Environmental Health*, vol. 3, *The Biogeochemistry of Mercury in the Environment*, ed. J. O. Nriagu. Elsevier North-Holland Biomedical Press, Amsterdam

Bielecki, E. (1977). *Acta Biol. Cracov. Sér. Bot.*, **20**, 67

Brown, G. I. (1961). *A Simple Guide to Modern Valency Theory*. Longmans, London

Byford, W. J. (1978). *Ann. Appl. Biol.*, **88**, 377

Cardarelli, N. F. (1978). *Mosquito News*, **38**, 328

Corbett, J. R. (1974). *The Biochemical Mode of Action of Pesticides*. Academic Press, London

Czuba, M. and Mortimer, D. C (1982). *Ecotoxicol. Environ. Safety*, **6**, 204

Danielli, J. F. and Davies, J. T. (1951). *Adv. Enzymol.*, **11**, 35

de Waard, M. A. and van Nistelrooy, J. G. M. (1980). *Pestic. Biochem. Physiol.*, **13**, 255

FAO (1974). *The Use of Mercury and Alternative Compounds as Seed Dressings*, Report of a Joint FAO/WHO Meeting, Geneva, March, 1974, FAO Agricultural Studies Report no. 95. FAO, Rome

Green, M. B., Hartley, G. S. and West, T. F. (1977). *Chemicals for Crop Protection and Pest Control*. Pergamon, Oxford

Hatzios, K. K. and Penner, D. (1978). *Pestic. Biochem. Physiol.*, **9**, 70

Horsfall, J. G. (1956). *Principles of Fungicidal Action*. Chronica Botanica, Waltham, MA

Jacob, F. and Neumann, St. (1987). In *Modern Selective Fungicides*, ed. H. Lyr, p. 13. Longmans, Harlow; Wiley, New York

Kairu, G. M., Nyangena, C. M. S. and Crosse, J. E. (1985). *Plant Pathol.*, **34**, 207

Kingsland, G. C. and Sitterly, W. R. (1986). *Trop. Pest Managem.*, **32**, 31

Leow, A. C. T., Towns, K. M. and Leaver, D. D. (1979). *Chem.–Biol. Interact.*, **27**, 125

Lyr, H. (1987). In *Modern Selective Fungicides*, ed. H. Lyr. Longmans, Harlow; Wiley, New York

McBrien, D. C. H. (1964). Aspects of the uptake of copper and its physiological effects on *Chlorella vulgaris*, *Ph.D. Thesis*, University of Reading, UK

McBrien, D. C. H. and Hassall, K. A. (1967). *Physiol. Plant*, **20**, 113

McCallan, S. E. A. and Miller, L. P. (1957). *Contrib. Boyce Thompson Inst.*, **18**, 497

McGregor, A. J. (1984). *Plant Pathol.*, **33**, 81

MAFF (1984). *Use of Fungicides and Insecticides on Cereals 1984*, Ministry of Agriculture, Fisheries and Food, ADAS Booklet 2257. HMSO, London

MAFF (1986). *Pesticides 1986: Pesticides Approved Under the Control of Pesticides Regulations 1986*, Ministry of Agriculture, Fisheries and Food, UK, Ref. Book 500. HMSO, London

Mellor, D. P. and Maley, L. (1948). *Nature (London.)*, **161**, 436

Mottley, J. (1978). *Pestic. Biochem. Physiol.*, **9**, 340

Owens, R. G. (1960). *Dev. Ind. Microbiol.*, **1**, 187

Owens, R. G. and Miller, L. P. (1957). *Contrib. Boyce Thompson Inst.*, **19**, 177

Pan-Hou, H. S. K., Kajikawa, Y. and Imura, N. (1982). *Ecotoxicol. Environ. Safety*, **6**, 82

Riedel, B. and Grün, G. (1986). *Nachrichtenbl. Pflanzenschutz DDR*, **40**, 147

Rose, M. S. and Aldridge, W. N. (1972). *Biochem. J.*, **127**, 51

Seinen, W., Vos, J. G., Brands, R. and Hooykaas, H. (1979). *Immunopharmacology*, **1**, 343

Sempio, C. (1932). *Mem. R. Accad. Ital. Cl. Sci. Fis. Mat. Nat., 3, Biol.*, **2**, 1 (cited from Horsfall, 1956)

Somers, E. (1961). *Ann. Appl. Biol.*, **49**, 246

Somers, E. (1963). *Meded. Landb. Hoogesch. Opzoek. Stn. Gent*, **28**, 580

Tezuka, T. and Tonomura, K. (1978). *J. Bacteriol.*, **135**, 138

Thomson, W. T. (1985). *Agricultural Chemicals*, Book IV, *Fungicides*, rev. edn. Thomson, Fresno, CA

Tröger, R. (1960). *Phytopathol. Z.*, **40**, 91

Tweedy, B. G. (1964). *Phytopathology*, **54**, 910

Ulfvarson, U. (1969). *Fungicides, an Advanced Treatise*, vol. 2, ed. D. C. Torgeson, p. 303. Academic Press, New York

Vallee, B. L. and Ulmer, D. D. (1972). *Annu. Rev. Biochem.*, **41**, 91

Webb, J. L. (1966). *Enzyme and Metabolic Inhibitors*, vol. 2. Academic Press, New York

11 Non-systemic organic fungicides

11.1 CLASSIFICATION OF NON-SYSTEMIC FUNGICIDES

Fungicides used in crop protection can be divided into two types, namely those that remain near the point at which they are deposited and those that enter the plant (either through the root or the leaves) and are transported within the plant in xylem or phloem. The former are non-systemic or loco-systemic (section 4.8) compounds, the latter are systemic. A few substances possess the ability to enter plants in very small amounts (e.g. prochloraz, some dinitro compounds and morpholines) and can be classified in either group.

The substances considered in this chapter are listed in table 11.1. They are predominantly contact in action; when deposited on plant surfaces, they give protection against fungal spores arriving after the time of application, the spores being killed as they try to germinate.

Non-systemic fungicides were in use long before systemic compounds became popular. Some are still used in large quantities, although a straw-poll of titles of articles in the scientific press does not leave this impression. One reason for this is that the modes of action of certain systemic compounds are of particular scientific interest from a fundamental viewpoint. In contrast, the targets of non-systemic fungicides sometimes seem to be 'ordinary' and general. For example, several groups of non-systemic fungicides attack a range of thiol compounds, thereby (and almost incidentally) blocking thiol groups present at active sites of important enzymes. In addition, from a practical and commercial viewpoint, the ease of application of systemic fungicides, their duration of action, and the prospect of tailoring molecules with both insecticidal and systemic fungicidal properties, all make them attractive targets for industrial research initiative.

However, the potential importance of non-systemic fungicides discussed in this chapter should not be underestimated; problems of resistance have arisen during the use of systemic fungicides which are very serious—worse than any encountered using contact fungicides. In fact, as will be seen later, the judicious use of non-systemic compounds, either admixed with systemics or alternating with them chronologically, may be the only way to avoid serious long-term problems associated with many (but not all) groups of systemic fungicides.

Table 11.1 Classification of non-systemic organic fungicides other than organometal compounds. Section references are shown in parentheses

Group	Examples
Organosulphur compounds	
1. Dithiocarbamates (11.2, 11.3)	Thiram, zineb, mancozeb
2. Phthalimides (11.4)	Captan, folpet, captafol
Dinitrophenol derivatives (11.5)	Dinocap, binapacryl
Chlorinated aromatics (11.6)	
1. Chlorinated nitro compounds	Quintozene
2. Chlorinated amino compounds	Dicloran
3. Chlorinated nitriles	Chlorothalonil
4. Chlorinated quinones	Dichlone
Other non-systemic or poorly systemic compounds (11.7)	
1. Guanidine derivatives	Dodine acetate
2. Imidazoles (others are systemic)	Imazalil, prochloraz
3. Dicarboximides	Iprodione, vinclozolin

Before considering individual fungicides it is desirable to stress that the correct and efficacious use of chemicals to control fungi is much more difficult than is the use of chemicals to control insects or weeds, especially in the conditions found in the developing world. Many insects are clearly visible and the nature of the problem is obvious. In any case, since many insecticides are not particularly selective, precise identification of the insect or precise choice of insecticide may not be all-important. But, as has been seen, most organic fungicides, both non-systemic and systemic, tend to be selective; consequently, success or failure in fungal control may depend upon an accuracy of identification beyond the skills of the average farmer unless he is supported by adequate advisory or extension services. Not only may identification be essential, but the effectiveness of a fungicidal application may be intimately dependent on timing, and hence upon an understanding of the life cycle of the organism causing the disease. Some of the principles involved, and various practical problems associated with the control of fungi, have been discussed by Fry (1982).

Some of the difficulties just described are well illustrated by a report by Black *et al.* (1985). It refers to surveys done in Thailand over several years, concerning the use of various fungicides by peasant farmers to control *Alternaria porri*, the organism causing purple blotch disease of garlic. In the first instance, there were cultural difficulties; the disease problem was always more severe if the farmer, in the interests of early planting, omitted the conventional preceding rice crop. Next, a wide range of fungicides was in use and the farmers had no idea which controlled *A. porri* (and most systemic fungicides, including the benzimidazoles were, in fact, unsuitable). Other fungicides were in use even though no one anywhere had apparently researched their use against this particular purple blotch disease. As the authors say, these facts, if confirmed, reflect erratic marketing (the present writer would put it less graciously) and extension activities that were insufficiently supportive. Moreover, few of the farmers knew about the relevance of timing to the control of free-swimming zoospores, or were aware of the importance of rates of application, or of waiting for optimal weather conditions to occur. Thus, in one survey, most farmers did not spray at the right time (45 days post-planting) and, of those who did, only one actually achieved good control of purple blotch. Failure was due to ineffective spraying, spraying too late, spraying too infrequently, spraying the wrong fungicide, and using defective spraying equipment.

11.2 DITHIOCARBAMATES: CHEMISTRY, UPTAKE AND USES

In terms of tonnage employed, the dithiocarbamates are among the most used organic fungicides. They fall into two main groups, the most noteworthy difference between them being that the molecules of substances in group 2 have a hydrogen atom attached to the carbamate nitrogen (figure 11.1).

The fungicides in group 1 of table 11.2 are all derivatives of dimethyldithiocarbamic acid, although two sorts of derivatives are in use. Most are metallic complexes (except in the case of sodium, they are not salts), but one, thiram, is a disulphide oxidation product (figure 11.2b). Thiram is the only disulphide used as a fungicide but its diethyl analogue is used medically to treat alcoholics. All forms of one substance may be biologically interconvertible since disulphide forms can be reduced to thiol forms and metal complexes can dissociate.

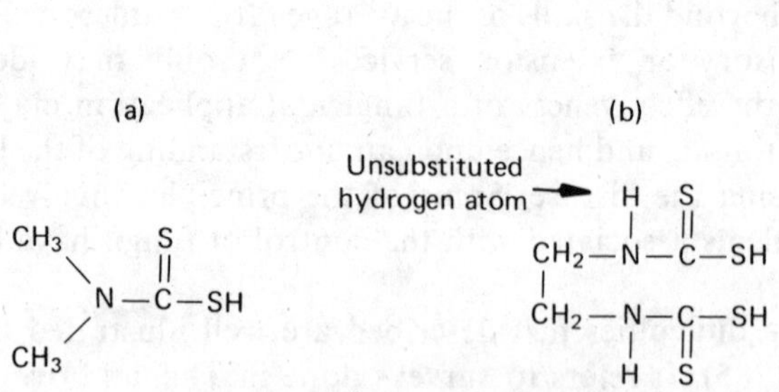

Figure 11.1   Structure of (a) a disubstituted and (b) a monosubstituted dithiocarbamate: (a) dimethyldithiocarbamate (group 1) (examples of fungicidal derivatives appear in figure 11.2); (b) ethylene bisdithiocarbamate (group 2a) (zineb and maneb are fungicidal derivatives)

Table 11.2 Classification of dithiocarbamate fungicides

Group; main feature	Chemical designation	Types of derivatives—with example
Group 1. No hydrogen atom on the nitrogen atom	Dimethyldithiocarbamates (figures 11.1, 11.2)	(i) Metal derivatives (a) Zinc complex (ziram) (b) Iron complex (ferbam) (iii) Oxidation product (thiram)
Group 2. One hydrogen atom on the nitrogen atom	(a) Bisdithiocarbamates (figure 11.1b)	(iii) Metal derivatives (a) Sodium salt (nabam) (b) Zinc complex (zineb) (c) Manganese complex (maneb) (d) Mn/Zn mixed complex (mancozeb)
	(b) Monomethyldithio-carbamate	(a) Sodium salt (metham-Na)

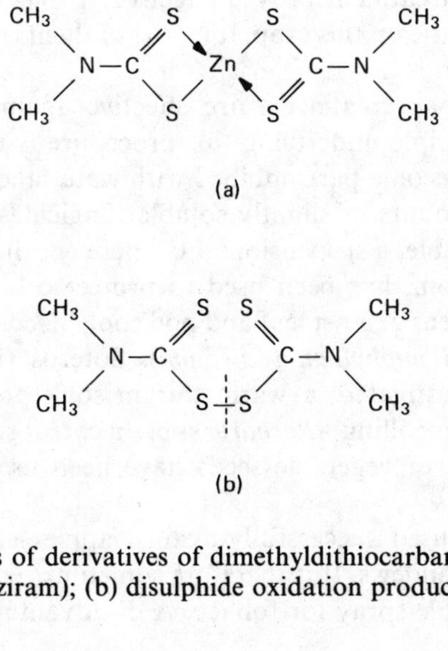

(a)

(b)

Figure 11.2 Two types of derivatives of dimethyldithiocarbamate: (a) chelate metal complex (ziram); (b) disulphide oxidation product (thiram)

The dithiocarbamates of both groups probably enter fungi as un-ionised molecules of a weak acid, of a disulphide derivative, or of a covalent complex. Nabam, for example, which is soluble in water and highly ionised, is of low toxicity to spores of *Monilia* spp. if environmental conditions do not favour oxidation. In contrast, the water-insoluble and lipophilic zinc complex, ziram, is toxic whether or not oxidising conditions exist. For toxicity at the site of action, however, it may be essential for an ionic form to be readily assumed, no matter in which form the substance penetrates the fungus.

Soluble dithiocarbamates are used for soil treatment whereas the insoluble heavy-metal complexes and disulphides are valuable for foliage spraying, seed treatment and post-harvest protection. Some of the more important uses of these and other non-systemic fungicides appear in table 11.3.

Metham-sodium is not only a fungicide but a general soil sterilant. At about 100 kg/ha it destroys soil arthropods (e.g. millipedes and woodlice), nematodes (e.g. the potato cyst nematode) and weed seedlings (e.g. *Oxalis*, chickweed) as well as soilborne fungi. For reasons of cost, its use is normally restricted to glasshouse soil and to land to be used for high-value crops. It decomposes to give methyl isothiocyanate, $CH_3.NCS$, which probably acts as a fumigant. It is essential that both metham-sodium and isothiocyanate should have disappeared before a crop is introduced into the soil.

Thiram was originally introduced to control *Botrytis* spp. although it is used nowadays for seed treatment, especially as a protection against damping-off in beans, peas and maize and against *Verticillium* wilt of lucerne. The report of Ellis and Paschal (1979) is one of several illustrations of the use of thiram for seed treatment. They found that thiram (and also captan) moved into the tissues of the seed coat of the pigeon pea (*Cajanus cajan*) but did not penetrate to the embryo. The treatment proved effective against seven pathogens that are internally seedborne on this crop, for none of them is normally to be found deeper than the testa.

Warm chemical soak treatments are effective against many deep-seated pathogens. The principle underlying this procedure is that seeds soaked for about 24 h at 30°C become part-imbibed with water and in consequence they absorb sufficient amounts of slightly soluble fungicides to eliminate specific pathogens. For example, a suspension of 0.2 per cent thiram, the solubility of which is about 30 ppm, has been used to protect celery against leaf blight (*Septoria apiicola*), peas against leaf and pod spot (*Ascochyta pisi*) and carrots against black rot (*Stemphylium radicinum*). Soteros (1979) found that, of several methods investigated, a warm thiram soak proved to be the most effective means of controlling *Alternaria* spp. on carrot seeds. Many aspects of antifungal treatment of vegetable seeds have been usefully summarised by Maude (1978).

Ferbam has been used successfully against apple scab, but it gives poor control of powdery mildews. It is therefore sometimes employed with elemental sulphur as a double spray for foliage. A disadvantage is that it leaves an

Table 11.3 Some of the more important uses of protective (non-systemic) fungicides

Fungicide	Uses (foliage-applied unless otherwise stated)
Metham-Na	Soil sterilant — soil fungi, nematodes, millipedes
Thiram	Botrytis, cane spot, rusts; post-harvest dip for strawberries; seed treatment against damping off, *Verticillium* wilt, *Fusarium* spp. and root rots
Maneb, mancozeb	Potato, tomato blight; tulip fire; black spot of roses; cereal rusts
Zineb	Potato, tomato blight; downy mildew on hop, lettuce; tomato leaf mould and root rot; celery leaf spot
Captan	Apple, pear scab; *Botrytis* on strawberries, lettuce; black spot of roses; stem rot of tomato
Folpet	Black spot on roses; some other diseases of ornamentals; grape downy mildew
Captafol	Potato blight; *Rhynchosporium* leaf blotch of barley
Dichlofluanid	*Botrytis* on several bush and cane fruits and on strawberries; septoria glume blotch of wheat
Dinocap	Powdery mildews and red spider mites on apples, strawberries, gooseberries, roses
Binapacryl	Powdery mildew and red spider mites on apples
Tecnazene	Seed treatment of potato tubers against dry rot; inhibits potato sprouting; a smoke for *Botrytis* on greenhouse plants
Dicloran	Dust for *Botrytis* on tomatoes, lettuce, cyclamen
Chlorothalonil	Several diseases on bush and cane fruit and on soy beans; also on strawberries
Dichlone	Seed treatment, especially for legumes
Dodine	Apple scab, especially when infection incidence high

unsightly black deposit, which can only be washed off picked fruit with difficulty.

Maneb, zineb and **mancozeb** (a complex containing both manganese and zinc) are the most important dithiocarbamate sprays for foliage application. Much of their importance rests in the fact that they have partly replaced copper fungicides for the control of potato and tomato blights. **Maneb** is used against late blight of tomato and potato, *Phytophthora infestans*, as well as tomato leaf mould and tulip fire (MAFF, 1985). **Zineb** is employed against potato and tomato blight, against downy mildew of hops, lettuce and onions, and against bubble and cobweb of mushrooms. It is less frequently applied to top fruit for, like thiram, it can taint produce or cause the corrosion of cans. It sometimes reduces rust infection but does not necessarily totally control it. For vegetables, it has been partly replaced by maneb and mancozeb since these often provide superior control.

Mancozeb is tending to supersede maneb for the control of potato blight — half the crop in the UK is currently being sprayed with a mixture of mancozeb and metalaxyl (section 12.8). Dithiocarbamates generally persist on sprayed potato leaves for a shorter time than do copper fungicides, a property that can be disadvantageous in seasons when conditions favour potato blight, for more spray applications are then necessary. Kingsland and Sitterby (1986) investigated the effectiveness and the cost–benefit of several fungicides against *Corynespora* leafspot of tomatoes in the Seychelles. Mancozeb was not as effective as some other fungicides (and especially not as satisfactory as a mixture containing copper oxychloride and chlorothalonil) but, on the basis of cost–benefit per kilogram of fruit, mancozeb was better than any other substance or mixture of substances used.

It has been found that mixtures of dithiocarbamates with other fungicides are often more effective than are the individual components used alone. This is especially so when the components of such mixtures have a different mode of action. Sometimes, one of the components is a systemic compound, and in such cases a second, but vital, advantage of the mixture is that the development of resistance, so characteristic of many types of systemic compounds when these are used alone, occurs far less readily. Samoucha and Cohen (1984) showed that foliar applications of mancozeb/metalaxyl mixture provided better control of downy mildew, *Pseudoperonospora cubensis*, and of blight, *Phytophthora infestans*, than either mancozeb or metalaxyl used alone. Similarly, Samoucha and Gisi (1987) demonstrated that a mixture of mancozeb and oxadixyl (section 12.8) exerted a control efficiency 31 times higher than expected when applied to tomato plants one day before inoculation of the plants with *Phytophthora infestans*.

An illustration of the way that a non-systemic fungicide can moderate the tendency of a systemic compound to cause resistance to develop is provided by the work of Lalancette *et al.* (1987). Mancozeb was mixed with the systemic fungicide, benomyl (section 12.2), in various (but roughly equitoxic) ratios and applied to apple trees inoculated with *Venturia inequaelis*. When the proportion of benomyl was great, the development of resistance occurred quickly, but, as the proportion of mancozeb increased the build-up of resistance was delayed. In this case the two active ingredients apparently had additive rather than synergistic effects.

For both of the reasons outlined above—possible synergism and prevention of resistance—it is now common practice to apply mixtures of such dithiocarbamates as mancozeb with other (often systemic) fungicides for the control of late blight of potatoes. In the UK it is common to mix a dithiocarbamate with metalaxyl, but many other variants exist; the Ministry of Agriculture reference book of approved pesticides under the 1986 regulations (MAFF, 1986) lists at least 10 mixtures containing mancozeb; these include benalaxyl, carbendazim (section 12.2), cymoxanil and oxadixyl (section 12.8). An even larger number of mixtures contain maneb.

It should be added that although, in the field, it is unusual for serious resistance to develop, nevertheless the potential always exists for this to happen and, in appropriate laboratory conditions, it does. An example is provided by the work of Anilkumar and Sastry (1979). Starting with a sensitive strain of *Rhizoctonia bataticola* that just tolerated 25 µg/ml of thiram, the strain was subjected to selection pressure on a growth medium containing increasing concentrations of thiram. After six serial passages through such media it was able to grow on a medium containing 500 µg/ml of thiram.

Various dithiocarbamates have also found use for *post-harvest protection* of foodstuffs. Banana hands are often dipped in a suspension of **maneb**; **thiram**, applied as a post-harvest dip, has been used to control strawberry rot. Such uses are feasible because of the low toxicity to higher animals of insoluble dithiocarbamates. Post-harvest uses of dithiocarbamates and other fungicides have been reviewed by Eckert (1967).

11.3 DITHIOCARBAMATES: MODE OF ACTION AND METABOLISM

Despite their chemical similarity, there is evidence that dialkyldithiocarbamates (group 1, table 11.2) and the bisdithiocarbamates (group 2, table 11.2) act in different ways on fungi, or at least have different secondary effects. The difference is often attributed to the fact that only the group 2 compounds (such as mancozeb and zineb) possess a reactive N–H bond associated with the thiocarbamyl group (figure 11.1). Briefly, compounds in group 1 may form toxic complexes with copper or, alternatively, may sequester essential trace metals. Group 2 compounds appear to react with thiol groups in enzymes, coenzymes or biological carriers (group 1 compounds may do this too, but to a lesser degree). In addition, group 2 compounds break down to give isothiocyanates and thiourea derivatives; such compounds are known to react with enzymes or proteins, and, indeed, in biochemistry, are often used as reagents for this purpose.

(a)   Group 1 dithiocarbamates

Several of these, including the sodium salt and the disulphide, thiram, exhibit a remarkable and rare phenomenon termed a *bimodal* response curve. As increasing amounts of dithiocarbamate are added to mould cultures growing in the presence of a little copper, it is found that toxicity first increases with dithiocarbamate concentration, then diminishes, and finally increases again (figure 11.3). In other words, over a restricted concentration range, increasing the external concentration of fungicide elicits a decreasing response from the fungus.

A bimodal curve probably reflects in some way the mechanism whereby group 1 dithiocarbamate fungicides bring about their toxic action on the fungus. It is commonly agreed, but not proven, that the bimodal curve could be a function of the relative abundance, at different dithiocarbamate concentrations, of different molecular species at an (unspecified) site of action. The proponents of this theory consider that free dithiocarbamate ions are formed within the cell, irrespective of which complex or oxidation product is applied externally. Once inside, it is assumed that the ions form a complex with internal heavy metals, of which copper is an obvious candidate. At low dithiocarbamate concentrations a resonating complex is believed to be formed comprising one metal ion united to one dithiocarbamate molecule (figure 11.4).

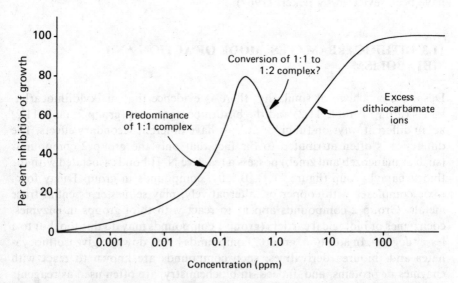

Figure 11.3   Bimodal dosage–response curve of *Aspergillus* to sodium dimethyldithio-carbamate (1:1 complex, one copper to one dithiocarbamate; 1:2 complex, one copper to two dithiocarbamates)

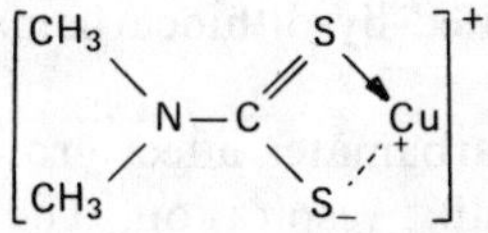

$$\left[\begin{array}{c} CH_3 \\ \diagdown \\ N-C \\ \diagup \\ CH_3 \end{array} \begin{array}{c} S \\ \diagdown \\ \diagup \\ S_- \end{array} \begin{array}{c} Cu \\ \stackrel{+}{\cdots} \end{array} \right]^{+}$$

Figure 11.4 The charged, resonating 1:1 complex formed between copper ions and dimethyldithiocarbamate

This complex is believed to be extremely toxic to those fungi whose dosage–response curves are bimodal; if so, *in vivo* fungitoxicity of dimethyldithiocarbamate to sensitive fungi could be attributed to it. It is this species of ion that is presumed to be responsible for the left-hand rising portion of the curve in figure 11.3. The toxic effect increases on addition of more dithiocarbamate until all the available copper (and possibly other heavy metals) has been converted to a 1:1 complex. There is spectrophotometric evidence for the existence of such a complex, for, on addition of a solution of copper sulphate to dimethyldithiocarbamate, a characteristic absorption peak occurs at 380 nm. As more dithiocarbamate is added, this peak decreases and eventually disappears, a fact that is attributed to the formation of a more stable and less toxic complex containing one copper atom associated with two molecules of dithiocarbamate. When, *in vivo*, a large excess of dithiocarbamate ions is present, they appear to be toxic in their own right and to account for the right-hand rising part of the curve in figure 11.3; their toxicity is often ascribed to their ability to inactivate thiol groups (and hence, at this level, the mode of action of all dithiocarbamate fungicides appears to be similar).

It was observed in early studies (Goksøyr, 1955) that oxygen uptake by yeast supplied with sodium acetate as carbon source was inhibited by the group 1 compound, sodium dimethyldithiocarbamate; moreover, in the presence of zinc ions, respiratory inhibition was depressed even more severely. It is therefore of some interest that Soni and Atri (1986), working with *Botryodiplodia theobromae*, observed that mycelial growth was suppressed by thiram but was reversed by magnesium ions or by ferrous ions. Cysteine also reversed the effect (which is consistent with the comment above that group 1 compounds may also owe part of their toxicity to interaction with thiol groups).

(b) Group 2 dithiocarbamates

An important clue to the mode of action of bisdithiocarbamates may be provided by the observation that spores, the germination of which has been inhibited by nabam, commence to germinate normally when cysteine is added to the growth medium. Presumably a thiol group of an enzyme (or of some other essential biological component) is the target, although which of the many possible candidates is actually involved remains undetermined. Data on enzymes that can be inhibited by dithiocarbamates have been tabulated by Owens (1969, p. 243).

Precisely how bisdithiocarbamates affect growth is uncertain, but a common view is that they inhibit respiration. The evidence for this has been outlined by Kaars Sijpesteijn (1982). More recently, however, Russian workers have studied the effect of zineb on yeast using electron microscopy as well as biochemical and genetic methods. It was concluded (Emnova *et al.*, 1986) that the initial changes were anabolic, with an increase in the RNA and protein content of cells; in addition, an enlargement of the mitochondria was evident, while genetic effects were induced by zineb at approximately 500 μg/l.

The nature of the active species (if it is not the applied bisdithiocarbamate) is also uncertain, for the labile hydrogen atom referred to above renders these compounds very unstable. At least 14 breakdown products are feasible, any one of which might be, or might give rise to, the actual toxicant. Of the two principal theories, one implicates an isothiocyanate as the active species whereas the other suggests that it is ethylenethiuram disulphide (figure 11.5).

The isothiocyanate theory is based upon the fact that the soil fumigation action of **metham-sodium** (table 11.2) arises from the formation of a volatile isothiocyanate. However, Owens (1969) failed to confirm any similarity in the (abnormal) internal balance of metabolic acids after treating *Rhizoctonia* with authentic methyl isothiocyanate and with nabam. The work of Morehart and Crossan (1965) revealed rather that there was a similarity in the pattern of free amino acid distribution in *Colletotrichum* spp. after the mycelium had been treated with maneb or with ethylenethiuram disulphide. The latter (figure 11.5) is probably formed from all the common fungicides in group 2, and it has therefore been proposed that this disulphide is the actual toxic agent.

All dithiocarbamate fungicides, but especially the ethylene derivatives, are unstable and can be broken down chemically and photochemically as well as by enzymes in plants and fungi. Some common breakdown products of various dithiocarbamates are shown in figure 11.5, which is based on data quoted by Menzie (1980). Common products include ethylenethiuram disulphide and ethylene diisothiocyanate, as well as ethylenethiourea, ethyleneurea and (secondarily) carbon disulphide, sulphur and various imidazoline derivatives. Many of these are chemical decomposition products rather than true metabolites.

It is noteworthy that the formation of a significant amount of ethylenethiourea has been observed during the cooking of food treated with maneb (Watts *et al.*, 1974). It may well be a degradation product of other dithiocarbamates as well. It is therefore a matter of concern that this substance is suspected of being a potential hazard, possibly teratogenic, goitrogenic and (in the presence of nitrite) carcinogenic at some dose levels and in some test organisms. Trotter and Pardue (1982) have reviewed the evidence for the occurrence of these chronic effects and have also demonstrated that the amount of ethylenethiourea in a formulation of ethylene bisdithiocarbamate

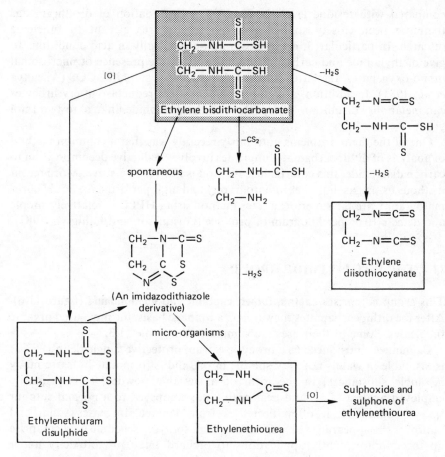

Figure 11.5 Some common breakdown products, including possible fungitoxic derivatives, of ethylene bisdithiocarbamates

increases on storage if the product is kept at 49°C and at 80 per cent humidity. Working with raw, unwashed spinach they detected up to 2.3 ppm ethylene-thiourea on dithiocarbamate-treated leaves and between 5 and 80 ppm (μg/g wet weight) of the dithiocarbamate. Upon washing the leaves, most of the dithiocarbamate was removed but most of the ethylenethiourea was not.

High residues of dithiocarbamates have occasionally been observed in vegetable crops sprayed with these fungicides and a fear that possible chronic toxic effects of the kinds referred to above might occur has led to the use of dithiocarbamates being restricted in Canada and some other countries. In this regard it is worth recalling that tetraethylthiuram disulphide, which is closely related to thiram, is prescribed medically to help people break dependence on alcohol. The dose levels of 'disulfiram' used for this purpose are very high compared with residue levels in foods. The degradation of disulfiram has therefore been closely studied and the results are relevant to fungicide research. In particular, it decomposes non-enzymically in acid conditions to give diethylamine and carbon disulphide and, in the presence of microsomal mono-oxygenases, the latter is oxidised to carbonyl sulphide, COS (Aneanya *et al.*, 1981). In addition, a glutathione-dependent reductase in erythrocytes can metabolise disulfiram by reduction of the disulphide linkage to two thiol groups.

One of the main problems until fairly recently was that a common method of analysis of dithiocarbamate fungicides involved reductive decomposition to carbon disulphide; this colorimetric method is not very sensitive. More recent methods using gas–liquid chromatography and high-performance liquid chromatography are far superior; a later method using HPLC is relatively simple and detects 10 ng per kilogram of produce (Gustafsson and Fahlgren, 1983).

11.4 THE PHTHALIMIDE GROUP

This group comprises **captan**, **folpet**, **captafol** and **dichlofluanid** (figure 11.6). After the dithiocarbamates they are, on a tonnage basis, the most used organic fungicides. Some of their uses are summarised in table 11.3.

Captan was introduced as a broad-spectrum protective fungicide in 1952. It is insoluble in water, not very soluble in oil, and is formulated (as are many insoluble substances) in the form of a wettable powder. It is primarily employed against apple and pear scab, and, compared to a normal sulphur spray programme, it often decreases fruit damage, increases yield, and improves the appearance of fruit skins. A full spraying schedule may comprise up to eight fortnightly applications to orchard trees: phytotoxicity under

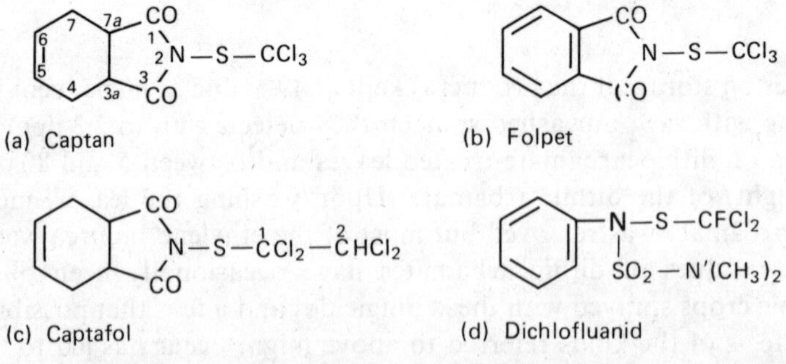

Figure 11.6 Fungicides of the phthalimide group: (a) 3a,4,7,7a-tetrahydro-N-(trichloromethylthio)phthalimide; (b) N-(trichloromethylthio)phthalimide; (c) 3a,4,7,7a-tetrahydro-N(1,1,2,2-tetrachloroethylthio)phthalimide; (d) N-(dichlorofluoromethylthio)-N',N'-(dimethyl)phenylsulphamide

British conditions is usually low. However, it does not control powdery mildews, so if these are present in a mixed infection, a double spray containing captan together with a fungicide that controls powdery mildews is usually essential. It also controls *Botrytis* mould on strawberries and lettuces, potato and tomato blight, and *Didymella* stem rot of tomatoes. It is also quite useful for the control of bitter rot of apples, a disease caused by *Gloeosporium* spp., which affects apples in storage.

Folpet is a white insoluble solid similar in properties to captan, but it is somewhat more phytotoxic to top fruit. In consequence, it is used more frequently for disease control on ornamentals, and especially to control black spot of roses.

Captafol is superior to captan for the control of potato blight but it is more expensive. It is often used against *Rhynchosporium* leaf blotch of barley, against *Septoria* glume blotch of wheat and against white tip of leeks. Northover (1978) found that an application of captafol after leaf-fall reduced the incidence of peach leaf curl caused by *Taphrina deformans* in the following spring, and that it was more effective than captan under conditions that favoured severe infestation. Captafol has also been shown to be more effective than several other fungicides at inhibiting the recolonisation by *Fusarium oxysporum* of freshly steamed soil; a 200 µg/ml solution kept the soil pathogen-free for three weeks (Rowe and Farley, 1978). As was mentioned elsewhere, a frequent device nowadays is to use combined sprays with compounds with different modes of action; some synergism often occurs, while resistance problems with systemic components can be minimised. An instance of this is described by O'Neill and Griffin (1987) in relation to the control of *Phytophthora fragariae*, which causes red core disease of strawberries. A half-rate soil drench of captafol and a half-rate leaf spray of the systemic compound, fosetyl-Al, in the autumn gave better disease control and higher yield next season than did full-rate separate treatments.

Dichlofluanid controls *Botrytis* on a number of bush and cane fruits, as well as *Botrytis* and leaf mould on glasshouse tomatoes, and downy mildew on cauliflower seedlings. In Europe it is widely used for the control of *Botrytis* on grape vines (MAFF, 1985).

The entry of **captan** into fungal spores from an external medium occurs very rapidly, the rate increasing with rising temperature. Richmond and Somers (1963) observed a correlation between the amount of captan absorbed and the thiol content of the spores. They concluded that captan was taken up by thiol sites, but they were unable to show any correlation between thiol content of spores of different fungi and the susceptibility of these fungi to captan. They also observed that, when spores were pretreated with thiol-inactivating agents, the treated spores absorbed less captan than untreated controls, but nevertheless the treated and untreated spores were equally susceptible to the fungicide. Richmond and Somers concluded that captan attaches itself indiscriminately to thiol groups. In consequence, they argued, much of it is immobilised by less vital thiol groups and thus is unable to reach vital thiol groups at the site of action. The precise nature of this site of action remains unclear but, somewhat unusually, an observation of a negative nature is worthy of note. In insects, there is evidence that phthalimide fungicides inhibit chitin synthetase in circumstances that implicate its reaction with thiol groups of the enzyme. However, the chitin synthetase in yeast and in *Sclerotium rolfsii* is insensitive to phthalimides (Cohen, 1987). There have also been reports that phthalimides can inhibit non-thiol enzymes; an example is a carboxylesterase, isolated from *Penicillium duponti*, that is capable of splitting *p*-nitrophenylpropionate (Neidert *et al.*, 1985).

A common criterion of toxicity is the amount of toxicant that needs to be absorbed per gram of spore substance in order to effect a response. On this basis, captan cannot be regarded as a very toxic substance, for whereas penicillin or organophosphorus compounds can exert their toxic effects on appropriate organisms when only $0.1–10\,\mu g$ are present per gram of cell or body weight, the toxic dose of captan is often of the order of $10^3\,\mu g/g$ spore weight (Somers, 1962). It is the ability of fungi to absorb captan (and several other organic fungicides) from large volumes of very dilute external solutions that gives the impression that these substances are intrinsically very toxic. Their low inherent toxicity and limited persistence probably account, at least in part, for the low incidence of fungal resistance so far observed under field conditions.

Using a marine fungus, *Lagenidium collinectes*, Ruch and Bland (1979) have studied the cytological changes that occur at lethal doses of captan. Ultra-structural changes in zoospores exposed to 3.2 ppm captan included the 'washing out' of mitochondrial matrix and disappearance of the mitochondrial cristae. They concluded that the main effect of the fungicide is on mitochondria, but they also observed the disappearance of the nuclear matrix and the swelling of the cisternae of the endoplasmic reticulum.

It is unlikely that intact molecules of captan or its analogues are responsible for the fungitoxic effect. Whether the thiol is located at the primary site of action, or elsewhere, reaction with fungicide probably involves the participation of two thiol groups and leads to the formation of phthalimide, a disulphide, HCl and **thiophosgene** (figure 11.7). The latter is both unstable and volatile and at most sites it soon disappears. At the site of toxic action the same reaction probably occurs, but the conversion of thiol to disulphide may in this case provide the mechanism that blocks enzyme activity. In addition, it is also possible that at such sites the very reactive thiophosgene may attack more thiol groups to form thiocarbonates or may attack amino acids to form thiourea derivatives.

In addition to reaction with thiol groups at the site of action or with inactivating non-essential thiols, it is probable that the breakdown of phthalimides is accentuated by the endogenous thiol, glutathione, which plays a part in cellular defence mechanisms (section 3.5). Barak and Edgington (1984)

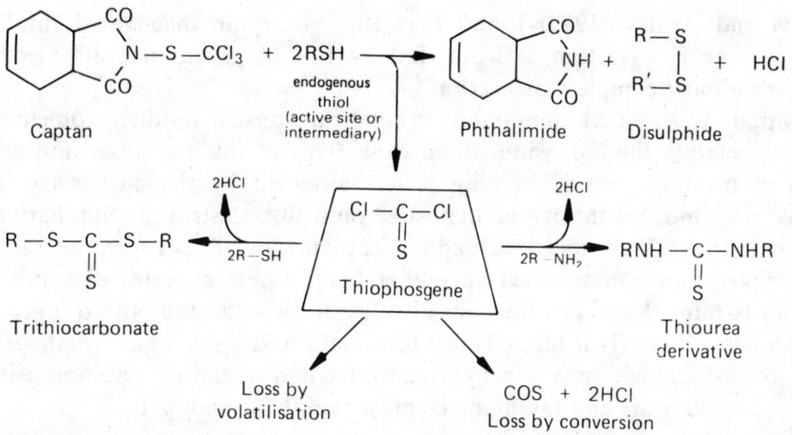

Figure 11.7   Reaction of captan with thiol groups and possible subsequent reactions of thiophosgene

measured the quantities of glutathione in two strains of *Botrytis cinerea*, one of which was resistant to captan. At the time of adding captan to the growth medium, the amount of glutathione present in the two cultures was similar but, one day later, the more resistant strain had apparently responded by producing much more glutathione (the other strain produced extra gluta-thione more slowly). These data seem to suggest that phthalimides stimulate the production of a substance that leads to their own detoxification; moreover, comparison of the responses of the two strains of fungus suggest that stimulation of glutathione production could be a mechanism leading to resistance.

Fungicides of the captan group are toxic to fish but the oral toxicity to mammals is very low. This low toxicity probably reflects hydrolysis of the fungicide by acid gastric juices, for the LD_{50} by intraperitoneal injection is less than 100 mg/kg. Chronic tests in which captan was fed to dogs for 66 weeks showed that the no-effect level was at least 300 mg/kg per day. Nevertheless, the captan group of fungicides has been exhaustively tested, for these substances are distantly related to the teratogenic drug, thalidomide. Specific teratogenic effects have, in fact, been observed in chick embryos, and much detailed evidence has been collected by Fishbein (1977).

Mutagenicity can be investigated in well established tests (e.g. the **Ames test**) using bacteria such as *Escherichia coli* or *Salmonella typhimurium*, and in such investigations, captan, captafol and folpet can give positive reactions. Moriya *et al.* (1978) contrasted such results with the absence of symptoms in chronic tests on mammals and demonstrated that the results of bacterial tests can be altered if the medium contains sulphydryl compounds or drug-metabolising enzymes. They concluded that these may in practice protect most mammals from small doses of potential mutagens. It is therefore of some interest that

Dalvi and Ashley (1979) found that 10^{-4} M captan inactivated rat liver cytochrome P_{450} (section 3.4) but that 5×10^{-4} M glutathione afforded the enzyme almost complete protection.

Captan and related compounds present an unusual residue problem, for they accelerate the corrosion of tin cans. This is able to cause tainting of canned produce, but if canning is accompanied by the customary heat processing, most of the captan deposited on fruit is destroyed. Nutahara and Yamamoto (1978) found that captan, captafol and folpet were all rapidly decomposed in homogenised cucumber fruit, 1 ppm captafol disappearing within 10 min. Decomposition was also fast in cabbage and potato tuber but was much slower (half-life, 60 min) in tomato and apple homogenates. The rate of decomposition was roughly correlated with the pH, decomposition being non-enzymic and taking place most rapidly at high pH.

11.5 DINITROPHENOL DERIVATIVES

Various dinitrophenol derivatives have found uses as insecticides, fungicides and herbicides. One member of the group was employed for moth-proofing as early as 1892, the first herbicide was patented in 1932 and the first fungicidal dinitrophenol derivative was discovered in 1949.

It was in that year that Sprague observed that an esterified dinitrophenol, dinocap (figure 11.8), controlled both mites and powdery mildews (Erysiphales). It differs from the herbicidal members of the dinitrophenol group in being both insoluble in water and non-ionic. It was historically fortunate that dinocap and its analogue, binapacryl, are able to control powdery mildews, for it will be recalled that the fungi that cause these diseases are not readily controlled by most non-systemic organic fungicides. Recently, the use of dinitrophenol compounds has, on the grounds of risk to health, been phased out in many countries in favour of the use of systemic fungicides, which, it is currently believed, are safer to higher animals. Greater use of systemic fungicides does, however, increase the risk of fungal resistance developing over the next decade, and for this reason it is desirable that a brief account be given of the chemistry of dinitro compounds. The two main members of the group are dinocap and binapacryl.

Dinocap and **binapacryl** are crotonic and methylcrotonic acid esters respectively. Both are hydrolysed by alkalis to dinitroalkylphenates. Formulation is usually as a wettable powder or, for low-volume application, as an emulsifiable (or miscible) liquid. They have some eradicant as well as protective action, the eradicant properties being accentuated by factors that favour increased penetration.

Dinocap is a mixture of at least two isomeric substances (figure 11.8a, b). Dinocap-4 is probably more fungitoxic than dinocap-6, but the latter is more acaricidal. In this respect dinocap is somewhat atypical, because most dinitro-

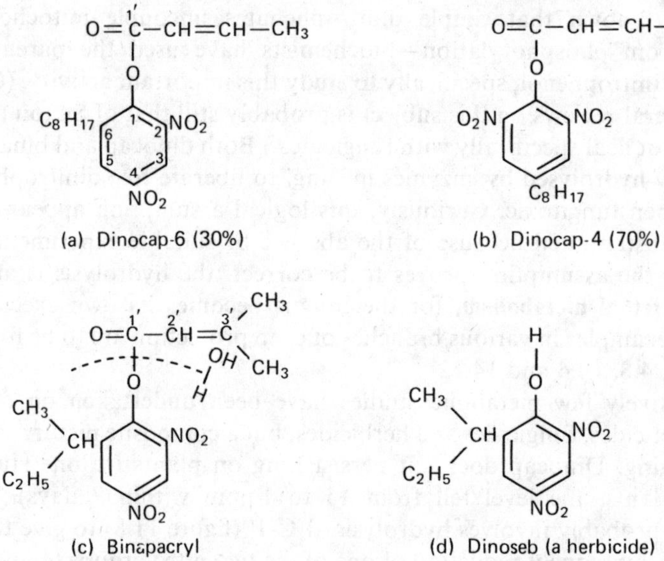

Figure 11.8 Dinitroalkylphenol derivatives: (a) 2,4-dinitro-6-sec-octylphenyl croto-nate; (b) 2,6-dinitro-4-sec-octylphenyl crotonate; (c) 2,4-dinitro-6-sec-butylphenyl-3′-methyl crotonate; (d) 2,4-dinitro-6-sec-butylphenol (this is formed when the fungicide, binapacryl, is hydrolysed)

phenols employed in crop protection are 2,4-dinitro-6-alkylphenol derivatives (compare binapacryl and the herbicide, dinoseb: figure 11.8c, d). The principal use of dinocap is for the control of powdery mildews on apples, strawberries, gooseberries and roses. Until recently, a combined spray much used in apple orchards comprised a mixture of dinocap to control powdery mildews and captan to control pathogenic Oomycetes and Deuteromycetes. Nowadays systemic compounds have replaced dinocap in such mixtures.

Binapacryl is (or was) mainly employed to control powdery mildew and red spider mites on apples, often in combination with pyrazophos (section 12.9). Livestock should be excluded from the treated area for a month after spraying. In a study lasting six years, Locke and Andrews (1986) compared the effects of dinitrophenol and systemic fungicides on the powdery mildew, *Podosphaera leucotricha*, and on the trees in apple orchards. Binapacryl proved to be superior to dinocap and to systemic fungicides in this study. Over a period of six years, the heaviest accumulative yield of marketable fruit was obtained when binapacryl was used, while the percentage of vegetative shoots with primary mildew fell from 53 to 10 and the percentage of infected leaves fell from 64 to 32. It was also pointed out that tree vigour, as assessed by extension growth, was higher for binapacryl than it was for triadimefon or for fenarimol, both of which are systemic and have some (negative) growth regulatory properties (section 12.5).

It is well known that simple dinitrophenates uncouple mitochondrial oxidation from phosphorylation—biochemists have used the parent substance, 2,4-dinitrophenol, specifically to study this important activity. (One of the best general reviews on this subject is probably still that of Simon (1953), but it does not deal specifically with fungicides.) Both dinocap and binapacryl are probably hydrolysed by enzymes in fungi to liberate free dinitrophenols, which are then fungitoxic. Curiously, this logical assumption appears to be largely unsubstantiated because of the absence of suitable experimentation. However, if the assumption proves to be correct, the hydrolysis is another example of **lethal metabolism**, for the fungus becomes its own executioner (analogous examples in various branches of crop protection are to be found in sections 3.4, 4.8, 10.4 and 14.12).

Comparatively few metabolic studies have been undertaken on dinitrophenol insecticides, fungicides and herbicides, but a composite picture appears to be emerging. Dinocap does not persist long on plants (in one study on cucumber plants, the level fell from 15 to 1 ppm within 7 days). Initial metabolism probably involves hydrolysis at C-1' (figure 11.8) to give the free phenol, with subsequent reduction of one of the two nitro groups to an amino group. The latter is analogous to what happens to the weedkiller, dinoseb (Hawkins and Saggers, 1974). Menzie (1978) referred to several other instances where the nitro groups of dinitro compounds are converted to amino groups (in studies variously carried out on locusts, rats and rabbits). Some dinitroalkylphenols are also known to be degraded by oxidation of the C-6 alkyl group: for example, the sec-butyl side-chain of dinoseb is oxidised to an isobutyric acid derivative when this herbicide is sprayed on apples (Hawkins and Saggers, 1974) and when it is fed to rats and rabbits (Ernst and Bar, 1964). No similar work appears to have been reported on dinocap, but it would be surprising if the octyl group on C-6 could not be hydroxylated by microsomal systems (chapter 3).

In view of the universal importance of oxidative phosphorylation it might appear surprising that the LD_{50} value to mammals of both dinocap and binapacryl are moderately high (oral LD_{50} of dinocap to rats is 1000 mg/kg body weight) whereas the corresponding figure for DNOC (dinitro-ortho-cresol) is about 30 mg/kg. The difference probably reflects different penetration ability of various dinitro compounds into fungi and mammals, as well as being related to the fact that free phenol (not the crotonic ester) is the actual toxicant. The importance of the latter is illustrated by the work of Bough *et al.* (1965), for it happens that the hydrolysis of binapacryl produces the herbicide, dinoseb (this is why this substance has been included in figure 11.8) and dinoseb is very toxic to animals. They showed that, on feeding *binapacryl* to guinea pigs, death of the animals occurred when the level of *dinoseb* in the blood was the same as that which led to death when *dinoseb itself* was fed to the animals.

11.6 CHLORINE-SUBSTITUTED AROMATIC FUNGICIDES

This group comprises a number of chlorinated substances that have limited but local importance, often but not exclusively for soil or seed treatment (table 11.3). There has recently been renewed interest in some, such as chlorothalonil, as possible non-systemic components of mixed formulations containing a systemic and a non-systemic fungicide in an attempt to decrease the risk of systemic compounds causing resistance to develop (sections 11.1 and 12.1).

PCNB (**pentachloronitrobenzene, quintozene**) has the structure shown in figure 11.9. It is employed to control soil- and seedborne fungi, including those which cause damping off on brassicas. It is also used against *Rhizoctonia* spp., which infect many vegetables, including lettuce and cucumber. It can be used as a seed treatment or worked into the soil before planting. For example, Elango (1986) investigated its use in soil in Peru to control pre- and post-emergence damping off of potatoes caused by *Rhizoctonia solani*; it was found that pre-emergence damping off was partly controlled and that crop yield increased significantly. In contrast, Hoffman and Sisson (1987) applied it to the surface of the soil at 2.7 kg/ha to control dwarf bunt of wheat, caused by *Tilletia controversa*. It proved to be the best of several experimental treatments when applied in late autumn. Hagan *et al.* (1986) applied it to soil to control stem rot of peanuts, which is caused by *Sclerotium rolfsii*; a beneficial effect was reported, especially when it was applied jointly with the insecticide, chlorpyrifos.

In soils, the half-life of PCNB varied from 5 months (in sandy loam) to 10 months (in organic soil). In water-saturated unsterilised soil a major metabolite is pentachloroaniline. This same metabolite is one of several found in potatoes grown in PCNB-treated soil (Gorbach and Wagner, 1967) and is one of 14 metabolites found in the Rhesus monkey (Menzie, 1980). Cairns *et al.* (1987) identified four new metabolites of PCNB in parsnips grown in PCNB-treated soil; these included a tetrachlorophenylmethyl sulphoxide and three sulphones. In all of these studies it is probable that the amino group originates by reduction of the nitro group, especially in locally anaerobic conditions. The 14 metabolites listed by Menzie (1980) include a family of pentachloro derivatives and another containing only four chlorine atoms; in addition, each family contains methylthio derivatives. Examples are given in figure 11.9. These facts can be explained by assuming that a glutathione-dependent system forms conjugates with PCNB, with possible loss of chlorine (compare example 3a in table 3.2), in which case the sulphur of the thioethers above probably originates from the cysteine moiety of glutathione. This thioether may then oxidise to sulphoxide and sulphone (compare 5(a) in table 3.1).

Macris and Georgopoulos (1969) observed that PCNB is not effective against species of fungi that possess little chitin in their cell walls (e.g. *Phytophthora*). Conversely, sensitive fungi such as *Neurospora*, when analysed after treatment with PCNB, contained less hexosamine in their cell walls than

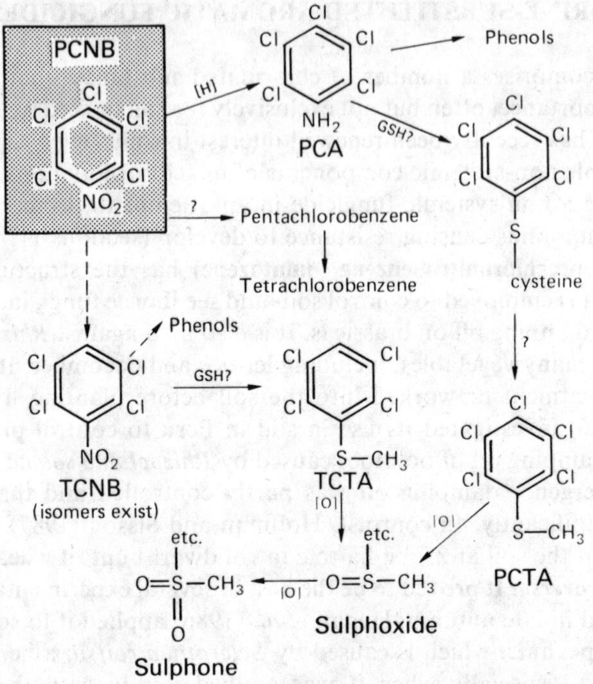

Figure 11.9   Some PCNB derivatives and possible relationships between them: PCA, pentachloroaniline; TCNB, tetrachloronitrobenzene; TCTA and PCTA, tetra- and pentachlorothioanisole

did untreated specimens of the same fungus. It thus seems possible that PCNB interferes with chitin synthesis.

Tecnazene (TCNB, tetrachloronitrobenzene) is closely related to PCNB and forms metabolites similar to those just discussed. It was introduced for use against dry rot of seed potatoes but it was soon evident that it also inhibited the sprouting of potato tubers in storage and it is now marketed as a dust for this purpose. In addition, smoke formulations are used to control *Botrytis cinerea* on greenhouse plants. Since tecnazine is mixed with soil, it is of interest that it has been reported to have nematicidal properties (Rodriguez-Kabana *et al.*, 1978). At a rate of 0.025 g/kg soil a significant decrease in numbers occurred for several species of nematodes, including *Meloidogyne* spp., *Pratylenchus* spp. and *Tylenchorhynchus* spp.

Dicloran is a dichlorinated nitroaniline (figure 11.10a). It is used both as a soil-applied fungicide and as a foliar spray. Being insoluble in water and strongly adsorbed by clay particles, it is rather persistent in soils, in which its half-life is often upwards of a year. It is used as a foliar spray on lettuces and tomatoes to control *Botrytis cinerea*. Other fungi against which it can be used to protect many types of vegetables and ornamental plants are *Rhizopus*,

Sclerotium and *Monilinia* spp. Its acute oral toxicity is very low (LD_{50} above 3000 mg/kg) but, in view of its persistence, a safety period of three weeks should elapse between the last application and harvesting.

Dicloran is taken up by plant roots, and moves in the transpiration stream to the leaves, where it is soon destroyed enzymatically. Primary metabolism in plants and animals probably occurs by the same major route, namely the reduction of the nitro group to amino and the conversion of the (newly formed) amino group to hydroxyl. In animals, the hydroxyl group may then conjugate with sulphate or with glucuronic acid in the manner outlined in chapter 3.

The mode of action of dicloran remains uncertain. Early work indicated that it delayed the germination of conidia of *Botrytis cinerea* and that it caused 36 per cent inhibition of the rate of uptake of radioactive leucine into proteins of *Rhizopus arrhizus*. More recently, Craig and Peberdy (1983) observed that, at concentrations near the LD_{50} level, it decreased total lipid synthesis but stimulated the incorporation of tritium-labelled adenine into RNA.

Chlorothalonil (figure 11.10b) is a tetrachlorinated dinitrile of benzene. It controls a wide range of crop pathogens, especially on fruit canes and bushes, and shows particular promise for the control, by foliar application, of *Botrytis cinerea*, *Phytophthora infestans* and *Rhizoctonia solani*. It has been reported to be the most promising of several substances tested, as foliar sprays, for the control of *Ascochyta fabae*, the cause of blight of faba beans (Kharbanda and Bernier, 1979). Patel and Vaishnav (1986) found chlorothalonil to be the most effective of nine fungicides against *Puccinia arachidas* on groundnuts. In addition, it is often used as one component of a mixture in order to widen the spectrum of action or to reduce the rapidity with which resistance develops. In regard to the latter, it often provides one component of a non-systemic/ systemic pair (section 12.1), an example being the use of a mixture of chlorothalonil and benomyl to control root rot caused by *Rhizoctonia solani* on Egyptian lupins (Sahab *et al.*, 1985/86). It is also useful in the control of cercospora disease of Australian subterranean clover, for Barbetti (1987) observed that chlorothalonil, alone or mixed with benomyl, gave fair control

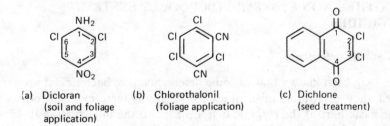

(a) Dicloran
(soil and foliage
application)

(b) Chlorothalonil
(foliage application)

(c) Dichlone
(seed treatment)

Figure 11.10 Chloro aromatic protective fungicides: (a) 2,6-dichloro-4-nitroaniline; (b) tetrachloroisophthalonitrile; (c) 2,3-dichloro-1,4-naphthoquinone

of *Cercospora zebrina*. Four mixtures of chlorothalonil with different systemic fungicides are approved for use in Britain (MAFF, 1986). It is of interest that cross-resistance has been noticed in *Botrytis cinerea* between captan and chlorothalonil, a situation somewhat unusual for two fungicides that possess low target specificity (table 10.2). The explanation appears to be that cross-resistance in this instance is a consequence of the two substances sharing a common mechanism of detoxification. Barak and Edgington (1983; 1984) have provided evidence that this mechanism involves the production by the resistant strain of the organism of larger amounts of glutathione than are produced by the sensitive strain; this additional glutathione is believed to provide non-vital thiol groups with which captan, chlorothalonil (and also some dithiocarbamates) react before they reach too many essential thiols in proteins and other vital cell components.

Chlorothalonil appears to react rather indiscriminately with thiol groups of cell constituents. Although the most vulnerable endogenous substance is not known, the thiol reaction possibly accounts for its biological activity, for exogenous thiol compounds reverse its fungitoxic action (Vincent and Sisler, 1968). However, glutathione is a substance frequently involved in detoxication (section 3.5) and is itself a thiol, so this same reactivity of chlorothalonil with thiols may be one mechanism whereby it is detoxified.

Dichlone (figure 11.10c) is a dichlorinated naphthoquinone. In the USA it is occasionally used as a seed treatment for legumes because it has a somewhat similar biological spectrum to organomercury compounds (section 10.6) and yet it is of much lower toxicity to man. It is not very useful as a foliar spray because it is decomposed by light. Dichlone is taken up rapidly by fungal spores and, on the basis of weight absorbed per gram of spores, it is among the most effective of protectant organic fungicides. Typically, the dose of dichlone causing 50 per cent inhibition of spore germination (I_{50}) is of the order of 500 µg/g, whereas the I_{50} of most non-systemic fungicides is many thousands of micrograms per gram. It must, however, be remembered that the high figure for many fungicides (e.g. copper, captan) often reflects attachment to inert or less vital constituents of cell or cell wall.

11.7 OTHER NON-SYSTEMIC OR POORLY SYSTEMIC FUNGICIDES

(a) Cationic detergents

It has long been known that cationic detergents have bactericidal properties; indeed, they have found medical use for sterilising instruments. Modification of the basic part of the cationic detergent led to the introduction in 1956 of **dodine**, which is a substituted guanidine acetate:

$$C_{12}H_{25}-NH-C(NH)-NH_3^+ \cdots \cdots {}^-OOC.CH_3$$

Dodine has a narrow but useful antifungal spectrum, being especially useful for the control of apple scab, caused by *Venturia inaequalis*, in seasons when the incidence of the disease is high. In addition to its protective function, it can eradicate recent (but not well established) scab infections. It is regarded as being safe to the consumer (being related to domestic detergents*) and apples can be picked within a day or two of the final application.

Dodine probably attacks lipoprotein membranes, disrupting vital membrane-dependent processes such as selective permeability and oxidative phosphorylation. In common with other detergents, it probably causes lysis of membranes by masquerading as membrane phospholipid; the more hydrophobic parts of the molecule become embedded in, and in part replace, the membrane lipid while the polar region of the molecule attaches itself to membrane protein. It is of interest that a mixture of cationic and non-ionic detergents has been used to solubilise membrane-bound components of hepatic microsomes precisely because such detergents attack lipoprotein membranes. The mono-oxygenase function (section 3.4) can then be reconstituted by putting the separated, solubilised components together again.

(b) Imazalil and prochloraz

These two compounds (figure 11.11a, b) belong to a group of imidazoles that inhibit steroid synthesis (see section 12.5). They have *weakly* systemic properties especially when entry is by root uptake or through the seed testa. They have proved to be effective against several important Ascomycetes and Deuteromycetes, are sometimes useful against Basidiomycetes, but do not control pathogenic Oomycetes. They are particularly useful against pathogens that are seed- or soilborne. With the safety-dictated decline in use of organomercury seed treatments, much work has centred on the use of imazalil (and some other less known members of the group) as replacement treatments, especially for the control of rusts, leaf blotch and eyespot diseases of cereals.

Imazalil is used mainly for seed treatment in cereals and is particularly useful against seedborne and soilborne pathogens such as *Pyrenophora* and *Septoria* spp. After seed treatment a small proportion has been found in the shoot but it is doubtful whether this weakly systemic action is responsible for its action against *Pyrenophora graminea* (Scheinpflug and Kuck, 1987). If present in too high a concentration it can retard the growth of plant roots.

Prochloraz is a more recent introduction; when used as a foliage spray it controls the organisms that cause several diseases of cereals (e.g. *Septoria* spp.) but is especially important because of its ability to control strains of *Pseudocercosporella herpotrichoides* that are resistant to the benzimidazoles (section 12.2). Gallimore *et al.* (1987) collected 194 isolates of this organism,

---

*How long will it be before domestic detergent residues come under suspicion of being health hazards?—see the next paragraph.

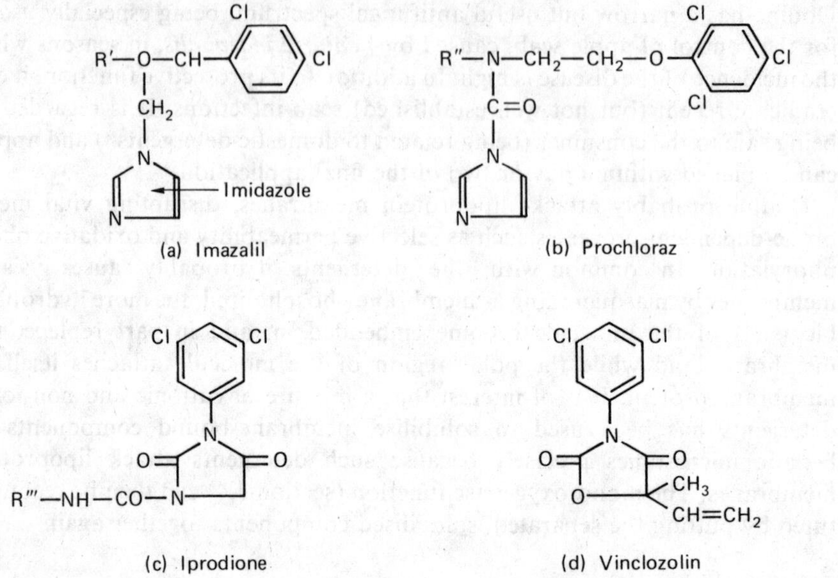

Figure 11.11 Examples of imidazoles (a, b) and dicarboximides (c, d): R′ is $CH_2=CH-CH_2-$; R″ is C_3H_7; R‴ is iso-C_3H_7

the cause of eyespot of cereals, and found that 191 did not grow on agar containing 2 µg/ml prochloraz. Moreover, prochloraz gave good control of both benzimidazole-sensitive and benzimidazole-resistant strains of *P. herpotrichoides*. Absence of cross-resistance is probably a consequence of the fact that the two types of fungicides have very different modes of action (sections 12.1 and 12.2). In Britain, the Ministry of Agriculture (MAFF, 1984) listed mixtures of prochloraz with carbendazim (a benzimidazole fungicide) for use to control eyespot, powdery mildew, net blotch and rhynchosporium disease of wheat.

Prochloraz has also been found to control effectively most of the major fungal pathogens of mushrooms (Fletcher *et al.*, 1983). Such pathogens include *Verticillium fungicola* and *Mycogone perniciosa*; here, too, prochloraz was found to be particularly efficacious against benzimidazole-resistant strains, especially when used in a formulation containing a manganese complex. The advantage of manganese formulations in another context (the control of sigatoka of bananas) has been mentioned by Mabbeth (1986).

Prochloraz has an interesting and occasionally important secondary effect on higher animals when used in high concentrations. When fed to rats, it induces enzymes present in the endoplasmic reticulum of cells. Among these are the cytochrome P_{450} mono-oxygenase system and glutathione-*S*-transferases and some hydrolases (chapter 3). In consequence, hepatic microsomal preparations prepared from animals exposed to prochloraz are able to metabolise certain foreign compounds, including pesticides, much more rapidly than can similar preparations from uninduced animals (Rivière, 1983). Different inducing agents often induce different types of cytochrome P_{450} possessing somewhat different substrate specificities, rather than simply stimulating the production of more of the same mixture of types that are characteristically present in the uninduced animal.

(c) Dicarboximides

These compounds are weakly systemic when root-applied and should not be confused with the systemic carboxamides discussed in section 12.3. The formulae of two important dicarboximides are shown in figures 11.11c and d. They are remarkable for their rather specific toxicity to the grey mould, *Botrytis cinerea*, and to *Sclerotinia* spp., although a useful level of control is sometimes evident against species of *Alternaria*, *Didymella*, *Helminthosporium* and *Phoma*. As foliar sprays they are frequently applied mixed with dithiocarbamates (section 11.2) in order to widen the biological spectrum.

Nair *et al.* (1987) reported that the three best-known dicarboximides, namely **iprodione**, **vinclozolin** and **procymidone**, applied as solutions containing 1 mg/ml, were more effective in controlling bunch rot on grapes in Australia than were five other fungicides, some of which were systemic and some not. Bunch rot is caused by *Botrytis cinerea*. The authors point out that the timing of sprays depends upon whether the fungus enters through splits in the mature fruit or is a latent infection established earlier in the flowers; on the assumption that the latter was a significantly frequent event, they applied two sprays, one pre-bloom and another during blooming. These two sprays accomplished a level of control that sometimes took seven applications when other fungicides were used.

Vinclozolin has been used since about 1975 for the control of *Botrytis cinerea* on grape vines in Europe, but from about 1978 serious resistance was evident first in Germany (Holz, 1979) and then elsewhere (Löcher *et al.*, 1987). The last-named authors have outlined the general principles of resistance management, namely to reduce the number of treatments, to combine active ingredients, to alternate fungicides possessing different modes of action, or to use alternative equally effective substances. The most satisfactory solution of their own problem proved to be the use of a mixture of vinclozolin with chlorothalonil. They did, however, also find that the percentage of R strains had risen to 90 per cent by harvest time, whether vinclozolin was used alone or in a mixture, although this high incidence fell back to a base level of about 20 per cent over the winter.

Dicarboximides have been used extensively to protect lettuce in the UK; Wang and Coley-Smith (1986) found that 47 per cent of isolates from protected lettuce in one district were moderately resistant to all three common members of the group (cross-resistance was almost complete). They pointed out, however, that no extreme case of resistance was observed in samples collected from the field despite the ease with which high resistance can be developed in laboratory selection tests.

Hunter *et al.* (1987) found that the ability of dicarboximides to control *B. cinerea* on strawberries had greatly diminished because of the development of resistance. They concluded that chlorothalonil was a better partner for a dicarboximide in a mixture than was the (sometimes employed) dichlofluanid, because the latter, when used alone, led to an increase in dicarboxamide resistance. These workers also reported that there is a gradual decline in the proportion of dicarboximide-resistant forms in the population during the winter season.

Walker *et al.* (1986) described instances, both in laboratory tests and in field trials, of enhanced degradation of dicarboximides in soils to which these fungicides had been repeatedly applied. Thus, for both iprodione and vinclozolin, 3 per cent of a standard dose remained after 77 days on the first occasion. The treatment was then repeated. On the third occasion treatment was followed by analysis, when it was found that only 1 per cent remained after 10 days. Similarly, in another instance quoted by Walker *et al.* (1986), a failure of iprodione to control white rot disease of onions (caused by *Sclerotium cepivorum*) was ascribed not to the development of resistance by the fungus but to increased degradation of the fungicide by soil organisms.

The mode of action of the dicarboximides is uncertain, cell division, nucleic acid metabolism, lipid and steroid metabolism all having being implicated as targets in various fungi (Edlich and Lyr, 1987). These authors favour the view that dicarboximides induce lipid peroxidation in sensitive fungi, possibly because of an interaction with flavin enzymes such as cytochrome C reductase.

REFERENCES

Anilkumar, T. B. and Sastry, M. N. L. (1979). *Phytopathol. Z.*, **94**, 126

Barak, E. and Edgington, L. V. (1983). *Can. J. Plant Pathol.*, **5**, 200 (abstract)

Barak, E. and Edgington, L. V. (1984). *Pestic. Biochem. Physiol.*, **21**, 412

Barbetti, M. J. (1987). *Aust. J. Exp. Agric.*, **27**, 107

Black, R., Jonglaekha, N., Bruin, G., Sukasem, S. and Buranaviriyakul, S. (1985). *Trop. Pest Managem.*, **31**, 47

Bough, R. G., Cliffe, E. E. and Lessel, B. (1965). *Toxicol. Appl. Pharmacol.*, **7**, 353

Cairns, T., Siegmund, E. G. and Krick, F. (1987). *J. Agric. Fd Chem.*, **35**, 433

Cohen, E. (1987). *Annu. Rev. Entomol.*, **32**, 71

Craig, G. D. and Peberdy, J. F. (1983). *Pestic. Sci.*, **14**, 17

Dalvi, R. R. and Ashley, W. M. (1979). *Drug Chem. Toxicol.*, **2**, 245

Eckert, J. W. (1967). In *Fungicides: An Advanced Treatise*, vol. 1, ed. D. C. Torgeson, p. 287. Academic Press, New York

Edlich, W. and Lyr, H. (1987). In *Modern Selective Fungicides*, ed. H. Lyr, p. 107. Longmans, Harlow; Wiley, New York

Elango, F. (1986). *Ann. Appl. Biol.*, **109**, 279

Ellis, M. A. and Paschal, E. H. (1979). *Seed Sci. Technol.*, **7**, 75

Emnova, E. E., Merenyuk, G. V., Biryozuva, V. I., Kodryan, V. A. and Tsurkan, L. G. (1986). *Mikrobiologiya*, **55**, 612 (in Russian; from *idem*. (1987). *Rev. Plant Pathol.*, **66**, abstract 2192)

Eneanya, D. I., Bianchine, J. R., Duran, D. O. and Andresen, B. D. (1981). *Annu. Rev. Pharmacol. Toxicol.*, **21**, 575

Ernst, W. and Bar, F. (1964). *Arzneimittel Forsch.*, **14**, 81

Fishbein, L. (1977). In *Antifungal Compounds*, eds M. R. Siegel and H. D. Sisler, chap. 14. Marcel Dekker, New York

Fletcher, J. T., Hims, M. J. and Hall, R. J. (1983). *Plant Pathol.*, **32**, 123

Fry, W. E. (1982). *Principles of Plant Disease Management*. Academic Press, New York

Gallimore, K., Knights, I. K. and Barnes, G. (1987). *Plant Pathol.*, **36**, 290

Goksøyr, J. (1955). *Physiol. Plant*, **8**, 719

Gorbach, S. and Wagner, U. (1967). *J. Agric. Fd Chem.*, **15**, 654

Gustafsson, K. H. and Fahlgren, C. H. (1983). *J. Agric. Fd Chem.*, **31**, 463

Hagan, A. K., Weeks, J. R. and Reed, R. B. (1986). *Peanut Sci.*, **13**, 36

Hawkins, D. R. and Saggers, V. H. (1974). *Pestic. Sci.*, **5**, 497

Hoffman, J. A. and Sisson, D. V. (1987). *Plant Dis.*, **71**, 839

Holz, B. (1979). *Weinberg Keller*, **26**, 18

Hunter, T., Brent, K. J., Carter, G. A. and Hutcheon, J. A. (1987). *Ann. Appl. Biol.*, **110**, 515

Kaars Sijpesteijn, A. (1982). In *Fungicide Resistance in Crop Protection*, eds J. Dekker and S. G. Georgopoulos, p. 32. Centre for Agricultural Publishing and Documentation, Wageningen, Holland (quoted from Samoucha and Gisi (1987))

Kharbanda, P. D. and Bernier, C. C. (1979). *Can. J. Plant Sci.*, **59**, 661

Kingsland, G. C. and Sitterby, W. R. (1986). *Trop. Pest Managem.*, **32**, 31

Lalancette, N., Hickey, K. D. and Cole, H., Jr (1987). *Phytopathology*, **77**, 86

Löcher, F. J., Lorenz, G. and Beetz, K.-J. (1987). *Crop Prot.*, **6**, 139

Locke, T. and Andrews, L. (1986). *Plant Pathol.*, **35**, 241

Mabbeth, T. H. (1984). *SPAN*, **29**, 78

Macris, B. and Georgopoulos, S. G. (1969). *Phytopathology*, **59**, 879

MAFF (1984). *Use of Fungicides and Insecticides on Cereals*, Ministry of Agriculture, Fisheries and Food, ADAS Booklet 2257. HMSO, London

MAFF (1985). *1985 List of Approved Products and their Uses for Farmers and Growers*, Ministry of Agriculture, Fisheries and Food, Agricultural Chemicals Approval Scheme (UK). HMSO, London

MAFF (1986). *Pesticides, 1986. Pesticides Approved Under the Control of Pesticides Regulations, 1986*, Ministry of Agriculture, Fisheries and Food, Health and Safety Executive (UK). HMSO, London

Maude, R. B. (1978). *Seed Treatment*, CIPAC Monograph 2, ed. K. Jeffs, chap. 9

Menzie, C. M. (1978). *Metabolism of Pesticides, Update II*. US Dept Interior, Fish and Wildlife Service, Special Scientific Report, Wildlife no. 212. Washington, DC

Menzie, C. M. (1980). *Metabolism of Pesticides, Update III*. US Dept Interior, Fish and Wildlife Service, Washington, DC

Morehart, A. L. and Crossan, D. F. (1965). *Delaware Univ. Agric. Exp. Sta. Bull.*, no. 357

Moriya, M., Kato, K. and Shirasu, Y. (1978). *Mutation Res.*, **57**, 259

Nair, N. G., Emmett, R. W. and Parker, F. E. (1987). *Plant Pathol.*, **36**, 175

Neidert, K., Epps, L. V. and Welch, W. (1985). *Pestic. Biochem. Physiol.*, **23**, 221

Northover, J. (1978). *Plant Dis. Reptr*, **62**, 706

Nutahara, M. and Yamamoto, M. (1978). *J. Pestic. Sci. Jap.*, **3**, 101 (in Japanese; reported from abstract only)

O'Neill, T. M. and Griffin, G. W. (1987). *Plant Pathol.*, **36**, 258

Owens, R. G. (1969). In *Fungicides: An Advanced Treatise*, vol. 2, ed. D. C. Torgeson, chap. 5. Academic Press, New York

Patel, V. A. and Vaishnav, M. U. (1986). *Indian J. Plant Prot.*, **13**, 79

Richmond, D. V. and Somers, E. (1963). *Ann. Appl. Biol.*, **52**, 327

Rivière, J.-L. (1983). *Pestic. Biochem. Physiol.*, **19**, 44

Rodriguez-Kabana, R., King, P. S. and Adams, J. R. (1978). *Nematropica*, **8**, 69

Rowe, R. C. and Farley, J. D. (1978). *Phytopathology*, **68**, 1221

Ruch, D. G. and Bland, C. E. (1979). *Can. J. Bot.*, **57**, 2116

Sahab, A. F., Osmam, A. A., Soleman, N. K. and Mikhail, M. S. (1985/86). *Egypt. J. Phytopathol.*, **17**, 23

Samoucha, Y. and Cohen, Y. (1984). *Phytopathology*, **74**, 1434

Samoucha, Y. and Gisi, U. (1987). *Ann. Appl. Biol.*, **110**, 303

Scheinpflug, H. and Kuck, K. H. (1987). In *Modern Selective Fungicides*, ed. H. Lyr, p. 173. Longmans, Harlow; Wiley, New York

Simon, E. W. (1953). *Biol. Rev.*, **28**, 453

Somers, E. (1962). *Sci. Prog. (Lond.)*, **50**, 218

Soni, N. K. and Atri, D. C. (1986). *Acta Bot. Indica*, **14**, 167 (from *idem.* (1987). *Rev. Plant Pathol.*, **66**, 341 abstract)

Soteros, J. J. (1979). *NZ J. Agric. Res.*, **22**, 191

Trotter, W. J. and Pardue, J. (1982). *J. Fd Safety*, **4**, 59

Vincent, P. G. and Sisler, H. D. (1968). *Physiol. Plant*, **21**, 1249

Walker, A., Brown, P. A. and Entwistle, A. R. (1986). *Pestic. Sci.*, **17**, 183

Wang, Z.-N., Coley-Smith, J. R. and Wareing, P. W. (1986). *Plant Pathol.*, **35**, 427

Watts, R. R., Storherr, R. W. and Onley, J. H. (1974). *Bull. Environ. Contam. Toxicol.*, **12**, 224

12 Systemic fungicides

12.1 CLASSIFICATION; ADVANTAGES AND DISADVANTAGES OF SYSTEMIC FUNGICIDES

Following the success of systemic insecticides and translocated herbicides, the strenuous efforts made to develop systemic fungicides were increasingly rewarded from about 1965. The work was based on the premise that a systemic fungicide might well be able to attack internal mycelium and penetrating haustoria and thereby overcome the problem (section 10.1) that arises from the fact that even small pieces of surviving mycelium can regenerate. It was also hoped that systemic fungicides would reduce dependence upon external protective poisons, which suffer from the double disadvantage that they are subject to weathering and that they cannot give protection to plant growth initiated after spraying.

In table 12.1 the principal systemic fungicides are divided into groups distinguished by molecular structure and by mode of action. Members of most of the main classes of plant pathogens are attacked by members of one or other of these eight groups. Until recently, however, the armoury against Oomycetes was non-existent and, as will be seen later, the situation is still not entirely satisfactory. Of the eight groups, the benzimidazoles tend to have a wide spectrum of action (although even these seldom control Oomycetes), whereas members of most of the other groups tend to be more or less selective in action. For example, the oxathiins are particularly effective against rusts, smuts and bunts, which are members of the Basidiomycetes, while most of the fungicides that inhibit steroid biosynthesis are particularly useful in the control of one group of Ascomycetes (the powdery mildews). In a few cases fungicides are genus- or even species-specific; thus the antibiotic, kasugamycin, is used almost exclusively against the rice blast fungus, *Pyricularia oryzae*, and the hydroxyaminopyrimidine, ethirimol, is particularly useful for the control of *Erysiphe graminis*, the species of *Erysiphe* that attacks cereals.

When considering systemic fungicides, a little caution is necessary about the precise meaning of 'systemic'. It was mentioned elsewhere that this term does not necessarily imply highly efficient uptake through plant *leaves*. Several systemic fungicides (e.g. benomyl) can indeed be effectively applied to leaves, which they may enter to some extent. This entry is followed by translocation across leaves and by acropetal movement towards the leaf tips and margins. There is little translocation out of sprayed leaves, so the action cannot be

Table 12.1 Classification of some systemic fungicides (figures in parentheses are section references)

Group	Examples
Benzimidazoles (12.2)	Benomyl, carbendazim, thiophanate, thiabendazole
Oxathiins or carboxamides (12.3)	Carboxin, oxycarboxin
Morpholines (12.4)	Tridemorph, dodemorph
Inhibitors of steroid C-14 demethylation (12.5)	
(a) Triazoles	Triadimefon, triadimenol, propiconazole, diclobutrazole
(b) Pyrimidines	Fenarimol, nuarimol
(c) Pyridines	Buthiobate
(d) Piperazines	Triforine
(e) Imidazoles	Imazalil (11.7), prochloraz, ketoconazole, triflumizole
Hydroxyaminopyrimidines (12.6)	Ethirimol, bupirimate, dimethirimol
Antibiotics (12.7)	Kasugamycin, streptomycin
Phenylamides that target Oomycetes (12.8)	Metalaxyl, ofurace, oxadixyl
Miscellaneous antifungal compounds (12.9)	
(a) Ethylphosphonates	Fosetyl
(b) Others	IBP, chloroneb, pyrazophos, cymoxanil, prothiocarb

regarded as truly systemic. However, many fungicides that are little more than loco-systemic (compare section 4.8) when applied to foliage are nevertheless absorbed excellently when they enter plants through the roots (after soil or seed application), or through the testa (following seed treatment).

Most systemic fungicides appear to attack very specific processes in fungi. Such site-specific activities are usually influenced by single gene selection, amplification or modification. The types of specific activities that have been attributed to various systemic fungicides include interference with nucleotide base synthesis, with polynucleotide or protein formation and with the synthesis of steroids and of components of lipoprotein membranes. It is perhaps because of their highly specific effects that they select out existing mutants or even favour rapid gene mutation. In consequence, the use of many systemic fungicides has led to a serious complication. In the decade or so since they were introduced, more *resistance* has appeared than in the previous 50 years when only protective fungicides were employed. Furthermore, resistance of fungi engendered by systemic fungicides tends to be long-lasting—that is to say, it persists for many generations after use of the compound has ceased—whereas resistance caused by protective fungicides is sometimes rather ephemeral.

Georgopoulos (1977) listed 41 instances of resistance developing to only one systemic compound—thiabendazole—in 23 fungi during the period 1970–76. Similarly, Ogawa *et al.* (1983) listed more than 100 pathogens that had become resistant to various fungicides under field conditions. In some cases the situation became so serious that local disease control failed, especially when metalaxyl, kasugamycin or certain benzimidazoles were employed. The use of systemic fungicides is increasing and the potential seriousness of the resistance problem cannot be overemphasised. The worst scenario is that the semipermanence of resistance and the frequency of its occurrence may yet threaten the long-term success of systemic fungicides. However, various techniques and strategies introduced in recent years have diminished the rate at which resistance has developed and some newer systemic fungicides are less liable to cause resistance than were earlier compounds.

Strategies to avoid resistance, or, at least, to decrease the probability that it will occur, have been reviewed by Dekker (1982). Measures must be taken before the onset of a resistance problem, otherwise the only possible action is to change the fungicide or to desist with application altogether.

Selection pressure experiments in the laboratory often demonstrate that a particular fungicide has a tendency to cause the development, in the reasonably short term, of either a high level or a low level of resistance. When, from such work, a high level is anticipated in the field, it is probably best, when treating crops, to reduce selection pressure by the use of combined or alternating treatments, or to use the minimal effective number of applications. Another strategy is to arrange that not all farms in a locality spray chemicals of the same high-risk group.

When lower levels of resistance are to be expected, as may happen, for example, when vinclozolin is used (section 11.7), it may be best to increase selection pressure by the use of saturation treatment of some kind (compare strategies against insect resistance, section 9.1). A tactic often recommended to minimise resistance problems is to ensure that treatment involves the use of two fungicides with different modes of action. Usually, although not inevitably, one member of the pair is a systemic compound and the other is not; a fundamental requirement in any case is that appropriate laboratory work has been done to ascertain that no cross-resistance readily occurs. There is no consensus as to whether the use of two such substances in a mixture is better than to alternate their use. A third possibility, favoured by some, is regularly over several seasons to use that member of a pair of active ingredients which is less likely to cause resistance but to use the second (systemic) substance on alternate treatments only.

At the present state of knowledge it is often the case that the best treatment can only be determined by trial and error, for it probably depends on the crop, on the fungus, on the fungicide and on various environmental factors. It should be added that, although so far in its early stages, a search is under way to find pairs of fungicides that encourage negative cross-resistance; this could be envisaged, for example, if one of a pair in a mixture interferes with the mechanism by which resistance to the second member of the pair would otherwise develop (De Waard, 1984). Three or four possible cases are quoted by Dekker (1987).

12.2 BENZIMIDAZOLES

Benzimidazole (figure 12.1a) is the parent substance of a family of systemic fungicides, including benomyl, thiophanate-methyl and thiabendazole. If one of the hydrogen atoms of the amino group of carbamic acid is replaced by the benzimidazole radical, benzimidazolyl carbamate is formed, the methyl ester of which is called carbendazim and is shown in figure 12.1b. Benomyl is a n-butylcarbamoyl derivative of carbendazim, the carbamoyl substitution being on N-1 of benzimidazole (figure 12.1c). Note that, in compounds such as *butylcarbamate*, one of the amino nitrogen atoms is replaced by the substituent, whereas in *carbamoyl* compounds the carboxylic acid group is attached, with loss of water, to a base (in this case, to a substituted benzimidazole).

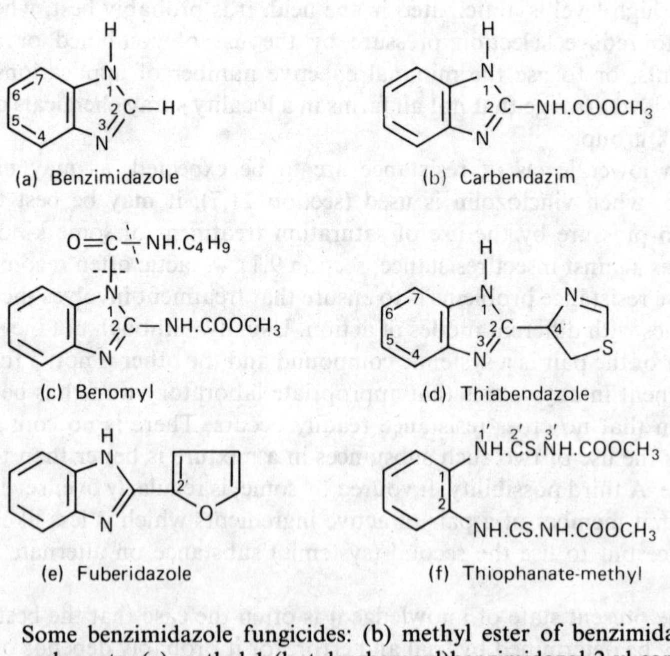

(a) Benzimidazole

(b) Carbendazim

(c) Benomyl

(d) Thiabendazole

(e) Fuberidazole

(f) Thiophanate-methyl

Figure 12.1   Some benzimidazole fungicides: (b) methyl ester of benzimidazol-2-yl carbamate; (c) methyl 1-(butylcarbamoyl)benzimidazol-2-yl carbamate; (d) 2-(thiazol-4′-yl)benzimidazole; (f) 1,2-di(3′-methoxycarbonyl-2-thioureido)benzene

Table 12.2 Important fungi that respond to one or more benzimidazoles and some of the crops that the fungi attack[a]

Pathogen	Crops
Ascochyta	Ornamentals, peanuts, tobacco
Aspergillus	Peanuts
Botrytis	Apple, beans, citrus, grapes, lettuce
Ceratocystis	Banana, sugar cane
Cercospora	Beet, carrot, celery, rice, strawberry
Cladosporium	Apple, plum, tomato
Colletotrichum	Beans, soybean, tomato
Fusarium	Brassicas, pineapple, plum, potato
Gloeosporium	Banana, tea
Erysiphe	Cucumber, wheat
Monilinia	Cherry, plum
Mycosphaerella	Apple, pea, pear, strawberry
Oidium	Plum, tomato
Phoma	Brassicas, potato, tomato
Podosphaera	Pear
Pseudocercosporella	Cereals
Rhizoctonia	Pineapples, potato, wheat
Sclerotinia	Lettuce, tomato
Septoria	Soybean, tomato, wheat
Sphaerotheca	Currants, plum
Ustilago	Cereals

[a] Not all benzimidazoles are suitable in every case, so they should only be used according to the manufacturer's instructions; in addition, users should bear in mind that resistance may exist.

Benzimidazoles are of three types: some are carbamates, others are non-carbamates and the thiophanate family do not become benzimidazoles until after application. These differences are to some extent reflected in their field uses, but all are wide-spectrum systemic fungicides useful against many Ascomycetes and Basidiomycetes as well as some Deuteromycetes (or Fungi Imperfecti). Nevertheless, pathogenic Oomycetes and some Deuteromycetes are insensitive, both *in vitro* and in the field. Thus they do not control downy mildews, damping off by *Pythium* spp. or late potato blight caused by *Phytophthora infestans*. Some of the more important fungi controlled by various benzimidazoles on a variety of crops are listed in table 12.2.

The limited systemic action of benzimidazoles when applied to leaves was mentioned earlier. The main movement appears to be translaminar rather than from leaf to leaf and is facilitated by non-ionic detergents, which not only increase the area of contact but probably soften cuticular wax. Penetration is usually more rapid through the abaxial surface of the leaf, where wax is thinner and more stomata are often present. In one study, in the absence of detergent only 5 per cent of a dose of benomyl penetrated the adaxial surface of cucumber leaves.

When uptake is through the soil, some differences exist between the behaviour of various benzimidazoles. Some of them are loosely sorbed onto soil organic matter and clay particles but eventually enter roots. After root uptake, benomyl is hydrolysed to carbendazim (see below) and it is principally the latter that moves up the plant. Indeed, it has been suggested that benomyl and thiophanate-methyl are normally bound to root constituents sufficiently strongly to act as a reservoir of insoluble fungicide from which an active component is released slowly into the transpiration stream, so maintaining a lethal concentration in the meristematic regions. In contrast, thiabendazole is probably translocated unchanged. Usefully, from a residue viewpoint, since movement is predominantly in the xylem, the translocated substances pass predominantly to the leaves and meristems rather than to the fruit.

In order to take advantage of the superior systemic action following root uptake, it is necessary to get compounds of low solubility near to the roots of growing crops. This difficulty increases as the root system becomes deeper, so that the root uptake method is, in practice, limited to shallow-rooted plants, to potted plants and to greenhouse plants. An alternative approach is that of seed treatment, which ensures that the fungicide is readily available to the plant with minimal interference from soil constituents.

Benomyl (figure 12.1c) is applied to *foliage* to control a variety of powdery mildews (Erysiphales). Little actually enters the leaves by this route of application, most of the deposit acting as a superficial protectant. It is very effective against brown rot of stone fruit and when it is used in apple orchards prior to leaf fall it prevents the formation of perithecia during wintertime. Attempts have been made to decrease spoilage during storage by application at flowering time. Thus Mason and Dennis (1978) applied it to raspberries to decrease berry contamination by *Botrytis*. Such pre-harvest sprays decreased the percentage of berries with *Botrytis* mycelium developing in the proximal row of drupelets (i.e. arising from infection of the flower parts) but the fungicide did not translocate or persist sufficiently to prevent mycelium developing elsewhere on the berry.

Benomyl has been used as a bulb or corm dip to control, *inter alia*, various rots caused by species of *Botrytis*, *Fusarium* and *Sclerotinia*. It is also employed as a seed treatment to control loose smut of winter wheat as well as *Ascochyta* infections of pea seeds and, mixed with captan, to control anthracnose disease (*Colletotrichum*) of beans. Post-harvest protection can often be afforded by dipping or dusting; an example is the treatment of banana hands to prevent the spread of *Gloeosporium musarum*. Ricci *et al.* (1979) reported that the use of 10 min dips no later than three days after harvest controlled post-harvest rot in stored tubers of the cush-cush yam (*Dioscorea trifida*). This is caused by *Penicillium oxalicum*. Other examples of post-harvest protection have been provided by Eckert (1969).

Soil treatment with benomyl and other systemic compounds can be a very effective, if sometimes expensive, approach to disease control. It is particularly useful for high-value crops such as strawberries, for which even vascular wilts can sometimes be economically controlled. The main problem is that high treatment levels are needed to maintain a toxic dose for uptake by roots. However, it is often financially feasible to use it in greenhouses and sometimes also in the field. It can be applied either as a soil drench or by soil mixing. Examples are the control of *Verticillium* wilt of tobacco by applying benomyl as a pre-plant soil treatment and of *Verticillium* and *Fusarium* wilts of tomato by using it as a soil drench.

Carbendazim (figure 12.1b) is fungitoxic and is marketed as a systemic fungicide, especially to control eyespot (*Pseudocercosporella herpotrichoides*) on European cereals. It is also formed within plants by the hydrolytic removal of the butylcarbamoyl side-chain from benomyl and is probably the active substance at the site of action no matter which of several benzimidazoles has been applied to the plant. The latter view is supported by the fact that, if an aqueous suspension of benomyl is hydrolysed by boiling, the fungicidal effectiveness in plants decreases whereas the antifungal activity *in vitro* increases (i.e. it is more toxic to fungi but has greater difficulty reaching the site of infection).

In most soils, **benomyl** breaks down rapidly; of several soils investigated in one study, only one contained a residue of *intact* benomyl 4 weeks after application and in this case no benomyl was present after 12 weeks. The half-life of total detectable benzimidazole derivatives is, however, often six months or more, and 30 per cent of the original benomyl could in one case still be accounted for as breakdown products containing the benzimidazole ring two years after application (Zbozinek, 1984). Carbendazim is a major primary breakdown product and is fungitoxic but with passage of time more and more of the non-fungitoxic 2-aminobenzimidazole is formed. Benomyl and its breakdown products are largely immobile in soil; very little leaches out unless the soil is very sandy. Adsorption onto soil constituents increases with rising organic matter content but is inversely related to pH. Conversely, uptake by plants is greater as the pH is raised or the content of organic matter decreases. Formulations may contain detergents or other adjuncts which assist benomyl and similar products to penetrate soil, thus enabling more of the fungicide to enter roots and reach loci of infection. However, adsorption onto soil organic matter may be so intense in some soils that fungitoxicity is greatly diminished.

Since 1972, when Helwig reported the isolation from soil of microorganisms capable of using benomyl as a sole source of carbon, several similar reports have appeared. This phenomenon has been investigated by Fuchs and de Vries (1978) using strains of *Pseudomonas*. These workers were unable to detect growth when benzimidazoles other than benomyl were employed and concluded that the probable explanation was that the n-butylamine moiety was removed from N-1 (figure 12.1c) and that this aliphatic component was used as an energy source.

In rats, breakdown of benomyl occurs rapidly following oral ingestion

(Axness and Fleeker, 1979). Within 24 h of feeding, 40 per cent of the ^{14}C and 55 per cent of the tritium originally in the labelled benomyl appeared in the urine. One major metabolite comprised butylamine attached to glucuronic acid, so in this case hydrolysis presumably occurred at the CO–NH linkage indicated in figure 12.1c. In addition, butylcarbamoyl derivatives of cysteine and acetylcysteine were recovered from the urine. This possibly implies that transfer to glutathione of a butylcarbamoyl group occurred by rupture of the linkage between C and N-1 indicated in figure 12.1c, followed by further metabolism of the sort described in section 3.6.

Carbendazim, as well as being a breakdown product of benomyl, is used as a fungicide in its own right. In Britain, it has been used as a spray on winter-grown cereals for the control of mildews, *Septoria* and, especially, eyespot disease, which is caused by *Pseudocercosporella herpotrichoides* (MAFF, 1984). Unfortunately, resistance of the latter pathogen to carbendazim is now widespread and prochloraz (section 11.7) is then often used instead. Where resistance does not yet exist, a mixture of carbendazim and prochloraz is probably the best way to avoid its rapid development. In addition to these uses on cereals, it is used in the UK for the control of *Botrytis cinerea*, powdery mildews, leaf mould, leaf spot and chocolate spot on various vegetables, fruit canes and fruit bushes (MAFF, 1985). It is of interest that Panwar *et al.* (1987) have reported that the mycelial growth *in vitro* of *Pythium aphanidermatum* shows a bimodal response to carbendazim, an event which means that, over a limited concentration range, toxicity of the fungicide actually decreases with increasing concentration (compare dithiocarbamates, section 11.3).

Thiabendazole (figure 12.1d) is a non-carbamate member of the group. It is principally employed in Britain to reduce the damage done by various diseases to stored potatoes. These diseases include dry rot, skin spot, silver scurf and gangrene. It has also been used as a bulb dip to protect certain bulbs against *Fusarium* rot, as a seed treatment against bunt (*Tilletia*) of wheat and as a dressing to control blue and green mould on citrus fruit (see Cremlyn, 1978). It is one component (the others being ethirimol and flutriafol) of a seed treatment against barley powdery mildew, which has been claimed to offer better mildew control and better crop yields than previous products (Northwood *et al.*, 1984). It has also been used to check Dutch elm disease of American elms. In a technique described by Stennes and French (1987), a solution of thiabendazole hypophosphite (at 5.6 g per centimetre trunk diameter) was injected into exposed root flares and found to become evenly distributed in outer sapwood in the crown of mature elms; the treatment afforded protection for the year. An unusual observation claims an **iatrogenic** (disease-promoting) effect in relation to the incidence of *Alternaria radicina* on carrot seeds grown on malt agar; after thiabendazole treatment the incidence of black rot was nearly 30 per cent greater than in the untreated controls.

Free thiabendazole disappears more rapidly from plants than does carbendazim, but little is known of the routes by which it is metabolised. High-molecular-weight materials are formed, which seem to be firmly attached to plant constituents. In soil, it is strongly adsorbed to clay soil constituents and is nearly immobile (Zbozinek, 1984). It is moderately persistent; in one study 2 per cent of an applied dose was still present after 121 days in a loam held at 26°C.

In many species of higher animals, hydroxylation occurs in the aromatic ring and the hydroxyl group is then conjugated with glucuronic acid or with sulphate (compare section 3.6). In one investigation, 40 per cent of a dose of thiabendazole was excreted in the urine in the first 4 h by several mammals, although, in the dog, enterohepatic circulation probably accounted for the fact that most elimination occurred in the faeces. In man, only 38 per cent of the urinary metabolites were derived from hydroxythiabendazole, probably because the thiazolyl ring (right, figure 12.1d) had been cleaved (Zbozinek, 1984). The routes of metabolism in mammals are of some importance, for thiabendazole has veterinary uses as an anthelmintic.

Fuberidazole (figure 12.1e) is closely related to thiabendazole but has a furane ring attached to benzimidazole. It is used in Europe for seed treatment. It was early shown to be valuable as a seed treatment against *Fusarium*, and both *F. culmorum* of peas and *F. nivale* of rye can be controlled by it. Good control of the snow mould, *Calonectria nivalis*, and some reduction in the incidence of infections by *Puccinia triticini* have also been reported. In common with other benzimidazoles it inhibits mycelial growth rather than the germination of spores, probably because it interferes with DNA synthesis (see below).

Thiophanate-methyl (figure 12.1f) is another fungicide with a wide biological spectrum. It is used to control *Botrytis*, *Gloeosporium* and powdery mildews. In addition, it controls scab of apples as well as *Sclerotinia* on several crops and *Cercospora* on sugar beet. It is used as a paint for pruning cuts and as a seed treatment for onions. It is included in the benzimidazole group because it undergoes decomposition and rearrangement within the crop plant to give rise to carbendazim. As in the case of benomyl, this is probably the actual toxicant at the site of action, a fact that helps to explain why benomyl, carbendazim and thiophanate-methyl have similar biological spectra.

Benomyl, thiabendazole, fuberidazole and thiophanate-methyl/ethyl all act on fungi at concentrations ranging from 1 to 100 ppm. Within this range, lower concentrations prevent elongation of germ tubes of sensitive species while higher concentrations reduce spore germination. Bourgois *et al.* (1977) observed that benomyl alters the ultrastructure of the microconidia of *Fusarium*, causing a marked thickening of the cell walls and the development of lysosome-like vesicles in the cytoplasm.

It is now almost certain that a major mode of action of the benzimidazoles is an interference with the division of cell nuclei by disrupting the assembly of tubulin into microtubules. Much of the work was done by Davidse and colleagues; the subject has been reviewed by Davidse (1987) and the present section will therefore be confined to a brief survey.

All eukaryotic cells possess what has been termed a cytoskeleton (Borisy *et al.*, 1984). Units of two proteins, tubulin and actin, are responsible for various types of intracellular movement of cellular organelles and of macromolecules, as well as organisation needed for effective budding, flagellar action and (of importance in the present context) for nuclear division. Tubulin comprises two amino acid chains, known as the α- and the β-chains. In order that tubulin should function at cell division, the molecules have to be assembled into microtubules, which in turn are assembled into the spindle fibre system that is visible at cell division under the light microscope. If the spindle fibres fail to operate properly at cell division, post-metaphase chromosomal separation is imperfect, leading to mitotic abnormalities.

Valuable work undertaken by Davidse (1975) and by Davidse and Flach (1977) showed that labelled carbendazim is able to bind to a protein, molecular weight about 100 000, present in mycelial extracts of a benzimidazole-sensitive strain of *Aspergillus nidulans*. Moreover, a similar protein, originating from a strain of this organism that showed resistance to carbendazim, binds this substance much less firmly. Later work, by these and other investigators, showed that many naturally tolerant species of fungi contain similar proteins which bind carbendazim rather loosely and, moreover, that the binding protein had the chromatographic properties of tubulin. In addition, fungicidal specificity may be accounted for by the fact that the microtubule assembly of higher animals is not readily affected by carbendazim. Plant cells do appear to suffer mitotic abnormalities if directly exposed to benzimidazoles (Richmond and Phillips, 1975) but these systemic fungicides move predominantly in the non-living apoplastic system. A useful account of the interaction of benzimidazoles with tubulin subunits, and an effect of mutation of the gene for β-tubulin, has recently been given by Burland and Gull (1984).

The propensity of benzimidazoles and other systemic fungicides to induce *resistance* in fungi has been referred to (section 12.1) and this tendency is further illustrated by the following examples. Hisada *et al.* (1979) reported that *Botrytis cinerea* on rose plants became highly resistant after the plants had been sprayed only five times. Chandler *et al.* (1978) isolated benomyl-tolerant strains of *Cladosporium carpophilum* from peach orchards in Georgia after benomyl had been applied between four and seven times a year for four years. They found that the strain retained its resistance for at least two years after isolation. Penrose *et al.* (1979) reported that tolerance of *Sclerotinia fructicola* to benzimidazoles was first recorded in New South Wales in 1976, since when it has been observed in 11 orchards of stone fruit trees. Other examples include resistance in strains of *Venturia* (the cause of apple scab) and in strains of *Cercospora* on sugar beet in Greece; resistance in the latter case has proved to be very persistent. Ogawa *et al.* (1983) listed 100 fungi that had developed resistance to a variety of fungicides, many of them benzimidazoles. In view of these serious difficulties, it is of interest that de Waard (1984) has described cases where **negative cross-resistance** involving benzimidazoles appears to exist, and predicted that either this phenomenon, or synergism between benzimidazoles and other fungicides, may shortly be exploited to control resistant strains of fungi.

Resistance to benzimidazoles commenced in the 1970s in consequence of their widespread, overconfident use as single-substance sprays. The rate of development of resistance tends to be greater when the cause of resistance is associated with a single site of action or a single altered gene, the problem being exacerbated when the alteration that has led to resistance confers no disadvantage *vis-à-vis* non-resistant strains. Unfortunately, these two criteria both apply when benzimidazoles are used as fungicides. When fungi become resistant to these compounds it is seldom, if ever, due to increased detoxication (a situation that should be contrasted with that which frequently occurs in cases of insect resistance), nor is it usually greatly dependent on changes in uptake, distribution or elimination. It is, instead, usually a consequence of some alteration in the fine structure of the site of action in resistant strains of the fungi. In most cases, this difference is not initiated by the fungicide but exists already in a more or less small proportion of the natural population. The methods recommended to avoid benzimidazole resistance, or at least to minimise the rate at which it develops, are the same general strategies described in sections 11.1 and 12.1.

The altered site of action when benzimidazoles select for resistance, as work by the Davidse school has shown, is almost certainly the protein, tubulin, from which microtubules are constructed. It appears to be an alteration in the β-strand, which leads, in resistant strains, to diminished binding of benzimidazoles by the complete tubulin molecule. At least in the relatively few fungi investigated, the two or more β-protubulins characteristically present are products of the same single gene (Sheir-Neiss *et al.*, 1978).

It was mentioned earlier that carbendazim is believed to be the primary toxicant whether applied as such, or in the form of benomyl or thiophanate-methyl. It is therefore not surprising that the development of resistance to one member of the group usually confers an automatic tolerance of most of the others. An illustration is provided by the work of Shabi and Katan (1979), who isolated nine cultures of carbendazim-resistant *Venturia pirina* from different pear orchards in which benomyl no longer controlled scab. Crosses between these resistant strains and sensitive wild types showed that carbendazim resistance is conferred by a mutation in a single gene and that the mutation is unaffected by modifying genes or by cytoplasmic components.

Nevertheless, the formulae in figure 12.1 illustrate that thiabendazole and fuberidazole form a separate subgroup of the benzimidazoles; there is no obvious way in which carbendazim is likely to be formed from them *in vivo*. The conclusion must be drawn that molecules other than carbendazim probably combine with tubulin (for thiabendazole undoubtedly affects the microtubule assembly). Consequently, although cross-resistance between the two groups of benzimidazoles is common, it is possible to imagine that some mutations could, by chance, lead to tubulins which bind better than does normal tubulin to carbendazim but which bind poorly to thiabendazole (or a metabolite formed from it). Should this occur, negative cross-resistance could occur. By means of ultra-violet light, Van Tuyl *et al.* (1974) induced mutations in *Aspergillus nidulans* and found examples of mutants that had become highly resistant to thiabendazole and yet had not lost their sensitivity to benomyl. Davidse (1987) described an example in which the binding affinity of mutant tubulin derived from a thiabendazole-resistant strain of *Penicillium expansum* was lower for thiabendazole, yet higher for carbendazim, than was the tubulin from the wild biotype.

The acute oral toxicity of most benzimidazoles to higher animals is low; for example, the oral LD_{50} to rats of benomyl is 7500 mg/kg, which makes it about half as poisonous as aspirin. Acute toxicity, however, is not the whole story, and for several years until 1983 benomyl was, in the USA, under the cloud of an Environmental Agency RPAR Notice on the grounds of suspected teratogenic effects (very approximately, a Rebuttal of Presumption Against Registration (RPAR) is an indication that registration may be withdrawn unless further evidence of safety is forthcoming)*. In invertebrates, there is some evidence that, in unusual circumstances, teratogenicity can occur; when tails of earthworms are amputated, teratogenic defects occur during repair if benomyl is applied to the surface within the normal post-operative 7–10 day period of segmental replication (Zoran *et al.*, 1986).

Various benzimidazoles have also been suspected of weak antimitotic activity (as has been seen, they bind with tubulin, but the ease with which this occurs varies very greatly with the species). This could be important, for mitotic abnormality can be associated with mutagenic and carcinogenic potential. Ficsor *et al.* (1978) carried out comprehensive monitoring using mutants of *Salmonella typhimurium* with captan as a positive control compound in variants of the Ames test (section 1.5). Over the range of 50–2000 µg of benomyl per plate, no positive results were obtained, either in simple *Salmonella* tests or in *Salmonella*/microsome tests (which provide evidence as to whether host enzyme systems may lead to the production of mutagens). It should be added, however, that these authors gave references to work that had led to ambiguous or to occasional positive results when modifications of the Ames test were used.

---

*In view of the similarity of mode of action and metabolism of different benzimidazoles, the author has always thought it a bit odd that tiny doses of benomyl should cause alarm while its near neighbour, thiophanate, is one of several benzimidazoles administered to animals in large amounts as an anthelmintic.

12.3 OXATHIINS OR CARBOXAMIDES

The discovery of the first two members of this group, carboxin and oxycarboxin, was reported in 1966, and they are still the two most important fungicides of this type. Their unique characteristic is their specific action on Basidiomycetes, and especially on the rusts, smuts and bunts that cause serious losses of cereals. Susceptible genera include *Puccinia, Tilletia, Urocystis* and *Ustilago*. They also often control members of the form genus, *Rhizoctonia*, which causes some types of damping off and which may be the conidial stage of the Basidiomycete, *Hypochnus*. Both carboxin and oxycarboxin are systemic, the former being almost exclusively used for seed treatment and the latter often being applied to foliage. They appear to have a beneficial effect on the growth of some crops even in the absence of a pathogen.

   Carboxin (figure 12.2b) contains the oxathiin ring; additionally, it will be noted, the crotonic acid amide grouping, $CH_3-CH{=}CH-CONH-$, is present, the $-CH_3$ being orientated *cis* to the $-CONH$ moiety. It is this grouping that is believed to be the toxophoric entity, and carboxin and oxycarboxin are consequently often referred to as *cis*-crotonanilides. The reason for this newer nomenclature is that several fungicides with similar specific action against Basidiomycetes have now been discovered that are all *cis*-crotonanilides (figure 12.2d) even though they may lack an oxathiin ring (Kulka and von Schmeling, 1987). Examples are **pyracarbolid**, which contains a pyrane-type ring (and is used against rusts), **mepronil** (benzene ring; rice sheath blight) and **fenfuram** (furane ring; smuts and bunts).

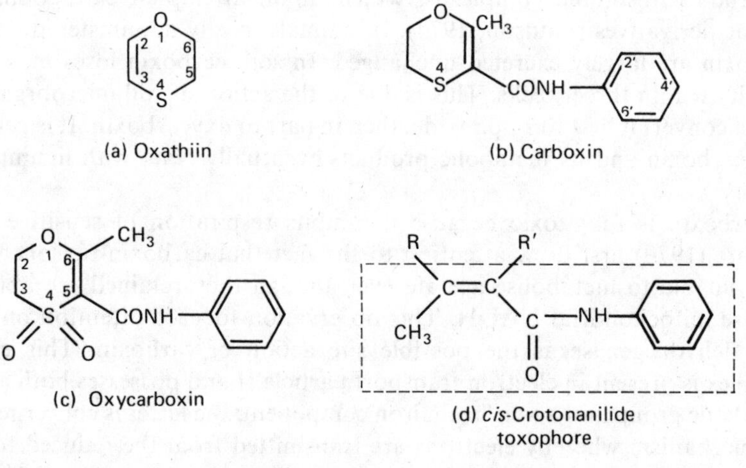

Figure 12.2   Structures of carboxin and oxycarboxin: (b) 2,3-dihydro-6-methyl-5-phenylcarbamoyl-1,4-oxathiin; (c) sulphone of (b)

Carboxin is used in the UK exclusively as a seed treatment against rusts, smuts and bunts of cereals. Elsewhere, it is used to control damping off of cotton caused by *Rhizoctonia solani* and sheath blight of rice caused by *Corticium sasakii*. It is usually mixed with other fungicides (e.g. thiram) to widen the spectrum of control. Very approximately, 1 g of active ingredient is used per kilogram of seed. In contrast oxycarboxin, the sulphone of carboxin (figure 12.2c), is more polar and tends to be used as a foliar spray rather than as a seed treatment. It is frequently formulated as an emulsifiable concentrate.

In the UK carboxin seed treatment is particularly useful as a means of controlling loose smut (*Ustilago*) of wheat, barley and oats. For this purpose the systemic action is most valuable because loose smut mycelium penetrates deeply into seed and thus cannot be readily controlled by superficial protectants. Care is necessary to ensure that the moisture content of treated seed is not too high (above 16 per cent) and treated seed should not be sown immediately after treatment. Carboxin is also active against the soil fungus, *Rhizoctonia solani*, and Oyekan (1979) found that it controlled wet blight of cowpea, caused by this fungus, at one-tenth of the dose of captafol needed to obtain a similar result.

Initial metabolism of carboxin follows predictable routes. In some organisms, *para* hydroxylation of the phenyl moiety takes place; for example, Larson and Lamoureux (1984) found that this was the predominant metabolic route in peanuts. In barley, on the other hand, although some workers have reported that hydroxylation takes place, the oxidation of the sulphide sulphur to sulphoxide has also been reported. In plants, the sulphoxide, which is of low fungitoxicity, does not appear readily to add another atom of oxygen to give the sulphone, namely oxycarboxin. Both the hydroxylation product and the sulphoxide undergo further changes, the former, at least, reacting with lignin to produce insoluble complexes, which, upon attempted extraction, yield aniline derivatives (Paulson, 1977). In animals, orally administered doses of carboxin are largely excreted unchanged. In soil, carboxin loses most of its activity within three weeks. This is due to the action of soil microorganisms, which convert it first to sulphoxide, then in part to oxycarboxin. It is probable that carboxin and its metabolic products eventually react with lignin in soil humus.

Carboxin is fungitoxic because it inhibits respiration of sensitive fungi. Mathre (1970) first drew attention to the fact that carboxin-poisoned fungi were unable to metabolise acetate even though they retained the ability to oxidise mitochondrial NADH. This observation focused attention on succinate dehydrogenase as the possible site action of carboxin. This enzyme complex is present in electron transport particle II and possesses both a flavin prosthetic group and a non-haem iron component; the latter is concerned with the mechanism whereby electrons are transmitted from the reduced form of the flavin to ubiquinone, the next electron carrier in the mitochondrial electron transport chain (figure 12.3). It is now recognised that carboxin inhibits succinate oxidation in membrane preparations from animals and plants as well as some fungi. The succinate dehydrogenase of Basidiomycetes appears to be more sensitive than that in higher plants, but it is not certain whether this selectivity reflects differential uptake into mitochondria or unique topography of the succinate dehydrogenase in the vicinity of the non-haem iron centre. Whatever the reason, it is a fortunate coincidence, for it allows carboxin to express systemic activity in higher plants without phytotoxic complications (Schewe and Lyr, 1987).

It appears that there are both non-specific and specific binding sites for carboxin on the inner mitochondrial membrane, only the binding to specific binding sites being reversible (Coles *et al.*, 1978). Mitochondrial damage caused by carboxin has, in fact, been directly observed by electron microscopy, but so also has damage to other membranes. The probable importance of interaction with succinate dehydrogenase has been strikingly confirmed by White *et al.* (1978). These workers chose a number of strains of *Ustilago maydis* and *Aspergillus nidulans* of varying resistance to carboxin and isolated succinate dehydrogenase complex from each. They found a marked parallelism between tolerance of the fungus to carboxin *in vivo* and the amount of carboxin needed to inhibit the succinate dehydrogenase from each of them *in vitro*.

The non-haem iron site of succinate dehydrogenase is, more specifically, an iron–sulphur protein, which is similar to ferredoxin in that there is a group of several sulphur and iron atoms at each active site (figure 12.4). This iron–sulphur site is reduced by electrons originating from succinate (via the FAD prosthetic group). Its reduction proceeds normally in the presence of carboxin but its reoxidation is prevented. In consequence, electrons do not flow to ubiquinone, the next carrier in the transport system. The technique of electron paramagnetic resonance spectroscopy has proved to be of major importance

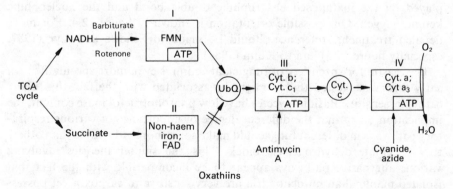

Figure 12.3 Mitochondrial electron transport and proposed sites of action of some pesticides and other poisons

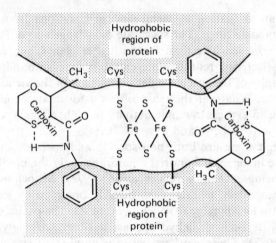

Figure 12.4   Site II active centre of succinate dehydrogenase (after Lyr, 1987). Carboxin appears to act on a complex, rich in iron and sulphur, which comprises succinate dehydrogenase linked to a coenzyme Q-binding protein. In this model, two molecules of carboxin intrude into the (active) Fe–S cluster of the complex, anchored by phenyl and methyl groups which fit into the hydrophobic region of the complex

in the elucidation of these events; its use has been reviewed by Schewe and Lyr (1987).

The precise mode of action is still uncertain. A popular view is that the molecule of carboxin is structurally designed to fit into the active site of the iron–sulphur part of succinate dehydrogenase and, by so doing, disorganises the flow of electrons to ubiquinone. In this respect the *cis*-crotonanilide 'toxophore' (figure 12.2d) is crucial to the argument, for the theory not only requires that the dimensions of the molecule are correct but that a role is played by the juxtaposed electrophilic double bond and the nucleophilic ketone oxygen. One possible orientation is shown in figure 12.4. For more detailed treatment, reference should be made to Schewe and Lyr (1987, especially figure 10.3) and to Kuhn (1984).

The reason for specificity of fungicidal action is even more speculative. An early theory suggested that it might be associated with the fact that many carboxin-sensitive Basidiomycetes have low phosphofructokinase content, the implication being that the different degree of importance of various respiratory pathways in different fungi could make some more vulnerable than others to a succinate dehydrogenase block. This and similar theories involving various alternative pathways appear to be incompatible with the fact that isolated mammalian mitochondria are very sensitive to carboxin yet possess no alternative respiratory mechanism. As was mentioned earlier, the possibility of carboxin penetrating to its site of action with varying ease in different types of fungi cannot be excluded. The most popular current view is that it is a consequence of specific stereochemistry at the site of action and that there is something about the structure of succinate dehydrogenase in Basidiomycetes that makes them more susceptible to oxathiins than are other fungi.

Resistance of fungi to oxathiins appears often, but not always, to be caused by single gene mutation and probably involves a decreased affinity of the site of action for the fungicide (White *et al.*, 1978). When it occurs, cross-resistance to other fungicides of the '*cis*-crotonanilide' family is common but not universal; White and colleagues reported an example of negative cross-resistance between carboxin and one of its analogues. In the laboratory both ultra-violet radiation and normal selection pressure procedures can lead readily to strains of Basidiomycetes that are resistant to carboxin, but, in the field, rather few examples have been reported. This is possibly because carboxin is primarily used as a seed protectant and this method of application seems to develop less selection pressure. On the other hand, oxycarboxin, which is frequently used as a foliar spray, has been reported to have caused problems in several countries.

12.4 MORPHOLINE INHIBITORS OF STEROL SYNTHESIS

The morpholine ring structure is somewhat similar to that of oxathiin, but has a nitrogen atom instead of sulphur (figures 12.2a and 12.5a). The best-known fungicides of this group are tridemorph and dodemorph although, more recently, fenpropimorph and aldimorph have been introduced. Their primary use is to control diseases caused by powdery mildews (Erysiphales) but some are also quite effective against rusts and a few Deuteromycetes. Much of the work on fungicidal morpholines has been done by Pommer and his colleagues. A publication in 1984 has summarised work on morpholines in which alkyl and aryl groups had been *N*-substituted and has listed some of the requirements for good fungitoxicity (Pommer, 1984).

Tridemorph (figure 12.5b) is of particular importance because it has been used for many years to control *Erysiphe graminis*, the cause of powdery mildew of cereals. It also shows activity against *Puccinia striiformis*, the cause of yellow rust of cereals in the UK. It is used on several cereals but it is particularly safe on most cultivars of barley. On various crops (which include banana, cotton, potato, rubber and tea) it has, at various locations, controlled species of *Exobasidium*, *Fomes* and *Mycosphaerella* (Pommer, 1987). In practice, it is frequently used mixed with one or more fungicides from different groups to extend the range of activity of the spray. In the UK it is frequently used in a spray mixture with carbendazim and with a dithiocarbamate such as maneb; such a mixture has been recommended to control yellow rust, brown rust (*Puccinia recondita*), eyespot (*Pseudocercosporella*), powdery mildew and *Septoria* (MAFF, 1984).

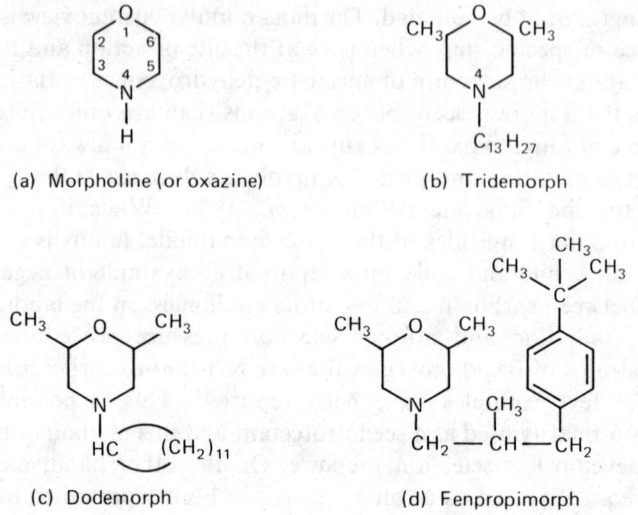

(a) Morpholine (or oxazine)   (b) Tridemorph

(c) Dodemorph   (d) Fenpropimorph

Figure 12.5   Morpholine fungicides: (b) 2,6-dimethyl-4-tridecylmorpholine; (c) 2,6-dimethyl-4-cyclododecylmorpholine; (d) N-[(3-p-t-butylphenyl)-2-methylpropyl]-2,6-dimethylmorpholine

Tridemorph is strongly absorbed onto soil particles, so little leaching occurs. Published data upon the metabolism of tridemorph have been collated by Menzie (1978). In one study, after tridemorph had been used on cereals, residues fell to less than 0.05 ppm after 48 days, with a half-life of about 6 days. In another investigation, 80 per cent of the tridemorph added to Limburgerhof soil was degraded within a month. Metabolic products included an unstable amine oxide (compare 5b, table 3.1), one or more hydroxylated derivatives and the N-dealkylated product, 2,6-dimethylmorpholine.

Dodemorph (figure 12.5c) is used principally on ornamental plants and especially on roses. In common with other morpholines, it is often used in mixtures with benzimidazoles or with non-systemic fungicides to increase its spectrum of activity. The marketed product contains both *cis* and *trans* isomers, but these are of approximately equal fungitoxicity, at least to powdery mildews (Pommer, 1984).

Aldimorph, a newer member of the group, comprises a mixture of four isomers and is marketed primarily for the control of *Erisyphe graminis* on barley. Jumar and Lehmann (1982) reported that metabolism in barley plants leads to the formation of one or more hydroxylation products; these then eventually form conjugates with glucose.

Fenpropimorph is another member of the morpholine group; it has found acceptance in the UK for the control not only of powdery mildew of cereals but also of yellow rust on wheat and *Rhynchosporium secalis* leaf blotch on barley. It has also been used as a seed treatment on cabbage seed infected with *Alternaria* and with *Phoma* (Pommer, 1987). It is often used in mixtures with other fungicides, such as carbendazim, iprodione or chlorthalonil. It rapidly enters wheat plants after spraying, being rain-fast within a few minutes of application (Saur and Löcher, 1984).

The mode of action of morpholines is now partly understood. It was observed quite early on that various morpholines, at realistic concentrations, interfere with normal growth of fungal hyphae. Sometimes haustoria cease to grow out and penetrate leaves; sometimes the tips of hyphae swell out and then dry up; and on other occasions sporulation is inhibited. In the case of *Botrytis* spp., short but branched germ tubes emerge from germinating spores and, eventually, chitin is deposited in an irregular manner in fungal cell walls. Significantly, perhaps, when suitable fungi are grown *in vitro* in the presence of morpholines, very little effect is observed until the number of cells has doubled or quadrupled; initially, the increase in dry weight is almost normal and the first observed symptom is that certain sterols, characteristic of the particular fungus, are in short supply. It seems likely that the main, and perhaps the only, action of morpholines at economic concentrations is to inhibit one or both of two steps in the complex process of biosynthesis of sterols. A consequence of such a blockage late on in the synthesis can be that, while an overall shortage develops of those sterols which are natural end-products, there may neverthe-less be present an excess of certain of the intermediates near where the molecular 'blockage' occurred. A brief outline of sterol synthesis follows; for further details, reference should be made to a biochemical text.

Sterol synthesis starts from acetyl coenzyme A; indeed, all 27 carbon atoms of cholesterol, a common mammalian sterol, originate from acetate. From acetate, acetoacetyl coenzyme A is formed, which reacts with a molecule of acetyl coenzyme A to give hydroxymethylglutaryl coenzyme A. The latter is subsequently converted to mevalonic acid (six carbon atoms). From this, a five-carbon compound of high energy is formed; it is called isopentenyl pyrophosphate. Six of these molecules combine together, with loss of phos-phate, to give the linear unsaturated compound, squalene. By rearrangement of the double bonds, ring formation occurs to give **lanosterol**, the parent or precursor of all other steroids in both fungi and mammals. We are not concerned with the side-chain at C-17 and the formulae in figure 12.6 have been simplified accordingly. A common end-product in fungi is ergosterol, and there are numerous intermediates between lanosterol and this substance. However, changes occur in a methodical manner; sometimes a methyl group is removed, sometimes a double bond swivels to an adjacent position and sometimes a double bond is reduced. The steps relevant to an understanding of the mode of action of the morpholines are simplified and linked together in figure 12.6; episterol is a few steps removed from the final product, ergosterol.

The most likely site of disruption is at A, where a reductase adds hydrogen atoms to the double bond between C-14 and C-15. The reason for believing this to be the case is that a C-14, C-15 unsaturated sterol called ignosterol accumulates in at least some morpholine-poisoned fungi. There is, however, some uncertainty, because most sterol identification involves the technique of mass spectrometry, and the mass spectra of these substances are sometimes very similar. Other workers claim to have identified an accumulation of fecosterol, which has a double bond in the C-8, C-9 position rather than the C-14, C-15 position; in this case, it would appear that the morpholines inhibit the action of the isomerase at position B of figure 12.6. In practice, of course, both groups of workers could be correct; results may depend on environmental conditions or upon the strain of fungus being investigated. In either case a cautionary footnote is perhaps appropriate; Kerkenaar (1987) has pointed out that Gram-positive bacteria are very sensitive to tridemorph yet such bacteria usually contain very few steroids.

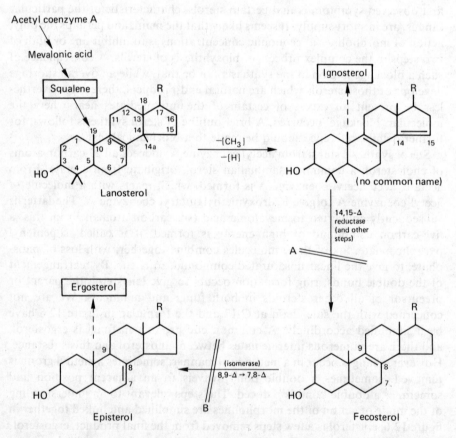

Figure 12.6   Some important steps in steroid biosynthesis by fungi, showing possible points of disruption by morpholines (Δ = double bond)

A few cases of resistance of *Erysiphe graminis* to morpholines have been reported but in most cases the problem has not been severe. In glasshouse experiments the development of resistance was indicated by the shortening of the time between successive sprays of tridemorph and the appearance of symptoms (Walmsley-Woodward *et al.*, 1979). It should be pointed out that there are several groups of fungicides which, while they function by preventing biosynthesis of sterols, nevertheless achieve this in a way quite different from that described above for the morpholines; cross-resistance between morpholines and these other compounds (which inhibit the removal of the methyl group from C-14 of the sterol nucleus) has so far been minimal. Indeed, one case has been reported where strains of *Penicillium italicum* that are moderately resistant to the demethylation inhibitor, imazalil (section 11.7), were more sensitive to fenpropimorph than was a susceptible strain, thereby exhibiting negative cross-resistance.

12.5 INHIBITORS OF C-14 DEMETHYLATION OF STEROLS

It will be recalled that natural sterols are constructed from acetyl groups derived from acetyl coenzyme A. Moreover, lanosterol lies on the synthetic pathway (section 12.4) and this sterol possesses a methyl group attached to carbon atom 14 whereas ergosterol, a major final product in fungi, does not (figure 12.6). It is therefore essential for this methyl group (carbon atom 14*a*) to be replaced by a hydrogen atom during biosynthesis and its oxidative removal is accomplished by the cytochrome P_{450} mono-oxygenase system (section 3.4). If its removal is prevented, sterols essential for the stability and functioning of lipoprotein membranes will be in short supply while unwanted intermediate sterols may accumulate (compare the morpholines in the previous section, although the location and the cause of the blockage are both different).

Several groups of nitrogen-containing heterocyclic fungicides function in this way. The largest of these groups contains compounds based on the triazole ring system; others are based on pyrimidine, pyridine, piperazine and imidazole (figure 12.7). The imidazoles were, in fact, mentioned in chapter 11 because two of major importance in crop protection (imazalil and prochloraz) are only marginally systemic in plants; others, however, are of considerable medical importance because of their systemic action in animals and are briefly considered in the present section.

The use in crop protection of steroid C-14 demethylation inhibitors (or ergosterol biosynthesis inhibitors (EBIs), as they are sometimes called) is of some importance since many are effective at less than one-tenth of the application rate needed for disease control employing conventional non-systemic fungicides. This high intrinsic toxicity is in part explained by the fact that they are not only systemic in action but many of them are sufficiently

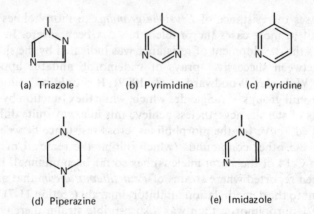

    (a) Triazole   (b) Pyrimidine   (c) Pyridine

          (d) Piperazine   (e) Imidazole

Figure 12.7   Heterocyclic nuclei present in C-14 demethylation inhibitors

volatile for some vapour-phase activity to occur within the crop plant. They can be usefully employed against many members of most groups of fungi other than the Oomycetes, although *Botrytis cinerea* and *Pseudocercosporella herpo-trichoides* are seldom fully controlled by some C-14 demethylation inhibitors. In view of the need, for safety reasons, to restrict the use of organomercury seed treatments it is of major importance that some C-14 demethylation inhibitors have proved to be useful replacements for these substances.

(a)   Group A: the triazoles

From a structural viewpoint, triazole derivatives that are used as fungicides in crop protection can conveniently be divided into two subgroups (figure 12.8), but it should be stressed that this does not imply any difference in three-dimensional geometry insofar as this is related to their mode of action. The triadimefon subgroup comprises three subsets, with molecular variations of the type shown in the figure. Triadimefon has been used since about 1973 whereas diclobutrazol and bitertanol derivatives have appeared more recently. The second subfamily is similar to propiconazole in that an extra carbon atom is present between the triazole nucleus and 'T-junction' of the molecule.

    Triadimefon consists of a mixture of two stereoisomers, which are of approximately equal toxicity (Krämer *et al.*, 1983). It is effective against a range of Ascomycetes and Basidiomycetes and against some Deuteromycetes, but, in common with other triazoles, it does not give satisfactory control of Oomycetes. It was originally introduced primarily for the control, by both eradicant and protective action, of such diseases of cereals as those caused by species of *Erysiphe*, *Septoria* and *Rhynchosporium*. It has, however, also found use in the control of non-Oomycetes that cause diseases of coffee and top fruit. It is mainly used for foliar application and partly acts in the vapour phase within the plant. It also controls a number of bacteria, including species of

Rhizobium, Pseudomonas, Corynebacterium and *Arthrobacterium* (Oros and Gasztonyi, 1986). Its metabolism in barley plants was studied by Rouchard *et al.* (1982); they found that about 10 per cent could be recovered unchanged 66 days after applying to young barley plants but that 28 per cent had been converted to triadimenol or its conjugated derivatives. More complete metabolism led to the formation of chlorophenol, which rapidly bound to plant constituents.

Triadimenol is similar to triadimefon except that the ketone group of the latter is reduced. Indeed, when triadimefon is applied, much of it is converted to isomers of the somewhat more active triadimenol (Buchenauer and Grossman, 1982). It is best known for its use as a seed protectant although foliar formulations also exist. It has a moderately wide spectrum of activity, including rusts, smuts, bunts and powdery mildews. According to Schwinn (1983) triadimenol applied at 30 g per 100 kg of seed controls many major seed-borne diseases of cereals, high translocation in the xylem ensuring that seed application can control foliar disease. Other than for the protection of cereals, its main use is for disease control on deciduous fruit trees and especially for high-yield cultivars used in Europe.

Diclobutrazol was introduced by ICI as a systemic foliar fungicide for the control of cereal diseases caused by such fungi as *Puccinia* spp., *Rhynchosporium* spp., *Erysiphe* spp. and *Typhula* spp. It has pronounced growth-regulating effects, especially on dicotyledonous plants (Buchenauer *et al.*, 1981). Baldwin and Wiggins (1984) studied the effect of diclobutrazol isomers on the growth and sterol composition of *Ustilago maydis*. They observed a decrease in the rate of growth during the lag phase with a marked increase in the proportion of methylsterols (see mode of action, above). The mixture of stereoisomers was 181 times as toxic to *U. maydis* as was triadimefon; moreover, on separating the four isomers, the one that was the most toxic was 600 times as toxic as triadimefon whereas another was only half as toxic. Clearly, in contrast to Krämer's observations on the toxicity of the two isomers of

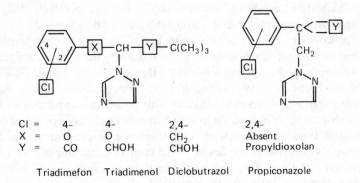

Cl =	4-	4-	2,4-	2,4-
X =	O	O	CH_2	Absent
Y =	CO	CHOH	CHOH	Propyldioxolan
	Triadimefon	Triadimenol	Diclobutrazol	Propiconazole

Figure 12.8 Triazole fungicides; triadimefon and propiconazole subfamilies

triadimefon, the molecular topography of diclobutrazol is crucial to its action. The same is true of triadimenol, which comprises four isomers that differ greatly in fungitoxicity. Subsequent observations suggest that fungal growth regulation and fungicidal activity are not parallel characteristics but are possessed to varying degrees by different enantiomers of triazoles.

Propiconazole is extensively used as a foliar spray to control a range of Ascomycetes, Basidiomycetes and some Deuteromycetes on cereals. Of particular importance is the control of species of *Erysiphe*, *Puccinia*, *Pyrenophora* and *Rhynchosporium* on winter wheat and on barley; in addition, the control of *Pseudocercosporella herpotrichoides* can be improved by using a mixture containing propiconazole and carbendazim (MAFF, 1985). Sutton and Roke (1984), working on the wheat cultivar, Favor, in Canada, found that propiconazole reduced the intensity of tritici blotch and nodorum blotch; it also increased yield, especially if two applications were made, a month apart. Prior (1987) attempted to control vascular streak dieback disease of cocoa (caused by *Oncobasidium theobromae*) in Papua New Guinea, using 18 fungicides. None was totally successful, but the best result was obtained by painting the rough bark on stems with a paint containing propiconazole dissolved in oil; this greatly reduced the incidence of the disease but did not eliminate it.

Propiconazole has been found to increase liver weight and to induce cytochrome P_{450} in Japanese quail, although to a lesser extent than has been observed for prochloraz and imazalil (section 11.7). These were the only ergosterol biosynthesis inhibitors found by Rivière *et al.* (1984) to have this effect to an important degree. For example, the ratio of liver weight to body weight was 1.5 times as great after treatment with propiconazole as it was for untreated birds (for prochloraz the ratio was 1.9). The same authors noticed that lanosterol concentration increased in quail liver after propiconazole treatment, implying some interference with avian sterol metabolism.

Hexaconazole has been marketed by ICI as a broad-spectrum fungicide (Shephard *et al.*, 1986). Structurally it is similar to propiconazole except that, for this substance, the two valencies directed towards Y in the formula shown in figure 12.8 are attached to hydroxyl and to butyl respectively. It is mainly active against Ascomycetes and Basidiomycetes and is especially employed against powdery mildew, rust and scab (all of apples), powdery mildew of some vegetables and black spot of grapes. These effects are achieved using solutions containing approximately 10–30 ppm. Brown *et al.* (1988) have reported excellent activity against *Venturia inaequalis*, *Hemileia vastatrix*, *Cercospora* spp. and *Rhizoctonia solani*. This success was ascribed to the fact that hexaconazole appeared to possess an optimal balance of protective, curative and translaminar activity. Furthermore, it penetrates rapidly into plants, and its curative action leads to the control of pathogens with a latent period of greater than 60 h, although effectiveness diminishes if it is applied more than 96 h after infection has occurred.

Hexaconazole is a foliar spray and moves exclusively in the xylem

(Shephard *et al.*, 1986). In common with other C-14 demethylation inhibitors, it has little activity against Oomycetes. It appears to be of low mammalian toxicity but to be somewhat more toxic to fish, earthworms and bees. It is rapidly degraded in soil and its soil mobility is low.

Other azoles, not discussed in this book, include terbinconazole, etaconazole, flusilazol, penconazole and myclobutanil. Many of these are used in specific circumstances to control, *inter alia*, powdery mildews, rusts, smuts, *Monilinia* spp., *Cercospora* spp., *Septoria* spp., *Puccinia* spp., as well as *Venturia inaequalis*, *Pseudocercosporella herpotrichoides* and *Uncinula necator*.

The effects of triazole fungicides on a variety of fungi have been studied by several investigators. Triadimefon at 5 µg/ml inhibited the budding process of sporidia of *Ustilago avenae* so that a filamentous promycelium was produced, the cells of which were larger than usual in diameter and, characteristically, possessed very thick walls and septa. Moreover, the mitochondria visible in electron micrographs of fungicide-treated organisms were more numerous than those of the controls but were irregularly shaped. Additionally, the plasmalemma of cells containing them appeared abnormally pitted, with deposits of substances that had apparently escaped from the cells (Hippe, 1984).

Allowing for differences in fungicide, fungus and concentration, analogous results have been obtained by other workers. Pring (1984) studied the effect of triadimefon on rust fungi. The mycelial walls of both *Uromyces vicia-fabae* and *Puccinia recondita* were abnormally thickened after treatment, with incomplete and multiperforated septa; sometimes the walls were so thick that they almost blocked the hyphae. Similarly, the electron micrographs of Richmond (1984) show that, on germination, the conidia of triadimefon-treated *Botrytis allii* produced stubby, swollen germ tubes, with unevenly thickened walls and incomplete septa; an increase in the number of vacuoles and of lipid vesicles was also evident. An increase in mitochondrial numbers and in endoplasmic reticulum has also been observed for *Sclerotinia sclerotiorum* when growing in the presence of triadimefon (Stiers *et al.*, 1980).

Smolka and Wolf (1986) carried out similar studies using propiconazole and its ethyl analogue, **etaconazole**. Cytological observations showed that these compounds did not prevent the germ tube of *Erysiphe graminis* from penetrating the plant but, once haustoria had formed, the penetrating hyphae became 'encapsulated' by a callose-like polysaccharide substance produced by the host plant. The authors referred to other work which demonstrated that triadimefon had led to encapsulation and have drawn attention to the similarity of this host response to that which has been observed when the hyphae attempt to enter cells of resistant strains of the host plant. The morpholines (section 12.4), which inhibit sterol synthesis in a different way from the triazoles, cause a distinctive type of encapsulation, whereas ethirimol, a hydroxyaminopyrimidine that is fungitoxic for reasons unrelated to sterol chemistry, does not cause encapsulation.

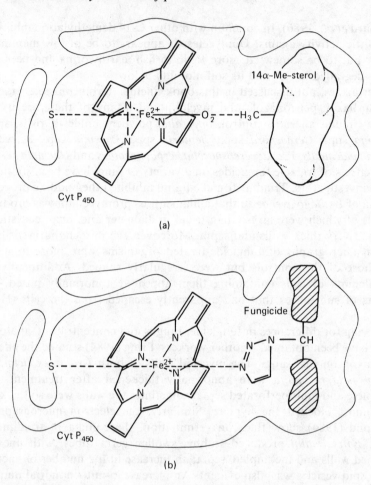

Figure 12.9   How C-14 demethylation inhibitors may block the active site of cytochrome P_{450} (after Gadher *et al.*, 1983). The porphyrin unit should be
visualised as being at right-angles to the plane of the paper

There is general agreement that the triazoles are fungicidal because they
interfere with sterol synthesis by preventing C-14 demethylation by the
cytochrome P_{450} system (figures 12.6 and 12.9). In addition to C-14 demethylation, the triazoles probably prevent the formation of double bonds in the R
group attached at carbon atom 17 of the sterol nucleus. This is another
reaction that involves the participation of cytochrome P_{450}. When sterol
biosynthesis is disorganised, a consequence appears to be that lipoprotein
membranes are defective, presumably because of a shortage of sterols of the
right kind or the presence of lipids of the wrong type. In either case, the
permeability of a membrane is affected and any specialist activity occurring on
such a membrane is disrupted (Sancholle *et al.*, 1984). In this respect, activities

such as those of fatty acid desaturase, ATPase and cytochrome oxidase could be affected, as could essential steps in the synthesis of chitin.

Oomycetes are not sensitive to C-14 demethylation inhibitors and it may be significant that these organisms differ from other fungi in their steroid composition (Sancholle *et al.*, 1984); in particular, members of the *Pythium* family lack significant amounts of sterols in their lipoprotein membranes (Weete, 1980). The enzyme, squalene epoxidase, an enzyme involved in an essential step in sterol synthesis, is apparently absent from some Oomycetes; this could well account for the differences that have been reported. It also worth recalling that Oomycetes are coenocytes, the hyphae being aseptate.

The triazoles are the largest of several groups of nitrogen-containing heterocyclic compounds with the ability to inhibit C-14 demethylation. Within the triazole group small changes of structure lead to large changes in fungitoxicity. Thus, as Köller (1987) has observed, there is a need to reconcile two facts. The first is that the sterol binding site of the cytochrome P_{450} responsible for C-14 demethylation shows high structural flexibility in that it can be blocked not only by certain triazole derivatives but also by substances that contain other heterocyclic structures. On the other hand there exists simultaneously a remarkable stereochemical specificity in that small changes within one such cyclic structure can greatly alter fungicidal effectiveness.

The paradox is resolved when it is remembered that cytochrome P_{450} is a complex membrane-bound protein, the active centre of which is in the vicinity of an iron-containing porphyrin prosthetic group. The iron of the cytochrome binds oxygen to form a complex that interacts with an oxidisable substrate XH, which is probably bound to the protein in the vicinity of the porphyrin. In consequence, X is converted to XOH (figure 3.2). All the heterocyclic compounds that are C-14 demethylation inhibitors contain a nitrogen atom that possesses a free electron pair and can bind to the porphyrin system and thus prevent oxygen uptake. Hence, several molecular species (triazoles, pyrimidines, imidazoles, etc.) have nitrogen atoms that can form coordination complexes with haem iron, yet the topography of the tertiary structure of the protein in the neighbourhood of the prosthetic group places severe stereo-chemical restrictions on the overall shape and size of molecules containing those nitrogen atoms. In normal circumstances, this active site accommodates lanosterol; oxygen molecules coordinate onto the ferrous iron (figure 12.9a) prior to the methyl group being oxidised to $-CH_2OH$. Gadher *et al.* (1983) have postulated that inhibitors of C-14 demethylation occupy this site, preventing access of both oxygen molecules and lanosterol, thereby impeding ergosterol synthesis (figure 12.9b).

A possible mechanism for C-14 demethylation is illustrated in figure 12.10. Although hypothetical, it provides one explanation of how demethylation could be achieved by well known reactions catalysed, *inter alia*, by cytochrome P_{450} (table 3.1). It also accounts for the intermediate formation of a double bond. The carbon atom of the methyl group attached at position 14 of the

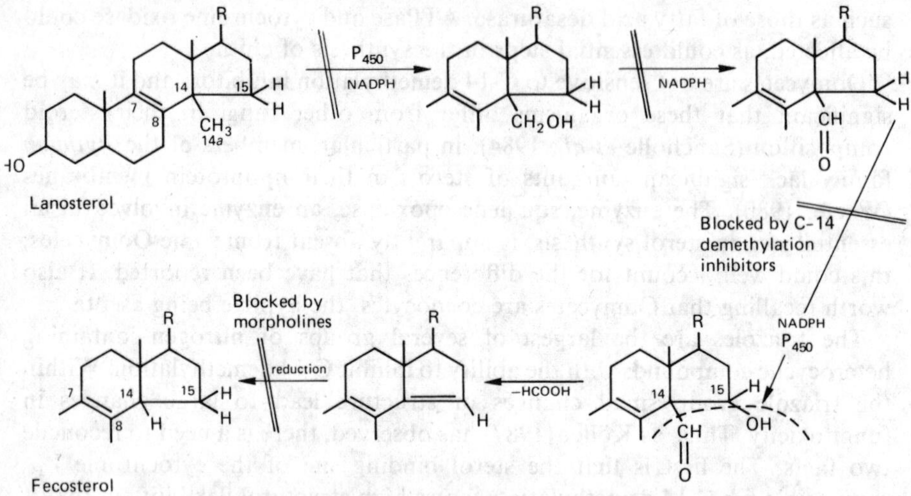

Figure 12.10   A possible mechanism for the role of cytochrome P_{450} in the conversion of lanosterol to fecosterol, with likely sites of action of C-14 demethylation inhibitors. (Hydrogen atoms are shown in positions 14 and 15)

polycyclic ring structure is labelled 14a. This methyl group is oxidised first to primary alcohol and then to aldehyde while, on the nearby C-15, C–H is oxidised in a separate reaction to C–OH. Removal of the elements of formic acid results in the formation of a double bond in the 14,15 position. The latter is then reduced by the 14,15 reductase (the latter being, as is shown in figure 12.6, one possible site of attack by the fungicidal morpholines).

Cytochrome P_{450} derived from mammalian systems is much less sensitive to many C-14 demethylation inhibitors than is fungal cytochrome P_{450}. Azoles appear to bind less firmly to the mammalian cytochrome than to that from yeast, for Vanden Bossche (1985) has reported that, using a spectral technique to measure binding, between 150 and 1500 times as great a concentration of certain azoles is necessary to obtain a similar binding effect using cytochrome P_{450} derived from rabbit liver than when using cytochrome P_{450} derived from yeast. Whether or not this is the full explanation, Vanden Bossche *et al.* (1987) have demonstrated that azole antifungal agents inhibited ergosterol synthesis in fungi when present in nanomolar concentrations whereas micromolar amounts were needed to obtain a similar inhibition of cholesterol synthesis in mammals.

Few cases have been reported of the development of resistance of fungi to C-14 demethylation inhibitors under field conditions, although several have been listed by Hippe and Köller (1986). Nevertheless, resistance can be induced in the laboratory. It is not fully understood why resistance to these substances develops so slowly in the field, despite an evident innate capability for this to happen. Lyr (1988) has discussed this problem and reported that up to 8 genes may be involved in the development of resistance to some C-14 demethylation inhibitors. He also suggested that these fungicides may have a secondary toxic effect on sensitive fungi such as *Ustilago maydis*; this toxic effect appears to involve damage to membranes by peroxidation of lipids within them. Hippe and Köller (1986) found that resistant and susceptible strains of *Ustilago avenae* have very similar lipid compositions prior to treatment with fungitoxic triazoles.

(b) Group B: the pyrimidines

The formulae of the two most important pyrimidines that are C-14 demethylation inhibitors are shown in figure 12.11a (fungicidal pyrimidines with a different mode of action exist and are considered in section 12.6). An earlier member, triarimol, not now used in the field, is an isomer of fenarimol. **Nuarimol** was introduced primarily for use on cereals but has been extensively used on top fruit, and especially in apple orchards, since about 1981. **Fenarimol** was specially developed for this purpose (Huggenberger, 1985). Both fenarimol and nuarimol act against a number of Ascomycetes and Basidiomycetes, as well as some Deuteromycetes; in particular, both are very effective against powdery mildews such as *Podosphaera leucotricha* and against scab caused by *Venturia inequaelis*. Both are locally systemic when applied to leaves, moving within the plant in the apoplast and possibly acting partly in the vapour phase (Buchenauer and Röhner, 1982). Nuarimol appears to be taken up by plant roots more readily than is fenarimol. When the incidence of disease is high, a co-formulation of fenarimol (or of nuarimol) with a non-systemic antiscab protectant fungicide such as captan often gives

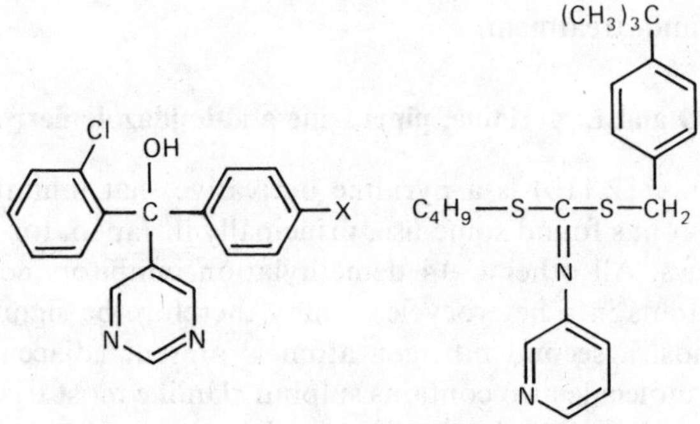

(a) Pyrimidines
X = Cl fenarimol
X = F nuarimol

(b) Pyridines
e.g. buthiobate

Figure 12.11 Some C-14 demethylation inhibitors containing pyrimidine or pyridine

more consistent control than does the use of a pyrimidine by itself (Huggenberger *et al.*, 1986).

The morphological effects of fungitoxic doses of nuarimol are very similar to those of the triazoles. Electron micrographs obtained by Hippe and Grossmann (1982) show that the cell walls of *Ustilago avenae* thicken and the plasmalemma invaginates on treatment with nuarimol. In addition, the septa are often perforated and extracytoplasmic material appears between the plasmalemma and the cell wall.

The mode of action of these pyrimidines is the same as that of the triazoles (figure 12.9). Fenarimol was one of the substances chosen by Henry and Sisler (1984) to investigate in more detail the way in which sterol C-14 demethylation inhibitors interact with fungal cytochrome P_{450}. They did this by studying several types of P_{450}-mediated reactions, including the demethylation of *p*-chloromethylaniline, the hydroxylation of steroids and steroid demethylation. It was found that *N*-demethylation of chloromethylaniline and 11α hydroxylation of progesterone were little affected by conventionally used levels of the fungicide, but that 14α hydroxylation of progesterone was more sensitive. The most sensitive system was the 14α demethylation of steroids. In the case of the 14α sterol hydroxylation, occurring in cells of *Curvularia lunata*, it was shown that the reaction was inhibited by carbon monoxide, an observation that strongly suggests that fenarimol (and similar inhibitors) are likely to act directly on the site of attachment of sterols to cytochrome P_{450} and not upon a linked non-haem system such as a sterol carrier protein.

As in the case of azoles, evidence is emerging that pyrimidines may have secondary fungitoxic effects. Cooke *et al.* (1989) have pointed out that plant lipoprotein membranes alter in composition in the presence of various fungicides, including nuarimol. Perhaps for this reason, these workers discovered that the activity of an Mg^{2+}-dependent, K^+-stimulated, ATPase located in the plasma membrane of winter cereal was increased about 40 per cent after nuarimol treatment.

(c) Groups C, D and E: pyridine, piperazine and imidazole derivatives

Buthiobate (figure 12.11b) is a pyridine derivative that inhibits sterol C-14 demethylation; it has found some use, principally in Japan, for the control of powdery mildews. All other C-14 demethylation inhibitors contain at least two nitrogen atoms in a heterocycle; it may therefore be significant that, in these compounds, a second nitrogen atom is present adjacent to the ring. Unusually, the molecule also contains sulphur. Unlike most triazoles, pyrimidines and piperazines (but in common with some imidazoles) its systemic properties are rather limited, movement after leaf application being mostly translaminar (Ohkawa *et al.*, 1976). Another difference from most sterol C-14 demethylation inhibitors is that it does not control rusts and smuts.

Triforine (figure 12.12a) is the only important fungicide of the piperazine group. It is also unusual among C-14 demethylation inhibitors in that it contains a completely saturated heterocyclic ring and the carbamic aldehyde moiety is also worthy of note. Triforine controls powdery mildews, rusts and a few other fungi such as *Colletotrichum* spp. It is of interest that, like some non-systemic fungicides that are effective against powdery mildews, it has acaricidal properties and gives partial control of red spider mites. It has been used on a range of fruit, vegetables and trees, but has proved to be phytotoxic to some varieties of lettuce.

Triforine is fully systemic following entry into roots (although not all of an applied dose may reach roots owing to absorption onto soil organic matter). After entering roots triforine rapidly moves above ground and accumulates in leaves. There is evidence that, when applied to leaves, there is a limited movement down to the roots. In this respect it differs from many systemic fungicides, including some pyrimidines, imidazoles and benzimidazoles, the movement of which is little more than translaminar when applied to leaves. Triforine therefore moves up the plant in the apoplast (section 13.4) but can also move down the plant in the phloem with food materials that are being stored; symplastic downward movement is therefore dependent on the physiological status of the plant and requires that photosynthesis should be actively occurring.

Some of the metabolic conversions undergone by triforine in different organisms have been summarised by Aizawa (1982). Non-enzymic hydrolysis slowly hydrolyses one trichloromethyl group to carboxyl. This can react with the adjacent carbamic aldehyde group with elimination of both from the molecule, leaving $=$N—H in position 1 (figure 12.12). This same product is also formed in barley and in rats.

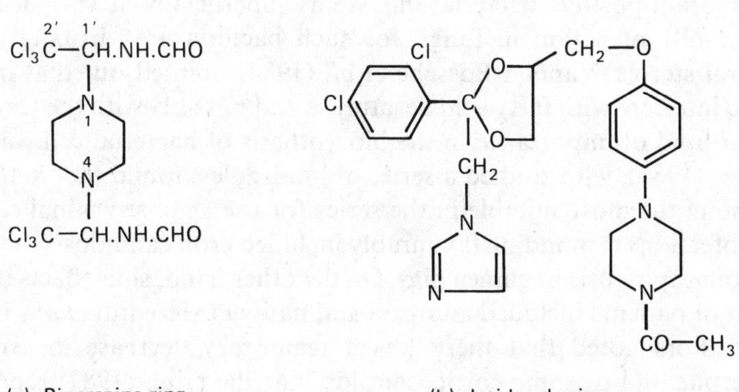

$$Cl_3C-CH.NH.CHO$$

(a) Piperazine ring
e.g. triforine

(b) Imidazole ring
e.g. ketoconazole

Figure 12.12 Examples of sterol C-14 demethylation inhibitors of the piperazine and imidazole groups

Imazalil and **prochloraz** (section 11.7) are two imidazole derivatives that have proved to be very useful in crop protection. Their mode of action is identical to that of the other compounds considered in this section, for they inhibit sterol C-14 demethylation. However, their systemic action in plants is so marginal that they have been more appropriately considered in the previous chapter. Briefly, however, they are used to control such important cereal diseases as rusts and smuts, as well as eyespot disease caused by strains of *Pseudocercosporella herpotrichoides* that are benzimidazole-resistant. They also control diseases caused by *Septoria* and by *Rhynchosporium*. The ability of prochloraz to induce the formation of cytochrome P_{450} in animal liver is worthy of especial attention (it has, in fact, been used as a means of inducing cytochrome P_{450} isoenzymes). A related phenomenon, the enlargement of livers of quails by propiconazole and some other C-14 demethylation inhibitors, was mentioned earlier (see propiconazole).

The agricultural imidazoles above are closely related to others that offer the prospect of major advances in human and veterinary medicine (Vanden Bossche *et al.*, 1984). These will be briefly mentioned, not only because work on them may give guidance as to possible side-effects of imidazoles used for crop protection but because some are systemic in animals and so justify the appearance of imidazoles in the systemic sections of some texts. Two important examples are ketoconazole and miconazole. **Ketoconazole** (figure 12.12b) is used against superficial fungal infections in animals but, since it can be orally administered, it is also used to control deep-seated fungi (Heeres, 1984). Unlike miconazole, it retains its antifungal activity when given by mouth and it is finding increasing clinical use for this reason. Sheets and Mason (1984) have referred to its possible use in the treatment of prostatic cancer (a use that might possibly be based on some effect on sex steroid biosynthesis). **Miconazole** and some other imidazoles have been shown to inhibit the growth of various Gram-positive bacteria; this seems superficially at variance with the known mode of action in fungi, for such bacteria are virtually devoid of structural sterols. Vanden Bossche *et al.* (1984) pointed out that imidazoles can also interfere with fatty acid desaturase and possibly with the formation of a carrier lipid of importance in the biosynthesis of bacterial cell walls.

Heeres (1984), who studied a series of imidazoles, found that ketoconazole was among the most suitable in the series for use against vaginal candidosis. Other infections responding favourably included crop candidosis in the turkey and dermatophytosis in guinea pigs. On the other hand, side-effects in up to 20 per cent of patients included anorexia and nausea (Meredith *et al.*, 1985). The same authors noted that there was a temporary decrease in synthesis of testosterone and of some corticosteroids. Latrille *et al.* (1987) reported that ketoconazole when fed to rats reduced the activities of three ovarian microsomal enzymes that are involved in the conversion of progesterone to oestrogen and that the same fungicide lowers the level of circulating oestradiol in humans.

(d) Development of resistance to C-14 demethylation inhibitors

Some members of this group of systemic fungicides have now been on the market for nearly 20 years and the dramatic development of resistance characteristic of earlier fungicides that attacked specific sites has not so far occurred. One possible reason for this is that, although demethylation inhibitors attack a very specific process, more than one gene often appears to be implicated in the mechanism of resistance (van Tuyl, 1977). Another reason why resistance has not so far been a major problem could be because, when these fungicides are not present in the environment, resistant strains may lack fitness or competitive vigour compared with non-resistant strains.

The qualification 'so far' was included above because it is quite easy, in the laboratory, to select for resistance to these fungicides; moreover, fairly recently, reports have appeared which suggest that powdery mildews may be developing moderate resistance in the field. Schepers (1985), for example, observed a correlation between the frequency of application of triforine, *inter alia*, in commercial greenhouses and the ease with which the cucumber powdery mildew, *Sphaerotheca fulginea*, responded to treatment. Other examples have been collated by Hippe and Köller (1986) and by Scheinpflug and Kuck (1987). The latter authors contrasted the slow stepwise development of resistance to C-14 demethylation inhibitors with the dramatic development of resistance that occurred after the introduction of benzimidazoles, hydroxy-aminopyrimidines (see below) and the phenylamides (section 12.8). Caution should however be exercised; should resistance develop, cross-resistance to all members of this group might be expected to occur.

12.6 HYDROXYAMINOPYRIMIDINE DERIVATIVES

These compounds were introduced specifically to control powdery mildews and they are of little use against other fungi. Dimethirimol was introduced in 1968 to control the cucumber powdery mildew, *Sphaerotheca fulginea*. Ethirimol is used almost exclusively against *Erysiphe graminis*, the powdery mildew of cereals, and bupirimate is used against another powdery mildew, *Podosphaera leucotricha*, on fruit trees. Their use has greatly diminished, at least temporarily, because of the high levels of resistance that rapidly developed to them. This section will therefore be mainly concerned with ethirimol (figure 12.13a). Dimethirimol is an isomer of ethirimol, with two methyl groups on the nitrogen atom attached to position 2 of the pyrimidine ring; bupirimate is a dimethylsulphamoyl ($(CH_3)_2N.SO_2.O-$) ester of ethirimol, the group being attached to C-4 of the pyrimidine ring instead of the hydroxyl group.

Ethirimol controls *Erysiphe graminis* on several cereals, but in practice it is largely used against powdery mildew on barley, where larger yields of grain are readily demonstrated, whereas on wheat the yield response is often less. In

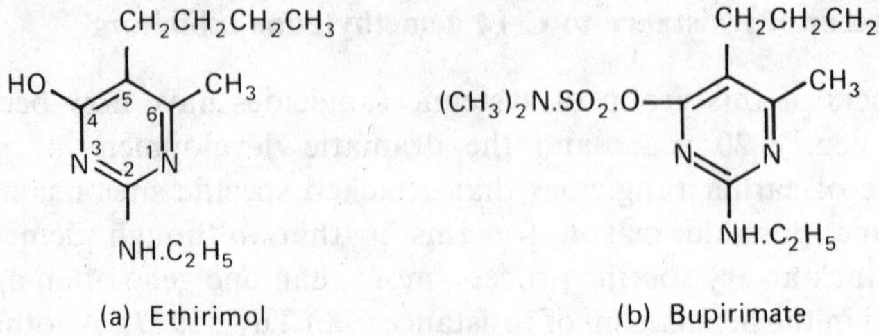

(a) Ethirimol   (b) Bupirimate

Figure 12.13 Structures of ethirimol and bupirimate. Ethirimol is 5-(n-butyl)-2-ethylamino-6-methylpyrimidin-4-ol

Britain it is often used for seed treatment, when the moisture content of the seed should not exceed 16 per cent; it should not be put on seed already treated with other fungicides (MAFF, 1985). It has also been formulated for application to foliage and as granules for application in the furrow at the time barley is drilled. Since relatively tolerant strains of the fungus are normally present in barley and are given a selective advantage when ethirimol is used, the incidence of tolerant strains can be reduced by restricting its use as a seed treatment to spring-sown barley (Shephard *et al.*, 1975).

Ethirimol is readily absorbed by roots of plants and moves upwards in the apoplastic system. No symplastic movement out of sprayed leaves usually occurs, so neither leaves formed after spraying nor lower parts of the plant are protected (i.e. it is not systemic when applied to foliage). Movement in leaves is towards their margins.

The primary metabolism of ethirimol is similar in plants and animals and takes routes that can be anticipated from the general reactions described in chapter 3. It can be *N*-de-ethylated to a primary amine of low but measurable biological activity. Alternatively, the butyl group can be hydroxylated, although this route does not appear to be as important in plants as it is in animals. Conjugation (which for many groups of compounds is a secondary stage in metabolism) can occur on hydroxyl C-4 *without* any preliminary change. In plants, a glucoside is usually formed, whereas in animals glucuronic acid is attached to C-4. A consequence of these changes is that ethirimol has a half-life of less than a week in barley plants when uptake is through the roots.

When ethirimol is absorbed through plant roots it inhibits the development of mildew spores prior to their penetration of the leaf and causes the vegetative hyphae to grow away from the leaf instead of being adpressed to it. Excellent electron micrographs that illustrate these morphological features have been published by Bent (1978). The mycological structure concerned is termed an appressorium; ethirimol prevents the formation of appressoria so long as the fungicide is applied within 8 h of the time the plant is infected. This suggests that, whatever its action, ethirimol must act upon existing machinery rather than have a long-term blocking effect. This is stressed because many explanations have been proposed for its action, including purine synthesis, mononucleotide synthesis and polynucleotide function. It is relevant to point out that powdery mildews probably do not need to synthesise purines in the early stages of their growth, since they get them from their host.

Currently, the most favoured theory is that ethirimol interferes with the action of the enzyme, adenosine deaminase, which normally catalyses the conversion of the amino group of adenine (in the form of adenosine) to the amino group of hypoxanthine (in the form of inosine). This enzyme, which also deaminates deoxyadenosine, appears, in powdery mildews, to differ from its counterpart in other organisms and is important during the early stages of infection by *E. graminis* (Hollomon and Chamberlain, 1981). Nevertheless, no quantitative or qualitative differences have yet been detected between adenosine deaminase in ethirimol-sensitive and ethirimol-resistant strains of the fungus.

Resistance management techniques were rapidly developed and, in the UK, little overall change in sensitivity of powdery mildew on barley appears to have occurred during the period 1973–77 (Dekker, 1985) although the situation must clearly be watched with great care (much of the early poor reputation of the hydroxyaminopyrimidines originated after glasshouse studies, which seem in retrospect to have exacerbated the resistance problem). Ethirimol is available on the British market for seed treatment and also for spraying spring-sown barley. It is usually co-formulated with other fungicides (e.g. with captafol, thiabendazole or flutriafol). It is of interest that triazole-resistant strains of powdery mildews were found by Butters *et al.* (1984) to be sensitive to ethirimol and, in the case of triadimenol, a **negative cross-resistance** appeared to exist.

12.7 ANTIBIOTICS

The medically important **streptomycin** has been used in crop protection as a bacteriostatic and antifungal agent. Its principal use is to control bacterial diseases of stone and pome fruits, but it has also been used for early spraying of downy mildew on hops. It is soluble in water and is readily taken up by the roots of plants. Streptomycin is somewhat phytotoxic, causing chlorosis by interfering with the synthesis of chlorophyll. It probably attacks prokaryotes by attaching itself to ribosomes, one molecule of streptomycin uniting with one 30-S ribosomal subunit. Streptomycin has a much lower affinity for non-bacterial ribosomes than it has for those in prokaryotes, and it does not affect protein synthesis in eukaryotic cytoplasm. Some yeasts and Oomycetes are sensitive to it and it probably affects *mitochondrial* protein synthesis in such organisms.

Blasticidin S, a complex pyrimidine derivative isolated from *Streptomyces griseochromogenes*, is effective against a range of bacteria. It is much less toxic to most fungi, an important exception being *Pyricularia oryzae*, the organism responsible for paddy blast of rice. It has been marketed to control this disease, but it damages rice at concentrations not greatly above those needed to control rice blast disease. At 5 ppm, blasticidin S inhibits the incorporation of glutamic acid into the protein of the rice blast fungus. This probably happens as a result of it attaching itself to the A site receptor of the 60-S subunit of the ribosome, which aminoacyl tRNA should occupy. This effectively blocks the peptidyltransferase reaction and in consequence prevents peptide chain elongation.

Kasugamycin is another antibiotic used against the rice blast fungus. It is an aminoglycoside and was isolated from *Streptomyces kasugaensis*. It is now used more widely in Japan than is blasticidin S, principally because the phytotoxicity is much lower. In addition, it is degraded in plants much less rapidly than is blasticidin S. Although it can enter rice plant roots, it is used as a foliar spray since it is not economic to add it in large quantities to paddy water. It is of interest that it is eradicant but not protective in action. The reason is that it has little effect on *Pyricularia oryzae* before the fungus penetrates the host plant. On the other hand, it prevents the spread of the organism within the plant and it inhibits sporulation. The mode of action of kasugamycin appears to be similar to that of blasticidin S, for it selectively inhibits the initiation of bacterial protein synthesis. It has no effect on nucleic acid metabolism.

12.8 PHENYLAMIDES USED AGAINST OOMYCETES

There are three main subgroups of substances in this group: (1) acylalanines, e.g. metalaxyl, furalaxyl; (2) butyrolactones, e.g. ofurace, cyprofuram; (3) oxazole ketones, e.g. oxadixyl. This account will be mainly confined to a consideration of metalaxyl. The Oomycetes are in important ways different from other fungi. In particular, the mycelium is aseptate, the cell walls contain cellulose, not chitin, and infection usually involves motile zoospores. They are, in consequence, regarded as being distinct from other fungi. Perhaps because of these differences, the Oomycetes have until recent times not been adequately controlled by systemic fungicides. This limitation was a serious problem, for the organisms concerned are the cause of numerous important diseases, among them being late potato blight and downy mildews of many crops. Some important genera of Oomycetes include *Phytophthora*, *Peronospora*, *Sclerospora*, *Pseudoperonospora* and *Plasmopara*. Initially, many of these organisms were controlled by copper fungicides. Later, these copper compounds were partly replaced by various dithiocarbamates, by phthalimides and by chlorothalonil (chapter 11). The phenylamides are of especial value in the control of diseases caused by those Oomycetes which live largely or entirely internal to the host plant.

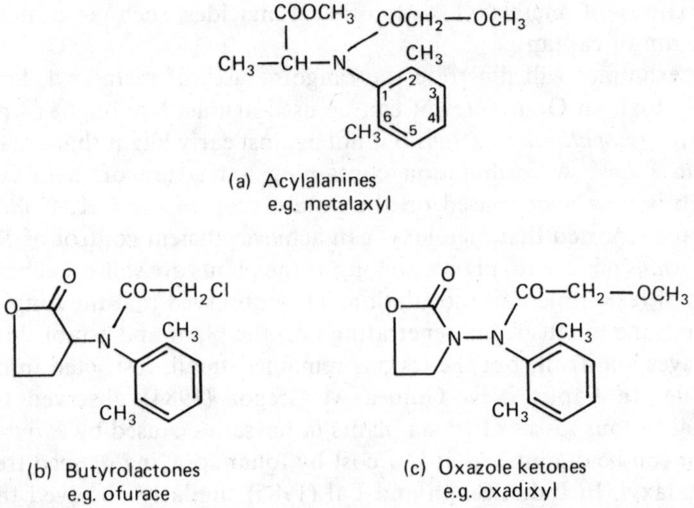

(a) Acylalanines
e.g. metalaxyl

(b) Butyrolactones
e.g. ofurace

(c) Oxazole ketones
e.g. oxadixyl

Figure 12.14 Three types of phenylamides that control many Oomycetes

The formula of metalaxyl is compared with structures of members of the butyrolactone and oxazole groups in figure 12.14. Furalaxyl and benalaxyl also contain the alanine ester ($-N-CH(CH_3)-COOCH_3$) moiety, which is the distinguishing feature of subgroup 1 above. Most members of all three groups also contain the xylyl (dimethylphenyl) group and all contain a substituted amide group ($=N-CO-$) attached to phenyl; it is this which gives the section its name.

Metalaxyl is predominantly active against Oomycetes belonging to the order Peronosporales, but, within this restriction, it is highly versatile, effectively controlling organisms that attack plants via the leaves, the lower stem or the roots. Many soilborne organisms belong to this order and have been difficult to control with conventional fungicides except when used as soil drenches; metalaxyl has therefore proved valuable in the prevention of crown and root rots that were hitherto not readily controlled. Moreover, following application as a seed treatment or as soil granules, apoplastic movement occurs, which can eliminate some diseases caused by Oomycetes that have gained access to the upper part of the plant (surface deposits are normally entirely protective in function). Common Oomycetes that live within plants include species of *Peronospora*, *Pseudoperonospora* and *Plasmopara*, while those that attack roots or stem include species of *Pythium* and *Phytophthora*. Metalaxyl has also been used as a root dip and a post-harvest dip for fruit. To achieve these different ends, metalaxyl has been formulated in several ways, including as a wettable powder (for spraying foliage), as granules for soil application, and in a form suitable for seed treatment. For the reason mentioned in section 12.1, most formulations of metalaxyl nowadays comprise mixtures of metalaxyl with other fungicides such as a mancozeb, carbendazim or captan.

A few examples will illustrate the range of uses of metalaxyl. Since it is selectively toxic to Oomycetes, it can be used against late blight of potatoes caused by *Phytophthora infestans* but not against early blight that is caused by *Alternaria solani*. A formulation containing a mixture of metalaxyl with mancozeb is now widely used on the potato crop in the UK. Cohen *et al.* (1979) have reported that metalaxyl can achieve efficient control of *Phytophthora infestans* on tomato plants, so long as the plants are soil-drenched within two days of (experimental) inoculation. They observed that the fungicide did not prevent the fungus from penetrating into the plant and establishing itself in the leaves and fruit, but the lesions remained small, restricted in number, and sterile. In Papua New Guinea McGregor (1984) observed that the occasional serious losses of cocoa plants in nurseries caused by *Phytophthora palmivora* can be diminished at low cost by foliar spraying or seed treatment with metalaxyl. In India, Singh and Lal (1985) similarly observed that seed treatment normally prevented serious damage to sugar cane by the downy mildew, *Peronosclerospora sacchari*, and that, if a sudden outbreak occurred in a standing crop, a foliar spray reduced the level of infection to one-third and increased the yield. The use of mixtures of metalaxyl with mancozeb as a foliar spray to control *Bremia lactucae* on lettuce in the UK has been discussed by Crute *et al.* (1987). The persistence of metalaxyl on foliage after exposure to artificial rain at various times after application has been studied by van Bruggen *et al.* (1987).

Utkhede (1987) has described a combined soil drench and trunk treatment technique for the control of crown rot in naturally infected apple trees. The symptoms of the rot, which is caused by *Phytophthora cactorum*, are arrested on lightly infected trees treated at 1 g per tree with metalaxyl; more importantly, healthy trees remained free from infection if two applications were made per year. Working in Italy, Marucchini *et al.* (1983) showed that metalaxyl was rapidly translocated in sunflower plants when either applied to the soil or used as a seed treatment. High concentrations were present in the leaves a few days after application, after which the concentration steadily declined (figure 12.15). Evidently, the maximal concentration in the shoot is achieved sooner when treatment is to the seed, but lasts longer when metalaxyl is applied to the soil.

Exconde and Molina (1978) evaluated the use of metalaxyl as a seed dressing for the Philippine maize downy mildew, *Sclerospora philippinensis*. Applying the fungicide at rates of from 2 g active ingredient per kilogram of seed it was found that all rates gave total protection from emergence to harvest, whereas untreated seed had 36–100 per cent incidence of infection. Any initial depressive effect on plant growth had disappeared by the end of the second week of growth. Similarly, Lal *et al.* (1979) reported that seed treatment of maize at 4 g/kg of seed adequately controlled *Peronosclerospora*

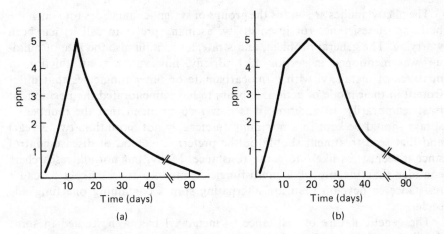

Figure 12.15   Rate of accumulation and decay of metalaxyl in sunflower plants after (a) seed treatment and (b) soil treatment (after Marucchini *et al.*, 1983)

sacchari on maize without affecting either seed germination or plant vigour. Finally, attempts were made by Edney and Chambers (1981) to control rot of apple fruits caused by *Phytophthora syringae* by dipping zoospore-inoculated fruit into a 0.03 per cent solution of metalaxyl. Control was only achieved if no more than five days had elapsed after inoculation, and it was concluded that in field conditions total eradication was not to be expected by post-harvest dipping.

At the physiological level it is clear that metalaxyl affects mycelial growth and subsequent sporulation rather than motile zoospore penetration into the host plant (see, for example, Fisher and Hayes, 1982). This contrasts with the action of dithiocarbamates, which, by protective action, prevent zoospores from entering cells of leaves. This complementary action, which has been excellently portrayed by Schwinn and Staub (1987), is a reason (other than that relating to resistance) why combined sprays of metalaxyl and maneb have proved efficacious. At the biochemical level, the mode of action is less certain. Early work demonstrated that metalaxyl inhibits the incorporation of uridine into RNA, although the inhibition remains incomplete at realistic concentrations of the fungicide (more precisely, **fungistat**, for it prevents growth rather than kills, at least initially). A likely explanation is that metalaxyl inhibits one form of RNA polymerase much more than others, for different polymerases are responsible for incorporating uridine into the three main forms of RNA (ribosomal, messenger and transfer RNA). Much of this work was pioneered by Davidse and his colleagues and has been reviewed by Davidse (1984). The most likely candidate appears to be the polymerase involved in the synthesis of ribosomal RNA, although whether the *specific* effect of metalaxyl on Oomycetes implies that the polymerase system in Oomycetes is different from similar systems in other fungi remains unresolved.

The phenylamides are one of the groups of systemic fungicides for which the build-up of resistance (or insensitivity, as many prefer to call it) has been worrying. The general problem, and strategies to minimise the rate of build-up, was mentioned in section 12.1. Briefly, however, the introduction of mixtures of metalaxyl with dithiocarbamate or other fungicides that differ from it in their mode of action, appears to have ameliorated the position, at least temporarily. In addition, it is now recommended that the number of sprays should be kept to a minimum (preferably not more than two a year) and that seed treatment should be the preferred method of disease control since it seems less likely to cause resistance. Many, but not all, researchers consider that the use of a multi-fungicide mixture is less likely to cause resistance to develop than are alternating sprays containing one fungicide each.

The genetic nature of resistance to metalaxyl has been studied in some detail. Using *Phytophthora infestans*, a series of experiments by Shattock (1986) led to the conclusion that resistance to metalaxyl is controlled by a single nuclear locus exhibiting incomplete dominance. In this work it was shown that the F_1 progeny of crosses between metalaxyl-resistant and metalaxyl-sensitive strains were of intermediate sensitivity; the F_2 progeny of F_1 sibling mating, on the other hand, segregated in a ratio close to 1:2:1 for sensitive, intermediate and resistant individuals. Different fungi appear, however, to give somewhat different results. Crute *et al.* (1987), working with *Bremia lactucae*, observed only two phenotypic responses in field isolates; they were either sensitive or they were highly resistant.

It is highly probable that the mode of action of metalaxyl and other phenylamides is similar. It is therefore no surprise to find that most work indicates that a considerable degree of cross-resistance exists within the group. Several studies are listed by Schwinn and Staub (1987). Another example is provided by the work of Diriwächter *et al.* (1987), who obtained nine isolates of *Phytophthora infestans* and eight of *Plasmopara viticola* of varying sensitivity to metalaxyl and tested them for their cross-sensitivity to various other fungicides active against Oomycetes. For both fungi, a marked cross-resistance to four phenylamides (cyprofuram, oxadixyl, ofurace and metalaxyl) was evident but no cross-resistance was noted between metalaxyl and fosetyl, prothiocarb or maneb. Moreover, a quantal effect appeared to exist; isolates were either sensitive or very resistant to ofurace and oxadixyl, but were never of intermediate resistance.

12.9 MISCELLANEOUS ANTIFUNGAL COMPOUNDS

(a) Fosetyl-aluminium

Work on phosphites that began in France in 1971 led to field trials which showed that a substance, now known as fosetyl (fosetyl-aluminium; phosetyl-aluminium), very effectively controlled *Plasmopara viticola*. This organism is the cause of downy mildew of vines and, according to Schwinn and Staub (1987, figure 17.1) it is the Oomycete disease upon the control of which most money was expended in 1983 (potato blight being the second). Nowadays, fosetyl is usually formulated as a mixture, often with folpet (section 11.4). In recent years fosetyl has been shown to control a moderately wide range of Oomycetes, including several species of *Phytophthora*. For example, it has been used against *Phytophthora parasitica*, the cause of heart rot of pineapples and of gummosis of citrus, and against *Phytophthora cinnamoni*, the cause of root rot of avocadoes (Beach, 1979). It is also marketed for the control of wilt and die-back in such hardy nursery stock as conifers, *Ericas* and rhododendrons, and for the control of strawberry red core, which is caused by *Phytophthora fragariae*. Utkhede (1987) found that, at 8 g active ingredient per tree, it arrested symptoms of crown rot of apples on trees lightly infested with *Phytophthora cactorum* and prevented the appearance of symptoms on healthy trees.

Fosetyl (figure 12.16a) is a water-soluble solid with a low vapour pressure. It enters plants rapidly, where it persists for a time of between four weeks and four months. Apart from being unusual in regard to its specific action against Oomycetes, it differs from most systemic fungicides in that it is able to move down the plant in the phloem as well as upwards in the xylem. It can therefore give protection to new tissue not formed at the time of foliar application, and such applications can protect root systems if the physiological state of the host plant allows basipetal (downward) movement.

The mode of action of fosetyl is disputed. One school of thought considers that the substance is not so much fungicidal as capable of stimulating the plant's defence system. If this were indeed the case, it would have exciting

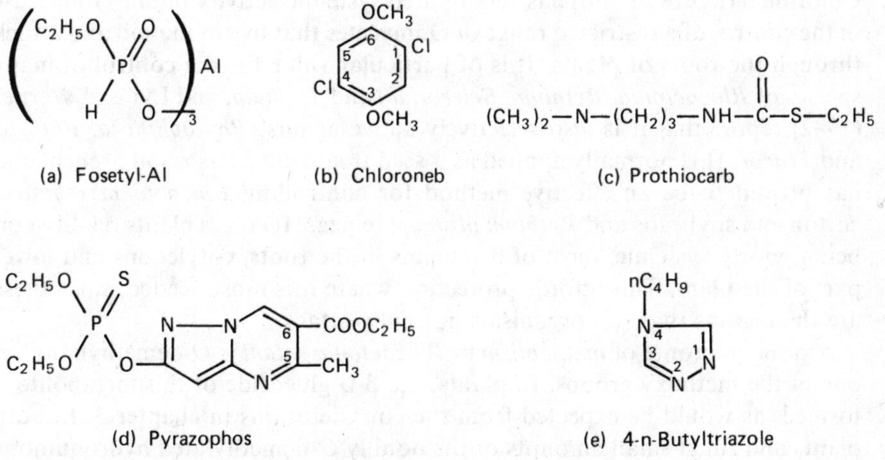

(a) Fosetyl-Al   (b) Chloroneb   (c) Prothiocarb

(d) Pyrazophos   (e) 4-n-Butyltriazole

Figure 12.16   Miscellaneous antifungal compounds

implications; unfortunately, the evidence that the *primary* effect is one of triggering the plant's defence system remains rather tenuous. It should however be recalled that fungicides evoke physiological changes on the part of the host plant (e.g. more vigorous growth; production of encapsulating secretions) which indirectly affect fungal access; no doubt fosetyl can have these types of effects as well, especially since phosphate is one of its decomposition products.

Fenn and Coffey (1984) found that fosetyl (and, indeed, even phosphorous acid) is very fungitoxic *in vitro* if tested in a growth medium low in phosphate, but that the fungitoxicity is reversed by higher phosphate. Such work would seem to exclude the obligatory involvement of the host in the antifungal effect. This possibility is strengthened by the observation that mutants tolerant of phosphorous acid are also resistant to fosetyl (Fenn and Coffey, 1985). Derks and Buchenauer (1987) found that, at the (high) concentration of 750 ppm, fosetyl caused morphological changes in three species of *Phytophthora* but not in *P. infestans*. In sensitive species, there was thickening of the mycelial tip and swelling occurred along the hyphae. Somewhat similar swellings had been noted earlier by Abu-Jawdah (1983) when fosetyl acted on *Colletotrichum lindemethianum*. Derks and Buchenauer also observed that fosetyl treatment decreased membrane permeability in the three sensitive species of *Phytophthora* but not in the more tolerant *P. infestans*. In the two most sensitive species (*P. cactorum* and *P. capsici*) a marked difference was observed in the phospholipid composition of the cell membranes. From these results it was concluded that the primary effect of fosetyl was probably on the fungus and somehow involved interference with membrane structure and function.

(b) Chloroneb

Chloroneb (figure 12.16b) has very limited systemic activity but has found use in the control of a restricted range of Oomycetes that live in the soil and attack through the roots of plants. It is of particular value for the control of many species of *Rhizoctonia*, *Pythium*, *Sclerotium* and *Typhula*, and Lyr and Werner (1982) report that it is also selectively active against *Phytophthora*, *Botrytis* and *Mucor*. It is normally applied as a seed treatment or as a soil drench, and has proved to be an effective method for controlling *Rhizoctonia solani* in cotton and soybeans and *Pythium ultimum* in peas. It enters plants readily but, being poorly systemic, most of it remains in the roots, cotyledons and lower part of the plant. This affords protection where it is most needed, since these are the regions that soil organisms normally attack.

A principal route of *metabolism* in *Rhizoctonia solani* is *O*-demethylation of one of the methoxy groups. In plants, the β-D-glucoside of this metabolite is formed, as would be expected from the considerations in chapter 3. In both plants and fungi small amounts of the doubly *O*-demethylated hydroquinone and of its quinone oxidation product are also produced.

The mode of action of chloroneb appears to be primarily on mitochondrial membranes, although the cell walls of sensitive species tend to be abnormally thick and, at high dosage, nuclear membranes are also affected. Lyr and Werner (1982) reported that it causes lysis of the inner membrane of mitochondria in sensitive strains of fungi such as *Mucor*, an observation that is supported by the electron micrographs that accompanied their publication. No uncoupling of oxidation from phosphorylation was detected but the binding capacity of the inner mitochondrial membrane for chloroneb appeared to be greater in sensitive strains of *Mucor* than in tolerant strains. This was attributed to the presence of higher levels of tyrosine in membrane lipoprotein of the more sensitive strains. For several species considered, there is also some evidence that a correlation exists between tyrosine levels in mitochondrial membranes and species sensitivity. The work of Lyr and colleagues supports the hypothesis that chloroneb induces lipid peroxidation in mitochondrial membranes (Lyr, 1987).

(c) Prothiocarb

Prothiocarb (figure 12.16c) is used as a soil drench or as an in-furrow spray near the roots of crops against species of *Pythium*, *Phytophthora*, *Pseudoperonospora* and some other Oomycetes. It enters plants readily and is in part translocated. In sandy soil it has a half-life of about 60 days and it persists longer in loams. Aqueous solutions give protection to cucumbers against the downy mildew, *Pseudoperonospora cubensis* (Cohen, 1979). It is toxic to sporangia and inhibits sporulation. In tomato plants it hydrolyses at the NH–CO linkage to give dimethylpropane-1,3-diamine as the major metabolic product. This has also been identified as a major metabolite in soil.

(d) Pyrazophos

This substance (figure 12.16d) is an organophosphorus compound used in Britain mainly to control powdery mildew on hops (*Spaerotheca humuli*). Mixed with binapacryl, it was used to improve the control of powdery mildew on apple trees (MAFF, 1985). Its uptake by roots or from a seed dressing is insufficient for adequate systemic control. It is oxidised to the fungitoxic oxon analogue by *Pyricularia oryzae*, a reaction that is reminiscent of the oxidative metabolism of insecticidal thionphosphates (section 4.8).

(e) 4-n-Butyltriazole

This substance (figure 12.16e) is of interest in that it is effective against the brown rust of wheat, *Puccinia recondita*, but not against other species of *Puccinia* or *Uromyces* causing rust disease (Erwin, 1973). It has proved better for this purpose in the field than oxycarboxin, giving total control under bad epidemic conditions when used at a rate of 0.56 kg/ha.

(f) Phenyl pyrrole derivative

A new fungicide based on phenyl pyrrole has been reported by Neville *et al.* (1988) to be an excellent seed treatment for the control of *Fusarium nivale*, *Tilletia caries* and *Septoria nodorum* when applied at about 20 g per 100 kg of seed. Admixed with imazalil (section 11.7) it has also proved useful against seedborne *Pyrenophora* spp. The molecule comprises a dichlorinated phenyl ring joined to pyrrole ring carrying a nitrile group.

(g) Dimethomorph

Dimethomorph is another new fungicide reported at the British Crop Protection Conference in 1988. It is a complex cinnamic acid derivative. It is systemic to certain Oomycetes by root application and is also loco-systemic when applied to foliage. It is very highly effective against fungi of the family *Peronosporaceae* (Albert *et al.*, 1988).

REFERENCES

Abu-Jawdah, Y. (1983). *Parasitica*, **39**, 3
Aizawa, H. (1982). *Metabolic Maps of Pesticides*. Academic Press, New York
Albert, G., Curtze, J. and Drandarevski, Ch. A. (1988). *Proc. Br. Crop Prot. Conf., Pests and Diseases*, p. 17
Axness, M. E. and Fleeker, J. R. (1979). *Pestic. Biochem. Physiol.*, **11**, 1
Baldwin, B. C. and Wiggins, T. E. (1984). *Pestic. Sci.*, **15**, 156
Beach, B. G. W. (1979). *Proc. Br. Crop Prot. Conf., Pests and Diseases*, p. 319
Bent, K. J. (1978). In *The Powdery Mildews*, ed. D. M. Spencer, chap. 10. Academic Press, London
Borisy, G. G., Cleveland, D. W. and Murphy, D. G. (1984). *Molecular Biology of the Cytoskeleton*. Cold Spring Harbor Press, New York
Bourgois, J.-J., Bronchart, R., Deltour, R. and de Barsy, Th. (1977). *Pestic. Biochem. Physiol.*, **7**, 97
Brown, M. C., Shephard, M. C. and Frank, J. A. (1988). *Proc. Br. Crop Prot. Conf., Pests and Diseases*, p. 229
Buchenauer, H. and Grossman, F. (1982). *Z. Pflanzenkr. Pflanzenschutz*, **89**, 309
Buchenauer, H., Kohts, T. and Roos, H. (1981). *Mitt. Biol. Bundesanst. Land- Forstw. Berlin-Dahlem*, **203**, 310
Buchenauer, H. and Röhner, E. (1982). *Z. Pflanzenkr. Pflanzenschutz*, **89**, 385
Burland, I. G. and Gull, K. (1984). In *Mode of Action of Antifungal Agents*, eds A. P. J. Trinci and J. F. Ryley, p. 299. Cambridge Univ. Press, Cambridge
Butters, J. A., Clark, J. and Hollomon, D. W. (1984). *Meded. Fac. Landbouww. Rijksuniv. Gent*, **49/2a**, 143
Chandler, W. A., Daniell, J. W. and Littrell, R. H. (1978). *Plant Dis. Reptr.*, **62**, 7c3
Cohen, Y. (1979). *Phytopathology*, **69**, 433

Cohen, Y., Reuveni, M. and Eyal, H. (1979). *Phytopathology*, **69**, 645

Coles, C. J., Singer, T. P., White, G. A. and Thorn, G. D. (1978). *J. Biol. Chem.*, **253**, 5573

Cooke, D. T., Burden, R. S., Clarkson, D. T. and James, C. S. (1989). *Pestic. Sci.*, **25**, 319

Cremlyn, R. J. (1978). *Pesticides: Preparation and Mode of Action*. Wiley, Chichester

Crute, I. R., Norwood, J. M. and Gordon, P. L. (1987). *Plant Pathol.*, **36**, 297

Davidse, L. C. (1975). In *Systemic Fungicides*, eds H. Lyr and C. Polter, p. 137. Akademie-Verlag, Berlin

Davidse, L. C. (1984). In *Mode of Action of Anti-fungal Agents*, eds A. P. J. Trinci and J. F. Ryley, p. 239. Cambridge Univ. Press, Cambridge

Davidse, L. C. (1987). In *Modern Selective Fungicides*, ed. H. Lyr, p. 245. Longmans, Harlow; Wiley, New York

Davidse, L. C. and Flach, W. (1977). *J. Cell. Biol.*, **72**, 174

Dekker, J. (1982). In *Fungicide Resistance in Crop Protection*, eds J. Dekker and S. G. Georgopoulos, p. 177. Pudoc, Wageningen

Dekker, J. (1985). In *Progress in Pesticide Biochemistry and Toxicology*, vol. 4, eds D. H. Hutson and T. R. Roberts, p. 165. Wiley, Chichester

Dekker, J. (1987). In *Modern Selective Fungicides*, ed. H. Lyr, p. 39. Longmans, Harlow; Wiley, New York

Derks, W. and Buchenauer, H. (1987). *Crop Prot.*, **6**, 82

De Waard, M. A. (1984). *Proc. Br. Crop Prot. Conf., Pests and Diseases*, p. 573

De Waard, M. A., Groeneweg, H. and van Nistelrooy, J. G. M. (1982). *Neth. Plant Pathol.*, **88**, 99

Diriwächter, G., Sozzi, D., Ney, C. and Staub, T. (1987). *Crop Prot.*, **6**, 250

Eckert, J. W. (1969). *Wld Rev. Pest Control*, **8**, 116

Edney, K. L. and Chambers, D. A. (1981). *Plant Pathol.*, **30**, 167

Erwin, D. C. (1973). *Annu. Rev. Phytopathol.*, **11**, 389

Exconde, O. R. and Molina, A. B., Jr (1978). *Philipp. J. Crop Sci.*, **3**, 60

Fenn, M. E. and Coffey, M. D. (1984). *Phytopathology*, **74**, 606

Fenn, M. E. and Coffey, M. D. (1985). *Phytopathology*, **75**, 1064

Ficsor, G., Bordes, S. and Stewart, S. J. (1978). *Mutation Res.*, **51**, 151

Fisher, D. J. and Hayes, A. L. (1982). *Pestic. Sci.*, **13**, 330

Fuchs, A. and de Vries, F. W. (1978). *Antonie van Leeuwenhoek J. Microb. Serol.*, **44**, 283, 293

Gadher, P., Mercer, E. I. Baldwin, B. C. and Wiggins, T. E. (1983). *Pestic. Biochem. Physiol.*, **19**, 1

Georgopoulos, S. G. (1977). In *Antifungal Compounds*, vol. 2, eds M. R. Siegel and H. D. Sisler, p. 409. Marcel Dekker, New York

Heeres, J. (1984). *Pestic. Sci.*, **15**, 268

Henry, M. J. and Sisler, H. D. (1984). *Pestic. Biochem. Physiol.*, **22**, 262

Hippe, S. (1984). *Pestic. Biochem. Physiol.*, **21**, 170

Hippe, S. and Grossmann, F. (1982). *Pestic. Sci.*, **13**, 447

Hippe, S. and Köller, W. (1986). *Pestic. Biochem. Physiol.*, **26**, 209

Hisada, Y., Takaki, H., Kawase, Y. and Ozaki, T. (1979). *Ann. Phytopathol. Soc. Jap.*, **45**, 283

Hollomon, D. W. and Chamberlain, K. (1981). *Pestic. Biochem. Physiol.*, **16**, 158

Huggenberger, F. (1985). *Technical Report*, Lilly Research Centre, Windlesham, Surrey, UK

Huggenberger, F., Farrant, D. M. and Bacci, L. (1986). *Proc. Br. Crop Prot. Conf., Pests and Diseases*, p. 299

Jumar, A. and Lehmann, H. (1982). *Proc. 5th Int. Congr. of Pesticide Chem.*, Kyoto, Japan

Kerkenaar, A. (1987). In *Modern Selective Fungicides*, ed. H. Lyr, p. 167. Longmans, Harlow; Wiley, New York

Köller, W. (1987). *Pestic. Sci.*, **18**, 129

Krämer, W., Büchel, K. H. and Draber, W. (1983). In *Pesticide Chemistry: Human Welfare and the Environment*, vol. 1, p. 223. Pergamon, Oxford

Kuhn, P. J. (1984). In *Mode of Action of Antifungal Agents*, eds A. P. J. Trinci and J. F. Ryley, p. 155. Cambridge Univ. Press, Cambridge

Kulka, M. and von Schmeling, B. (1987). In *Modern Selective Fungicides*, ed. H. Lyr, p. 119. Longmans, Harlow; Wiley, New York

Lal, S., Bhargava, S. K. and Upadhyay, R. N. (1979). *Plant Dis. Reptr.*, **63**, 986

Larson, J. D. and Lamoureux, G. L. (1984). *J. Agric. Fd Chem.*, **32**, 177

Latrille, F., Charuel, C., Monro, A. M., Stadler, J. and Sutter, B. Ch. J. (1987). *Biochem. Pharmacol.*, **36**, 1863

Lyr, H. (1987). In *Modern Selective Fungicides*, ed. H. Lyr, pp. 63 and 75. Longmans, Harlow; Wiley, New York

Lyr, H. (1988). *Pestic. Biochem. Physiol.*, **32**, 197

Lyr, H. and Werner, P. (1982). *Pestic. Biochem. Physiol.*, **18**, 69

McGregor, A. J. (1984). *Papua New Guinea J. Agric. Forestry, Fisheries*, **33**, 39

MAFF (1984). *Use of Fungicides and Insecticides on Cereals, 1984*. ADAS Booklet 2257 (84). HMSO, London

MAFF (1985). *Agricultural Chemicals Approved Scheme: Approved Products for Farmers and Growers*. UK Ministry of Agriculture, Fisheries and Food. HMSO, London

Marucchini, C., Patumi, M. and Zazzerini, A. (1983). *J. Agric. Fd Chem.*, **31**, 1123

Mason, D. T. and Dennis, C. (1978). *Hortic. Res.*, **18**, 41

Mathre, D. E. (1970). *Phytopathology*, **60**, 671

Menzie, C. M. (1978). *Metabolism of Pesticides, Update II*. US Dept Interior, Fish and Wildlife Service, Special Scientific Report, Wildlife no. 212, Washington, DC

Meredith, C. G., Maldonado, A. L. and Speeg, K. V., Jr (1985). *Drug Metab. Dispn.*, **13**, 156

Neville, D., Nyfeler, R. and Sozzi, D. (1988). *Proc. Br. Crop Prot. Conf., Pests and Diseases*, p. 17

Northwood, P. J., Paul, J. A., Gibbard, M. and Noon, R. A. (1984). *Proc. Br. Crop Prot. Conf., Pests and Diseases*, p. 47

Ogawa, J. M., Manji, B. T., Heaton, C. R., Petrie, J. and Sonoda, R. M. (1983). In *Pest Resistance to Pesticides*, eds G. P. Georghiou and T. Saito, p. 117. Plenum, New York

Ohkawa, H., Shibalke, R., Okihara, V., Moridawa, M. and Miyamoto, J. (1976). *Agric. Biol. Chem.*, **40**, 943 (abstract)

Oros, G. and Gasztonyi, M. (1986). *Rev. Plant Pathol.*, **66**, abstract no. 3215

Oyekan, P. O. (1979). *Plant Dis. Reptr.*, **63**, 574

Panwar, R., Singh, R. S. and Singh, U. S. (1987). *Pestic. Sci.*, **18**, 29

Paulson, G. D. (1977). *Antifungal Compounds*, vol. 2, eds M. R. Siegel and H. D. Sisler, chap. 4. Marcel Dekker, New York

Penrose, L. J., Davis, K. C. and Koffman, W. (1979). *Austr. J. Agric. Res.*, **30**, 307

Pommer, E.-H. (1984). *Pestic. Sci.*, **15**, 285

Pommer, E.-H. (1987). In *Modern Selective Fungicides*, ed. H. Lyr, p. 143. Longmans, Harlow; Wiley, New York

Pring, R. J. (1984). *Pestic. Biochem. Physiol.*, **21**, 127

Prior, C. (1987). *Plant Pathol.*, **36**, 355

Ricci, P., Coleno, A. and Fevre, F. (1979). *Ann. Phytopathol.*, **10**, 433

Richmond, D. V. (1984). *Pestic. Biochem. Physiol.*, **21**, 74

Richmond, D. V. and Phillips, A. (1975). *Pestic. Biochem. Physiol.*, **5**, 367

Rivière, J.-L., Leroux, P., Bach, J. and Gredt, M. (1984). *Pestic. Sci.*, **15**, 317

Rouchard, J., Moons, C. and Meyer, J. A. (1982). *Pestic. Sci.*, **13**, 169

Sancholle, M., Weete, J. D. and Montant, C. (1984). *Pestic. Biochem. Physiol.*, **21**, 31

Saur, R. and Löcher, F. (1984). *Mitt. Biol. Bundesanst. Land- Forstw. Berlin-Dahlem*, **223**, 224

Scheinpflug, H. and Kuck, K. H. (1987). In *Modern Selective Fungicides*, ed. H. Lyr, Longmans, Harlow; Wiley, New York

Schepers, H. T. A. M. (1985). *Doctoral Thesis*, Wageningen (abstract)

Schewe, T. and Lyr, H. (1987). In *Modern Selective Fungicides*, ed. H. Lyr, p. 133. Longmans, Harlow; Wiley, New York

Schwinn, F. J. (1983). *Pestic. Sci.*, **15**, 40

Schwinn, F. J. and Staub, T. (1987). In *Modern Selective Fungicides*, ed. H. Lyr, p. 259. Longmans, Harlow; Wiley, New York

Shabi, E. and Katan, T. (1979). *Phytopathology*, **69**, 267

Shattock, R. C. (1986). *Proc. Br. Crop Prot. Conf., Pests and Diseases*, p. 507

Sheets, J. J. and Mason, J. I. (1984). *Drug Metab. Dispn.*, **12**, 603

Sheir-Neiss, G., Lai, M. H. and Morris, N. R. (1978). *Cell*, **15**, 639

Shephard, M. C., Bent, K. J., Woolmer, M. and Cole, A. M. (1975). *Proc. 8th Br. Insectic. Fungic. Conf.*, vol. 1, p. 59.

Shephard, M. C., Noon, R. A., Worthington, P. A., McClellan, W. D. and Lever, B. G. (1986). *Proc. Br. Crop Prot. Conf., Pests and Diseases*, vol. 1, p. 19

Singh, I. P. and Lal, S. (1985). *Trop. Pest Managem.*, **31**, 327

Smolka, S. and Wolf, G. (1986). *Pestic. Sci.*, **17**, 249

Stennes, M. A. and French, D. W. (1987). *Phytopathology*, **77**, 707

Stiers, D. L., Fellman, J. K. and Le Tourneau, D. (1980). *Environ. Exp. Bot.*, **20**, 181

Sutton, J. C. and Roke, G. (1984). *Proc. Br. Crop Prot. Conf., Pests and Diseases*, vol. 1, p. 121

van Bruggen, A. H. C., Milgroom, M. G., Osmeloski, J. F., Fry, W. E. and Jacobson, J. S. (1987). *Phytopathology*, **77**, 401

Vanden Bossche, H. (1985). In *Current Topics in Medical Mycology*, ed. M. R. McGinnis, p. 313. Springer, New York

Vanden Bossche, H., Lauwers, W., Willemsens, G., Marichal, P., Cornelissen, F. and Cools, W. (1984). *Pestic. Sci.*, **15**, 188

Vanden Bossche, H., Marichal, P., Gorrens, J., Bellens, D., Verhoeven, H., Coene, M.-C., Lauwers, W. and Janssen, P. A. J. (1987). *Pestic. Sci.*, **21**, 289

Van Tuyl, J. M., Davidse, L. C. and Dekker, J. (1974). *Neth. J. Plant Pathol.*, **80**, 165

Van Tuyl, J. M. (1977). *Meded. Landbouwh. Wageningen*, **77-2**, 1

Utkhede, R. S. (1987). *Pestic. Sci.*, **19**, 289

Walmsley-Woodward, D., Laws, F. A. and Whittington, W. J. (1979). *Ann. Appl. Biol.*, **92**, 199

Weete, J. D. (1980). *Lipid Biochemistry of Fungi and Other Organisms*. Plenum, New York

White, G. A., Thorn, G. D. and Georgopoulos, S. G. (1978). *Pestic. Biochem. Physiol.*, **9**, 165

Zbozinek, J. V. (1984). *Res. Rev.*, **92**, 114

Zoran, M. J., Heppner, T. J. and Drewes, C. D. (1986). *Pestic. Sci.*, **17**, 641

13 Herbicides: general considerations

13.1 INTRODUCTION

The global weed control problem is somewhat different from that relating to the control of insects and pathogens. Weeds only seriously reduce yield or quality of produce when they compete with the crop for available moisture, nutrients and light, and when soil quality does not, in itself, limit food production. In some areas, soil or climate may be so inhospitable that weeds may fare little better than crop plants. Elsewhere, especially in areas of subsistence farming, the hands and hoes of the family unit may be sufficient to provide adequate weed control; pathogens and insects cannot be controlled so readily. When cash crops are grown in simpler agricultural systems, the area under cultivation may be small and labour cheap, making chemical weed-killers at best a luxury.

The turning point probably occurs when groups of neighbouring farmers cooperate to cultivate larger areas (e.g. ujamaa villages in Tanzania or farming cooperatives in Libya), especially when local labour is scarce or more profitably employed on other activities. Moreover, even in some developing countries, weedkillers are often necessities on tea, sugar or coffee plantations run by private, national or international organisations. In advanced farming communities, where densely packed crops are grown on good soil over vast areas, the financial loss caused by weeds can be enormous (Shaw, 1963). Moreover, when the area of monoculture is extensive, as in the wheat belt of the USA or some of the potato and sugar beet areas of Europe, the use of chemical weed control is usually imperative.

Crop rotation has been practised in many parts of the world for hundreds of years, e.g. the Norfolk four-course rotation (wheat, root crops, barley, seeds ley). Although originally introduced to protect soil fertility, rotation often also acted as a means of weed and pest control. However, modern agricultural methods tend to make farms more profitable when they are larger and more specialised, because specialisation reduces the number of types of costly equipment needed. A related requirement for profitable agriculture is that farms should be less labour-dependent. In consequence, rotation is less often practised nowadays and herbicides provide an alternative mechanism for weed control. Furthermore, chemicals have in some circumstances found use in minimal cultivation or 'ploughless' farming, where shallow cultivators or even direct drilling replace the energy-consuming and tedious use of the plough. This can be particularly useful in areas where ploughing leads to excessive water loss.

Herbicide manufacture is big business—more so than the manufacture of insecticides (figure 1.1). It has been estimated that some $18 000m are currently spent world-wide on toxic agricultural chemicals and, of this, probably some 40 per cent is spent on weedkillers. The most-used herbicides are members of the 2,4-D family, certain carbamates, triazines and also propachlor. From a farmer's point of view this huge expenditure is justifiable—often representing a four-fold return on outlay. This saving is explained by larger yields and higher-quality produce; it does not include the potential costs of labour that would have been needed to achieve the same ends, and 2,4-D alone is estimated to save hundreds of millions of man-hours of labour each year. This, in turn, can mean that if an appropriate political climate exists, excess produce can be exported to less fortunate parts of the world. Indeed, since the first edition of this book was written, disasters in East Africa and elsewhere have shocked the world; the obverse of the contribution of pesticides to the embarrassing mountains of grain in two continents is the fact that disasters in Africa and elsewhere would have been worse but for this readily available source of produce.

This chapter deals with some of the fundamentals of chemical weed control, including a partial classification of weedkillers according to the principal method of application and the structures of the herbicides concerned. The next three chapters consider respectively herbicides that are principally applied to foliage, those usually applied to soil just before or just after crop emergence and those that are applied to the soil at other times or have strong residual action. For updating purposes the Handbook of the Weed Science Society of America is recommended (the Journal, *Weed Science*, carries on the back cover of each publication the recommended names of the latest additions).

13.2 NON-SELECTIVE AND SELECTIVE HERBICIDES

Herbicides are used in agriculture to remove weeds that would otherwise compete with the crop. This can, however, be done in a number of ways, not all of which require the weedkiller to possess an intrinsic selectivity between weed species and crop plants. By 'intrinsic selectivity' it is meant that, if the chemical were to be applied to crop and weeds in such a way that equal amounts were uniformly deposited, the weed species would succumb but the crop would not. Some herbicides do indeed possess such selectivity. Many others are relatively non-selective, yet may nevertheless be used to control weeds by exploiting a variety of methods of application at various stages of crop development (section 13.6). Whether a herbicide is best described as selective or non-selective often depends on what happens when the substance is used at economic dosage. If the dosage of a selective compound is increased, the selectivity is eventually lost but reduction of the dosage of non-selective compounds does not necessarily make them act selectively.

Non-selective, total and long-term weed control is sometimes wanted in a domestic or industrial context—for example, to keep garden paths or railway lines free from weeds. In such cases the herbicide does not need to—and usually should not—differentiate between one type of plant and another. Weed control in these circumstances is usually straightforward, except when weeds are well established, deep-rooted, or near to a cropped area. Non-selective soil-acting herbicides can be chosen, and their dosage calculated so that the length of time that the substance remains in a particular type of soil can be predicted with reasonable precision (section 13.5). For example, of the compounds in figure 13.3, dichlobenil at about 60 g active ingredient per 100 m^2 of soil surface normally remains active for up to a year, while diuron and simazine (200 g/100 m^2) may well persist for several years. In addition, sodium chlorate (4000 g/100 m^2) can give effective weed control for up to a year.

Compounds applied to soil for non-selective weed control differ greatly in their structure, in their physical properties and in the way that they are applied. Highly insoluble substances (e.g. diuron, simazine) can have a long-term residual action and, if misused, may incapacitate land for up to a decade. Others such as trichloroacetic acid (TCA) and sodium chlorate are water-soluble and at appropriate concentrations are of relatively low persistence: these are capable of giving a 'short sharp shock' to weed-infested land. They are therefore used for certain land clearance programmes or for pre-planting treatments for certain crops. The same is true of some foliage-applied substances (e.g. paraquat) applied in a non-directed manner.

Selective weed control involves the destruction of weeds without simultaneous damage to the crop among which the weeds are growing; this is often (but not always) a requirement in an agricultural context. On some occasions the crop may comprise relatively large established plants, but on others it may consist of seeds or of seedlings that have not broken through the surface of the ground at the time that the spray is applied. In the former case there is a great biological similarity between the crop and the weeds growing among it and selective weed control may consequently be more difficult than, say, the control of insects living upon crops.

Biochemical differences can seldom be exploited to achieve selectivity because of the diversity of types of weeds usually found growing in one crop. In such cases the crop plant would need to possess a defence mechanism absent in most of the competing weed species. A few such cases are in fact known: for example, the absence of β-oxidase in some legumes enables them to withstand 2,4-DB (section 14.12), while a special defence system in maize protects the plants from the effects of atrazine (section 15.2). It is probable that, in the near future, cases of this kind will be multiplied by genetic engineering (see at the end of this section), but for the time being less subtle attributes than enzymic differences must usually be exploited to achieve selectivity. In practice, selective action often depends on the possibility of using differences in life style, plant morphology, etc., to ensure that the crop plant is exposed to a lower effective dose than the weeds receive. Some examples follow.

Morphological differences may enable selectivity to be shown by a substance which, in other circumstances, might be almost equally toxic to all plants. Thus dicotyledonous plants often have meristematic tissue vulnerably exposed to a foliage spray. This is particularly evident when the leaves spread out and direct the toxicant to the growing point situated at the centre of a rosette (figure 13.1a). In contrast, monocotyledonous plants often have upright leaves which retain little of the spray and form a protective sheath around the meristem. This, in part, explains the selectivity of herbicides based on phenoxyacetic acid (section 14.4). Since grasses provide the staple diet for most of mankind and for many farm animals, this form of selectivity, characteristic of several translocated post-emergence herbicides (section 13.4), is of great importance to the human race.

Chronological selectivity exploits the fact that in certain crops (e.g. sugar beet) weeds are shallower-rooted and grow more rapidly than the crop plants (figure 13.1b). In consequence, many of the potentially more competitive weeds emerge before the crop and can be sprayed by a foliage spray such as diquat or glyphosate (sections 14.1 and 14.2). For chronological selectivity to be successful, the timing of the application is all-important. If it is done too early, many of the germinating weed seedlings will escape for they will not have broken through the surface; if it is done too late, non-selective foliage sprays such as those mentioned above will damage the crop. A modification of the method is the 'stale seed-bed' technique, in which the ground is prepared for sowing but the seeds are not put in immediately. Instead, the weeds are allowed to germinate before the crop is sown. Eventually, sowing is done with minimal soil disturbance, after which spraying is carried out in the time interval before crop emergence. Soil disturbance by hoeing would, of course, enable another batch of weed seeds to germinate.

Positional selectivity can often be achieved when seeds (also tubers, etc.) of the crop are large compared with those of the weeds and in consequence are sown or placed quite deeply in the soil compared with the shallow lie of the majority of potentially competitive weed seeds. A soil-acting herbicide, usually of low water solubility, sprayed on to the soil surface or only gently tined in, is able to destroy weed seeds growing in the top few millimetres of the soil, whereas a large-seeded crop (e.g. beet, potato tubers) is protected by the fact that it is usually sown deeper in the soil (figure 13.1c). Even very sparingly soluble chemicals slowly move down in the soil, but two factors combine to

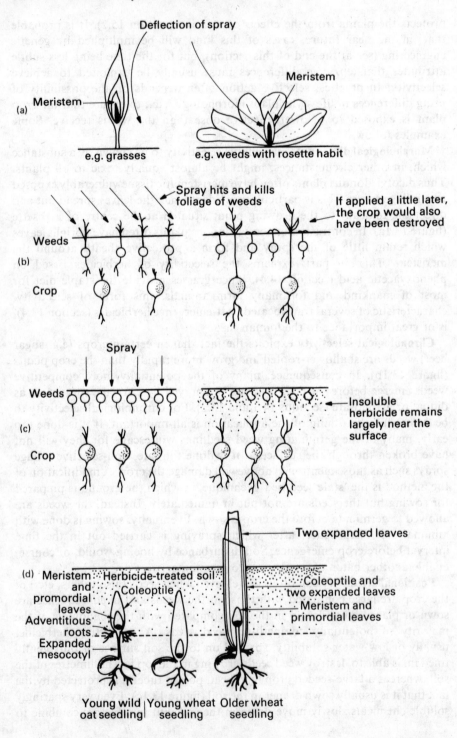

Deflection of spray

Meristem

(a) Meristem

e.g. grasses   e.g. weeds with rosette habit

Spray hits and kills
foliage of weeds

If applied a little later,
the crop would also
have been destroyed

Weeds

(b)

Crop

Spray

Weeds

Insoluble
herbicide remains
largely near the
surface

(c)

Crop

Two expanded leaves

(d) Meristem   Herbicide-treated soil
and
promordial   Coleoptile
leaves
Adventitious
roots
Expanded
mesocotyl

Coleoptile and
two expanded leaves
Meristem and
primordial leaves

Young wild | Young wheat | Older wheat
oat seedling | seedling | seedling

reduce the potential hazard to the crop. The first of these is the time factor: when used at economic concentrations bacteria and other microorganisms attack and inactivate most herbicides. Secondly, there is the dispersion factor: under field conditions, a nearly insoluble substance is seldom washed down as a single concentrated layer (as it might be in a suitable chromatographic column) but instead becomes more and more diluted by admixture with soil as some of it penetrates more deeply into the soil while the rest is held back by adsorption on soil constituents.

A somewhat different example of positional selectivity is provided by the use of triallate to control wild oat (*Avena fatua* and *A. ludoviciana*) germinating in wheat. The triallate is incorporated carefully into the soil so that there are a couple of centimetres of triallate-free soil above the wheat seeds before the triallate-contaminated layer is reached (figure 13.1d). When any wild oat present among the weed seeds starts to germinate, its mesocotyl elongates rapidly, so raising the nearly unprotected meristematic region into the triallate-treated zone. This does not happen in the case of the wheat, which has no extending mesocotyl, and by the time the meristematic region reaches the treated soil it is protected by mature sheathing leaves.

Placement selectivity is achieved when it is possible to direct a foliar spray in such a way that it makes contact only with the leaves of the weeds. By this means a substance that is not in itself intrinsically selective can still be used for weed control in a standing crop. Many variants of this approach exist; two examples are weed control in orchards and weed control in dormant or near-dormant fruit bushes and canes. Thus non-selective substances such as diquat or glyphosate can be used to clear grass from around raspberry canes in early spring, or some moss killers can be applied to dormant fruit trees. Requirements of such methods are, of course, that contact with trunks of trees does no harm and that damaging entry through crop roots does not occur.

Genetic engineering, as was mentioned above, will almost certainly soon make it possible to protect crops from the action of certain herbicides—in other words, to improve selectivity. Briefly, if the mode of action of a herbicide is known, and the target proves to be a protein, genetic engineering may well allow the gene coding for that protein to be isolated. It is then possible, by already established techniques, to alter that gene so that it is less affected by the herbicide. The altered (and resistance-coding) gene can be cloned in a virus or microorganism and eventually inserted into plant cells growing in culture; from such cell cultures it is already possible for botanists to generate clones of

Figure 13.1 Factors exploitable to achieve selectivity of herbicides: (a) morphological (some foliar applications); (b) chronological (contact pre-emergence); (c) positional (residual pre-emergence); (d) the special case of wild oat control in wheat, where growth habit of wild oat can be exploited by careful soil incorporation of herbicide

thousands of whole plants. By these means it will soon be possible to make strains of crop plants that are resistant to particular herbicides: indeed, successes have already been achieved. Parallel procedures could be anticipated to lead to amplification of genes coding for enzymes that could help crop plants to detoxify herbicides.

An example that illustrates the role genetic engineering is likely to play in the protection of crops from adverse effects of herbicides is provided by the work of Shah *et al*. (1986). Knowing which enzyme is inhibited by glyphosate, they isolated a complementary DNA clone that encoded for this enzyme in a glyphosate-resistant variety of *Petunia*. It was found that resistance occurred because the enzyme was overproduced, and that this happened because the gene had undergone a 20-fold amplification (compare insect resistance, section 9.3). A 'poly-gene' was then constructed using a cauliflower mosaic virus and introduced into glyphosate-sensitive *Petunia* cells in culture; the regenerated transgenic plants were tolerant of glyphosate. A second example is illustrated by the work of Lee *et al*. (1988). Knowing the target enzyme of sulphonylureas (section 15.5), Lee and her colleagues isolated the modified gene that confers resistance to sulphonylurea in resistant mutants of *Nicotiana tabacum*. Introduction of mutant genes into sulphonylurea-sensitive tobacco cells led to regenerated plants that were highly resistant to this herbicide. The authors suggest that it might also be possible to put the resistant gene from *tobacco* plants into cultured cells of *other types* of crop plants and so create numerous crops with strains tolerant of this herbicide.

13.3 WEED CONTROL: AN OVERVIEW

The different circumstances in which weed control may be desirable will be discussed in succeeding chapters but a brief summary, with terminology, is appropriate here.

A common circumstance is weed control in a standing crop, but several possible scenarios exist. One of these was mentioned above, namely weed control in such perennials as fruit trees, fruit and ornamental bushes or shrubs, and weed control in fruit canes. If done in the dormant season, the approach is quite different from, say, controlling weeds in cereals to facilitate harvesting or to avoid contamination of grain with weed seeds. So long as suitable techniques have been used, only in the cereal example is selectivity essential. In all of these cases, however, a standing crop is present, and the herbicide is being used (late) **post-emergence**. Thus the different situations just mentioned are similar in that some of the weeds to be controlled are very conspicuous, established plants, the weedkiller being applied to the weeds as a foliar spray (although some of this will reach the soil and could also kill germinating seeds).

It is important to note that the term 'post-emergence', if used unqualified, always means 'post-emergence of the crop'. If in some circumstances it is convenient to refer to the state of the weeds, the expression 'post-emergence (or pre-emergence) of the weeds' should be used. When a foliar-acting herbicide reaches the leaves of the weeds, its movement away from the point of contact may be very limited. If this is the case it is said to be a **contact** poison. If it moves away from the point of contact in either xylem or phloem (see section 13.4) it is said to be **translocated** in the plant (compare, **systemic** insecticides).

Pre-emergence use of herbicides almost always involves applying herbicides to seedling weeds, rather than large established plants. The purpose is to remove weeds that are rooted shallowly, grow rapidly and thereby are serious competitors with the seedling crop for light and nutrients. The weeds may be either visible above the surface, or germinating but invisible beneath the surface. Clearly, from a practical viewpoint, the farmer wishes to have chemicals that are able both to attack the foliage of seedling weeds and to contaminate the ground in such a way that the seeds or seedlings weeds still below the surface are killed as they germinate or emerge. In many circumstances the timing of such applications is critical, for there is no guarantee that a chemical marketed for this purpose would spare the crop if it made contact with it. Such substances, whether they act on foliage or through the soil, will normally be applied in a late pre-emergence situation.

In addition, it is possible to apply herbicides to soil long before the crop is due to emerge, or before the crop is planted or sown, or after a crop has been harvested. Such **soil-acting** herbicides range from soil fumigants to non-selective universal soil sterilants. A common crop protection use for a herbicide of this type is to apply it late in autumn, often to clear land of subterranean parts of perennial weeds. They can, however, also be used in other contexts, such as around cultivation time or as an alternative to ploughing. Such chemicals persist for varying times in the soil and some (but by no means all) can be used late on in the spring before the sowing or planting of specific (somewhat tolerant) crops. Substances used for these purposes have different properties from soil-acting herbicides used in late pre-emergence situations and are discussed in more detail in section 13.5.

13.4 UPTAKE OF HERBICIDES BY LEAVES OR BY ROOTS

It is frequently found that the physicochemical properties of herbicides that are applied to foliage are very different from those of compounds normally applied through the soil. The factors influencing the uptake of herbicides are many and interacting, and the total process is, in consequence, poorly understood. However, some of the physical and chemical characteristics determining uptake by, and distribution within, plants can often be predicted in general terms by assuming that the upper part of the plant is hydrophobic by virtue of the waxy cuticle of the leaves whereas the lower part is essentially hydrophilic since the major function of roots is to take in water and various water-soluble substances.

When a toxic substance with a measure of oil solubility is applied to leaves, it will tend to penetrate through the waxy cuticle, especially if it is so formulated that it is soluble in a covalent carrier solvent (section 2.7). Similarly, weak acids or bases will tend to penetrate most easily if the formulation favours low polarity. This can be achieved by using covalent esters or by suppressing the ionisation of suitable salts by the addition of an activator that alters the pH of the total spray medium. If a leaf-applied herbicide is sufficiently soluble in both oil and water, it may enter the waxy cuticle, penetrate it, and then leave on its inside, so as to enter the aqueous phase of the plant.

The sieve tubes of the phloem constitute a special part of the interconnected living parts of the plant, or **symplast**. Photosynthetic products (assimilates) move through the intercommunicating plasmadesmata of mesophyll cells and thence to the companion cells of the sieve tubes. **Translocated** leaf-applied herbicides enter the symplast with such assimilates and so move out of the leaf. Very young leaves do not export photosynthetic products, but assimilates from leaves placed low on the stem often pass to storage areas in the roots and those from leaves higher up the plant pass to the apical meristems.

Movement of solutes in the phloem reflects the general metabolic activity of the plant and the majority of systemic foliage-applied herbicides are translocated most readily when the weeds are growing rapidly. At certain times of the year many species of plants pass assimilates down to the roots in order that food stores can be created in tap roots, rhizomes, etc. This provides a botanical Trojan horse, in that it enables translocated foliage-applied herbicides to move downwards and to destroy subterranean parts of perennial weeds. Conversely, herbicides usually move out of the leaves rather slowly at times when poor light intensity restricts photosynthesis. However, some herbicides damage leaf tissue in such a way as to reverse the natural flow of water in the xylem. When this happens, xylem transportation of herbicides from foliage can occur, as it does, for example, at certain levels of application of quaternary ammonium compounds.

Naturally, many of these generalisations are, at best, oversimplifications. Corrosive or caustic substances may gain access in successive stages by first destroying cuticle of cells in their vicinity, then soaking further in, thus enabling the process to be repeated (e.g. sulphuric acid, which has been used for weed control in onions and kale). Another complication is that a water-insoluble herbicide may be oxidised after deposition, giving rise to a more water-soluble but still toxic substance capable of being translocated. Again, salts of weak acids or bases may undergo considerable hydrolysis so that the ionisation of such substances as the amine salts of 2,4-D is less than would otherwise be the case. Moreover, plant cell walls and cell cytosol have different pH values, so that the overall effect on uptake followed by systemic movement may be, for some herbicides, very complex.

Root uptake involves somewhat different considerations. Roots exist to absorb water and some solutes, but the relative amounts of solutes within plants is quite different from their relative amounts in soil water. This difference implies a selective uptake of natural soil constituents and it would not be surprising if herbicidal molecules were also absorbed in a discriminatory manner. Some may move in passively, others may masquerade as natural substances: some may be actively pumped out as they enter, while others may destroy cells and so nullify the plant's normal protective system.

Once within the root, the substance may be strongly adsorbed onto cellular or extracellular components near to the point of entry. Such compounds may kill roots by contact action. Others may not be strongly bound, in which case they will tend to move upwards in the transpiration stream. Substances usually enter roots via the non-living, or **apoplastic**, part of the plant, a system that not only includes the cell walls and the intercellular spaces, but also the xylem vessels of the transpiration stream. The water-impermeable Casparian strip of the root presents an apparent barrier to free entry. It is probably by-passed by aqueous solutions entering the symplast of the cells and then passing back into the apoplast via the parenchyma cells of the xylem.

The rate of upward movement of herbicide will be influenced by factors such as elevated temperature or reduced humidity, which affect transpiration, as well as by any tendency of the herbicides to bind to macromolecules in root cells or to constituents in the walls of xylem vessels. For very slightly soluble substances, the slowest process in the uptake sequence may in practice be physicochemical, namely the rate at which 'insoluble' herbicide particles in soil dissolve in the surrounding water and thus acquire the opportunity to reach plant roots. Movement in the xylem normally carries most of the herbicides to the leaves, a process that enables those that are photosynthetic inhibitors to reach their site of action. However, a proportion of the total dose absorbed usually escapes from the xylem to the phloem on the way up, a movement that allows growth-inhibiting herbicides such as trifluralin to reach meristematic tissue by conduction in the phloem. In addition, although the rate of apoplastic movement should be a function of such environmental factors as humidity and temperature, it is often found that, in practice, stomata are readily damaged by herbicides, and such damage can alter the rate of transpiration.

13.5 PERSISTENCE OF HERBICIDES IN SOIL

Stable substances with low vapour pressures and with low solubilities in water usually tend to persist in soil. On the other hand, if a substance is volatile, or chemically unstable, and often if it is soluble in water, it is unlikely to persist for long, although the extent of persistence is considerably influenced by temperature, soil type and soil microbiology.

Volatile materials such as dichlobenil (section 16.2), certain thiolcarbamates (section 15.1) and nitroanilines (section 16.4) have relatively short half-lives in many soils. Trifluralin (section 16.4) illustrates a general point of some importance. At normal rates of application it may persist in soil for as little as 15 weeks or for as long as eight months. In common with many other volatile soil-acting herbicides, it is lost more rapidly from moist soil than it is from the same soil when it is dry. The explanation is that water successfully competes with herbicide molecules for adsorption sites on soil constituents. Consequently, the molecules of herbicides that are strongly adsorbed on dry soils are often readily dislodged under damp conditions. When the substance is volatile, dislodgement allows diffusion to the surface where loss can occur by evaporation and sometimes also by photodecomposition.

One potential danger inherent in the use of soil-acting herbicides is that build-up of concentrations could occur from year to year. If this occurred, the first intimation of disaster to the unwary farmer might be poor crop emergence. The trouble with soil application is that to use the technique is to walk a scientific tight-rope; if the chemical disappears too readily the technique is an expensive failure and if it lasts too long it is a dangerous and expensive failure. In practice, the sort of build-up that would be disastrous is unlikely to occur for substances applied at the correct (selective) soil concentration. Figure 13.2 shows, for example, that, if, year after year, 30 per cent of a dose (in the diagram, a dose of 10 arbitrary units) still remains in the soil when the next year's application is made, the maximal cumulative dose, A′, is only 40 per cent above the applied dose in the first year (14 as against 10 units); such an 'overdose' would normally be well within the tolerance limit. Even if half an applied dose remains at the end of the year (curve B), the theoretical maximal cumulative dose, B′, achieved after several years of similar 'mistakes' is only twice the 'recommended' application rate (20 units instead of 10). In practice, of course, sensible crop husbandry avoids difficulties of this sort. Ashton (1982) has given references to work on which the relevant mathematical models have been based.

In view of what has just been said, it is somewhat ironic that another major problem that can follow repeated dosing of the same soil with the same herbicide is that degradation can actually take place more rapidly than might be anticipated from initial laboratory studies. The reason for **enhanced degradation** is that, on continued exposure to (selective) doses of many herbicides, the 'living' soil becomes **enriched** with types of microorganisms

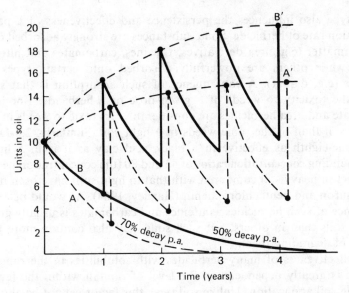

Figure 13.2   Theoretical build-up of soil residues of a herbicide: A, decay curve for 70% disappearing per year; A′, cumulative residue if reapplication at the same rate each year (the maximal residue rises little after the first year); B, decay curve for 50% disappearing per year; B′, cumulative residue rises towards a maximum of twice the annual rate. (In each case, the annual dose is 10 arbitrary units)

that can break down the herbicide more readily than the types that were originally present. Consequently, the herbicide may disappear more and more quickly from year to year (some workers in the USA describe such soils as *problem* soils). The history of enhanced degradation of pesticides, with references, has been reviewed by Walker and Suett (1986); other examples of enhanced degradation of pesticides are to be found in sections 4.11, 5.6, 5.7, 14.4 and 16.1.

Most herbicides are degraded more or less easily by **microorganisms**, being attacked by their oxidative, reductive and hydrolytic enzymes (chapter 3). It is the high activity of these enzymes in soil organisms present after 'enrichment' that leads to enhanced degradation. However, if an insoluble and *chemically* stable herbicide (e.g. some triazines*, uracil and urea derivatives) is applied at such a high concentration that potentially destructive microorganisms cannot recolonise the area, the substance may persist for a long time.

---

*The author recalls upsetting half a teaspoonful of a solid simazine formulation on the much-prized lawn of the University of Reading in 1964. Twice since, the lawn has been returfed over several square metres, yet the area still shows. Several members of Senior Common Room have been heard condemning the Rag-day vandalism of irresponsible undergraduates.

Soil type also influences the persistence and effectiveness of a particular application rate of herbicide. Some substances are strongly adsorbed onto soil organic matter (e.g. urea derivatives, triazines, carbamates and nitrophenyl ethers) while others are powerfully adsorbed onto certain types of soil particles (e.g. diquat). A consequence of such adsorption is that soil type affects the toxicity to weeds of a given dose of a herbicide. For instance, carbamate and urea herbicides are considerably less toxic to weeds in a heavy organic soil than to the same weeds in a light soil. Similarly, 2,4-D is only about one-eighth as effective in a black acid clay as it is in a light soil. Corresponding **concentration ratios** of 43 and 80 (the concentration needed for unit effect in heavy soil compared with that in light soil) have been observed for monuron and pentachlorophenol (Hartley, 1964). As would be expected, persistence of such herbicides as ureides and carbamates is usually greater in organic soils than in others, but such soils may also contain more bacteria capable of degrading them.

The effectiveness of many herbicides with solubilities in the range of 1–100 ppm is greatly dependent on the level of rainfall within the few weeks following soil application. Unlike soil type, this factor cannot be allowed for in advance of application. Difficulties can therefore arise in seasons where the rainfall in the period shortly after spraying is atypical. If rainfall is light, wash-down may be insufficient to bring the chemical into contact with even shallow-rooted weeds. On the other hand, if rainfall is excessive, even nearly insoluble substances may be washed down to the level of the germinating crop and so become **phytotoxic** (i.e. damage the crop).

Since herbicides vary widely in their physical properties and biochemical stability, the persistence in soil of different substances varies greatly. It is thus necessary to select with care a herbicide for a particular purpose, especially when using soil-acting compounds. Moreover, since the family names of certain groups of herbicides are somewhat similar (e.g. leaf-applied triazoles and soil-acting triazines), it is essential that users of commercial products double-check the names and the instructions on containers before applying a product.

Figure 13.3 illustrates on a logarithmic timescale the probable range of persistence for each of several herbicides. It is important to remember that rate of application, rainfall, soil type, temperature and microbial population all affect persistence, so such schemes can only be indicative of probable persistence. In addition, some crops are relatively tolerant of some of these compounds so can be sown or planted a shorter time after application than would be possible for other crops. For example, brassicas and carrots are relatively tolerant of trifluralin and can be drilled between three and 14 days after incorporating this substance into soil. Similarly, brassicas and some types of beet can be sown in land recently treated with diallate.

The **mobility** of a given herbicide in a particular type of soil is a function of the intensity with which it is adsorbed by one or more kinds of soil

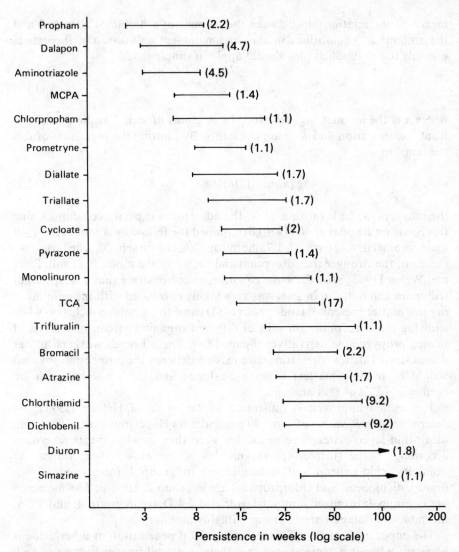

Figure 13.3 Persistence of herbicides in soil: approximate maximal and minimal persistence at levels toxic to susceptible plants when used in average soils at normal dosage. Figures in parentheses indicate the dose (kg/ha) often used

constituents and the level of rainfall after application. Attempts have been made to quantify the relative mobility of various herbicides either by measurement of adsorption constants or by measuring R_f values in thin-layer chromatography systems for which the thin layer is a standard soil.

The first approach is illustrated by the work of Rhodes *et al.* (1970), who measured the relationship between the amount of a herbicide adsorbed and the amount in equilibrium in the circumambient solution. On theoretical grounds the Freundlich plot should apply in simple cases:

$$x/m = KC^{1/n} \tag{13.1}$$

where x is the amount (µg) adsorbed by m grams of soil, C is the circumambient concentration and K, n are constants. By plotting the logarithm of this relationship

$$\log(x/m) = (1/n)\log C + \log K \tag{13.2}$$

the intercept is the logarithm of K, the adsorption capacity constant. Using this equation Rhodes *et al.* (1970) determined the following K values for a silt loam: bromacil, 1.5; terbacil, 1.7; monuron, 2.6; chloroneb, 20. The larger the constant, the stronger the adsorption and the lower the mobility in soil. Peter and Weber (1985) used the same equation to demonstrate that adsorption of trifluralin and butralin in soils was very highly correlated with the amount of organic matter present. Bastide *et al.* (1981) came to a similar conclusion when studying the adsorption, on soils of different organic content, of a series of related propyzamide derivatives (figure 13.4). These French workers further demonstrated that a correlation also existed between the adsorption (by unit weight of organic matter) of each analogue and the oil–water partition coefficient (K_{ow}) of that analogue.

The second approach is illustrated by the work of Helling (1971). He determined the R_f values of some 40 pesticides on Hagerstown silty clay loam, using thin-layer plates. The pesticides were then divided into five groups according to the (increasing) magnitudes of the observed R_f values. As examples, chloroxuron and trifluralin are in group 1 (highly immobile); diuron, dichlobenil and chlorpropham are in group 2; atrazine and monuron are in group 3; bromacil, aminotriazole and 2,4-D are in group 4; and TCA, dicamba and dalapon are in group 5 (highly mobile).

The importance of the effective depth of soil penetration of a herbicide is apparent when it is remembered that there may well be, per hectare of soil, tens of millions of viable weed seeds at any one time. Most of those which germinate are probably in the top 3 cm of soil, although seeds of some troublesome weeds can develop from a depth of up to 12 cm. It is clearly desirable to know the distribution of the more important weed species in the soil before calculating what dose of a soil-acting herbicide to apply, or before deciding to what depth a soil-mixed pre-planting herbicide should be incorporated into the soil.

The length of time a herbicide persists in soil is evidently important for soil-applied herbicides since the duration of herbicidal effectiveness (and therefore, often, of potential phytotoxicity) must be matched against the time likely to

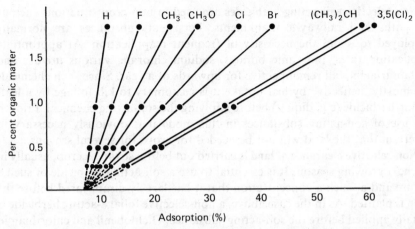

Figure 13.4 Relation of adsorption to percentage organic matter for each of eight propyzamide analogues (after Bastide *et al.*, 1981, with permission). Substituent groups are shown at the top of each line; for further details the original article should be consulted

elapse between applying the herbicide and sowing a suitable crop. It must not be overlooked, however, that persistence *in soil* may also be important in relation to the use of *foliar-applied* herbicides, since a considerable proportion of a foliar-applied substance usually misses the leaves and ends up on the soil. Moreover, plants killed by foliar weedkillers may inadvertently be collected for compost and any remaining active substance or its breakdown products could actually get applied to soil in concentrated form.

13.6 SITUATIONS INVOLVING THE APPLICATION OF HERBICIDES TO SOIL

The following situations in which soil-applied herbicides can be employed should be carefully distinguished:

(a)   Non-selective weed control (e.g. on paths); here long-term persistence is often desirable.

(b)   Non-selective clearance some time prior to sowing (i.e. a non-crop situation, but only temporarily so).

(c)   Pre-planting and pre-sowing treatments (i.e. as (b) but nearer to the deadline, so that the rate of disappearance is even more critical and the herbicide must be matched to a tolerant crop).

(d)   Soil application after sowing the crop but before the crop emerges (residual pre-emergence treatment).

(e)   Soil application to kill seedling weeds in an established crop (residual post-emergence treatment).

Non-selective soil-acting herbicides are used in non-crop situations such as on paths and railway embankments. Persistent substances are normally employed to avoid the necessity of frequent reapplication. At appropriate application rates, inorganic borates, sodium chlorate, various ureides and certain triazines all remain active for upwards of a year. Since such chemicals are mostly ineffective by leaf uptake it is customary to kill foliage by a leaf-acting herbicide (e.g. diquat) before applying the soil-acting chemical. Prior to the use of soil-acting substances in this mode it is obviously necessary to ascertain that the land will not be needed for crops for several seasons.

Non-selective clearance of land is carried out before sowing a crop, usually in the next growing season. It is essential to use a soil-acting herbicide of such a nature and at such a concentration that it has largely disappeared before the crop is planted. As in the case above, a non-selective foliage-acting herbicide is usually applied before the soil-acting substance. Dichlobenil and chlorthiamid (section 16.2) are often applied in autumn to clear ground that is to be sown in spring.

Pre-sowing and pre-planting applications are made between about three weeks and three months before sowing or planting the crop. Exact timing and correct application rate may be essential to success and nearly always a herbicide must be chosen to which the would-be crop shows a degree of tolerance. The advantage of this type of treatment is that it can reduce the density of troublesome perennial weeds, which are difficult to deal with once the crop is present. An example of a herbicide often used in this manner is trifluralin (section 16.4), which is applied to soil to control weeds in land where brassicas are to be grown within a few weeks. In addition to soil-acting substances, downward-translocated foliar herbicides such as glyphosate and aminotriazole are used in pre-sowing and pre-planting situations (sections 14.2 and 14.3). Another use of pre-sowing applications of soil-applied herbicides is in relation to 'no-till' farming. This method of growing crops is becoming increasingly popular in some areas because it can reduce soil erosion and water loss, yet simultaneously decrease operating costs. Many possibilities exist but, essentially, visible weeds are removed, post-harvest, by a universal foliage killer and the bare ground kept more or less clear of weeds during winter and spring by the use of a herbicide that is applied to the soil surface. The crop is sown or planted 1–3 months after the last herbicide application. A useful illustration of the use of early pre-planting applications in a 'no-till' situation has been published by Stougaard et al. (1984) for the particular case of weed control in soybeans; after removal of large weeds by paraquat, a mixture of cyanazine (section 15.2) and oryzalin (section 16.4) was applied at intervals of one month, respectively three, two and one month before planting no-till soybeans.

Residual pre-emergence treatment involves killing weeds by uptake through their roots or subterranean shoots at a time when the crop is still beneath the surface. It contrasts with *contact* pre-emergence treatment, where a foliar application kills emerged seedling weeds before the crop appears. Some of the problems associated with the residual pre-emergence method are considered in section 13.5. Unless the crop is tolerant (e.g. as maize is tolerant of atrazine), it must be protected against wash-down, and this is usually done by deep planting. In practice, this usually means that the method is primarily applicable to large-seeded crops such as beans as well as to sets such as bulbs, corms and tubers.

Residual post-emergence sprays are applied to soil to control germinating weeds when a crop is visible. The chemicals employed are often the same as those used for residual pre-emergence weed control although the application procedure or concentration of herbicide may be different. The method is often used for weed control in orchards and in established fruit bushes. Chloroxuron (section 15.1) can be used in established celery and strawberries, and ametryne (section 15.2) is used after planting pineapples. In some crops, greater safety can be achieved by the use of placement spraying. Granular formulations are sometimes an advantage for residual post-emergence treatment because the granules bounce off foliage of the crop plants and come to rest on the ground beneath them.

13.7 THE USE OF MIXTURES OF HERBICIDES

It is evident from the preceding section and from the classification of herbicides in table 13.1 (see section 13.8) that considerable specialisation exists in respect to herbicidal function. Some are applied to foliage of well established plants while others attack germinating weed seeds. Others preferentially attack dicotyledonous weeds in the presence of foliage of a monocotyledonous crop while a few selectively destroy seeding monocotyledons. Yet others destroy existing weeds but have no long-term effect, and so on. It follows that if certain biological and chemical compatibilities exist, the application of appropriate mixtures containing two or more herbicides can achieve a versatility not possessed by either active ingredient used singly, thereby saving time and effort in weed control and diminishing the overall cost of weed control measures.

Problems of a biological and of a chemical nature can in practice restrict the types of substances that can be usefully mixed together. One biological requirement is that an active ingredient must be applied at a time and in a manner that allows its herbicidal potential to be realised. It is, for example, not economically sensible to apply a foliage-acting compound so early that little foliage is present, in order that the soil-acting compound with which it is mixed can fulfil its function. Similarly, the mode of action of the active ingredients should be complementary rather than antagonistic. On the other hand, chemical compatibility must exist not only between all the active ingredients but also between all the supplementary substances that may be present. Usually, of course, these problems will have been resolved by the manufacturer of a purchasable mixture, but they become important if the farmer makes his own mixtures (a practice which, for safety reasons, is often undesirable, and, in many countries, illegal).

In order to illustrate the usefulness and versatility of herbicidal mixtures, one or two examples will now be given to illustrate each of the four principal purposes for which such mixtures are used. Section references are given to indicate where the individual active ingredients are discussed in more detail.

First, a number of refractory weeds are very difficult to control at economic rates of application of individual chemicals, but they often succumb to 'cocktails' of herbicides. The following examples are among the recommendations of Fryer and Makepeace (1978). These recommendations provide a valuable source of information on special weed control problems. Ground elder (*Aegopodium podagraria*) is a particularly annoying weed in many parts of the British Isles: it has been found that a mixture of aminotriazole (section 14.3) and 2,4,5-T (section 14.4) applied in late summer controls it moderately well. Again, the docks (*Rumex obtusifolius* and *R. crispus*) are usually quite readily controlled by a mixture of dicamba (section 14.5) and MCPA (section 14.4) applied around midsummer.

A second common requirement is for a mixture of two foliage-acting herbicides, one of which attacks grasses. For example, total but temporary weed control can be obtained with mixtures of dalapon (section 14.8) and 2,4-D (section 14.4) for clearing rather neglected ground that is required for growing crops in the next growing season. The dalapon acts on the grasses and the 2,4-D kills the dicotyledonous weeds.

Thirdly, mixtures containing a soil-acting and a foliar herbicide are employed for several different purposes (Fryer and Makepeace, 1978). Some of these mixtures are designed so that planting can be done fairly soon afterwards, while others contain active ingredients that keep the ground weed-free throughout a complete season. A specific example is the use of a mixture of ioxynil (section 14.6) and linuron (section 15.1) for post-emergence treatment in onions: the ioxynil controls annual dicotyledonous weeds by foliar action and the linuron provides a degree of permanence by killing newly germinating weeds by soil action. A dinoseb (section 14.13) and monolinuron (section 15.1) mixture is used rather similarly for pre-emergence weed control in dwarf beans and potatoes. An aminotriazole (section 14.3) and simazine (section 15.2) mixture is used for weed control in apple orchards, the former removing mature weeds around trees while the simazine provides longer-term control.

Finally, it is sometimes useful to apply a mixture of two soil-acting herbicides. One procedure is to choose two active ingredients that control different weeds. For example, a mixture of diallate (section 16.1) and pyrazon (section 15.3) is used as a pre-sowing treatment in ground later to be sown with fodder beet or sugar beet. The diallate is particularly efficacious against wild oat (*Avena fatua* and *A. ludoviciana*) while the short-term action of pyrazon rapidly removes many other annual weeds. A second procedure is to choose two soil-acting substances, one of which has a quick clearing action while the other prevents new weeds from recolonising the area. An example is a mixture of bromacil (section 15.3) and borate. In this case the bromacil rapidly removes annual and shallow-rooted perennial weeds while the borate helps to prevent reinfestation. Cromack and Davies (1982) carried out an extensive study in which 15 herbicides were applied alone, or as mixtures, or in particular sequences, to control weeds in swedes growing on nine sites. They concluded that mixtures usually gave better results than did substances used individually; among the best pairs of substances for this particular purpose was a mixture of trifluralin and propachlor.

13.8 CLASSIFICATION OF HERBICIDES

Active ingredients with herbicidal properties belong to many chemical families and have been formulated in numerous ways. Thus, in a list of products approved in the UK, the entries for herbicides occupy more space than those for insecticides and fungicides combined (MAFF, 1986). It is therefore necessary to divide herbicides into manageable subgroups, and one way to do this is shown in Table 13.1. Here, the initial division relates to overall agricultural function (foliar or soil application, control of seedlings or of established weeds). Further subdivision utilises probable mode of action or (for leaf-applied substances) types of plants that are selectively killed or selectively protected. Later, in tables located at the beginning of the relevant

Table 13.1   Classification of herbicides. The sequence presented in this table is followed in the next three chapters

Group 1.	**Applied to foliage**
Type A:	Kill all foliage unless directionally sprayed
Type B:	Kill broad-leaf weeds in cereals, grass
Type C:	Kill grasses (sometimes in a broad-leaf crop)
Type D:	Kill grasses in cereals
Type E:	Kill broad-leaf weeds in various dicotyledonous crops
Group 2.	**Foliar and soil action on young weeds**
Type A:	Inhibitors of photosynthesis
Type B:	Herbicides that affect cell division
Type C:	Substances that disrupt membrane structure or function
Group 3.	**Soil-acting, often soil-incorporated**
Type A:	Substances that disrupt fatty acid metabolism
Type B:	Herbicides that affect meristematic growth

chapters, the classification is taken further, division occurring according to the chemical structures of the herbicides involved.

Group 1 foliar herbicides are usually applied to established weeds, some-times to clear ground for crops or, more often, to kill established weeds in a standing crop. Group 2 herbicides usually have a quite different function, since they are mainly used against weeds that have just emerged or are expected to emerge shortly after application. The stage of growth of the crop at the time of application may vary; it may be an established crop, like trees in an orchard, or an annual crop in an early stage of growth (possibly still below the ground at the time of application). The soil-acting herbicides of group 3 have yet other functions; for example, they may be applied long before a crop is sown or planted in order to eradicate subterranean growth of troublesome perennial weeds, a task that is often difficult to achieve in the presence of an annual crop.

REFERENCES

Ashton, F. M. (1982). In *Biodegradation of Pesticides*, eds F. Matsumura and K. Murti. Plenum, New York

Bastide, J., Cantier, J. M. and Coste, C. (1981). *Weed Res.*, **21**, 227

Cromack, H. T. H. and Davies, W. I. C. (1982). *Proc. Br. Crop Prot. Conf., Weeds*, p. 931

Fryer, J. D. and Makepeace, R. J. (1978). *Weed Control Handbook*, vol. 2, *Recommen-dations*, 8th edn. Blackwell, Oxford

Hartley, G. S. (1964). *Physiology and Biochemistry of Herbicides*, ed. L. J. Audus, chap. 4. Academic Press, London

Helling, C. S. (1971). *Soil Sci. Soc. Am. Proc.*, **35**, 737

Lee, K. Y., Townsend, J., Tepperman, J., Black, M., Chui, C. F., Mazur, B., Dunsmuir, P. and Bedbrook, J. (1988). *Embo. J.*, **7**, 1241

MAFF (1986). *Pesticides 1986, Reference Book 500, Pesticides Approved under the Control of Pesticides Regulations 1986*. UK Ministry of Agriculture, Fisheries and Food. HMSO, London

Peter, C. J. and Weber, J. B. (1985). *Weed Sci.*, **33**, 861

Rhodes, R. C., Belasco, I. J. and Pease, H. L. (1970). *J. Agric. Fd Chem.*, **18**, 524

Shah, D. M., Horsch, R. B., Klee, H. J., Kishore, G. M., Winter, J. A., Turner, N. E., Hironaka, C. M., Sanders, P. R., Gasser, C. S., Aykent, S., Siegel, N. R., Rogers, S. G. and Fraley, R. T. (1986). *Science*, **233**, 478

Shaw, W. (1963). *Nat. Agric. Chem. Assoc. News*, **21**(2), 14

Stougaard, R. N., Kapusta, G. and Roskamp, G. (1984). *Weed Sci.*, **32**, 293

Walker, A. and Suett, D. L. (1986). *Aspects Appl. Biol.*, **12**, 95

14 Herbicides applied to foliage

The herbicides that are applied to foliage can be divided into the five main sections listed in table 14.1. Some foliar herbicides selectively control grasses, others control dicotyledonous weeds and others are general weedkillers. It should, however, be stressed that no classification can take account of the many peripheral, overlapping or exceptional cases that exist. The compounds described in this chapter usually control well established plants (e.g. plants that are at least 10 cm high) although the effect is sometimes limited to the foliage with which they come into contact, leaving underground parts of the plants intact.

Table 14.1   Foliage-applied herbicides

Type A: Kill all foliage unless directed
   Section 14.1   Quaternary ammonium compounds (e.g. diquat)
           14.2   Glyphosate
           14.3   Aminotriazole

Type B: Kill broad-leaf weeds in cereals, grass
   Section 14.4   Phenoxyacetic acids (e.g. MCPA, 2,4-D)
           14.5   Chlorinated benzoic acids
           14.6   Phenolic nitriles (e.g. ioxynil, bromoxynil)
           14.7   Bentazon

Type C: Kill grasses (sometimes in a broad-leaf crop, sometimes non-crop)
   Section 14.8   Dalapon (pre-plant, pre-emergence, with exceptions)
           14.9   Fluazifop and sethoxydim groups

Type D: Kill grasses in cereals
   Section 14.10 Carbamates (e.g. barban)
           14.11 Difenzoquat, oxadiazon, chlorfenprop, propanil

Type E: Kill broad-leaf weeds in various dicotyledonous crops
   Section 14.12 Phenoxybutyric acids (e.g. 2,4-DB)
           14.13 Dinitrophenols (e.g. dinoseb)
           14.14 Hydrocarbon oils and the concept of physical toxicity

Type A: Herbicides that kill all foliage

14.1 QUATERNARY AMMONIUM COMPOUNDS

Paraquat and **diquat** (figure 14.1a, b) are bipyridinium herbicides and were discovered around 1955 at the Jealott's Hill Research Station of ICI; more recently, the monopyridinium compound, **cyperquat**, has been introduced (figure 14.1c). In view of what is now known about their mode of action, it is of interest that paraquat was used as early as 1933 as the redox indicator, methyl viologen, because of its ability to form a rather stable free radical.

Salts of paraquat and diquat are nearly colourless in the dry state. They are very soluble in water and the solutions are corrosive to some metals. A solution of paraquat absorbs light at 260 nm and that of diquat absorbs at 310 nm. On reduction, paraquat is reduced to a purple-coloured free radical and diquat to one that is coloured green. These free radicals *autoxidise* in the presence of oxygen. The standard redox potentials, E_0', are respectively -0.45 and -0.35 V, values that are, perhaps significantly, similar to the E_0' value for the biological electron carrier, ferredoxin.

A free radical is a substance that contains an unpaired electron—according to classical valence theory, it contains an 'unsatisfied chemical bond'. Such substances, although common, are usually so unstable that their half-lives are measured in micro- or milliseconds. When, however, the molecule contains a system of alternating double bonds (π-electrons), the energy can be delocalised to give molecules of much greater stability; the stability is said to be provided by 'resonance energy'.

The unique attribute of the quaternary ammonium group of herbicides is that they kill exclusively by **foliage contact** so long as the plants are growing in

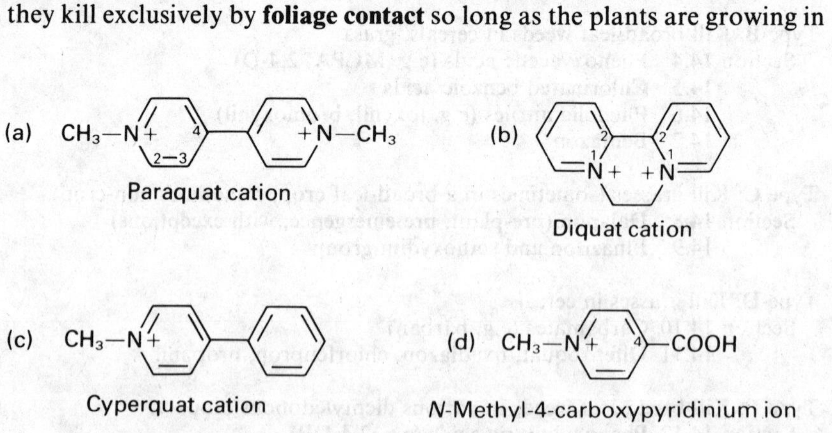

(a) CH_3-N^+ ⬡(4, 2—3) — ⬡ $^+N-CH_3$
       Paraquat cation

(b) ⬡(2, 1) ⬡(2, 1) $=N^+$ $^+N=$
       Diquat cation

(c) CH_3-N^+ ⬡ — ⬡
       Cyperquat cation

(d) CH_3-N^+ ⬡(4) $-COOH$
       N-Methyl-4-carboxypyridinium ion

Figure 14.1 Quaternary ammonium herbicides: (a) 1,1'-dimethyl-4,4'-bipyridinium ion; (b) 1,1'-ethylene-2,2'-bipyridinium ion; (c) 1-methyl-4-phenylpyridinium ion

Table 14.2 Some general uses of quaternary ammonium herbicides (all are used after emergence of weeds; they may be used pre-emergence of a crop or applied to an established crop by placement techniques)

Herbicide	Uses
Diquat	Often preferred where broad-leaved weeds predominate Non-crop situations, e.g. clearing heavily infested land For pre-harvest desiccation of foliage To control submerged aquatic weeds
Paraquat	Often preferred where grassy weeds predominate Non-crop situations, e.g. clearing heavily infested land Applied after harvesting one crop and before planting the next To destroy an old sward before reseeding Control of aerial parts of perennials For minimal cultivation farming
Cyperquat	To control annual weeds in cereals Control of *Cyperus* (nutsedge) in many crops
Difenzoquat	To control wild oats in wheat, barley

soil*. They cannot enter plant roots in such circumstances because they are inactivated by total adsorption on clay minerals. Montmorillonite and similar minerals adsorb these substances most strongly because they hold the doubly charged planar cations firmly within the negatively charged crystal lattice. Except in highly sandy soils, the cation exchange capacity of the soil is little diminished by such uptake. The affinity of clay minerals for bipyridinium cations is so high that neither fertilisers nor lime normally displace them.

Unlike the urea herbicides (section 15.1) they are not strongly bound to soil organic matter. This is demonstrated by the fact that soil that has been treated with peroxide loses little of its paraquat-adsorbing capacity. Paraquat and diquat slowly disappear from soil, although it is not clear whether physical or biochemical processes contribute most to this loss.

Some of the uses of quaternary ammonium herbicides are listed in table 14.2, and the following selected examples will illustrate the versatility of these substances. First, paraquat can be used as a **between-crop application**. For example, it can be used to clean up land before drilling cereals or kale or before planting cotton, asparagus or tomatoes. Another example is its use to

---

*That is, plants growing in culture solutions are rapidly killed by root uptake. Similarly, seedling crops can be killed before emergence above the soil when that soil is very light and lacks clay particles.

destroy an old sward prior to renovating grassland by reseeding. Mat grass (*Nardus stricta*), one of the least valuable British grasses, is killed by paraquat, although, in the absence of cultivation, such treatment may encourage the growth of *Agropyron repens* (couch grass or quack grass). A second range of uses requires that the herbicide be applied to the foliage of fast-growing weeds **before the crop emerges**. Thus paraquat can be sprayed over dormant bulbs, maize, rhubarb, soybeans and around some fruit bushes. Thirdly, paraquat is often applied by **directed spraying** around established fruit trees, forestry trees and sugar canes. Rather similarly, it can be used for inter-row spraying to reduce weed competition so long as protective shields are used to prevent the spray touching the crop.

Diquat is also used as a **pre-harvest desiccant** to dry up foliage and so to make harvesting easier and cheaper. It is particularly useful for potato haulm destruction but it is also employed as a desiccant for seed clovers, oil seed rape and peas (MAFF, 1985). In the USA it is similarly used for alfalfa, sorghum, soybeans, sunflowers and sugar cane.

Quaternary ammonium compounds are rain-fast soon after application because they are rapidly absorbed by foliage. At high light intensities they tend to be contact poisons whereas at low light intensities some limited translocation may take place. This difference arises from the fact that, in strong light, the leaf tissue is killed before appreciable translocation can occur. They cause wilting and water-soaking within a few hours of application, with rapid foliar discoloration. The target leaves soon show signs of scorching and desiccation, the unsprayed leaves becoming chlorotic somewhat later. A consequence of the rapid failure of translocation is that these herbicides are unable to control the subterranean growth of perennial plants.

Electron microscopy has shown that the tonoplast of cells in paraquat-treated leaves is damaged in the vicinity of chloroplasts within 6 h of application (Harris and Dodge, 1972). It is probable that peroxidation of membrane phospholipids causes chloroplastic and other membranes to rupture, with loss of potassium ions from the leaf (see below). It is now known that death occurs after some days even in the dark, but the more dramatic toxic effects mentioned earlier require the presence of light, oxygen and photosynthetic tissue. The importance of light makes the light reaction of photosynthesis (figure 14.2) an obvious candidate as the primary target of bipyridinium herbicides, yet paraquat does not inhibit the **Hill reaction** in isolated chloroplasts.

Around 1973 Hill found that isolated chloroplasts upon illumination were unable to reduce carbon dioxide. They could, however, remove electrons from water and pass them to a suitable artificial electron acceptor. Consequently, not only was the artificial electron acceptor reduced but oxygen was simultaneously evolved. Hill himself originally used ferric potassium oxalate as the terminal acceptor, but it is now known that numerous electron acceptors can replace carbon dioxide in this reaction, among them being indigo carmine

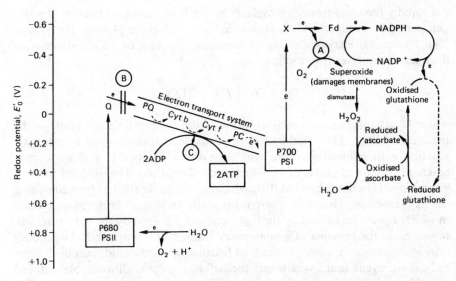

Figure 14.2 Light reactions of photosynthesis and probable sites of action of some herbicides. PQ, plastoquinone; Cyt b, cytochrome b_{559}; PC, plastocyanin; PS, photosystems I and II; Q, X, unidentified electron acceptors. A, site of electron deflection by quaternary ammonium compounds; B, primary site of action of ureides, triazines, uracils; C, site of action of uncouplers such as nitrophenols. In strong light superoxides are produced in small quantities naturally but inactivated by photosynthetically produced NADPH. In the presence of quaternary ammonium herbicides, electron deflection leads to increased superoxide levels but to decreased levels of NADPH

($E_0' = -0.12$ V) and methyl viologen (which, as was mentioned earlier, is now known as paraquat).

Paraquat ($E_0' = -0.45$ V) inhibits the reduction of $NADP^+$ and thereby prevents the reduction of carbon dioxide in the photosynthetic carbon cycle. It does this by replacing ferredoxin ($E_0' = -0.43$ V) as electron acceptor in photosystem 1 (figure 14.2). Thus light energy is re-routed, paraquat being reduced by a one-electron transfer and automatically reoxidised by atmospheric oxygen to form superoxides. The superoxide free radicals attack unsaturated fatty acids in membrane lipids and lead to the deleterious consequences described earlier. Since it is the autoxidation that does the damage, quaternary ammonium herbicides would be expected to act *catalytically* rather than stoichiometrically.

In normal circumstances a protective system exists that ensures that any peroxides, superoxides or hydrogen peroxide formed during the light reaction are rapidly removed from chloroplasts before they can cause damage (hydrogen peroxide, in particular, is highly damaging to green plants). The system involves several enzymes acting in sequence, the first of which, superoxide dismutase, catalyses the reaction

$$O_2^- + O_2^- + 2H^+ \rightarrow H_2O_2 \tag{14.1}$$

where O_2^- is superoxide, a radical formed from oxygen by green tissue in the presence of light. The toxic hydrogen peroxide is then reduced to water by reaction with reduced ascorbic acid. The oxidised ascorbic acid so formed reacts with reduced glutathione, which is itself oxidised. The oxidised form of glutathione is reduced by NADPH, which, it will be recalled, is formed during the light reaction. Therefore, there is normally an elegant failsafe mechanism in which a problem caused by the light reaction is solved by the light reaction. However, in the presence of a quaternary ammonium compound, the production of superoxide is greatly enhanced because of the autoxidation of the free radical, an event that overwhelms the defence system; all available reduced ascorbic acid is oxidised and thereafter hydrogen peroxide accumulates. The essential free-radical reactions of the ascorbate defence system have been described by Bowyer and Camilleri (1987) and are shown in simplified form on the right of figure 14.2.

It is of interest that paraquat-tolerant lines of various plants have been isolated. Harvey and Fraser (1980) have shown that paraquat-tolerant *Lolium perenne* has higher activity of several defence enzymes, including superoxide dismutase, than have susceptible plants of the species. It has been suggested that this increased activity could be the mechanism responsible for the tolerance, for Shaaltiel and Gressel (1986) detected greatly elevated levels of this enzyme, and also of ascorbate peroxidase and glutathione reductase, in a paraquat-tolerant strain of *Conyza bonariensis*. Faulkner and Harvey (1981) reported that the seeds of a tolerant strain of *Lolium perenne* are also tolerant when grown in paraquat-treated hydroponic culture and concluded that the mechanism of tolerance operates outside as well as within the photosynthetic tissues. They postulated that the (up to 10-fold) resistance to paraquat shown by this line of *Lolium perenne* could possibly be exploited to allow direct drilling after a sward destroyed by paraquat is reseeded.

Quaternary ammonium compounds have rather low LD_{50} values (table 1.2) but their correct field use probably presents no serious hazard. Small amounts can irritate the skin or, if inhaled, can cause nose bleeding, but such amounts are rapidly and completely eliminated from the body. However, when larger amounts are ingested, a non-cancerous multiplication of lung cells occurs, accompanied by proliferation of mitochondria within them. According to Hemberger and Schanker (1983) this uptake, over a 10 000-fold concentration range, occurred by diffusion; there was no evidence of saturation of any absorption mechanism. Gaudreault *et al.* (1984), however, working with lung slices, concluded that paraquat was taken up by lung cells by the active transport system normally employed to accumulate putrescine. Mitochondrial proliferation occurs long after all traces of the herbicide have disappeared and leads to respiratory failure and death. Medical treatment is only possible if administered soon after ingestion, although Wright *et al.* (1987) have reported the isolation of paraquat-neutralising antibodies, which, by binding to paraquat, were able to prevent its *in vitro* accumulation in rat lung tissues; the equivalent of about 1 mg of immunoglobin G was needed to bind 2.5 µg of paraquat.

In view of the hazards just described, it is evident that concentrated solutions of bipyridinium compounds must be handled with the greatest care and never subsampled into unauthorised containers. In particular, the removal of samples into beer or soft-drink bottles has been responsible for numerous tragedies. For home gardeners and usage in the developing world a soft granular formulation is preferable to a liquid concentrate on grounds of safety, for granules are less easily splashed or swallowed; the soft granules (section 2.6) disintegrate in water, liberating the soluble diquat or paraquat.

In contrast to what happens to most other pesticides, paraquat and diquat undergo little metabolism in plants or in animals. When paraquat is applied to plants kept in the dark, very little loss occurs, whereas in the light it rapidly disappears. Similarly, *in vitro*, diquat and paraquat keep almost indefinitely in the dark, but 85 per cent of the radioactivity is lost from ^{14}C-labelled diquat within seven days upon exposure to ultra-violet light. In the case of paraquat, it is believed that in both of these cases ultra-violet light causes one of the pyridine rings to split open to leave eventually the *N*-methyl-4-carboxypyridinium ion (figure 14.1d).

Environmental effects of quaternary ammonium compounds include a striking propensity to accumulate in water plants, which, in turn, implies that a possible hazard exists for aquatic animals that eat such plants. For example, Ernest (1971) found a 2000-fold accumulation in *Chara* spp. after water treatment with 1.14 ppm paraquat. Environmental concentrations of paraquat of between 0.5 and 100 ppm (a range of values incorporating figures reported in several publications) have been found to cause malformation of fish embryos or of developing tadpoles. Diquat has similar effects although it is possibly somewhat less toxic. Examples are provided by the work of Murray and Schreiweis (1977), who found that paraquat induced teratogenic effects in a teleost fish, and Dial and Dial (1987), who observed that both paraquat and diquat had lethal effects on developing frog embryos and on tadpoles.

In addition to these delayed effects, direct damage can occur to mammals that run through treated areas. Such animals tend to lick their contaminated fur, with fatal consequences; the effects are, however, difficult to quantify since death may occur weeks later and miles away.

14.2 GLYPHOSATE

This organophosphorus herbicide was introduced in 1971 for foliar application to many annual and perennial weeds. It is employed in non-crop situations as well as for pre-emergence treatment. It can also be used in appropriate established crops where shielding or placement is possible. It resembles the quaternary ammonium compounds in that it is **inactivated by soil**, and consequently material that runs off weed leaves cannot damage crop plants by being taken up by their roots (in the absence of soil, root uptake is rapid and lethal). In the case of glyphosate, inactivation may result from interaction with iron in soil minerals.

Glyphosate is an acidic substance containing phosphonate and derived from glycine (figure 14.3a). It is usually formulated as the water-soluble isopropylamine salt. There have been several reports of apparent incompatibility with formulations containing other pesticides, so considerable care is necessary to ensure spray apparatus is clean before glyphosate is used. For example, the presence of 1 per cent organic matter or montmorillonite in the spray-tank can reduce the activity of the sprayed glyphosate by up to 90 per cent. This is presumably a consequence of physical binding. Similarly, Stahlman and Phillips (1979) found that various formulations of seven herbicides all decreased the activity of glyphosate when mixed with it (some, but not all, of these seven formulations were wettable powders based on clays). Shea and Tupy (1984), using greenhouse-grown wheat, observed that the phytotoxicity of glyphosate was greatly reduced if small amounts of calcium ions were present in the medium, but that the metal chelator, EDTA, interacted with calcium (and other heavy-metal) ions and restored the

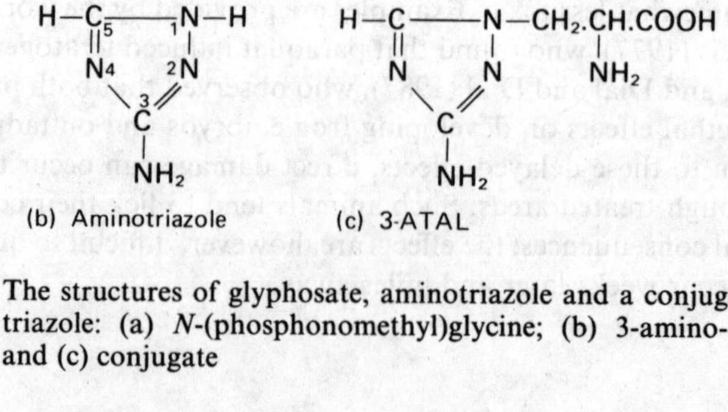

HO   O
 \\ //
  P
 / \\
HO $CH_2.NH.CH_2.COOH$

(a) Glyphosate

(b) Aminotriazole   (c) 3-ATAL

Figure 14.3   The structures of glyphosate, aminotriazole and a conjugate of aminotriazole: (a) *N*-(phosphonomethyl)glycine; (b) 3-amino-1,2,4-triazole; and (c) conjugate

phytotoxicity; they provided a useful three-dimensional histogram model to illustrate these results. They also pointed out that some hard waters are alkaline and that the toxicity of glyphosate will be reduced if the pH of the solution containing it is greater than the pK_a of this weak acid. If too alkaline, the addition of an acidic salt (e.g. ammonium sulphate) to the spray mixture can improve performance.

Absorption by leaves is followed by translocation and it is this property which enables it to be used in circumstances where the quaternary ammonium compounds would fail. The rate of translocation depends not only on the species of plant, but also on environmental conditions. Many workers have shown that movement of glyphosate is high in environmental circumstances that favour translocation of photosynthetic products to storage regions. Within biological limits, these environmental conditions include high temperature, high light intensity and high humidity. The physiological state of the plant also affects translocation, for movement of glyphosate is essentially symplastic and moves with the photo-assimilates. A few specific examples will illustrate this.

Devine *et al.* (1983) studied the absorption and translocation of glyphosate by *Agropyron repens* growing under three different day/night temperature regimes. Translocation was initially slower at the lower temperatures used but caught up within 24 h; after 120 h, 67 per cent had been absorbed and 47 per cent of the labelled glyphosate was recovered in rhizomes (and predominantly, in new rhizomes). McAllister and Haderlie (1985) compared the movement of labelled photo-assimilates and of labelled glyphosate out of treated mature upper leaves of *Cirsium arvense* at the mid-flower stage. It was found that the photo-assimilates and the glyphosate moved (to both roots and shoots) at almost the same rate. For example, eight days after treatment, 25 per cent of the radioactivity associated with the photo-assimilates and 31 per cent of that associated with glyphosate was recovered in the roots. They further noted that in one case the concentration of glyphosate was as high in the rhizome 95 cm from the treated shoot as it was at the base of the treated shoot itself.

Chase and Appleby (1979), working with the purple nutsedge (*Cyperus rotundus*), found that glyphosate was more effective at 90 per cent relative humidity than it was at 50 per cent. Similarly, it was more effective at -2 bar plant water potential than it was at -11 bar. Furthermore, these differences could be ascribed to consequential differences in translocation, for three times as much was translocated to underground parts at 90 per cent humidity than at 50 per cent, and twice as much was translocated at -2 bar water potential than at -11 bar.

Dewey and Appleby (1983) studied the movement of glyphosate and photo-assimilates in *Ipomoea purpurea* (tall morning glory). The overall conclusions were similar to those of McAllister and Haderlie (1985), although minor differences were noted between movement of labelled glyphosate and labelled photo-assimilates. In particular, when glyphosate was applied to the stem, apoplastic movement into transpiring tissues above the site of application was evident. This suggests that glyphosate can 'leak' from the translocation system of the phloem to the transpiration stream of the xylem. A substance with this capability is **ambimobile**; Dewey and Appleby gave references to some work that supports the view that glyphosate is ambimobile and some that does not; no doubt the extent to which this occurs varies with plant species and with environmental conditions. The effect of the stage of growth of perennial plants on the efficiency of translocation has been investigated by Neal *et al.* (1985) using *Ligustrum japonicum* and *Juniperus conferta*. Labelled glyphosate was applied to leaves at five stages of growth, from winter dormancy to active shoot extension. For the juniper about 2 per cent was absorbed in 14 days at the shoot elongation stage, otherwise absorption was negligible. *L. japonicum*, on the other hand, absorbed significant amounts at shoot elongation and at budbreak. They concluded that the season of the year at which application was made to woody weeds (or beneath woody fruit trees) could greatly affect success in the control of the one and danger to the other; fruit trees are more likely to be damaged by autumn applications.

The uses and limitations of glyphosate follow from the work described in the last few paragraphs. It has little selectivity of action and kills all foliage it touches. On the other hand, it is inactivated by most types of soil; consequently, ground sprayed with glyphosate can be cultivated and sown soon after application. Moreover, unlike most universal foliage poisons, it can in the right conditions be translocated to underground parts of perennial plants and bring about their death. When it is remembered that perennial weeds are becoming a major problem now that most annuals can be controlled satisfactorily, this is a valuable attribute. It is usually employed prior to planting or seeding annual crops, prior to crop emergence or for post-crop clean-up. For best results the weeds must be mature enough to present a large target for foliar uptake and, where applicable, glyphosate must be applied at a time when photo-assimilates are being actively transported to underground parts. In addition, it is best that rain should not fall for several hours after application. For the control of perennial weeds that possess rhizomes and tubers it is often found that cultivation after glyphosate application can be more effective than chemical treatment alone. A probable reason for this is that the glyphosate breaks the dormancy of buds on rhizomes of such important perennial weeds as *Agropyron repens* and *Cyperus rotundus*, the cultivation then leading to desiccation of the new growth. In the case of *C. rotundus* the optimal interval between applying glyphosate and tillage has been found to be about three days.

Cyperus rotundus is, in fact, a good example to illustrate these generalisations. According to Doll and Piedrahita (1982) it is one of the world's worst weeds in tropical areas, spreading vegetatively and not readily controlled by any herbicides. It can be a serious nuisance in citrus, banana and oil palms. In work done in Colombia these workers established that glyphosate was translocated underground, but nevertheless gave imperfect control. The failure could be due to two things: it may be that the emerged, sprayed plants did not fully succumb or that dormant tubers, separated from sprayed plants, later produced new plants. In their own study, Doll and Piedrahita found that, at 2 kg/ha, 36 h were needed for translocation to the tubers and that 89 per cent of the tubers died within the next 180 days. They concluded that glyphosate did control tubers attached to sprayed plants but that poor control was caused by the survival of dormant and unattached tubers. Later tillage or repeated spraying appears to be necessary to control newly emerged plants. Other workers have shown that even 1–5 per cent of viable tubers can cause significant reinfestation.

Other uses of glyphosate involve its careful placement in areas in which perennial crops are growing, such as in orchards, citrus groves and forestry plantations. Again, it can be used for pasture renovation, where it is used to kill undesirable stoloniferous grasses prior to reseeding. For this purpose it may take 10 days for toxic symptoms to appear but reseeding can proceed once the foliage has started to turn yellow. At lethal dosage plants yellow before dying, while at sublethal doses glyphosate affects apical dominance and leads to marked extra tillering at the base of treated shoots. In various countries it is also used to control *Sorghum halepense* (Johnson grass) and *Cynodon dactylon* (Bermuda grass) as well as to eliminate such troublesome weeds as *Aegopodium podagraria* (ground elder), water lilies, various reeds, *Convolvulus* spp. and *Polygonum* spp.

Decomposition of glyphosate in plants appears to occur rather slowly and the major product is aminomethylphosphonic acid. In soil, rapid inactivation occurs but, as was seen earlier, this is caused by sorption, since glyphosate complexes strongly with clay that contains aluminium, iron, zinc or manganese. Chemical decomposition is slow and it is not rapidly degraded in sterilised soils. However, in most soils, microorganisms rapidly degrade it with the release of carbon dioxide, the rate of release being reduced by the addition of trivalent ions of iron or aluminium. Literature upon degradation of glyphosate has been collated by Menzie (1980).

Plants that have been exposed to glyphosate suffer chlorosis as they die, while sublethal amounts affect apical dominance, with proliferation of buds, shoots and tillers (Fryer and Makepeace, 1977). Its main action appears to be upon the biosynthetic pathway whereby aromatic amino acids are synthesised in plants. The pathway is termed the **shikimic acid route** of synthesis and it is absent in higher animals (for which phenylalanine, tyrosine and tryptophan are, consequently, 'essential' amino acids). Other effects have, however, been observed, some or all of which may be secondary consequences of disruption of this pathway. These effects include interference with indolyl acetic acid metabolism (Lee *et al.*, 1983), reduction of the uptake and translocation of calcium ions (Duke *et al.*, 1983), inhibition of chlorophyll formation and inhibition of nitrite reductase (Cole *et al.*, 1983). Foley *et al.* (1983) have demonstrated that a 36 per cent rise in ATP levels in roots of *Xanthium pensylvanicum* coincides with the arrival of glyphosate there, and, simultaneously, the incorporation of leucine into protein declines to 35 per cent of the controls. The authors considered that these events are linked and concluded that glyphosate has an effect upon protein biosynthesis.

Jaworski (1972) was the first to suggest that the mode of action of glyphosate could be to disrupt aromatic amino acid biosynthesis. The disruption leads to a shortage of phenylalanine, tyrosine and tryptophan, which is well illustrated by the work of Shaner and Lyon (1980) using excised shoots of *Phaseolus vulgaris*. It was observed that, within 6 h of placing the shoots in water that contained 60 µmol/l glyphosate, the levels of endogenous aromatic amino acids were 50 per cent lower than in corresponding leaves of the controls (table 14.3).

Jaworski (1972) and others first directed attention to the excessive activity of the enzyme, phenylalanine-ammonia lyase, in glyphosate-poisoned plants; this is an enzyme that destroys aromatic amino acids. It is now realised that the pathway of aromatic amino acid biosynthesis is one that is subject to feedback control and some of the emphasis placed upon the importance of the phenylalanine-ammonia lyase may have been misplaced; the observed effects appear to be caused by the fact that a shortage of phenylalanine leads to derepression of this enzyme.

The shikimic acid pathway commences with erythrose-4-phosphate (formed in the photosynthetic carbon cycle) and phosphoenol pyruvate (formed in the glycolytic pathway) and passes, via shikimic acid-3-phosphate, to chorismate. Thereafter the path branches to tryptophan (via anthranilate) and to phenylalanine/tyrosine (via prephenate). For more details, the text by Lehninger (1975, chap. 25) is recommended. Essentially, however, a substantial body of evidence suggests that glyphosate is a specific inhibitor of one enzyme in that pathway, namely the synthase that catalyses the conversion of shikimic acid-3-phosphate to the 3-phosphate derivative of 5-enolpyruvyl shikimate (figure 14.4b).

Much of the evidence concerning the effects of glyphosate on the shikimic acid pathway was collected in the laboratory of Amrhein (e.g. Steinrücken and Amrhein, 1980). These workers demonstrated that the action of glyphosate

Table 14.3   Effect of 60 µmol/l glyphosate on the aromatic amino acid content of transpiring cuttings of *Phaseolus vulgaris* (after Shaner and Lyon, 1980)

Amino acid	Amount (nmol/mg leaf dry weight)		Percentage of control value
	Control	Glyphosate	
Phenylalanine	1.19	0.56	47
Tyrosine	0.73	0.42	58

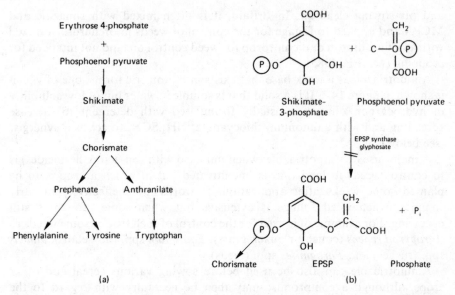

Figure 14.4 (a) Outline of the shikimic acid pathway; (b) the step in the pathway that appears to be most vulnerable to glyphosate. EPSP, 5-enolpyruvyl shikimate-3-phosphate

resulted in a massive accumulation of shikimic acid and a shortage of phenylalanine, leading to a decrease in the rate of protein synthesis. However, the effects of glyphosate cannot always be reversed by adding these amino acids, a fact that suggests that the growth-inhibiting effect of glyphosate in plants is still not fully understood. This is why some workers (e.g. Cole *et al.*, 1983) consider that the ultimate effect may be upon membrane structure and function. Pihakaski and Pihakaski (1980) have published electron micrographs showing the damaging effects of glyphosate on the plasmalemma and on the chloroplastic membranes of the liverwort, *Pellia epiphylla*.

14.3 AMINOTRIAZOLE (AMITROLE)

The practical uses of aminotriazole in some ways resemble those of the compounds in the previous two sections, for it is predominantly a foliar herbicide that rapidly disappears after it has destroyed weeds. It is also particularly efficacious against stoloniferous grasses and certain refractory weeds. However, it is not inactivated by soil and it is therefore able to reach roots of crops under conditions when quaternary ammonium compounds and glyphosate would be harmless. It was introduced in 1954; although non-selective, its relatively low persistence in soil can be exploited for pre-planting and pre-sowing clean-up. In Britain, it is often mixed with simazine and MCPA and applied to foliage for the control of weeds in orchards, or mixed with atrazine, diuron or dichlorprop for weed control on land not intended for cropping (MAFF, 1985).

Aminotriazole is a weak base that exists in tautomeric forms, one of which is shown in figure 14.3. It is a solid that is soluble in water but of low solubility in hydrocarbon oils. It is usually formulated with detergent to increase spreading and with ammonium thiocyanate, $NH_4.SCN$, to act as a synergist (see below).

A major use of aminotriazole (when unmixed with soil-acting herbicides) is to control weeds in land that is uncultivated but in which a crop is to be planted some weeks after application. It works more effectively in early summer, when weed foliage is extensive but when some growth is still occurring. For example, it is used for the control of such troublesome weeds as *Agropyron repens* (couch or quack grass), *Equisetum* spp. (horsetails), *Juncus* spp. (rushes) and *Phragmites* spp. (reeds).

Aminotriazole can also be used before sowing various cereal and other crops, although a compromise may then be necessary with regard to the optimal time of application. It can be applied in autumn prior to sowing winter wheat or oats, or any spring crop; it can also be applied in the spring at a suitable time before sowing wheat, maize and potatoes (MAFF, 1985). For weed control before kale, it can also be applied in spring or summer when the foliage of weeds is about three or four inches high, the ground being ploughed some three to six weeks later. If this ploughing completely inverts the soil it is possible to plant kale almost immediately (Fryer and Makepeace, 1978).

Since aminotriazole is able to penetrate soil it is able to reach plant roots. It is therefore *seldom employed in the presence of a crop* unless, like some trees, the root system is deep. It is somewhat sorbed onto soil constituents and its phytotoxicity is roughly proportional to the amount that is readily recoverable from a particular type of soil. Its persistence in soil varies but is usually between one and three months; sowing is sometimes, but not always, possible about one month after application.

Chemical and microbial processes, as well as leaching, play a part in the disappearance of aminotriazole from soil. When soil is autoclaved, the rate of release of carbon from aminotriazole is greatly decreased. In some soils, up to half the aminotriazole may be destroyed by microbial action but, in others, non-biological degradation possibly predominates.

In plants, detoxication involves conjugation reactions that result in metabolites that are of higher molecular weight and are less readily translocated than aminotriazole itself. The best authenticated of these is aminotriazolyl-aminopropionic acid (3-ATAL), which may be formed from aminotriazole and serine (figure 14.3b). The abbreviation presumably reflects the fact that the conjugate can be regarded as the 3-aminotriazole (3-AT) derivative of alanine (AL). Any substance able to decrease the rate of conversion of aminotriazole into 3-ATAL would be expected to make a given dose of aminotriazole more effective. **Ammonium thiocyanate** appears to act in this way, for Carter (1975) reported that only 6.7 per cent of a dose of aminotriazole was converted to 3-ATAL in the presence of thiocyanate whereas 63 per cent was converted to it in the absence of this supplement. Thus ammonium thiocyanate is an example of a substance with a **synergistic action**.

Typical symptoms of the herbicidal action of aminotriazole are chlorosis of leaves and retardation of growth. It moves in both symplast and apoplast and accumulates in active meristems. The numerous effects of aminotriazole on plants have been reviewed by Carter and Keeley (1987). One of them is to decrease the concentration of the plant hormone, indolylacetic acid (IAA). Others include a delayed increase in free amino acids, decreased protein and nucleic acid synthesis and effects on the movement of ions and on membrane integrity. Above all, however, as the chlorotic symptoms indicate, aminotriazole affects plant pigments (the action of aminotriazole has sometimes been described as a *bleaching* action but this term is best avoided).

It now seems probable that the primary action of aminotriazole is upon **carotenogenesis**; that is to say, it interferes at one or more points in the pathway that leads from acetyl coenzyme A and mevalonic acid, via isopentenyl pyrophosphate, to geranyl pyrophosphate, farnesyl pyrophosphate, terpenyl pyrophosphate, phytoene, lycopene, and eventually ends at the cyclic carotenes. This is one stem of the biosynthetic pathway by which complex lipids, carotenoids, sterols and terpenes (e.g. rubber) are made from common precursors. For details, a biochemical text should be consulted but a basic version is shown in figure 14.5. Essentially, the terpenoid building unit, isopentenyl pyrophosphate (IPPP), is first formed from acetyl coenzyme A. The IPPP molecules condense in pairs to give geranyl pyrophosphate. From here, the paths of synthesis for some pigments and terpenoids branch off, but the path that is of major immediate interest involves the union of two geranyl pyrophosphate molecules to give terpenyl pyrophosphate, which contains 20 carbon atoms and four double bonds. It is to this that attention is now drawn, for if it is reduced it eventually gives phytol (present in chlorophyll) or if two terpenyl pyrophosphate units condense together, an important 40-carbon precursor of all carotenoid pigments is formed. This precursor is termed **phytoene**; many of the steps from this substance to β-carotene involve the creation of double bonds (i.e. dehydrogenation reactions). It should be added that other pathways lead from geranyl pyrophosphate to the steroid precursor, squalene (section 12.4) and to such carrier quinones as plastoquinone.

It is now possible to consider the likely mode of action of aminotriazole. It was recognised early on that aminotriazole does not affect the Hill reaction in isolated chloroplasts; from this and other observations it has been concluded that aminotriazole has no direct effect on the structure or function of fully formed chloroplastic membranes. For example, if plants are kept in darkness until mature leaves have formed, whereupon they are treated with aminotria-

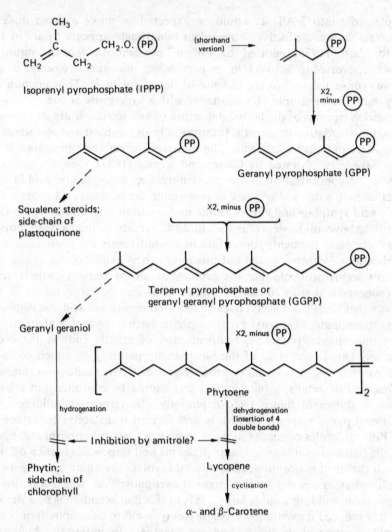

Figure 14.5   Carotenogenesis and the probable effect of amitrole

zole and exposed to light, it is found that the leaves turn green when the plant is illuminated. On the other hand, if germinating plants are exposed to aminotriazole in the dark, the leaves remain white on exposure to light. Clearly, green tissues that exist before treatment with aminotriazole remain green (at least in short-term experiments and when the light intensity is low), whereas new growth that appears after treatment with aminotriazole becomes chlorotic.

Similar symptoms to those just described were noticed by Burns *et al.* (1971) in seedlings of a mutant wheat known to lack carotenoids; as is well known, a major function of carotenoids in leaves is to protect chlorophyll from photo-oxidation. Consequently, the possibility exists that the chlorosis occurring in leaves of aminotriazole-treated plants exposed to high light intensity is caused by lack of carotenoid pigments. If so, the primary effect of aminotriazole would appear to be upon the pathway by means of which terpenes are synthesised. One piece of confirmatory evidence is that several workers have observed that while aminotriazole-treated plants lack finished carotenoids, intermediates such as the 40-carbon phytoene accumulate (Fedtke, 1982).

Such evidence has been taken to imply that aminotriazole causes a blockage of the pathway of carotenoid synthesis at the point where dehydrogenase enzymes remove hydrogen atoms to form double bonds. There may, however, be effects on other parts of the pathway also. For example, Rüdiger and Benz (1979) observed that the pigment fraction from aminotriazole-treated wheat that had been germinated in the dark and then exposed to light contained chlorophyll to which was attached not the normal (saturated) side-chain, phytyl alcohol, but its unsaturated counterpart, geranyl geraniol. Thus, in this case, the interference, rather intriguingly, appears to involve a natural *reduction* process rather than the *oxidative* process mentioned above for carotenoids. In view of the role of cytochrome P_{450} and the endoplasmic reticulum in lipid biosynthesis, it is interesting to speculate whether aminotriazole affects a chloroplastic equivalent of such systems. Finally, it should be mentioned that plastoquinone is also synthesised by a branch of the terpenoid pathway and the synthesis of this important chloroplastic electron transport component (figure 14.2) could also be affected by aminotriazole.

Type B: Herbicides selectively toxic to broad-leaf weeds

14.4 PHENOXYACETIC ACID DERIVATIVES

These translocated compounds are the most extensively used of all weed-killers, for they are used to control broad-leaved weeds in cereal crops and grassland—and these crops play a crucial role in the diet of man and farm animals. Moreover, grass and cereals are often grown in large areas of monoculture, a method of farming that makes manual control of weeds impracticable but favours the use of aircraft for spraying. Naturally, aerial spraying is not possible except in extensive agriculture because of the likelihood of damage to dicotyledonous crops in nearby fields.

Phenoxyacetic acid herbicides were introduced as a result of work carried out both in the USA and in Britain around 1944, although the substance now known as 2,4-D was used earlier as a plant growth regulator by Zimmerman and Hitchcock (1942). Formulae of principal members of the group are shown in figure 14.6. All members of the group have a chlorine atom attached to C-4 of the benzene ring and either a chlorine atom or a methyl group on C-2. Sometimes an additional chlorine atom is present on C-5. In certain homologues of phenoxyacetic acid herbicides the alkanoic side-chain may contain three carbon atoms but, in such cases, one is always so placed that the substance is a methylacetic acid rather than a n-propionic acid derivative.

Formulation is usually either as esters emulsified in oil or as water-soluble amine or other salts. Amine salts are usually very soluble in water and such formulations are convenient for low-volume application. A typical alkylamine ion is $(HO.CH_2.CH_2)_3NH^+$. Ester formulations are insoluble in water and more toxic to weeds than are the ionised forms. They are, however, much less selective. Originally the esters were made using alcohols of low molecular weight but problems sometimes arose from *vapour drift*, resulting in damage to such sensitive crops as tomatoes growing nearby. Nowadays, esters containing long-chain alcohols such as iso-octanol are normally employed since their volatility is much lower (a different problem, *spray drift*, can of course still occur if weather conditions at the time of application are unsuitable). Sodium and alkylamine salts are more ionised and more selective than oil-emulsified esters and are safer to use on less tolerant crops.

The ease of entry of phenoxyacetic acid derivatives through cuticular lipids

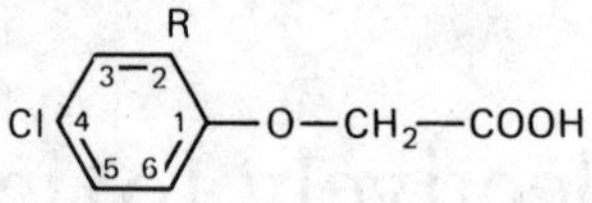

(a) R = CH$_3$; MCPA
(b) R = Cl; 2,4-D

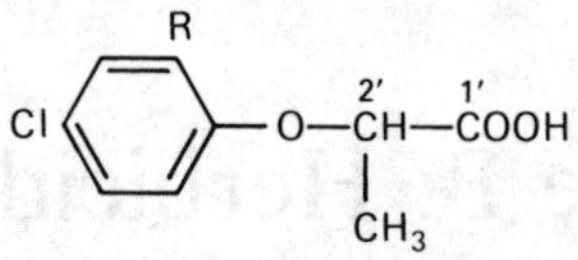

(c) R = CH$_3$; Mecoprop
(d) R = Cl; Dichlorprop

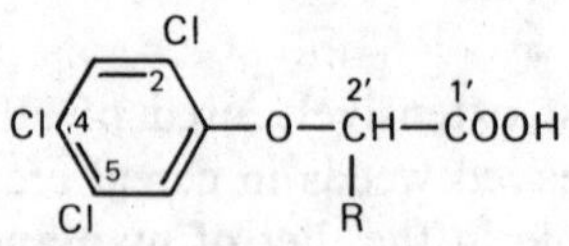

(e) R = H; 2,4,5-T
(f) R = CH$_3$; Fenoprop

Figure 14.6 Phenoxyalkanoic acid herbicides: (a) 2-methyl-4-chlorophenoxyacetic acid; (b) 2,4-dichlorophenoxyacetic acid; (c) 2'-(2-methyl-4-chlorophenoxy)propionic acid; (d) 2'-(2,4-dichlorophenoxy)propionic acid; (e) 2,4,5-trichlorophenoxyacetic acid; (f) 2'-(2,4,5-trichlorophenoxy)-propionic acid

is largely determined by molecular polarity. Covalent forms, and forms soluble in carrier oil, usually enter more readily than ionic or polar forms. In contrast, ionised forms are in equilibrium (at constant pH) with a fixed concentration of free, un-ionised acid and they enter more slowly. This slower or less complete entry of ionic forms is in part responsible for their selectivity, for in such circumstances the plant's enzymic defence system is more likely to be able to cope with the compound as it enters. In addition, morphological characteristics contribute significantly to the lower susceptibility of most grasses compared with broad-leaved plants (section 13.2).

Physicochemical factors similarly determine the relative ease of entry of various salts of phenoxyalkanoic acids. Salts of strong bases (e.g. MCPA-Na) are less hydrolysed at a given pH than are salts of weaker bases (e.g. amine salts of MCPA). Consequently, amine salts are often intermediate in phyto-toxicity and selectivity between covalent esters and highly ionised sodium salts. In a spray mixture, the pattern of uptake is further modified by the surfactants that are present since these can increase the availability and penetration of toxicant by reducing run-off and by softening surface lipids.

MCPA (figure 14.6a) is extensively used in Europe but **2,4-D** (figure 14.6b) is often preferred in the USA. The difference probably reflects the relative costs of raw materials at a regional level. The sodium salt of MCPA is more soluble in water than is that of 2,4-D (27 per cent as against 4.5 per cent) and may cause less jet blockage when the volume of application is low. MCPA-Na is more selective than 2,4-D-Na but it is also less effective against many (but not all) weed species. When comparisons are made between various phenoxy-alkanoic acid herbicides, or between different formulations of one such compound, all concentrations are expressed in terms of *acid equivalents* of active ingredients per gallon of applied liquid.

The alkali-metal and amine salts of MCPA are extensively used in European countries for the control of dicotyledonous weeds in cereal crops. The same is true of the amine salts of 2,4-D in the USA. In various countries these compounds are used on wheat, barley, oats, rye, rice, maize and sorghum. Both substances are frequently used in mixtures with one or more of the following herbicides: aminotriazole, 2,4-DB, dichlorprop, dicamba and dala-pon. Ester formulations of MCPA and 2,4-D are often used on non-cropped land as well as on grassland and turf; they are more persistent and control a wider range of weeds than do the sodium or amine salts. Ester-in-oil formulations are used to control some refractory weeds, especially in circum-stances where selectivity may not be essential (e.g. for the control of woody plants). Where selectivity is a requirement, the application rate for ester formulations is usually about two-thirds of that for the corresponding salt form.

Various formulations of 2,4-D and MCPA have been used for broad-leaved weed control on perennial grass pastures. An unusual hazard to farm animals is that the common ragwort, *Senecio jacobea*, which is toxic to cattle and normally avoided by them, is made more palatable after spraying with phenoxyacetic acid herbicides. Another aspect of the use of these herbicides in pastures is that they may alter the quality of forage. The evidence on this subject is somewhat conflicting, possibly because of differences in the nature of the sward or the rate of application of herbicide. Occasionally, a deleterious alteration of forage composition has been observed; for example Mislevy (1978) concluded that the dry matter and yield of crude protein was reduced when bahia grass, *Paspalum notatum*, was sprayed with 2,4-D. In other cases, however, no adverse changes in composition have been observed.

Mecoprop and **dichlorprop** (figure 14.6c, d) are best regarded as methylacetic acid derivatives. Their molecules contain an asymmetric carbon atom and it is of interest in relation to their mode of action that only one of the pair of stereoisomers possesses significant toxicity. Mecoprop can be applied to cereals somewhat earlier than can MCPA (i.e. before the five-leaf stage). Its weed control spectrum is similar to that of MCPA but it is more effective against chickweed (*Stellaria media*) and against cleavers (*Galium aparine*). The relative safety of mecoprop, and indeed of other foliar-applied substances, often depends on the fact that the soil acts as a barrier, which reduces or prevents root uptake, but herbicidal concentrations of mecoprop and of MCPA had adverse effects on lateral branches of roots of wheat plants grown in sand culture. Dichlorprop, often in the form of mixtures with 2,4-D, is used to control woody plants and *Polygonum* spp. (e.g. knotgrass and redshank).

Toxicological aspects of the phenoxyalkanoic acids have been discussed by Barnes (1976) and by Fagan and Pollak (1984). At very high dosage, animals lose the ability to maintain their body temperature when moved into either a hot or a cold environment. The reason for this loss of homoeostasis is unknown. At all dosages relevant to accidental exposure to spray or to spray residues, evidence for the occurrence of side-effects in man is tenuous. A mild neural disorder (peripheral neuropathy) has been reported in some individuals but it is by no means certain that most members of the population would develop these symptoms if exposed to occasional application-level doses of 2,4-D. It is even less likely that traces of phenoxyacetic acid herbicides present as residues in food cause neural disorders. In this respect, Hassall (1985) has drawn attention to the need, when discussing possible toxic side-effects of pesticides, to make a proper distinction between the risks associated with *industrial* levels, *application* levels and *residue* levels of pesticides.

At high concentrations, or after long times of contact with phenoxyacetic herbicides, deleterious effects have, of course*, been observed in several types of animals (Fagan and Pollak, 1984). At 1250 ppm in their diet, dogs showed no obvious immediate effects but the litter sizes were smaller than usual and the pups had lower than normal body weight. In Chinese hamsters, 2,4-D at

---

*Such a statement is not in any way specific for pesticides; the author does not consider it flippant to point out that four aspirins may cure a headache but that 40 will cure it for ever.

100 mg/kg body weight caused a proliferation of peroxisomes and the excess of free radicals that this implies could present a potential threat to the integrity of double-stranded DNA (and hence a possibility of chromosomal abnormalities, tumours and genetically transmissible effects). Lundgren *et al.* (1987) demonstrated that the livers of mice fed 0.125 per cent 2,4-D in their diet had higher hydrolase activity than normal and proliferation had occurred of hepatic peroxisomes and mitochondria.

By far the most important aspect of hazard relates not to 2,4-D or to MCPA but to their analogues containing three chlorine atoms. In 1970, it was shown that the use of some samples of 2,4,5-T could lead to teratogenic effects. The problem received adverse publicity as a result of the use of 'agent orange' as a defoliant during the Vietnam war. Unknown to the 'users' at that time, the impure 2,4,5-T then in use contained some 20 ppm of a highly toxic substance, dioxin (figure 14.7), which is formed as a side-reaction in the chemical preparation of 2,4,5-trichlorophenol, itself a precursor of 2,4,5-T. This is a highly toxic substance, the toxic properties of which have been reviewed by Poland and Knutson (1982). As well as teratogenic effects it can cause hyperplasia of gastric mucosa, pathological changes in epithelial tissue and degeneration of seminiferous tubules.

Dioxin remains a danger to those in or near factories making agrochemicals or their precursors (as the disaster at Seveso testifies) but the quantity of dioxin in 2,4,5-T herbicide formulations nowadays seldom exceeds 0.1 ppm. The crucial question to ask is whether this (or any other low level) of contamination presents a risk and to such a question there can never be a totally satisfactory answer. In matters such as this, no scientific experiment can ever prove a negative; it is possible to demonstrate toxicity when something undesirable is observed but not the absence of toxicity when something undesirable is not observed. The British Advisory Committee on Pesticides reviewed the safety of 2,4,5-T in 1980 and advised the Minister of Agriculture that it could continue to be used. The advice, reasserted in 1982, was accepted by the Minister. However, reports from Sweden and elsewhere (e.g. Hardell, 1981) gave cause for concern that some soft-tissue sarcomas are several times more common in workers who spray 2,4,5-T than in control groups. Consequently, many countries have severely restricted the use of 2,4,5-T, even though the level of hazard is disputed. The possibility of dioxin

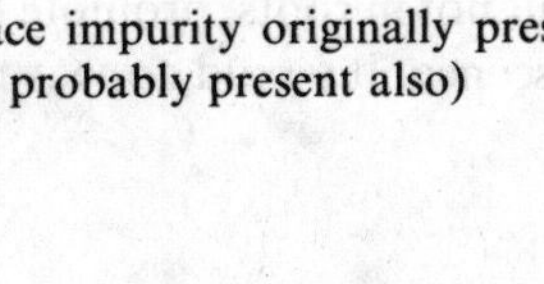

TCDD; 2,3,7,8-tetrachlorodibenzo-*p*-dioxin

Figure 14.7 Dioxin—a trace impurity originally present in 2,4,5-T (closely related analogues are probably present also)

being formed, photochemically or otherwise, from pure phenoxyacetic acid herbicides *after* application should also be borne in mind.

Typical members of the phenoxyalkanoic acid family are foliar poisons. At high dosage they can, however, penetrate through some types of soil to plant roots, which they readily enter (compare mecoprop above). Translocation from the leaves is normally in the *symplast*, and factors that favour photosynthesis, such as warmth, good lighting and high humidity, also favour translocation of both food materials and phenoxyalkanoic acid herbicides. This is illustrated by the work of Schultz and Burnside (1980), who demonstrated that 2,4-D was absorbed by, and translocated out of, leaves of hemp dogbane (*Apocynum cannabinum*) for 12 days after application, that higher light intensity resulted in more 2,4-D reaching the roots, and that autoradiographs showed a typical symplastic movement. These considerations are particularly important if the object is to kill subterranean parts of perennial weeds—the best time to do this is evidently when food reserves are being deposited in late spring and in early autumn. Since high concentrations of herbicide may cause premature collapse of aerial tissues, two or three applications at lower rates may be more advantageous than one application at a high rate.

If applied to soil, salts of MCPA and 2,4-D are readily washed away or decomposed by microorganisms. Degradation is promoted by environmental factors that favour microbial growth, including suitable temperature, moisture and air content of the soil. Consequently, at low rates of application the herbicides usually disappear in 1–4 weeks but they can persist much longer when the soil is cold or dry. An example is provided by Smith (1982) who applied ^{14}C-labelled MCPA to soils in a controlled environment (20°C and 85 per cent field moisture capacity). At 1 kg/ha equivalent, MCPA, whether it was alone or mixed with herbicides such as triallate, trifluralin and diclofop, had a half-life of about two weeks; with the exception of asulam, none of the co-herbicides had any adverse effects on the soil microorganisms that degrade MCPA. On the other hand, most if not all of the mono- and dichlorinated members of the phenoxyacetic acid family undergo **enhanced degradation** if applied on several occasions to the same soil. This process of 'enrichment' with microorganisms capable of rapidly metabolising the compound concerned was described in section 13.5. It should be noted that 2,4,5-T does not readily cause 'enrichment' and its greater persistence in soil is in part attributable to this fact.

Typical symptoms of the phytotoxic effects of MCPA and similar compounds include contorted growth, malformed leaves and severe epinasty of stems and petioles. Such symptoms probably reflect the fact that these herbicides are chemically related to the auxin group of plant growth regulators. Unfortunately, little is known about how natural auxins function (their effects cannot be demonstrated in cell-free systems). However, they promote cell enlargement in shoots but not in roots, promote the growth of lateral roots and of fruit, and delay senescence. It would appear that 2,4-D and MCPA act as **persistent auxins**, the concentration of which does not fluctuate in response to stimuli in the way characteristic of natural auxins. High concentrations of indolylacetic acid (IAA), a natural auxin, produce symptoms similar to those elicited by 2,4-D.

The primary effect of phenoxyacetic acid herbicides on plants is to cause aberrant growth of young, rapidly growing tissues near the meristem. The problem arises in trying to explain why such abnormal growth occurs, for much work over many years has shown a plethora of physiological and biochemical systems to undergo change. There is evidence that auxins stimulate cell wall development and, if so, phenoxyalkanoic acid herbicides may interfere with the metabolism of pectin methyl esters or of some other component of young cell walls. In addition, when hypocotyl cells are exposed to these herbicides, the quantity of ribonucleic acid produced increases several-fold. Microscopical examination of transverse sections of stems of susceptible plants often reveals that the extra RNA and protein translated from it has led to such cell proliferation that the vascular system is crushed (the arrangement of cambium and vascular bundles is different in the stems of monocotyledons and dicotyledons).

It has been postulated that *natural* auxins function by interacting with the plasma membrane of cells, causing an unknown factor (possibly a secondary messenger) to be released, which travels across the cytoplasm to the nucleus, where it modifies transcription in some way. Analogous events are known to occur in animals in response to circulating hormones. Since phenoxyacetic acid herbicides seem to be auxin-like, it has been further suggested that these also react with the plasma membrane and then, by their continued presence, cause transcription to be unnaturally prolonged. This could explain the symptomatic proliferation of RNA that was mentioned above.

These possibilities seem to be supported by work done by Hardin *et al.* (1972) on reconstituted systems containing RNA polymerase, cell membranes, calf thymus DNA and tritium-labelled nucleotides. In view of the obvious importance of this work it is surprising that few follow-up investigations have been reported in the last decade. Nevertheless, Guilfoyle *et al.* (1975) have shown that, whereas soluble RNA polymerase in plant cells only increases 30 per cent on application of auxin-type herbicides, the amount of chromatin-bound RNA polymerase increases up to eight-fold. The possibility therefore exists that auxins and auxin-like herbicides alter the pattern of gene expression and, in the case of the herbicides, the persistent auxin effect leads to such over-expression that a cataclysmic disturbance of the whole anabolic machinery takes place.

Whatever receptor or enzyme is the target of phenoxyacetic acid herbicides, clear structural requirements exist for auxin-like activity. All the compounds possess a carboxyl group (esters hydrolyse before acting at the site of action) and all are substituted in the 2 and 4 positions of the (aromatic) phenoxy ring. A variety of models have been proposed to explain such requirements, one of the earliest of which is the three-point attachment theory of Wain and Fawcett (1969). This theory postulates that an auxin receptor has three recognition sites, one of which associates with an ionised carboxyl group, one with an aromatic ring structure (or perhaps with a positive charge located on it) and one with a hydrogen atom (figure 14.8a). In addition, the overall dimensions of the molecule and its lipophilic–hydrophilic balance must be right, since it must fit into, rather than onto, a three-dimensional receptor surface. A refinement that extends the application of the model to natural auxin (IAA) and to other growth-regulating herbicides such as dicamba (section 14.5) suggests that a distance of 0.55 nm must exist between the negative charge of the carboxyl group and a positive charge associated with the aromatic centre (figure 14.8b).

The Wain–Fawcett model, with embellishments, adequately explains many structural features of molecules with auxin-like activity. In particular, it explains why, when a chiral centre (in this case, an asymmetric carbon atom) is present in the molecule, it is always found that only one of the two

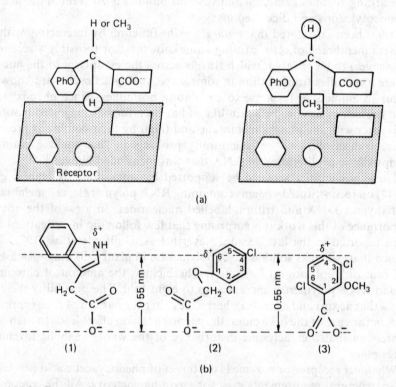

Figure 14.8   Proposed auxin–receptor binding: (a) the three-point attachment theory (only one of a pair of stereoisomers fits); (b) allowing for natural valency angles, the O^- and the δ^+ centre are 0.55 nm apart in (1) IAA, (2) phenoxyacetic acid derivatives and (3) dicamba

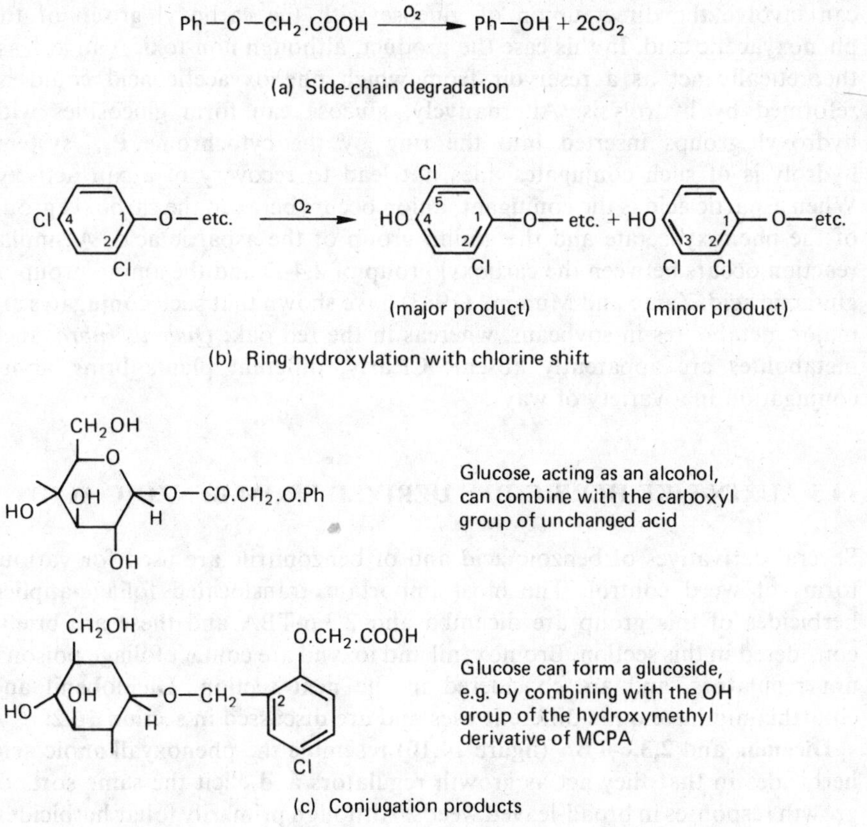

$$Ph-O-CH_2.COOH \xrightarrow{O_2} Ph-OH + 2CO_2$$

(a) Side-chain degradation

(major product)   (minor product)

(b) Ring hydroxylation with chlorine shift

Glucose, acting as an alcohol, can combine with the carboxyl group of unchanged acid

Glucose can form a glucoside, e.g. by combining with the OH group of the hydroxymethyl derivative of MCPA

(c) Conjugation products

Figure 14.9 Detoxication of phenoxyacetic acid herbicides

stereoisomers is biologically active (stereoisomers are, in this context, as different from one another 'as chalk and cheese'). Examples among the phenoxyacetic acid herbicides are mecoprop and dichlorprop (figure 14.6c, d). A more sophisticated model has been proposed by Katekar (1979).

The metabolism of phenoxyacetic acid herbicides conforms to the general principles outlined in chapter 3. Literature on their metabolism in plants has been reviewed by Loos (1975) and that on the metabolism of 2,4-D in animals has been covered by Menzie (1980).

In most plants, side-chain degradation of phenoxyacetic acid herbicides is probably a minor metabolic route, although it may be relatively more important in redcurrants, bedstraws (*Galium* spp.) and some varieties of apples. A substituted phenol is the final product. **Ring hydroxylation** is usually the major metabolic route. Aromatic compounds chlorinated on C-4 are often hydroxylated in this position and, in such cases, the chlorine atom is not substituted but 'migrates' to the C-3 or C-5 position (figure 14.9). **Conjugation** can involve the direct union of glucose with the carboxyl group of the phenoxyacetic acid. In this case the product, although non-toxic, can at least theoretically act as a reservoir from which phenoxyacetic acid could be reformed by hydrolysis. Alternatively, glucose can form glucosides with hydroxyl groups inserted into the ring by the cytochrome P_{450} system; hydrolysis of such conjugates does not lead to recovery of auxin activity. When aspartic acid is the conjugant, union occurs between the carboxyl group of the phenoxyacetate and the amino group of the aspartic acid. A similar reaction occurs between the carboxyl group of 2,4-D and the amino group of glutamic acid. Zama and Mumma (1983) have shown that such conjugates are major metabolites in soybeans, whereas in the red oak, *Quercus rubra*, such metabolites are apparently absent. Clearly, different plants bring about conjugation in a variety of ways.

14.5 AUXIN-LIKE HERBICIDES DERIVED FROM BENZOIC ACID

Several derivatives of benzoic acid and of benzonitrile are used for various forms of weed control. The most important translocated foliage-applied herbicides of this group are dicamba and 2,3,6-TBA and these are briefly considered in this section. Bromoxynil and ioxynil are contact foliage poisons, not regulators, and are considered in the next section. Dichlobenil and chlorthiamid have quite different uses and are discussed in section 16.2.

Dicamba and **2,3,6-TBA** (figure 14.10) resemble the phenoxyalkanoic acid herbicides in that they act as growth regulators and elicit the same sorts of growth responses in broad-leaved weeds. Although primarily foliar herbicides, they are much more effective than are most phenoxyalkanoic compounds when applied to the soil. In Britain, dicamba and 2,3,6-TBA (in the form of potassium or sodium salts) are only available in mixtures with various phenoxyalkanoic acids, so their main purpose is to add range and versatility to the herbicidal spectrum of these compounds. According to the recommendations of Fryer and Makepeace (1978) they are used in circumstances where one or more of the aggressive or refractory species shown in table 14.4 are present.

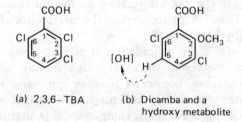

(a) 2,3,6–TBA (b) Dicamba and a hydroxy metabolite

Figure 14.10 Growth regulators based on benzoic acid: (a) 2,3,6-trichlorobenzoic acid; (b) 3,6-dichloro-2-methoxybenzoic acid

Table 14.4 Troublesome species that often respond to mixtures of a benzoic acid herbicide and a phenoxyacetic acid herbicide such as mecoprop or MCPA

Black bindweed (*Polygonum convolvulus*)	Knotgrass (*Polygonum aviculare*)
Camomile (*Anthemis arvensis* and *A. cotula*)	Mouse-ear (*Cerastium holosteoides*)
Chickweed (*Stellaria media*)	Pineapple weed (*Matricaria matricarioides*)
Cleavers (*Galium aparine*)	Redshank (*Polygonum persicaria*)
Corn spurrey (*Spergula arvensis*)	Scented mayweed (*Matricaria recutita*)
Docks (*Rumex* spp.)	Yarrow (*Achillea millefolium*)

Auch and Arnold (1979) reported that 31 per cent of soybean farmers whom they surveyed in South Dakota used dicamba on this crop. The yield of crop was adversely affected if dicamba was used at the flowering stage and germination was reduced if it was used at the pod-fill stage. Residues could be detected on foliage seven days but not 18 days after application. Barlow and Hicks (1985) investigated the use of dicamba to control problem broad-leaf weeds in maize in France and Germany. When used early post-emergence, tank-mixed with atrazine, it gave good control of *Amaranthus* spp., *Polygonum* spp. and *Solanum nigrum*; used alone at a higher application rate it controlled *Calystegia sepium*, *Convolvulus arvensis* and *Cirsium arvense*, although slight crop damage sometimes occurred.

The major route of dicamba metabolism in several plant species studied involves the hydroxylation of position C-5 of the benzene ring. Little of this hydroxylated metabolite accumulates in most species because it is rapidly conjugated with glucose. In soil, dicamba is poorly adsorbed onto soil constituents, so it washes down nearly as rapidly as does the wash water. Adsorption is strongest in soils of low pH value. It is of intermediate persistence in most soils, its disappearance being most rapid under conditions that favour bacterial growth.

In contrast to dicamba, 2,3,6-TBA does not appear to be readily metabolised by plants (compare this with the relative rates of metabolism of methoxychlor and DDT, which have respectively a methoxy and a chlorine substituent in the ring). Nor does 2,3,6-TBA disappear rapidly from soil; in one North Carolina soil, active residues could still be detected 18 months after applying 9 kg/ha. On the other hand, adsorption onto most soil constituents is very limited, so it tends to disappear from damp soils by leaching. Loss by volatilisation probably also limits soil persistence.

Two minor herbicides have structures somewhat similar to dicamba and probably have auxin-like properties since they affect RNA synthesis and protein metabolism. They are chloramben (3-amino-2,5-dichlorobenzoic acid) and picloram (3-amino-3,5,6-trichloropyridine-2-carboxylic acid). **Chloramben** is used for pre-emergence weed control in legumes and is active both through foliage and via the soil. It is reported to be useful for pre-emergence weed control in maize and soybeans, especially when used in combination with atrazine.

Picloram, in common with other auxin-like compounds, stimulates cell elongation at low concentrations (1 µM) and causes an increase in the rate of RNA synthesis within a few hours of treatment. It is readily translocated and is used to control deep-rooted perennials and some annual weeds in cereals and sugar cane, for which purposes it is often used jointly with 2,4-D. In the UK it has been used against *Rumex* spp. and *Senecio jacobea*, both of which can be problem weeds. It has also been used to control certain woody species. In soil, it is only slowly decomposed by microorganisms.

14.6 BROMOXYNIL AND IOXYNIL

These contact herbicides have *little or no action through the soil*. Their practical importance rests in the fact that, while most grasses tolerate them, they attack the seedlings of several troublesome broad-leaved weeds that are not readily controlled by phenoxyalkanoic acid herbicides. The range of species they attack when used at economic concentrations is limited, a disadvantage that is usually offset by using them in mixtures with other herbicides.

As well as being nitriles (figure 14.11) these sparingly soluble solids are also halogenated phenols and are, in consequence, acidic substances ($pK_a \simeq 4.0$) capable of forming both salts and esters. As would be expected, the salts are more soluble in water and less persistent as foliar sprays than are the esters. Many formulations contain octanoic acid esters, together with adequate spreading agent to achieve the good coverage that is essential for successful contact action.

Bromoxynil and ioxynil enter leaves through the cuticle, killing by a rapid contact action. Nevertheless, studies with radioactive bromoxynil have shown that very small quantities are translocated. Most of the radioactivity of ^{14}C-labelled bromoxynil does, however, remain in the treated leaves of both resistant and susceptible species.

Bromoxynil and ioxynil were introduced in the 1960s primarily for the control of a narrow range of broad-leaf weeds in cereals, sugar cane, flax, onions and grasses. Although they are in many ways similar, both weeds and crops can vary in relative sensitivity, as Sanders and Pallett (1986) have illustrated in respect to their effects on *Matricaria inodora* and *Viola arvensis* (actually, they used these differences to investigate the mode of action of this group of herbicides). Ioxynil is the preferred herbicide for weed control in newly sown lawns and it is also used for weed control in onions and leeks. In all of these cases, for maximal benefit, they should only be applied under optimal environmental conditions.

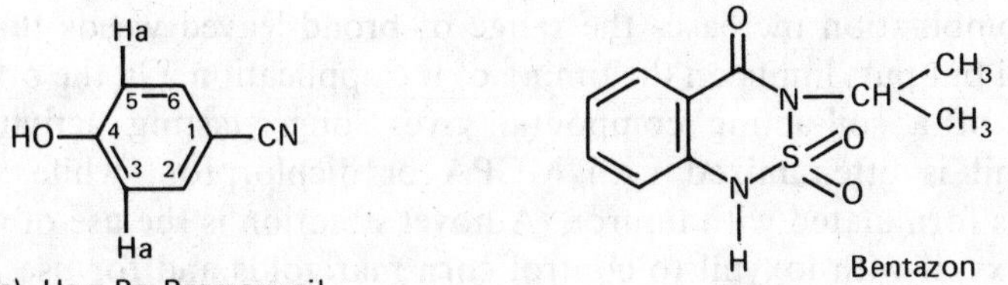

(a) Ha = Br; Bromoxynil
(b) Ha = I; Ioxynil

(c)

Bentazon

Figure 14.11 Bromoxynil, ioxynil and bentazon

Bromoxynil and ioxynil are often used in spring cereals to control *weeds resistant to MCPA and 2,4-D*. Some of these weeds are listed in table 14.5. Timing of the application is critical for good results—when weed seedlings have passed beyond the four-leaf stage they often respond poorly. Established weeds are usually resistant. The stage of development of the crop is usually not very critical. This versatility is of some practical importance, since it makes possible the use of bromoxynil as an emergency spray on winter cereals that have passed the stage where phenoxyacetic acids can be safely employed.

With the exception of the use of ioxynil for weed control in newly sown lawns, both bromoxynil and ioxynil are usually applied in mixtures with a (translocated) hormone-type herbicide or with a soil-acting substance. The

Table 14.5 Weeds resistant to some phenoxyalkanoic acids but the seedlings of which can be controlled by bromoxynil or ioxynil

(a) *Weeds of frequent importance*

Mayweeds, several kinds (*Matricaria* spp.)	Hempnettle (*Galeopsis tetrahit*)[a]
Black bindweed (*Polygonum convolvulus*)	Corn marigold (*Chrysanthemum segetum*)[a]
Chickweed (*Stellaria media*)	Fiddleneck (*Amsinckia intermedia*)[b]
Knot grass (*Polygonum aviculare*)	Mustards (resistant)[b]
Speedwells, several kinds (*Veronica* spp.)[c]	Wild buckwheat[b]

(b) *Weeds of occasional importance*[d]

Fool's parsley (*Aethusa cynapium*)	Bugloss (*Lycopsis arvensis*)
Scarlet pimpernel (*Anagallis arvensis*)	Forget-me-not (*Myosotis arvensis*)
Chamomile (*Anthemis* spp.)	Corn poppy (*Popaver rhoeas*)
Mouse-ear (*Cerastium holosteoides*)[e]	Redshank (*Polygonum persicaria*)
Fumitory (*Fumaria officinalis*)	Groundsel (*Senecio vulgaris*)

[a] Better control when mixed with linuron.
[b] In the USA (Klingman and Ashton, 1975).
[c] A good way to control slender speedwell (*Veronica filiformis*) in established lawns (Fryer and Makepeace, 1977).
[d] Selected from Fryer and Makepeace (1978, pp. 15–20).
[e] Best control is at the young plant stage.

former combination increases the range of broad-leaved weeds that can be controlled but puts limits on the timing of the application. On the other hand, inclusion of a soil-acting compound gives longer-lasting activity. Thus, bromoxynil is often mixed with MCPA or dichlorprop, while ioxynil is sometimes formulated with linuron. A novel situation is the use of a mixture of bromoxynil with ioxynil to control corn marigolds and for use in under-sown cereals (MAFF, 1985).

Herbicidal action occurs in two stages. There is a rapid contact action that causes local blisters or necrotic spots within 36 h of spraying. Thereafter, the damage spreads, with deterioration of leaf tissue in target leaves and the development of chlorosis in untreated leaves. The latter occurs despite the fact that very little herbicide appears to move into untreated leaves, and it eventually leads to the death of the plant.

Merritt (1984) investigated the effect of environmental factors on the activity of ioxynil formulated as a salt and as an ester. Low soil moisture before spraying greatly reduced the susceptibility of *Stellaria media* to both formulations. Raising the temperature after spraying increased the toxicity of the ester but changes in humidity played a subordinate role. On the other hand, raising the humidity after spraying increased the activity of the salt. The author also stressed the interacting nature of environmental effects; for example, while factors that enhance transpiration (higher light intensity, higher temperature, higher wind speed) generally increase toxicity, they also increase the moisture stress in tissues for a plant growing in soil of a given moisture content, a situation that would tend to reduce toxicity.

Both bromoxynil and ioxynil interfere with a wide range of biochemical processes in plants or plant organelles. They destabilise lipoprotein mem-branes, inhibit the Hill reaction in isolated chloroplasts, affect mitochondrial electron transport and inhibit the synthesis of proteins. In addition, they prevent the incorporation of carbon dioxide into acetyl coenzyme A, and thus prevent the formation of the malonyl coenzyme A needed for fatty acid biosynthesis. They also inhibit the reduction of $NADP^+$, and therefore interfere with the photosynthetic reduction of carbon dioxide.

For bromoxynil-treated plants to respond quickly, the treated plants must be illuminated. This fact, together with other effects just mentioned, favours the hypothesis that these herbicidal nitriles affect the light reaction of photosynthesis. A likely target is the **electron transport system** that connects electrons from photosystem II with the positive moiety formed in photosystem I (figure 14.2). Some workers have suggested that a probable locus is the quinonoid carrier, plastoquinone. It is therefore of some interest that ioxynil, which also interferes with mitochondrial oxidative phosphorylation, appears to exert its effect at or near the quinone carrier, ubiquinone (Kirkwood, 1976).

It thus seems that the reduced levels of ATP evident in bromoxynil-poisoned plants could be caused by interference with *both photosynthetic and oxidative* phosphorylation. Interference with electron transport in illuminated chloroplasts probably leads to the formation of singlet oxygen or other powerful oxidants; such substances are known to cause peroxidation of membrane lipids with disruption of function and leakage of contents. This could explain the short-term action of bromoxynil and ioxynil. In addition, since almost all ATP is ultimately used to synthesise macromolecules, a lack of ATP could have the longer-term effect of slowing down the synthesis of nucleic acids and proteins, an effect likely to lead to the eventual death of the plant. This could account for the chronic second stage in the action of these herbicides.

Information on the metabolism of bromoxynil is limited and inadequate. Buckland *et al.* (1973) found that the octanoic acid ester was first hydrolysed by wheat seedlings and the nitrile group was then hydrolysed to give substituted benzamide and substituted benzoic acid. The latter then appears to undergo rapid decarboxylation. In addition, there is evidence that bromine is replaced by hydroxyl or by hydrogen in some metabolites. Microorganisms present in some soils appear to be able to degrade bromoxynil all the way to carbon dioxide (Hsu and Camper, 1975).

So far as selectivity is concerned, a large number of morphological and biochemical factors have been implicated from time to time but the reason for selectivity remains obscure. Sanders and Pallett (1986) provided excellent electron micrographs showing ultrastructural changes that occurred when bromoxynil and ioxynil were applied to a susceptible species, *Matricaria inodora*, and to a moderately resistant species, *Viola arvensis*. *M. inodora* developed necrosis within four days with concomitant inhibition of carbon dioxide fixation. The chloroplasts swelled and, by seven days, showed ultra-structural changes of the thylakoid membranes that are typical in other contexts of photo-oxidation. On the other hand, the more resistant *V. arvensis* recovered after a period of static growth, and an increase in granal stack size occurred, which the authors interpreted as a compensatory adaptation.

More generally, while differential spray retention has been excluded as a primary cause of selectivity, there is evidence that different rates of metab-olism may partly explain the different tolerances of monocotyledonous and of some dicotyledonous plants to these compounds. However, the possibility cannot be excluded that there might be an innate difference in sensitivity at the site of action in sensitive and tolerant plants. Szigeti and his colleagues at the University of Budapest have extensively studied many aspects of the chemistry and mode of action of the benzonitriles. For example, Bujtas *et al.* (1985) reported that benzonitrile esters affected uptake of potassium by excised roots of wheat seedlings and found that biological activity correlated well with lipophilicity if a steric parameter for a second ring structure was included in the equation; the trouble with any such mathematical approach, is, of course, that it does not take cognisance of different *intensities* of biological activity — i.e., for selectivity of action.

14.7 BENTAZON

Bentazon(e) has an unusual structure (figure 14.11c) in that the molecule contains a heterocyclic ring containing a sulphur atom as well as two nitrogen atoms. The substance has a solubility of about 500 mg/l at 20°C.

Bentazon is marketed as a post-emergence herbicide for the control of broad-leaf weeds and sedges in many graminaceous crops, including rice and maize, and in some Leguminosae, including peas, beans and soybeans. For these purposes it is often mixed with phenoxyacetic acid or other herbicides. In the USA, it is used to control cocklebur, morning glory, nightshade and shepherd's purse and to suppress Canada thistle and yellow nutsedge. In Tanzania Ritoine *et al.* (1982) found that a mixture of bentazon and propanil (3 kg + 2 kg per hectare) was superior to all other weedkillers tested for the control of weeds in transplanted rice for a time of up to 80 days post-treatment. Among the weeds controlled were *Scirpus maritimus*, *Ammania baccifera*, *Ludwigia abyssinica* and *Ipomea aquatica*. Similarly, in Nigeria, Akobundu (1981) reported that bentazon treatment of direct-seeded rice increased yields (mainly in consequence of its ability to control sedges) and that 2 kg/ha gave better results than were obtained by two hand-weedings. Bentazon gives best results when weeds are small but are nevertheless actively growing. It is predominantly a contact herbicide, for it is poorly translocated; moreover, it does not act efficiently through the soil. Those parts of leaves that come into direct contact with bentazon soon show signs of necrosis and this is followed by death within a few days.

The herbicidal efficiency of bentazon is dependent on the environmental conditions. Potter and Wergin (1975) demonstrated that its phytotoxicity was light-dependent. Teasdale and Thimijan (1983) showed that an increase in either light or temperature after treatment increased its toxicity to cucumber plants but that the influence of light was the more profound. The two important weeds, *Xanthium pensylvanicum* and *Chenopodium album*, both show accelerated necrosis as the intensity of light after treatment increases. More generally, the greatest toxicity has been observed when the light intensity was low before application but high after it. Other workers have demonstrated that most weeds are more susceptible when the temperature and the humidity are both high. When plants are exposed to bentazon, ultrastructural changes take place that are consistent with it having an effect on the electron transport system in chloroplasts (Moreland, 1980). However, as Corbett *et al.* (1984) illustrate in table 2.3 of their book, the I_{50} of bentazon for the Hill reaction using chloroplasts derived from both susceptible and tolerant plants of *Amaranthus retroflexus* is very large (approximately 40 µM). This compares with much smaller values for typical triazines, ureides and uracils (e.g. 0.36, 0.06 and 0.25 µM respectively) for susceptible plants.

It is therefore of interest that Cobb *et al.* (1985) have found that it induces rapid changes in turgor in both light and darkness of cells in four different plant systems, namely isolated chloroplasts, stomatal guard cells, abaxial epidermal cells and aetiolated coleoptiles. These systems have one thing in common; according to these authors, each system is sensitive to a specific cation (e.g. in stomata, potassium ions are actively pumped in to balance efflux of protons, while magnesium and calcium ions are similarly involved elsewhere). The authors postulate that the effect of bentazon is to interfere with this process, perhaps by binding with the cell membrane.

Type C: Herbicides to control grassy weeds

14.8 DALAPON

This substance is one of two chlorinated aliphatic acids commonly employed as herbicides, the other being trichloroacetic acid, TCA. Both compounds are used in the form of their sodium salts, but whereas TCA is usually applied pre-planting to soil to control couch and other grasses, dalapon is internally translocated after application to foliage. Dalapon has a high LD_{50} but is irritant to the skin. It is soluble in water and hydrolyses slowly in aqueous solution with the loss of chlorine from the molecule.

$$CH_3 - \underset{\underset{Cl}{|}}{\overset{\overset{Cl}{|}}{C}} - COO^- \cdots \cdots H^+$$

Dalapon

Dalapon is formulated as its sodium salt, dalapon-Na, and is particularly **effective against grasses**. In this respect it resembles aminotriazole, compared with which it is often somewhat cheaper for an equi-effective dose rate. It has to be applied at a rather high application rate (up to 16 kg/ha) and six months may need to elapse between the final spraying and the sowing of a new crop. It thus persists for considerably longer than aminotriazole.

Grasses, and especially perennial and stoloniferous grasses, have become increasingly troublesome in recent years as a consequence of the removal of broad-leaved competitors by the action of the very effective hormone-type weedkillers (section 14.4). In Britain, couch grass (*Agropyron repens*), wild oats (*Avena fatua* and *A. ludoviciana*) and blackgrass (*Alopecurus myosuroides*) are controlled by dalapon, while in the USA it is frequently used against bermuda grass (*Cynodon dactylon*) and couch or quack grass (*Agropyron repens*). For many of these, better control often follows the application of two smaller doses rather than one larger one, for this prevents too rapid a kill and hence allows greater time for subterranean translocation.

Millhollon (1985) reported partial success in the control of *Sorghum halepense* (Johnson grass), which is a serious competitor to such crops as sugar cane, sorghum, corn and cotton. The main problem in the control of this weed is that buds on the rhizomes are numerous and allow it to escape ready control either by cultivation or by application of foliar herbicides. Millhollon reported that only 40 per cent of plants were killed by repeated applications of (*inter alia*) dalapon at 8 kg/ha; however, the use of dalapon resulted in a diminution of the number of surviving buds on the rhizomes to only 20 per cent of those on untreated plants, thereby reducing the rate at which the weed spread.

Dalapon is used for pasture improvement and for the control of reeds and sedges. It can also be used pre-planting or pre-sowing of several crops, mainly but not exclusively to control grassy weeds. It can be used pre-emergence of potatoes and sugar beet as well as in dormant, established perennial crops such as some fruit trees, canes and bushes. In a few instances it has been used after the crop has emerged, examples being sugar beet, carrot and oilseed rape (MAFF, 1985). Bamboo has been reported to be susceptible to a 1 per cent solution applied to the foliage.

Dalapon-Na can enter plants through their roots but it is usually uneconomic to use it in this manner. In the presence of adequate surfactant it enters leaves rapidly and thus, like aminotriazole, it is not very vulnerable to early rain. Once inside the plant it is not firmly bound to tissues, for it can be readily extracted by water. It is **readily translocated**, moving in both the apoplast and the symplast, and it accumulates in meristematic tissues. It appears to move in unchanged form, for few well defined breakdown products have been recognised in plants. Some soil bacteria can, however, decompose it. On the other hand, nitrifying bacteria (but not nitrogen-fixing bacteria) are somewhat sensitive to it.

Considering how many years dalapon has been in use, it is surprising that so little is known about its mode of action. There are no obvious primary targets and it is often said to combine with proteins in a non-specific manner (it resembles its near-relative, trichloroacetic acid, in that it precipitates proteins when used in unbuffered, acidic solutions at concentrations exceeding about 5 mM, but dalapon, it will be recalled, is actually used as its sodium salt). Working with sodium trichloroacetate, Hassall (1961a) found that concentrations above 12 mM caused a three-fold increase in the ratio of acid-soluble phosphate to acid-insoluble phosphate in cells of the alga, *Chlorella vulgaris*, growing in illuminated culture but not when growing heterotrophically in darkness. Again, however, such an alteration is likely to be a secondary effect. More recently, other workers have observed that it inhibits RNA synthesis by 44 per cent when present as a 1 mM solution. It also interferes with the synthesis of pantothenic acid and it disrupts the production of cuticular wax.

14.9 HERBICIDES THAT SELECTIVELY KILL GRASSES POST-EMERGENCE OF CROP

Ecology being what it is, success in one direction can produce problems in another. Nowhere is this more so than in relation to the success of such compounds as the phenoxycarboxylic acids in the control of dicotyledonous (broad-leaf) weeds; grasses can flourish in the absence of competitors, thereby causing considerable crop losses. Especially is this so for perennial grasses that spread vegetatively by development of buds on rhizomes, a problem that is exacerbated by minimum-till cultivation regimes.

For decades the problem was solved in many crops by the use of pre-sow or pre-emergence herbicides. For example, annual grasses and the foliage of perennial grasses can be killed by quaternary ammonium compounds (section 14.1) or, when perennial grass problems are serious, by the foliar application of glyphosate (section 14.2) to destroy subterranean growth. However, such an approach is more applicable to weed control in some crops than others; moreover, it lacks versatility in that the severity of the grass weed problem has to be anticipated, with indiscriminate application to a whole field. In addition, follow-up cultivations (e.g. to bring about desiccation of, or frost damage to rhizomes of perennial grasses) may be costly. The advantages and disadvantages of such pre-emergence use of non-selective herbicides have been discussed by Jones and Orson (1982).

More recently, a new dimension in weed control has been opened up by the discovery of several types of herbicides that are so selectively toxic to many grasses that they have been regarded as safe, at all reasonable concentration levels, to most other crops (Zwick *et al.*, 1985). Even non-graminaceous monocotyledons are usually quite tolerant. In annual crops their major potential is for the control of annual grass weeds (since cultivation, pre-sow or pre-emergence treatments may offer cheap alternative means of control of all kinds of perennial weeds). A section of the 1982 British Crop Protection Conference (BWCC, 1982) is devoted to the use of these new 'graminicides' in a variety of crops, including peas, autumn-sown oilseed rape, potatoes and sugar beet. In addition, they are of major importance for perennial weed control in no-till or minimum-till situations, and in circumstances where perennial (and some other) grasses have become major problems. Examples of grasses that frequently come under this heading are *Cynodon dactylon*, which has been cited as being the cause of one of the world's worst grass problems (Wills, 1984), as well as *Agropyron* (*Elymus*) *repens*, *Sorghum halepense*, *Echinochloa cruss-galli* and *Agrostis* spp.

Post-emergence herbicides that selectively control grasses belong to several different chemical families. Herbicides in one of these families have names that end in *-fop*; for reasons of space, only these will be considered in detail, but the general uses and mode of action of substances in the other families are usually similar to those described below for fluazifop. Substances in a second family have names that end in *-dim*, of which sethoxydim is the best-known example. The structures of these and of related compounds are shown in figure 14.12. In addition, a group of compounds with names ending in *-prop* could also be classified here but, since they are primarily used for the particular purpose of controlling wild oat in cereals, they are more conveniently considered in section 14.10.

Fluazifop-butyl

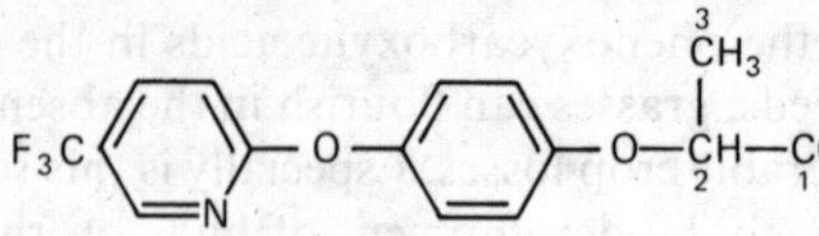

Others: diclofop-methyl; haloxyfop-methyl; quizalofop-ethyl

(a) Aryloxyphenoxy-2-propionate esters

Sethoxydim-sodium

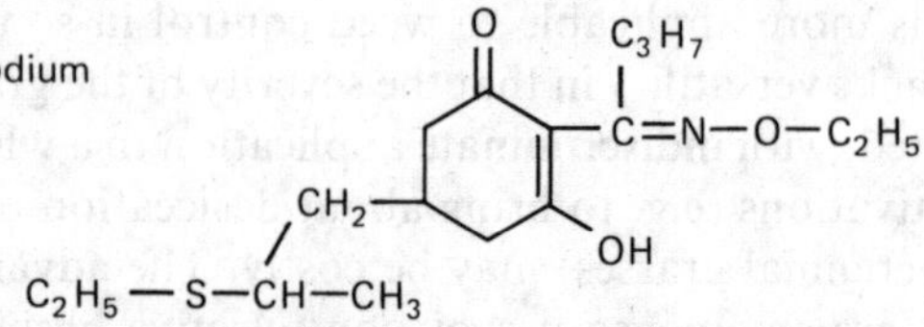

Others: alloxydim-sodium; cycloxydim

(b) Sethoxydim family

Figure 14.12 Structures of members of families of selective post-emergence grass-killers

Most selective grass-killers are formulated as emulsifiable solutions. They should not be used with unauthorised wetting agents (MAFF, 1985), nor should they ever be mixed with other herbicides unless the latter have been specifically recommended for the purpose. One important reason for this restriction is that several types of herbicides, but especially members of the phenoxyacetic acid group, tend to antagonise the action of fluazifop and sethoxydim.

The antagonistic interaction of auxin-type herbicides with 'graminicides' is already well documented (see Fedtke, 1982, p. 182) and some further illustrations are provided below. Rhodes and Coble (1984) investigated the action on *Brachiaria platyphylla* and *Paniculum dichotomiflorum* of sethoxydim and bentazon applied together or sequentially. Tank-mixing considerably reduced the grass-killing efficiency of sethoxydim, but by applying the substances sequentially the problem was avoided. Later, working with goosegrass, *Eleusine indica*, the same workers showed that bentazon decreased the foliar absorption of sethoxydim by 50 per cent. Moreover, 6 h after application, 3.5 per cent of the radioactivity was recovered from plant parts other than the treated leaf when sethoxydim was used alone whereas, when used mixed with bentazon, only 1.1 per cent appeared to have been translocated. Rather similarly, Liebl and Worsham (1987) observed that the control of Italian ryegrass, *Lolium multiflorum*, by diclofop was reduced by 27 per cent in the presence of chlorsulfuron; the authors did, however, comment that such a reduction was far less than was usually obtained with mixtures containing auxin-type herbicides such as 2,4-D. Knowledge about possible antagonistic effects of one highly selective herbicide upon another is clearly of practical importance since, for crop protection, there is often a need to attempt to control grasses and broad-leaf weeds simultaneously.

Some aspects of the practical potential for grass control of members of the fluazifop and sethoxydim families are demonstrated by the following examples. Members of both families are used in the UK to control *Agropyron repens*, *Agrostis* spp. and several annual grasses in circumstances that do not allow the use of glyphosate in the previous autumn. The method apparently suffers the disadvantage of being about 30 per cent dearer than is the use of soil-incorporated triallate to achieve similar ends, but this cost differential is often decreased by the fact that post-emergence treatment allows its selective use so that only those parts of a field that are heavily infested need be treated (Breay, 1982).

Targanyi and Mikulas (1982) have described the use of fluazifop for the control of *Cynodon dactylon* and *Agropyron repens* in severely infested Hungarian vineyards. Zwick *et al.* (1985) reported that non-graminaceous crops tolerate up to 2 kg/ha, a dose that is often 4–20 times the effective rate of application for grass control in cotton, potatoes, tobacco and vines. Lawson and Wiseman (1982) have, however, reported some damage to brassica crops, especially calabrese, at application rates of fluazifop and sethoxydim of as low as 1 kg/ha. Ivany (1984) has described the use of sethoxydim for the control of *Agropyron repens* in potatoes and Carter and Keeley (1987) used fluazifop for the control of *Sorgum halepense* in cotton. Reference has already been made to contributions in the 1982 British Crop Protection Conference (BWCC, 1982).

All uses of these compounds so far described have involved the spraying of foliage, but some of the compounds shown in figure 14.12 have also been used successfully as soil herbicides, albeit at somewhat higher rates of application to achieve comparable results. Stahlman (1984) used diclofop pre-emergence of wheat and alfalfa for the control of *Bromus tectorum* (which, like *Poa annua*, is not always readily controlled by post-emergence treatments). Diclofop is metabolised by microorganisms and has a half-life of 10–30 days in a normal range of soils. The persistence of sethoxydim in prairie soils has been investigated by Smith and Hsiao (1983); in 'living' soil its half-life is similar to that of diclofop but, in air-dried soils, 94 per cent of an applied dose was recovered unchanged 28 days later. Some compounds of the group have also been used for seed treatment. For example, Dale (1983) used fluazifop, mixed with oil, as an effective seed treatment for soybeans and cotton; 4.5 g/kg of cotton seed, planted into soil pre-seeded with *Eleusine indica*, resulted in a weed-free band 12 cm wide centred on the row of seeds.

Environmental factors often influence the rate of uptake of fluazifop and related substances. Kells *et al.* (1984) showed that foliar absorption in both the tolerant soybean and the susceptible *A. repens* increased as the temperature was raised from 20 to 30°C. It is noteworthy, however, that the level of tolerance is related neither to the rate of absorption nor to the rate of translocation. Thus, in the work just cited, absorption by the tolerant soybean, at 75 per cent of the applied dose in 6 h, was twice as fast as was absorption by the susceptible grass. Similarly Ikai *et al.* (1985) studied the rate of uptake of another aryloxyphenoxy derivative, quizalofop-ethyl, by 80 cm tall plants of *Sorghum halepense*. Small but lethal amounts of ^{14}C-labelled quizalofop were applied to leaves, which were removed and washed at different times after application. After 24 h about one-third of the herbicide had penetrated the leaf and small (but very important) amounts were found in untreated leaves (0.59 per cent), as well as at the stem base (0.14 per cent) and in the root system (0.11 per cent). By the sixth day over half had penetrated the leaf but the percentages translocated to the same three areas had not increased and so these small amounts are evidently sufficient to be lethal. Leaf yellowing and complete cessation of growth had occurred by 24 h after application and a rapid decrease in viability of rhizome buds occurred thereafter.

Carr *et al.* (1985) studied the uptake and translocation of fluazifop-butyl in *Setaria viridis*. Uptake by foliage at the 3–4 leaf stage was rapid, all except 5 per cent of the dose being absorbed within 24 h. However, only 2 per cent of the applied dose translocated from the treated leaf and only 0.75 per cent accumulated in the apical meristem. Similarly, Chandrasena and Sagar (1984) studied the effect of fluazifop-butyl on *Agropyron repens* under greenhouse conditions. At the lower range of the doses used (0.12–1.0 kg/ha equivalent) translocation to the rhizomes had occurred within 6–48 h of application and 90 per cent of rhizome buds had accumulated a lethal dose within 72 h of application. At 0.25 kg/ha 31, 72 and 92 per cent of the rhizome buds were found to be non-viable when investigated at 2, 24 and 48 h respectively.

For perennial grass control, environmental conditions and timing of the application must be carefully chosen for optimal effect. For example, to control *Agropyron repens* in sugar beet, it is essential that the grass is actively growing, with about 30 cm top growth on the largest shoots (Breay, 1982). The same author referred to the need to select optimal weather conditions; if the soil is too dry or the weather too hot, the drought stress will decrease translocation and thereby diminish herbicidal efficiency. Conversely, however, if the weather is too cold there will be slow grass growth and translocation will be poor. Warm, damp conditions encourage plant growth (one reason for waiting till some of the grass shoots are 30 cm high is that this gives the soil time to warm up and this, in turn, encourages activity of buds on rhizomes).

Dekker and Harker (1985) have provided useful bar charts to illustrate the effect of temperature on the translocation and distribution of a photosynthetic product, sucrose, and of three herbicides (haloxyfop, sethoxydim and glyphosate). Coupland (1986) has described the effect of environmental conditions on the ability of fluazifop to damage rhizome buds of *Agropyron repens*. At high light intensity the viability of rhizome buds had decreased significantly within 24 h of spraying; high humidity and (within limits) higher temperatures led to increased damage to rhizome buds (the viability of such buds being the best criterion of efficacy of herbicides used against perennial grasses). They also reported that if field water capacity fell below 50 per cent, complete bud kill was not achieved even at the highest application levels of fluazifop.

The twin questions of why selectivity exists and how aryloxyphenoxy herbicides function cannot be totally separated. Some graminaceous species are much more susceptible to the action of compounds in figure 14.12 than are others, and in such cases, selectivity appears to be closely connected to the rate at which metabolism occurs. Thus Gorecka *et al.* (1981) studied the metabolism of diclofop in shoots of wheat, oats and maize, and observed a high correlation between effectiveness and rate of metabolism (by a useful coincidence, wheat is more resistant than oats, allowing some of the substances shown in the figure to be used to control wild oats in wheat). On the other hand, work on less closely related plants, such as the sensitive maize and the tolerant soybean, has led to the conclusion that the major difference in sensitivity shown by graminaceous plants and dicotyledonous plants is very probably an expression of the existence of a fundamental biochemical difference at the site of action.

The aryloxyphenoxy herbicides have been shown to inhibit IAA-stimulated extension growth in coleoptiles (Shimabukuro *et al.*, 1978) and the uptake of ^{14}C-leucine (Peregoy and Glenn, 1985) and to destroy cells in intercalary meristems (Ikai *et al.*, 1985; Carr *et al.*, 1985). However, it now seems probable that the primary mode of action of compounds such as fluazifop, sethoxydim and flamprop involves some perturbation of **fatty acid biosynthesis** in susceptible plants. Hoppe and Zacher (1985) demonstrated that the incorporation of ^{14}C-labelled acetate into chloroplastic lipids of (susceptible) maize was inhibited by aryloxyphenoxy herbicides such as diclofop but that no such inhibition was evident using corresponding preparations from the tolerant bean. Other evidence to suggest that lipid biosynthesis is affected has been provided by Cho *et al.* (1986) who observed that 0.1 μM haloxyfop inhibited by 42 per cent the incorporation of acetate by cell suspension cultures of maize cells. Inhibition was also possible using cell suspension cultures of (tolerant) soybean but the effective dose was 47-fold greater. Carr *et al.* (1985) similarly demonstrated that 0.1 μM fluazifop inhibited acetate incorporation into lipids of *Setaria viridis*.

Fatty acid synthesis in green plants occurs in the chloroplasts, the membranes of which are strikingly different from other membranes in plants and animals (Gounaris *et al.*, 1986). In particular, the only important phospholipid is phosphatidyl glycerol while galactosyl diacyl triglycerides are very common. Whether any differences exist between the structures of thylakoid membranes in grasses and other plants that could account for the specific effects of aryloxyphenoxy herbicides is still under investigation. Nevertheless, the fatty acid synthetase, which is the site of action of these compounds, is bound to such membranes and is known to comprise seven individual enzymes and an acyl carrier protein. Harwood *et al.* (1987) have shown that fluazifop-butyl only affects fatty acid synthesis in chloroplasts of those plants that succumb to this substance when used in the field as a herbicide. Moreover, it was shown that the stereoisomer that was herbicidal was also the one that affected fatty acid synthase in susceptible plants. More specifically, in the case of sensitive barley, (*RS*)-fluazifop-butyl, used at 35 μM, reduced fatty acid synthesis to 14 per cent of the control, whereas even a 100 μM solution of this substance only reduced fatty acid synthesis by 4 per cent in the tolerant pea. The precise reason for the unique sensitivity of fatty acid synthase in chloroplasts of many grasses is unknown, but a possibly significant observation is that levels of fluazifop-butyl that cause only mild inhibition dramatically alter the relative percentages of fatty acids formed from labelled acetate or malonate (Harwood *et al.*, 1987).

Type D: Herbicides to control wild oats and some other grasses in cereals

Herbicides in the previous subdivision (type C) are substances that control grasses selectively in various crops (usually dicotyledons) or non-selectively before a crop is sown or planted. However, it will be recalled that compounds such as diclofop and sethoxydim are much more effective against some members of the Gramineae than others; thus wild oats (*Avena fatua* and *A. ludoviciana*) are very sensitive to such compounds and can be controlled by them if the species or the cultivar of crop is relatively tolerant of them. There is, therefore, some overlap between the uses of some (but not all) of the members of type C and the much narrower uses of the substances considered below in sections 14.10 and 14.11.

14.10 FOLIAGE-APPLIED CARBAMATES AND AMIDES

Barban (figure 14.13) is of low aqueous solubility (11 ppm) and it is formulated as an emulsifiable concentrate. It attacks such troublesome grasses as blackgrass (*Alopecurus myosuroides*) and reed canary-grass (*Phalaris arundinacea*) but it is marketed primarily for the control of wild oats (*Avena fatua* and *A. ludoviciana*) growing among wheat or among some varieties of barley. Such a use is pressing selectivity to its limit—in space-age parlance, there is a very narrow selectivity 'window' indeed, and precise timing is essential. The wild oats seedlings must usually be at the 1.5 to 2 leaf stage: if they are younger

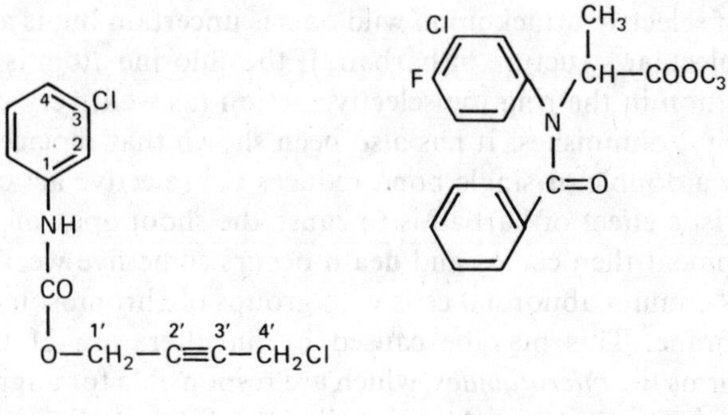

(a) Barban   (b) Flamprop-isopropyl

Figure 14.13 (a) Barban, 4'-chloro-2'-butynyl-3-chlorocarbanilate; (b) flamprop-isopropyl (others are benzoylprop-ethyl and flamprop-methyl)

or older, their growth may be retarded but recovery is likely. Barban is, in fact, not so much a *herbicide* as a growth-retarding substance, and for the full effect to be realised, the competitive growth of the crop is an essential component. Some crop damage has occasionally been reported, especially when cold weather follows immediately after spraying. Oats, buckwheat and some ryes are not tolerant, but an increase in the yield of wheat of as much as 50 per cent has been reported as a result of the suppression of wild oats grown in it. Where both wild oats and dicotyledonous weeds are present, wheat and some other small grains can be sprayed with a mixture of barban and MCPA, but the efficacy of wild oats control can diminish in the presence of phenoxyacetic acid herbicides, possibly because the latter tend to stimulate DNA and protein synthesis whereas barban has the opposite effect (Chow and Taylor, 1983). As well as its use to control wild oats in suitable cereals, barban is employed to control a wider range of grassy weeds in certain legumes, flax, sunflowers, soybeans and sugar beet.

Following foliar application, barban readily enters leaves but its translocation is somewhat restricted and occurs principally in the **apoplastic** system. Translocation is much more marked when contact is with the axils of the leaves. It is readily degraded within the plant, probably to a chloroaniline derivative, the peak of formation of which occurs around the third day after application. Few of the water-soluble metabolites have been unequivocally identified, but it seems probable that aryl hydroxylation is not a major metabolic route in plants. In this respect it is unusual, for most other carbamates are hydroxylated.

Whatever the mechanism of degradation, differential responses by different plants to barban are more likely to be related to differences in metabolism or differences at the site of action than to differences in retention or uptake. In soils, it persists for 2–4 weeks, amidases in soil organisms probably being responsible for most of the degradation.

The cause of selective attack upon wild oats is uncertain but is a function of the precise molecular structure of barban. If the chlorine atom is removed to any other position in the ring the selective action (as well, very often, as the absolute toxicity) diminishes. It has also been shown that replacement of the triple bond by a double or single bond reduces the selective action.

A characteristic effect of barban is to cause the shoot apex of wild oats to swell. Development then ceases and death occurs some five weeks later. The affected apices contain abnormal cells with groups of chromosomes devoid of nuclear membrane. This may be caused by an alteration of the globular protein that forms the *microtubules*, which are responsible for alignment of the chromosomes during mitosis. Additionally, the foliage of poisoned plants often turns dark green, a symptom that is frequently a sign of interference with protein synthesis.

Since barban is a carbamate derivative, its molecules contain the group $-NH.COOC-$. Another type of compound that selectively kills wild oats and some other grasses in cereal (and some other) crops has molecules containing the amide group, $=N.CO.C-$. Examples of members of this group are flamprop-isopropyl (figure 14.13b) and some other compounds with names ending in the suffix -*prop*. The uses of these latter compounds in some ways resemble those of fluazifop and sethoxydim, and the three groups are sometimes classified together. However, the structures of the -*fop* compounds are distinctive and, from a practical viewpoint, the -*prop* compounds control a much narrower range of grasses. Moreover, whereas the mode of action of compounds listed in section 14.9 is interference with lipid biosynthesis, the amides affect apical development and retard growth.

Benzoylprop-ethyl, an early member of the group, is marketed as an emulsifiable concentrate for the control of wild oats in wheat and some other crops, including crops undersown with clover (MAFF, 1985). The same publication recommended that application is not made to wheat crops that are thin, a comment that reinforces the observation above that, to get good results, crop competition is an essential contributory factor. Caution is necessary in the use of this compound on barley for some crop damage has occasionally been reported.

After entry into the plant, hydrolysis of the ester occurs and it is the free acid that is probably the actual toxicant. It is also the free acid that undergoes metabolism, principally by conjugation with glucose to give a glucosidic ester. Neither the ester nor the free acid appear to be freely mobile within plants, irrespective of whether the plants are tolerant of, or susceptible to, benzoyl-prop-ethyl.

The Shell company, who introduced benzoylprop, later produced **flamprop-isopropyl** (figure 14.13b) for use in barley. Its use is essentially the same as that of benzoylprop-ethyl except that it is more toxic to wild oats and less toxic to the crop; like benzoylprop-ethyl, it undergoes rapid hydrolysis, but unlike it, ring-hydroxylated derivatives have been detected in barley (Roberts, 1977). Its metabolism in rats was studied by Hutson *et al.* (1977); the general steps in the metabolism were apparently similar to those in plants, de-esterification being followed by conjugation (with glucuronic acid) and by hydroxylation of the benzoyl ring. However, the word 'de-esterification' was used above because, despite the apparent similarity, there is a possibility that, in some animals, ester cleavage may have been an oxidative rather than a hydrolytic process.

14.11 OTHER SUBSTANCES USED POST-EMERGENCE AGAINST GRASSES

Several other substances have limited or specialist uses in the control of grasses by foliar contact post-emergence of the crop. Among these are difenzoquat, chlorfenquat, oxadiazon and propanil.

Difenzoquat (figure 14.14a) is structurally somewhat similar to the bipyridinium compounds paraquat and diquat. Like them, it forms a quaternary ammonium ion, is soluble in water and is inactivated by soil particles. Unlike them, its principal use is for the control, post-emergence of crop, of wild oats in barley and in some cultivars of autumn-sown wheat. Timing of application is critical; the wild oat seedlings should be at the 3–5 leaf stage and, ideally, weather conditions should be warm and humid.

It rapidly enters foliage and is often said to be a contact poison, bringing about chlorosis and necrosis of the leaf some two weeks after application. For

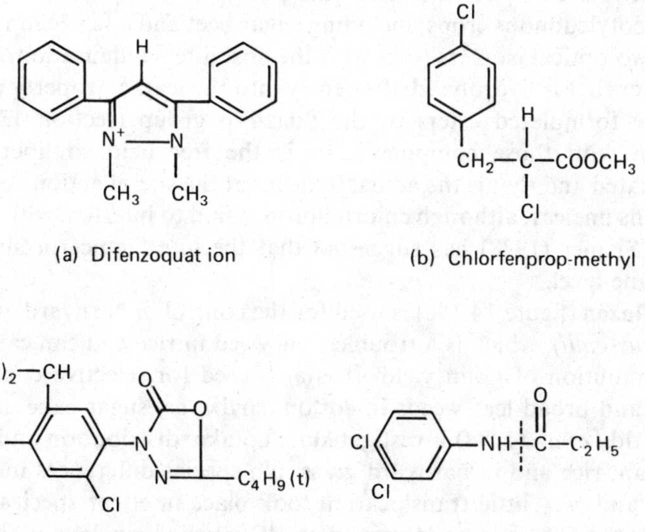

(a) Difenzoquat ion

(b) Chlorfenprop-methyl

(c) Oxadiazon

(d) Propanil

Figure 14.14 Miscellaneous substances that selectively control some grasses

this reason it is often classified with diquat, paraquat, cyperquat and mor-phamquat as a herbicide that inhibits electron transfer from photosystem II (Fedtke, 1982). However, Shaner (1983) has demonstrated that, in addition to this local (paraquat-like) action, a very small but sufficient amount moves from the leaf and inhibits cell division in the meristems. Halling and Behrens (1983) observed that spot applications just below the stem apex of wild oats were more effective than leaf-blade applications and concluded that stunting of growth was a more important symptom of toxicity than foliar damage. They also pointed out that severe symptoms were evident when wild oat was exposed to difenzoquat in the dark, so illumination was not an essential prerequisite to herbicidal activity. The same workers reported that, while it inhibited photophosphorylation at high concentrations (1000 μM), it affected mitochondrial energy transfer reactions of both sensitive and tolerant plants at 10 μM.

The reason why difenzoquat acts in such a selective manner remains obscure. Several groups of workers have established that any differences in retention, absorption or translocation that exist in sensitive species such as wild oat and various tolerant species of plants are apparently insufficient to explain its selective toxicity to *Avena fatua*. In common with paraquat and diquat, it is scarcely metabolised at all in either sensitive or tolerant plants. It is therefore to be suspected that the site of action is in some way structurally different in susceptible and tolerant species, but the nature of that difference is still unknown.

Chlorfenprop-methyl (figure 14.14b) is a liquid that is only slightly soluble in water. It is used to control wild oats post-emergence of barley, wheat and some dicotyledonous crops, including sugar beet and a few legumes. Only one of the two optical isomers (that with the absolute configuration *R*) is toxic. It is an ester that is hydrolysed after entry into the leaf, a property that it shares with the formulated esters of the fluazifop group (section 13.5). Also in common with those compounds, it is the free acid so liberated that is translocated and that is the actual toxicant at the site of action. What that site is remains unclear, although chlorfenprop is said to interfere with the action of auxins. Shaner (1978) has suggested that the interference occurs at the cell membrane level.

Oxadiazon (figure 14.14c) is used for the control of barnyard grass (*Echino-chloa crus-galli*), which is a troublesome weed in rice and can cause consider-able diminution of grain yield. It is also used for selective control of some grasses and broad-leaf weeds in cotton, soybeans, sugar cane and orchards. Achhireddy *et al.* (1984) investigated its uptake, distribution and metabolism in tolerant rice and in barnyard grass. No species differences in uptake were evident and very little translocation took place in either species. Seven days after treatment of barnyard grass with ^{14}C-labelled oxadiazon, 79 per cent of the applied radioactivity was still in the parent compound. Metabolism of oxadiazon in rice is apparently very limited, for at least 75 per cent of the applied radioactivity was still in the form of oxadiazon one month after application.

Propanil (figure 14.14d) is applied after the emergence of both weeds and crop. Its use in Europe is limited but a large percentage of the rice crop in the USA is treated with it (Anderson, 1977). Its primary use is to control barnyard grass, sedges and some broad-leaf weeds. The use of propanil and other herbicides in rice grown in upland dry land, in areas of irregular rainfall and in lowland shallow paddies has been described by Sankaran and De Datta (1985), who also observed that it did not persist for long in water. Kolhe *et al.* (1987) commented that the modern use of short-stature rice cultivars has exacerbated the weed problem, and they investigated the use of several herbicides, separately and in combination, for the control of major weeds in transplanted paddy. Such weeds included *Fimbristylis miliacea, Echinochloa colona* and *Cynodon dactylon*. One of the more successful treatments was a combination of thiobencarb, applied pre-emergence of weeds and four days after transplanting the rice, followed 16 days later by post-emergence application of propanil at 1.0 kg/ha. They reported that, compared with untreated plots, yield was increased by 37 per cent and weed dry matter decreased by 89 per cent.

A major reason why rice is not readily damaged by concentrations of propanil that damage many other Gramineae is that most cultivars are rich in an enzyme that hydrolyses this herbicide to 3,4-dichloroaniline and propionic acid. The enzyme, an (acyl)amidase, is, unusually, associated with the outer membrane of mitochondria (Gaynor and Still, 1983). It will be recalled (chapters 4 and 5) that many esterases are inhibited by organophosphorus and carbamate insecticides, and the same is true of the amidase that gives rice relative immunity to propanil. As a result, crop injury can occur if such *insecticides* are sprayed on to rice too soon after applying propanil. Pelsy *et al.* (1987) have succeeded in isolating a hydrolase from the fungus, *Aspergillus nidulans*, which behaves in a manner very similar to the enzyme in rice; it, too, is inhibited by the carbamate insecticide, carbaryl.

Eberlein and Behrens (1984) have shown that the selective action of propanil on green foxtail, *Setaria viridis*, growing in wheat, is similarly due to the presence in wheat of a mechanism that leads to rapid formation of dichloroaniline; for example, in a 72 h period, 66 per cent of a dose of propanil was converted to dichloroaniline in wheat but only 6.4 per cent was hydrolysed in the foxtail. They also showed that the foxtail retained 7.7 times as much of the applied dose as did the wheat and they regarded this difference as playing an important contributory role in the selective action.

Propanil at low concentrations is an inhibitor of photosynthetic electron transport, possibly at or near to the point at which plastoquinone participates. Whether, however, this is the main toxic action is uncertain. At higher concentrations it attacks chloroplasts and other types of cell membranes and at 1000 μM it uncouples oxidation from phosphorylation.

Type E: Herbicides to control broad-leaf weeds in various dicotyledonous crops

14.12 PHENOXYBUTYRIC ACID DERIVATIVES

MCPB and **2,4-DB** (figure 14.15) have very different uses from their phenoxyacetic acid counterparts. The latter are mostly used to control broad-leaf weeds growing in cereals or lawns; in contrast, these butyric acid derivatives are used to control broad-leaf weeds in certain (but not all) types of legumes.

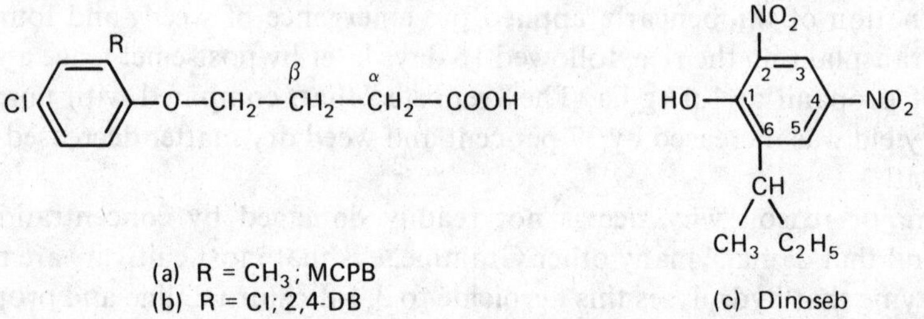

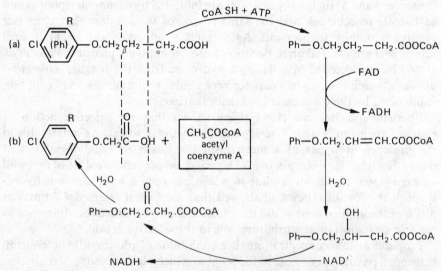

(a) R = CH$_3$; MCPB
(b) R = Cl; 2,4-DB

(c) Dinoseb

Figure 14.15   Herbicides that control broad-leaf weeds in certain broad-leaf crops

Figure 14.16   The β-oxidation of phenoxybutyric acid herbicides: (a) MCPB or 2,4-DB (see figure 14.15); (b) MCPA or 2,4-D (see figure 14.6). Compare the coenzyme A derivatives with those formed in fatty acid catabolism

There is a biological basis for the selectivity of the phenoxybutyric acid derivatives. Whereas the phenoxyacetic acid herbicides are the actual toxicants (except that when esters are used they first undergo hydrolysis), the butyric acid homologues are not. Instead, they are of low toxicity until they are converted by the plant to the acetic acid member of the series. The enzyme responsible appears to be a specific β-oxidase, although the degradation involves the formation of acyl coenzyme A derivatives analogous to those formed in plants and animals during fatty acid oxidation. The oxidation results in the removal of two carbon atoms in the form of the acetyl group of acetyl enzyme A (figure 14.16). The activity of this specific β-oxidase in some legumes is low and in consequence they are not damaged by concentrations of MCPB or 2,4-DB that kill weeds that possess a more active β-oxidase system. This type of event is termed **lethal metabolism**; other examples of it are referred to in sections 3.4, 4.8, 10.4 and 11.5.

14.13 DINITROPHENOL DERIVATIVES

Derivatives of 2,4-dinitro-6-alkylphenol have been used for various purposes for many years; binapacryl and dinocap are fungicides described in section 11.5 and dinoseb has herbicidal properties. However, dinitroalkylphenols have been shown to cause birth defects in laboratory animals and (as was mentioned earlier) many countries have restricted or are likely to restrict the use of these compounds. In the UK, approvals for dinoseb and other members of the group were revoked in 1988 and as from now their use is forbidden. The present writer is concerned that their use should not continue in developing countries, for, whatever the level of chronic toxic hazard may be, this group of substances has, over the years, caused numerous deaths by acute poisoning. Moreover, their use as weedkillers can no longer be justified since safer alternatives now exist. This section will consequently be brief. Nevertheless their mode of action is worthy of recall, for the parent substance, dinitrophenol, was historically employed in studies that contributed to an understanding of the biochemistry of oxidative phosphorylation.

Dinoseb (figure 14.15c) has been used as a foliage contact poison to control weeds in some tolerant legumes and in certain other specified crops such as cereals and onions. It is a deeply staining yellow solid that is sparingly soluble in water but, being a weak acid, it forms salts that are moderately soluble. The ammonium and alkylamine salts were commonly employed, as was the covalent acetate. Dinoseb formulations have usually been applied using middle- rather than low-volume application rates and such formulations are most toxic to plants when the weather is warm and humid.

For most herbicides that are weak acids or bases, maximal selectivity is usually obtained when ionisation is high. This is presumably because the rate of entry of covalent molecules through lipophilic barriers is greater than the rate of entry of anions. A consequence of such an assumption is that minor structural differences (e.g. in thickness or in composition) between such barriers in weeds and crop plants can best be exploited when some constraint (e.g. lipid insolubility or ionic charge) exists that impedes penetration. For dinoseb, as for the phenoxyacetic acids (sections 14.4), covalent formulations are more toxic to weeds, but also less selective, than the partly ionised amine or ammonium salts.

The acetate ester is often used in pre-emergence situations as well as post-emergence in certain tolerant crops such as forage legumes and onions. The ammonium and amine salts can be used pre-emergence in peas and beans as well as post-emergence in cereals undersown with clover or lucerne. When sprays are used in situations involving emerged legume crops, it is necessary that two or three trifoliate leaves are present. Similarly, dinoseb amine can be applied to control seedling weeds in new grass–legume mixtures, although some temporary damage is common. Dinoseb and other 2,4-dinitrophenols are highly toxic to mammals, birds and insects, as well as to plants. The universality of this toxicity implies impairment of some fundamental biological process. The effect is, in fact, to uncouple oxidation from phosphorylation in the mitochondrial electron transport system. Respiration not only continues in poisoned organisms but actually speeds up as the organism produces more and more NADH in a vain attempt to make ATP (figure 14.17). A commonplace analogy is that of trying to drive a car at constant speed while depressing the clutch more and more (depression equals higher dinoseb concentration). Uncoupling occurs in isolated animal mitochondria at a dinoseb concentration of about 1–10 µM.

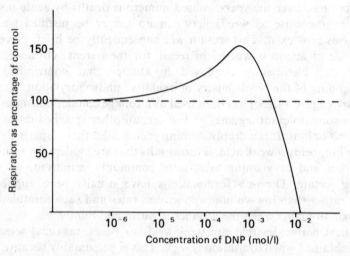

Figure 14.17   Effect of dinitrophenol on the respiration of *Chlorella vulgaris*

In mammals, the symptoms of poisoning reflect the 'slipping clutch' effect and the squandering of energy. The patient breathes rapidly and starts to flush and sweat. In an emergency, it is essential to keep the patient lying down in a cool place while awaiting a doctor. It is appropriate to recall that the numerous deaths that occurred in the early years of the use of dinitrophenol pesticides were in large measure the catalyst for the enactment of pioneering pesticide safety regulations in many countries.

14.14 OTHER HERBICIDES OCCASIONALLY APPLIED TO WEED FOLIAGE; OILS AND THE CONCEPT OF PHYSICAL TOXICITY

Pentanochlor controls annual weeds in carrots, parsnips and celery. Among weeds that are resistant to several other herbicides at the young plant stage but respond to pentanochlor are fat hen (*Chenopodium album*), fumitory (*Fumaria officinalis*), cleavers (*Galium alparine*), various *Polygonum* spp., wild radish (*Raphanus raphanistrum*) and smooth sow thistle (*Sonchus oleraceus*). These weeds can also be controlled in established gooseberry, blackcurrant and some other fruit bushes and trees if contact with leaves of the crop is avoided. For this last purpose a mixture with chlorpropham is occasionally employed.

Triazine herbicides are normally soil-acting compounds that are applied before the crop emerges (section 15.2), but several of them, when formulated with surfactant to promote good contact action, have also found uses as foliage sprays. Selectivity is limited and directed spraying is usually essential. **Desmetryne** (figure 15.3g) controls fat hen and many other weed seedlings in brassicas. Thus it can be used on cabbages and on brussels sprouts when the plants are about 13 cm high. **Prometryne** (figure 15.3e) is used for weed control in carrots, parsley and celery after the crop plants have reached specified stages of leaf development. It is also used for weed control in early potatoes, a technique that is particularly useful when the potatoes are to be followed by another crop (Fryer and Makepeace, 1978). In the USA it is also used post-emergence in maize. **Cyprazine** (figure 15.3c) is used to control seedling grasses and broad-leaved weeds in maize. The weeds should not be more than 4–6 cm high.

Endothall is a highly toxic substance sometimes used as a post-emergence spray to control emerged weed seedlings in sugar beet. It is also used as a pre-harvest desiccant (e.g. for soybeans) and defoliant (e.g. for cotton). It is the disodium salt of a hexahydrophthalic acid analogue that possesses an oxygen bridge *ortho* to each of the two carboxyl groups. It is not used in Britain.

Phenmedipham is a carbamate herbicide that is marketed principally to control seedlings of broad-leaved weeds in fodder beet, sugar beet and red beet (MAFF, 1985). It is also one of very few foliar herbicides that can be used, in appropriate circumstances, for seedling weed control in strawberries before flowering. A single application seldom controls weeds that have developed much beyond the cotyledon stage but some larger weeds respond if the treatment is repeated after an interval of three days. Mixtures with barban give improved control of *Polygonum* spp. in beet and, if wild oats are present, these can be controlled by increasing the proportion of barban. When used on beet and mangolds some crop damage may ensue if the temperature is above 21°C or if the light intensity is high; such damage is often minimised by evening spraying at a reduced application rate. The crop may also be damaged if it is suffering from manganese deficiency, frost or insect damage, or some other stress factor.

Petroleum spirits are refined petroleum distillates of high flammability. They are used for selective weed control in Umbelliferae. On the other hand, **diesel oil** has a high boiling point and a high viscosity and, together with **tractor vaporising oil** (TVO), has been used for non-selective weed control. Not infrequently, diesel oil is 'fortified' for this purpose by dissolving in it a powerful non-selective herbicide such as pentachlorophenol (PCP).

Many umbelliferous crops show tolerance to viscous oils that are damaging to most broad-leaved plants. For this reason—and if application is appropriately timed—highly refined oils can be used for weed control in parsnips and parsley; they are also occasionally used in carrots. If the oil is impure or contains unsaturated components there is a possibility that **tainting** will occur in plants that are actively depositing storage materials in tap roots.

In relation to herbicidal action, the 'physical' effect can be at the crude macroscopic level of blocking the stomata and damaging cuticular lipids. In less extreme cases a more gradual action probably involves damage to the cell membrane or to a lipoprotein membrane within the cell (i.e. to the tonoplast or to membranes of the chloroplast, nucleus or mitochondrion), with consequent loss of cell compartmentation. Plants sprayed with oil do, for example, often lose cell sap into the intercellular spaces, with a consequent change in the overall appearance of the leaf.

Hydrocarbon oils have played an important role in crop protection not only as herbicides but as insecticides and ovicides. In addition, they are still used in large amounts as spray adjuvants (chapter 2), often as solvents for other pesticides and to assist the main toxicant to penetrate into the surfaces of plants or insects by softening cuticular wax. For this reason, it is appropriate to end this chapter by reference to the role they have played in an understanding of a type of action that has been termed **physical toxicity**.

The problem can be stated like this: petroleum oils are predominantly alkanes, the older name for which was paraffins ('without activity'). Clearly, there is a difficulty in reconciling chemical inertness with the formation of specific chemical attachments with hypothetical receptors or with active sites of enzymes. A probable resolution of the paradox is that a non-specific sorption that can occur on all lipoprotein membranes can result in a highly specific event being disrupted on any one such membrane. This dilemma must be faced, for not only are hydrocarbon oils 'physical poisons' but Ferguson and Hawkins (1949) demonstrated that even inert gases such as argon can induce symptoms of physical toxicity. In the example below, the anaesthesia of mice has been chosen as the criterion of equitoxic physical action but it has been shown that physical toxicants also affect photosynthesis and cell division (e.g. Gavaudan and Brebion, 1945; Hassall, 1961b). Perhaps that process which is of the greatest consequence to an organism at the time the toxicant makes contact is the one which responds most obviously to the presence of a physical poison.

The nature of physical toxicity can best be explained and illustrated by considering what happens when alkanes or alkyl chlorides, related in homologous series, are used as toxicants of some biological process. It is found, first, that equitoxic concentrations of different homologues can be very different (P_t in table 14.6) but that each member of the series induces an approximately equal response when present in the external medium at the same relative saturation. For the present purpose, 'relative saturation' may be defined as the toxic concentration divided by the concentration needed to saturate the external medium (although, for rigorous treatment, several provisos must be added).

It has long been recognised that the effective concentration of any poison at the internal site of action need bear no simple relation to the concentration in the external medium. This is particularly so when the external medium in which the poison is applied differs greatly in its physical chemistry from the 'biophase' where the toxic action is manifest. In consequence, while LD_{50} values and similar measures of toxicity are of profound practical importance in that they determine such things as cost of medical treatment or level of danger resulting from accidental ingestion of poisons, they may reveal little about what is going on at the site of action. In order to investigate structure–activity relationships it is necessary to remove the complicating factor of **phase distribution** which is superimposed upon the **intrinsic toxicity** of the substance.

The use of the relative saturations of closely related substances as measures of toxicity removes the complicating factor of phase distribution so long as the compounds under consideration are of low chemical reactivity and so long as

Table 14.6 **Iso-anaesthetic concentrations and relative saturations of alkanes applied as vapours to mice (Badger, 1946)**

Substance	P_t toxic vapour pressure (mmHg)	P_s saturation vapour pressure (mmHg)	P_t/P_s
Pentane	85	794	0.11
Hexane	30	240	0.13
Heptane	12	81	0.15
Octane	6	28	0.20

a near-equilibrium condition between internal and external phases is rapidly achieved. Alkane hydrocarbons and chloroalkanes fulfil these requirements for physical toxicity. It can, perhaps, be postulated that all compounds could be physically toxic, but that chemically reactive substances cause irreversible damage at concentrations much lower than those which *would have been* physically toxic if such chemical reactivity had not existed.

Table 14.6 shows the concentrations of four hydrocarbons which induce an equal degree of anaesthesia in mice (Badger, 1946), and illustrates the value of the concept of relative saturation as a device for disentangling intrinsic toxicity from phase distribution. Anaesthesia, being reversible, is a more reliable and sensitive index of toxicity than LD_{50} to insects, herbicidal effects, etc., but the conclusions reached below are probably also valid for these less obviously quantifiable forms of toxicity.

The concentrations found to induce an equal level of anaesthesia are expressed as the toxic vapour pressure, P_t, of the toxicant at the temperature of the experiment. It is calculated from the number of moles per litre on the assumption that the substance acts as a perfect gas and so exerts a pressure of 760 mmHg at 273 K when present in 22.4 litres. P_s is the saturation vapour pressure at the same temperature. It can be shown that the relative saturation, P_t/P_s, is approximately the same as the thermodynamic activity, a, at which the stated toxic effect is manifest. For phases in equilibrium, the thermodynamic activity must be identical in the two phases, whether or not the solutions are ideal. However, for non-ideal solutions, the thermodynamic activity, a, is equal to γC, where C is the molar concentration of the toxicant in the phase under consideration. The other factor, γ, is known as the activity coefficient; the best way to visualise its significance is to remember that the more that it deviates from unity, the less 'ideal' is a solution of the solute in that phase (and the lower the solubility of the solute in that solvent). For present purposes there are two phases, an external phase and an internal phase. The experimenter has direct information about the external phase (in table 14.6, a solution of alkane vapour in air) but is seeking experimental information about the nature of the internal (or bio-) phase. Hence,

$a_{ext} = \gamma_{ext} C_{ext}$ for the external phase,

$a_{int} = \gamma_{int} C_{int}$ for the internal phase.

Consequently, at equilibrium,

$\gamma_{ext} C_{ext} = \gamma_{int} C_{int}$

Therefore,

$$\frac{\gamma_{ext}}{\gamma_{int}} = \frac{C_{int}}{C_{ext}}$$

This represents the ratio of the chemical concentrations in the two phases; in other words, the ratio $\gamma_{ext}/\gamma_{int}$ is the partition coefficient of the solute between the outside and the inside phases.

Those who wish to pursue the thermodynamic aspects of the subject further will find both theory and illustrative data in articles by Ferguson (1939) and by Brink and Posternak (1948). For others, the principal points are illustrated by the data in table 14.6. Heptane, for example, appears in the table to be about seven times as toxic as pentane when the external isotoxic concentrations are considered. Nevertheless, when seen from the point of view of the relative molar concentrations present at equilibrium in the internal phase, pentane is somewhat the more toxic of the two, for it acts at a lower relative saturation and hence at a lower molar concentration at the site of action.

The elimination of the complicating factor of phase distribution is a necessary preliminary to being able to 'recognise' physical toxicity. It is not, in itself, however, the point deserving attention here—phase distribution *always* has to be eliminated if one is studying in one phase an event that is actually occurring in another! The remarkable thing in the present instance is that, having eliminated phase distribution, there is a near-constancy of the internal concentrations that have equitoxic effects (this conclusion is derived from the near-constancy of the P_t/P_s values on the likely assumption that lipid solutions of hydrocarbons do not vary greatly in ideality; i.e. γ_{int} is nearly constant for the four alkanes). There was, in advance, no reason for believing that having corrected for phase distribution, the internal concentrations should have been expected to be similar—they are seldom similar for chemically active substances.

The significance of this near-constancy in biochemical terms is not entirely clear, but many people believe that equal numbers of molecules of all physical poisons sorbed onto a given area of lipoprotein surface distort it to roughly the same degree and so cause an equal level of abnormality of performance. Hydrocarbons, alkyl halides and ethers, are, of course, precisely the sorts of inert substances that would be expected to be absorbed into the lipid part of a lipoprotein membrane.

In various organisms, there are several types of membrane-located reactions, their relative importance depending not only on the species but on the age of the organism. Several workers have pointed out that candidate 'physical' poisons appear to affect various organised activities in different circumstances. For example, Gavaudan and Brebion (1945) observed that benzene and chlorobenzene have anaesthetic properties but they can also affect photosynthesis and cell division. Hassall (1961b) suggested that carbamates could act as narcotics and inhibitors of the Hill reaction (section 15.2) or interfere with nuclear division. Holan (1969) similarly concluded that DDT could not only affect neuronal activity but also interfere with oxidative phosphorylation and with the Hill reaction.

REFERENCES

Achhireddy, N. R., Kirkwood, R. C. and Fletcher, W. W. (1984). *Weed Sci.*, **32**, 727
Akobundu, I. O. (1981). *Weed Res.*, **21**, 273
Anderson, W. P. (1977). *Weed Science: Principles*, p. 291. West, New York
Auch, D. E. and Arnold, W. E. (1979). *Weed Sci.*, **26**, 471
Badger, G. M. (1946). *Nature (Lond.)*, **158**, 585
Barlow, J. N. and Hicks, B. R. (1985). *Proc. Br. Crop Prot. Conf., Weeds*, p. 857
Barnes, J. M. (1976). In *Herbicides: Physiology, Biochemistry, Ecology*, 2nd edn, vol. 2, ed. L. J. Audus, chap. 13. Academic Press, London
Bowyer, J. R. and Camilleri, P. (1987). In *Progress in Pesticide Biochemistry and Toxicology*, vol. 6, *Herbicides*, eds D. H. Hutson and T. R. Roberts, chap. 3. Wiley, Chichester
Breay, H. T. (1982). *Proc. Br. Crop Prot. Conf., Weeds*, p. 843
Brink, F. and Posternak, J. M. (1948). *J. Cell. Comp. Physiol.*, **32**, 211
Buckland, J. L., Collins, R. F. and Pullin, E. M. (1973). *Pestic. Sci.*, **4**, 149
Burns, E. R., Buchanan, G. A. and Carter, M. C. (1971). *Plant Physiol.*, **47**, 144
Bujtas, C., Cserhati, T., Cseh, E., Illes, Z. and Szigeti, Z. (1985). *Biochem. Physiol. Pflanz.*, **182**, 465
BWCC (1982). *Proc. Br. Crop Prot. Conf., Weeds*, pp. 793–855
Carr, J. E., Davies, L. G., Cobb, A. H. and Pallett, K. E. (1985). *Proc. Br. Crop Prot. Conf., Weeds*, p. 155
Carter, M. C. (1975). In *Herbicides; Chemistry, Degradation and Mode of Action*, eds P. C. Kearney and D. D. Kaufman, p. 377. Marcel Dekker, New York
Carter, C. H. and Keeley, P. E. (1987). *Weed Sci.*, **35**, 418
Chandrasena, J. P. N. R. and Sagar, G. R. (1984). *Weed Res.*, **24**, 297
Chase, R. L. and Appleby, A. P. (1979). *Weed Res.*, **19**, 241
Cho, H.-Y., Widholm, J. M. and Slife, F. W. (1986). *Weed Sci.*, **34**, 496
Chow, P. N. P. and Taylor, H. F. (1983). *J. Agric. Fd Chem.*, **31**, 575
Cobb, A. H., Rees, R. T., Nichols, K. J., Miller, P. R. and Pallett, K. E. (1985). *Proc. Br. Crop Prot. Conf., Weeds*, p. 1187
Cole, D. J., Caseley, J. C. and Dodge, A. D. (1983). *Weed Res.*, **23**, 173
Corbett, J. R., Wright, K. and Baillie, A. C. (1984). *The Biochemical Mode of Action of Pesticides*, 2nd edn. Academic Press, New York
Coupland, D. (1986). *Ann. Appl. Biol.*, **108**, 353
Dale, J. E. (1983). *Weed Res.*, **23**, 63
Dekker, J. and Harker, N. (1985). *Proc. Br. Crop Prot. Conf., Weeds*, p. 471
Devine, M. D., Bandeen, J. D. and McKersie, B. D. (1983). *Weed Sci.*, **31**, 461
Dewey, S. A. and Appleby, A. P. (1983). *Weed Sci.*, **31**, 308
Dial, N. A. and Dial, C. A. B. (1987). *Bull. Environ. Contam. Toxicol.*, **38**, 1006
Doll, J. D. and Piedrahita, W. (1982). *Weed Res.*, **22**, 123
Duke, S. O., Wauchope, R. D., Hoagland, R. E. and Wills, G. D. (1983). *Weed Res.*, **23**, 133
Eberlein, C. V. and Behrens, R. (1984). *Weed Sci.*, **32**, 13
Ernest, R. D. (1971). *Prog. Fish-Cult.*, **33**, 27
Fagan, K. and Pollak, J. K. (1984). *Res. Rev.*, **92**, 29
Faulkner, J. S. and Harvey, B. M. R. (1981). *Weed Res.*, **21**, 29
Fedtke, C. (1982). *Biochemistry and Physiology of Herbicide Action*. Springer, Berlin
Ferguson, J. (1939). *Proc. R. Soc.*, **127B**, 387
Ferguson, J. and Hawkins, S. W. (1949). *Nature (Lond.)*, **164**, 963
Foley, M. E., Nafziger, E. D., Slife, F. W. and Wax, L. M. (1983). *Weed Sci.*, **31**, 76
Fryer, J. D. and Makepeace, R. J. (1977). *Weed Control Handbook*, vol. 1, *Principles*, 6th edn. Blackwell, Oxford

Fryer, J. D. and Makepeace, R. J. (1978). *Weed Control Handbook*, vol. 2, *Recommendations*, 8th edn. Blackwell, Oxford

Gaudreault, P., Karl, P. I. and Friedman, P. A. (1984). *Drug Metab. Dispn.*, **12**, 550

Gavaudan, P. and Brebion, G. (1945). *Mem. Serv. Chim. Etat.*, **32**, 410

Gaynor, J. J. and Still, C. C. (1983). *Plant Physiol.*, **72**, 80

Gorecka, K., Shimabukuro, R. H. and Walsh, W. C. (1981). *Physiol. Plant*, **53**, 55

Gounaris, K., Barber, J. and Harwood, J. L. (1986). *Biochem. J.*, **237**, 313

Guilfoyle, T. J., Lin, C. Y., Chen, Y. M., Nagao, R. T. and Key, J. L. (1975). *Proc. Nat. Acad. Sci., USA*, **72**, 69

Halling, B. P. and Behrens, R. (1983). *Weed Sci.*, **31**, 693

Hardell, L. (1981). *Scand. J. Work Environ. Hlth*, **7**, 119

Hardin, J. W., Cherry, J. H., Morre, D. J. and Lembi, C. A. (1972). *Proc. Nat. Acad. Sci., USA*, **69**, 3146

Harris, N. and Dodge, A. D. (1972). *Planta*, **104**, 210

Harvey, B. M. R. and Fraser, T. W. (1980). *Plant Cell Environ.*, **3**, 107

Harwood, J. L., Walker, K. A., Abulnaja, D. and Ridley, S. M. (1987). *Proc. Br. Crop Prot. Conf., Weeds*, p. 159

Hassall, K. A. (1961a). *Physiol. Planta*, **14**, 140

Hassall, K. A. (1961b). *J. Exp. Bot.*, **12**, 47

Hassall, K. A. (1985). *Environmentalist*, **5**, 105

Hemberger, J. A. and Schanker, L. S. (1983). *Drug Metab. Dispn.*, **11**, 75

Holan, G. (1969). *Nature (Lond.)*, **221**, 1025

Hoppe, H. H. and Zacher, H. (1985). *Pestic. Biochem. Physiol.*, **24**, 298

Hsu, J. C. and Camper, N. D. (1975). *Pestic. Biochem. Physiol.*, **5**, 47

Hutson, D. H., Crayford, J. V. and Hoadley, E. C. (1977). *Xenobiotica*, **7**, 279

Ikai, T., Suzuki, K., Hattori, K., Igarashi, H. C. and Uchiyama, M. (1985). *Proc. Br. Crop Prot. Conf., Weeds*, p. 163

Ivany, J. A. (1984). *Weed Sci.*, **32**, 194

Jaworski, E. G. (1972). *J. Agric. Fd Chem.*, **20**, 1195

Jones, A. G. and Orson, J. H. (1982). *Proc. Br. Crop Prot. Conf., Weeds*, p. 793

Katekar, G. F. (1979). *Phytochemistry*, **18**, 223

Kells, J. J., Meggitt, W. F. and Penner, D. (1984). *Weed Sci.*, **32**, 143

Kirkwood, R. C. (1976). In *Herbicides: Physiology, Biochemistry, Ecology*, 2nd edn, vol. 1, ed. L. J. Audus. Academic Press, London

Klingman, G. C. and Ashton, F. M. (1975). *Weed Science: Principles and Practices*. Wiley, New York

Kolhe, S. S., Bhadauria, S. S., Mittra, B. N. and Tripathi, R. S. (1987). *Trop. Agric.*, **64**, 287

Lawson, H. M. and Wiseman, J. S. (1982). *Proc. Br. Crop Prot. Conf., Weeds*, p. 927

Lee, T. T., Dumas, T. and Jevnikar, J. J. (1983). *Pestic. Biochem. Physiol.*, **20**, 354

Lehninger, A. L. (1975). *Biochemistry*, 2nd edn. Worth, New York

Liebl, R. and Worsham, A. D. (1987). *Weed Sci.*, **35**, 383

Loos, M. A. (1975). *Herbicides: Chemistry, Degradation and Mode of Action*, 2nd edn, vol. 1, eds P. C. Kearney and D. D. Kaufman, chap. 1. Marcel Dekker, New York

Lundgren, B., Meijer, J. and De Pierre, J. W. (1987). *Biochem. Pharmacol.*, **36**, 815

McAllister, R. S. and Haderlie, L. C. (1985). *Weed Sci.*, **33**, 153

MAFF (1985). *Approved Products for Farmers and Growers*, Reference Book 380 (85). Ministry of Agriculture, Fisheries and Food. HMSO, London

Merritt, C. R. (1984). *Weed Res.*, **24**, 173

Menzie, C. M. (1980). *Metabolism of Pesticides, Update II*. US Dept Interior, Fish and Wildlife Service

Millhollon, R. W. (1985). *Weed Sci.*, **33**, 216

Mislevy, P. (1978). *Soil Crop Sci. Soc. Fla Proc.*, **37**, 50

Moreland, D. E. (1980). *Annu. Rev. Plant Physiol.*, **31**, 597

Murray, G. J. and Schreiweis, D. O. (1977). *J. Ariz. Acad. Sci.*, **12**, 41

Neal, J. C., Skroch, W. A. and Monaco, T. J. (1985). *Weed Sci.*, **34**, 115

Pelsy, F., Leroux, P. and Heslot, H. (1987). *Pestic. Biochem. Physiol.*, **27**, 182

Peregoy, R. S. and Glenn, S. (1985). *Weed Sci.*, **33**, 443

Pihakaski, S. and Pihakaski, K. (1980). *Ann. Bot.*, **46**, 133

Poland, A. and Knutson, J. C. (1982). *Annu. Rev. Pharmacol. Toxicol.*, **22**, 517

Potter, J. R. and Wergin, W. P. (1975). *Pestic. Biochem. Physiol.*, **5**, 458

Rhodes, G. N., Jr and Coble, H. D. (1984). *Weed Sci.*, **32**, 436

Ritoine, E. L., Lyatuu, H. A., Mosha, C. J., Sambai, L. M. and Mollel, S. L. (1982). *Proc. Br. Crop Prot. Conf., Weeds*, p. 875

Roberts, T. R. (1977). *Pestic. Biochem. Physiol.*, **7**, 378

Rüdiger, W. and Benz, J. (1979). *Z. Naturf.*, **34C**, 1055

Sanders, G. E. and Pallett, K. E. (1986). *Pestic. Biochem. Physiol.*, **26**, 116

Sankaran, S. and De Datta, S. K. (1985). *Adv. Agron.*, **38**, 284

Schultz, M. E. and Burnside, O. C. (1980). *Weed Sci.*, **28**, 13

Shaaltiel, Y. and Gressel, J. (1986). *Pestic. Biochem. Physiol.*, **26**, 22

Shaner, D. L. (1978). *Weed Sci.*, **26**, 513

Shaner, D. L. (1983). *Can. Plant Proc.*, **12**, 49

Shaner, D. L. and Lyon, J. L. (1980). *Weed Sci.*, **28**, 31

Shea, P. J. and Tupy, D. R. (1984). *Weed Sci.*, **32**, 802

Shimabukuro, M. A., Shimabukuro, R. H., Nord, W. S. and Hoerauf, R. A. (1978). *Pestic. Biochem. Physiol.*, **8**, 199

Smith, A. E. (1982). *Weed Res.*, **22**, 137

Smith, A. and Hsiao, A. I. (1983). *Weed Res.*, **23**, 253

Stahlman, P. W. (1984). *Weed Sci.*, **32**, 59

Stahlman, P. W. and Phillips, W. M. (1979). *Weed Sci.*, **27**, 575

Steinrücken, H. C. and Amrhein, N. (1980). *Biochem. Biophys. Res. Commun.*, **94**, 1207

Targanyi, J. and Mikulas, J. (1982). *Proc. Br. Crop Prot. Conf., Weeds*, p. 907

Teasdale, J. R. and Thimijan, R. W. (1983). *Weed Sci.*, **31**, 232

Wain, R. L. and Fawcett, C. H. (1969). In *Plant Physiology*, ed F. C. Steward, p. 231. Academic Press, New York

Wills, G. D. (1984). *Weed Sci.*, **32**, 20

Wright, A. F., Green, T. P., Robson, R. T., Niewola, Z., Wyatt, I. and Smith, L. L. (1987). *Biochem. Pharmacol.*, **36**, 1325

Zama, P. and Mumma, R. O. (1983). *Weed Sci.*, **31**, 537

Zimmerman, P. W. and Hitchcock, A. E. (1942). *Contrib. Boyce Thompson Inst.*, **12**, 321

Zwick, W., Merrick, B.-H. and Nuyken, W. (1985). *Proc. Br. Crop Prot. Conf., Weeds*, p. 85

15 Herbicides that are mainly soil-acting against seedling weeds

The substances appearing in this and the next chapter are usually described as soil-applied herbicides but the many types of such compounds differ greatly in the tasks that they fulfil. It is therefore convenient to subdivide soil-acting herbicides into two main groups, even though considerable overlap may occur, especially in non-crop or non-selective situations.

This chapter is concerned with substances in the first of these two main groups. Such substances can be (although not necessarily are) used during the relatively narrow time interval between sowing the crop and its emergence. At this time the weeds are delicate and shallow-rooted and it is often difficult to say what proportion of a toxic dose of herbicide enters by the root rather than by the shoot. Alternative uses include their application prior to planting, their application early post-emergence of tolerant crops and their use to control seedling weeds in established crops such as fruit trees.

The second possibility, considered in the next chapter, is the application of herbicides to soil at a time more or less distant from the date of sowing or planting the crop. Such an application is usually made to kill all seeds and underground parts of plants indiscriminately. Therefore, although very useful for the control of certain perennial weeds, the herbicide must disappear before a crop is sown unless the crop happens to be tolerant of it.

Table 15.1   Substances with a soil and foliar action on young weeds

---

Type A: Inhibitors of photosynthesis
  Section 15.1 Ureides (e.g. diuron, linuron, chlorbromuron)
       15.2 Triazines (e.g. atrazine, simazine, ametryne)
       15.3 Uracils, pyridazinones (e.g. bromacil, pyrazon)

Type B: Substances that act at, or before, cell division
  Section 15.4 Phenylcarbamates (e.g. chlorpropham)
       15.5 Sulphonylureas (e.g. chlorsulfuron)

Type C: Substances that disrupt membrane structure or function
  Section 15.6 Diphenyl ethers (e.g. nitrofen, acifluorfen)

The main types of herbicides considered in this chapter are listed in table 15.1. Such substances are most successfully used against weed seeds that have either just germinated, or are about to germinate, at the time that the herbicide is applied. Some seedlings are therefore already likely to be visible above the ground. The use of such substances is frequently preceded by the use of a conventional foliar spray, possibly applied months earlier, in order to eliminate the foliage of established weeds (most large, established weeds do not respond to soil-applied herbicides at economic application rates).

Since huge numbers of weed seeds are present in soil and they do not all emerge at the same time, it is useful that many of the substances employed in a pre-emergence* context are able to kill seedling weeds after entry through foliage as well as by entry through roots. The importance of weed control at this stage of crop growth is that the weeds often grow rapidly from seeds lodged near to the surface and therefore develop so rapidly that the crop is at a competitive disadvantage. This often arises from the fact that many crops are sown (or set) deeply; on the other hand, as was seen in chapter 13, this same circumstance often explains why selectivity can sometimes be achieved in the field even though many of the herbicides are intrinsically non-selective in their action.

Type A: Inhibitors of photosynthesis

15.1 UREA HERBICIDES

Urea is the amide of carbonic acid. In most members of the ureide (i.e. substituted urea) family of herbicides, urea is trisubstituted in the way indicated in figure 15.1. One of the amino groups carries either two methyl groups or one methyl and one methoxy group. The other amino group is substituted with a benzene ring which, in most cases, contains halogen atoms. Ureides are solids with a low vapour pressure (10^{-6}–10^{-8} mmHg) at room temperature and possess aqueous solubilities ranging from 4 to 700 ppm.

Diuron, **fluometuron** and **linuron** are quantitatively the most important urea herbicides manufactured in the USA (Green *et al.*, 1977), although at least nine ureides are used in Britain. Metoxuron resembles diuron except that it possesses a methoxy group in ring position 4. Similarly, chlortoluron resembles diuron but has a methyl group in this position. Monolinuron resembles linuron, and monuron resembles diuron, but, as the names partly

---

*Readers, at least in Britain, are reminded that, unless a specific qualification is inserted, the terms *pre-emergence* and *post-emergence* apply to a *crop*; these words should tell us nothing about the state of the *weeds*. Some authors deviate from this convention and thereby risk misunderstandings.

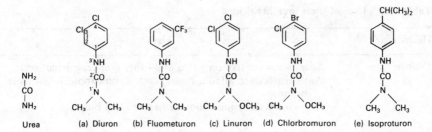

Figure 15.1 Urea herbicides (ureides): (a) 3′-(3,4-dichlorophenyl)-1′,1′-dimethylurea; (b) 3′-(3-trifluoromethylphenyl)-1′,1′-dimethylurea; (c) 3′-(3,4-dichlorophenyl)-1′-methoxy-1′-methylurea; (d) 3′-(4-bromo-3-chlorophenyl)-1′-methoxy-1′-methylurea; (e) 3′-(4-isopropylphenyl)-1′,1′-dimethylurea)

imply, each lacks a chlorine atom from ring position 3. Metobromuron resembles **chlorbromuron** except that it lacks the chlorine atom, and fenuron resembles diuron but is unchlorinated. It is noteworthy that the names of all the ureide herbicides terminate in -uron.

Some of the non-selective, pre-emergence and post-emergence uses of urea herbicides are listed in table 15.2. Needless to say, all the compounds become less selective as the application rate is increased. Some control with equal effectiveness seedling grasses and a range of seedling broad-leaved weeds whereas others are more selective in their action. Linuron, for example, is generally useful against seedling weeds in a number of crops just before emergence; diuron is often used in established or perennial crops; and chlortoluron is particularly useful to control the four types of wild oats and also blackgrass (*Alopecurus myosuroides*) in winter barley.

Atkin and Turner (1982) pointed out that about one-third of the cereal area of England is badly affected by wild oats and that blackgrass is troublesome in about one-third of some parts of England. They have advocated, for reasons of simplicity and cost, the use of microgranules containing **isoproturon** and triallate (section 16.1) to control these weeds pre-emergence or post-emergence of winter wheat or barley. In Nigeria, *Phalaris minor*, an important weed in wheat, can be controlled by the use of isoproturon or of metoxuron (Walia and Gill, 1985). Moreover, the same authors reported that some form of interaction between these herbicides and nitrogenous fertiliser leads to a profitable improvement in utilisation of the nitrogen. Gaur *et al.* (1986) reported that, in India, the growth of the opium poppy is slow and requires copious irrigation, a procedure that encourages weeds, which smother the crop; at 1.5 kg/ha the yield both of latex and of seed is roughly the same as can be achieved with two weedings by hand.

Of the substances in table 15.2, diuron and monolinuron are among the most persistent when used at higher rates of application. Fenuron is exceptional in that it is rather soluble in water and is not strongly adsorbed onto soil

Table 15.2   Uses of some urea herbicides

Herbicide	Uses
Diuron	Total weed control on paths and other non-crop situations Annual weeds in alfalfa, maize, cotton, pineapple, sugar cane, sorghum Annual weeds around some fruit trees and bushes
Fluometuron	Annual weeds in cotton and sugar cane
Linuron	Annual weeds pre-emergence of potatoes, carrots, sorghum, soybeans Kills corn marigold, pre-emergence of spring cereals Kills some grasses till 2 inches high, some dicots till 5 inches high Seedling weeds pre-emergence and post-emergence of ornamental bulbs, corms
Chlorbromuron	Annual weeds in potatoes, soybean, carrots, parsnips
Chlortoluron	Wild oats, blackgrass, dicot seedlings in some winter cereals
Fenuron	As pellets, for woody plant control in non-crop situations
Metobromuron	Annual grasses, dicots in potatoes
Metoxuron	Blackgrass, annual grasses, mayweed in some winter cereals
Monolinuron	Many seedling weeds in potatoes and post-planting of leeks Annual grasses and seedling dicots in carrots, onions
Chloroxuron	Annual weeds post-harvest in strawberries; seedling weeds in container plants

constituents. For these reasons it can wash down to plant roots, a property that is exploited for the control of woody weeds in the absence of a crop.

Ureides are **adsorbed** on soil organic matter and, to a lesser extent, on clay particles, with the consequences described elsewhere (section 13.5). Adsorption on soil constituents not only determines persistence, leaching characteristics and availability for root uptake but also influences the rate of degradation by microorganisms. Microbial action is largely limited to that fraction of a dose of herbicide that is present in soil water. It is therefore mainly determined by the aqueous concentration that results from an equilibration of the forces of adsorption on, and desorption from, soil particles. Kozak and Weber (1983) studied the adsorption of ureides by five Czechoslovak soils. They concluded that sorption fitted the Freundlich model better than it did the isotherm of Langmuir, and that soil organic matter was the most important factor influencing the level of adsorption. Similarly, Rahman *et al.* (1978) investigated the adsorption of five soil-acting herbicides using Horotiu sandy loam soils with organic matter varying from 8 to 19.3 per cent. Linuron was one of the substances used. For all five herbicides some 2–3 times as much was required for a similar level of weed control in the soil of highest organic content compared with that with the lowest amount of organic matter. Utulu *et al.* (1986) studied the leaching of fluometuron and atrazine (section 15.2) in Nigerian soils; rainfall increased the leaching of both substances but phytotoxic levels of fluometuron were still present in the top 15 cm of soil 12 weeks after application.

To summarise, the organic content of soil, and the amount of rain falling in the first few weeks after application, greatly influence the extent of adsorption, desorption and wash-down of ureides (as well as of triazines and uracils). Sorption is inversely related to solubility in water of a ureide. In the series fenuron, monuron, diuron, adsorption increases with increasing chlorine content and, when methoxy compounds are considered, it is usually found that compounds such as linuron are adsorbed more strongly than are their dimethyl counterparts.

Urea herbicides in solution or suspension readily enter plant roots but the extent of translocation of different substances varies greatly. Autoradiographic techniques have shown, for example, that chloroxuron and neburon tend to remain in the root system whereas monolinuron, fluometuron and metobromuron are largely translocated to the leaves. Once within leaves, some tend to stay near the leaf veins whereas others enter cells of the mesophyll. Since movement is apoplastic, it is accelerated by factors that increase the rate of transpiration, including higher temperatures, lower humidities and opening of stomata. Gross *et al.* (1979) have investigated the uptake and distribution of chlortoluron in wheat plants. Plants placed in a nutrient solution containing 3.1 ppm of ^{14}C-labelled chlortoluron absorbed 32 per cent of the total radioactivity within four days. Rapid translocation occurred since up to 80 per cent of the absorbed ^{14}C soon appeared in the shoots of the plants. Considerable species variation does, however, exist, for Owen and Donzel (1986), using radioactive chlortoluron, observed that only 42 per cent of the applied radioactivity was taken up in 13 days in suspension cell cultures of Italian ryegrass, *Lolium multiflorum*, whereas more than 72 per cent of the radioactivity was taken up by similar cultures of cotton cells in a period of less than 4 h. Metabolism of urea herbicides follows the pattern established in chapter 3, although the relative importance of routes of degradation depends on both the organism and the ureide. Hydrolysis of the (apparently vulnerable) amide linkage normally plays only a minor role, but there is some evidence that chlorbromuron is hydrolysed to a substituted aniline by microorganisms.

Figure 15.2 illustrates the probable major degradative routes for diuron and linuron. The metabolism of monuron follows a similar pattern (Menzie, 1978)

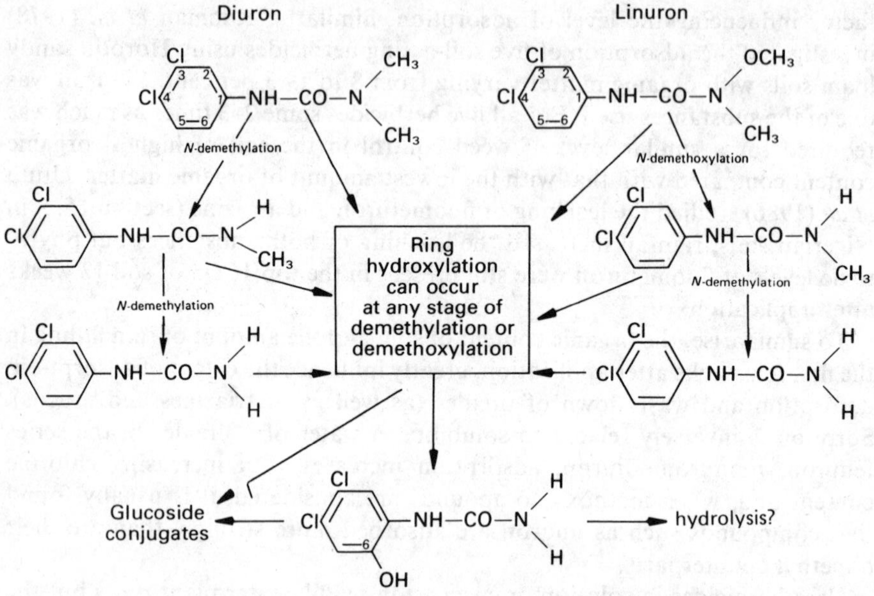

Figure 15.2   Probable metabolic routes of diuron and linuron

and the scheme probably applies to several other ureides also. Two major mechanisms operate, namely *N*-demethylation (or, where applicable, *N*-demethoxylation) and ring hydroxylation.

The mechanism of oxidative *N*-demethylation is described in section 3.4. Its oxidative nature is confirmed by the fact that intermediate hydroxymethyl derivatives or their glucose conjugates have been detected in plants. The reaction is probably NADPH-dependent and catalysed by microsomal mono-oxygenases. Ureides such as linuron appear to be metabolised by removal of the methoxy group and its replacement by a hydrogen atom (i.e. oxidation followed by elimination of the elements of formic acid). This probably happens in preference to the removal of the methyl group (figure 15.2). A further example is monolinuron, which has been studied by Schuphan and Ebing (1978), who found that both *N*-demethylation and *N*-demethoxylation occurred in three crop plants. They also detected the formation of the glucoside of a hydroxymethyl intermediate.

Another type of mono-oxygenase activity results in ring hydroxylation. Diuron and linuron and their demethylated (or demethoxylated) derivatives usually hydroxylate in the C-6 position. A third (and for the ureide group, unusual) type of oxidation occurs with chlortoluron (Gross *et al.*, 1979). For this substance the main route of metabolism in wheat cultivars involves the oxidation of the C-4 methyl group first to –CH_2OH (i.e. to a benzyl alcohol derivative) and then to carboxyl. In mature plants, the conjugates are mainly derivatives of the carboxyl oxidation product. Young wheat plants cannot oxidise the methyl group beyond the benzyl alcohol stage and the conjugates contain this product. These observations imply that a conjugate is not necessarily to be regarded as a terminal residue, for in this case, as the plant matures, the benzyl alcohol conjugates must be dismantled to allow further oxidation to occur, with subsequent reconjugation.

Differences in metabolism, with or without differences in uptake and translocation, are major factors contributing towards the selective responses of various crops and weeds to particular ureides. For example, Geissbühler *et al.* (1975, p. 271) have provided a list of species that are resistant to, or tolerant of, seven urea herbicides, and in almost all cases metabolic factors seem to be in part responsible for differences in susceptibility. Similarly, Ryan and Owen (1982) ascribed the partial tolerance to chlortoluron shown by wheat and barley to the ability of enzymes in these crops to hydroxylate the methyl group present in the benzene ring, a change that causes total loss of herbicidal activity. On the other hand, the methyl group of chlortoluron is much less readily oxidised in the relatively sensitive grasses, *Avena fatua* and *Alopecurus myosuroides*; instead, a principal route of metabolism in such plants is monodemethylation, and mono-*N*-demethylated ureides both retain some measure of herbicidal effectiveness and often disappear only slowly from the plant.

Metabolic differences are sometimes also responsible for differences in sensitivity between strains of the same plant species. For example, Müller and Frahm (1980) applied chlortoluron to wheat cultivars and showed that a relatively sensitive strain accumulated more of the mono-*N*-demethylated derivative than did the tolerant strain. On the other hand, Cabanne *et al.* (1985), working with the Corin and Clement cultivars of wheat, found that the metabolism of chlortoluron was only slightly greater in the tolerant Clement strain than it was in the susceptible Corin strain, and concluded that the difference was insufficient to account for the selectivity.

The principal **mode of action** of ureides, triazines and uracils is to disrupt the light reaction of photosynthesis. It will be recalled that green plants contain two light-induced electron excitation systems called photosystems I and II (figure 14.2). The second of these is responsible for the production of oxygen and supplies electrons, which move, via a chloroplastic electron transport system, to a positive moiety formed on excitation of photosystem I. As electrons move along the transport system, one molecule of ATP is probably formed from ADP for each electron entering the transport system. Photosystem I (PSI) produces the high-energy electrons that ultimately reduce $NADP^+$ to NADPH, and the latter is responsible for the reduction of carbon dioxide to sugar. Photosystem II (PSII) is activated by near-red rather than far-red light.

Some of these facts will now be considered in rather more detail. Light of wavelength about 680 nm stimulates the pigments in active centres of PSII (figure 14.2) and an energised electron is passed to an electron acceptor, Q, from where it normally enters the chloroplastic electron transport chain. An electron from water enters the (now positively charged) centre of PSII; this system is not fully understood but it is known to have a requirement for manganese ions. The overall effect is that water is oxidised to oxygen, which is evolved by green plants in sunlight:

$$2H_2O \rightarrow 2e + 2H^+ + O_2 \tag{15.1}$$

The (unknown) electron acceptor, Q, is so named because it fluoresces when activated but this fluorescence is *quenched* when it passes the energised electron to the electron transport chain. Should, therefore, the mechanism whereby an electron is lost from Q be blocked, the fluorescence persists.

The pioneering work of Wessels and Van der Veen (1956) showed that diuron inhibited by 50 per cent the Hill reaction (section 14.1) in isolated chloroplasts at concentrations below 1 μM. Later work extended this observation to other herbicidal ureas, as well as to triazines (section 15.2) and uracils (section 15.3). Moreover, these herbicides prevent non-cyclic photophosphorylation (the electrons for which originate from photosystem II) but do not affect cyclic phosphorylation.

All these data suggest that the ureides, triazines and uracils inhibit reactions at one or both ends of PSII. Very significantly, fluorescence of electron acceptor Q persists in the presence of these herbicides, indicating that the electrons are not entering the electron transport chain but that, instead, their energy is being squandered in the form of the energy of fluorescence. Such an observation strongly suggests that these herbicides interfere with the photosynthetic process in the position marked B in figure 14.2. Exactly how perturbation of photosystem II leads to lethal effects is not clear, but it is probable that the disruption leads to the production of free radicals and that these bring about lipid peroxidation and membrane disintegration (compare section 14.1).

Many attempts have been made to explain why ureides of different but related structures inhibit the light reaction of photosynthesis but do so at concentrations that differ greatly. In part, this could be a phase-distribution effect (section 14.14). Takemoto *et al.* (1985) showed that post-emergence herbicidal activity of a series of *N*-methoxy-*N*-methylphenylureas is correlated with their ability to inhibit the Hill reaction, modulated to some extent by parameters that reflect the lipophilic (or hydrophobic) qualities of the molecules. A similar conclusion was reached by Camilleri *et al.* (1987) using other substituted ureides. Concentrations of those substances that inhibited the Hill reaction by 50 per cent were plotted against parameters related to structure and to lipophilicity; the latter was found to be the most important molecular characteristic in relation to biological activity, although the position of substituents in the phenyl ring was also a contributory factor.

As was seen earlier, there is considerable evidence that the different susceptibilities of plants to equal levels of absorbed urea, triazine or uracil herbicides can often be explained in terms of rates or routes of detoxication. However, there are cases that apparently do not fit this explanation, for instances have been independently reported by several investigators where tolerance appears to be a consequence of some modification of the site of action, the change having been brought about by repeated exposure to ureides. For example, Santakumari and Das (1978) studied the Hill reaction in isolated chloroplasts from ureide-exposed and untreated plants of several species and found that it was less susceptible to diuron in plants pretreated with diuron than it was in plants that had received no pretreatment. A parallel phenomenon has been noted by Radosevich *et al.* (1979) in chloroplasts from two strains of *Senecio vulgaris* (groundsel), one of which was naturally tolerant of diuron and one not; a 60-fold greater concentration was needed for unit effect on the Hill reaction in the resistant strain than on that occurring in chloroplasts isolated from the susceptible strain. In the Hill reaction, as with other short-term *in vitro* experiments, results are unlikely to be greatly influenced by metabolic degradation (although metabolic activation could still affect the results).

Finally, it should be recalled that there is evidence that the action of ureides is not exclusively on photosynthetic tissues (seedlings may die before emerging from the soil and larger plants die even if kept in the dark). On the other hand, the concentrations that affect non-green tissues are frequently much higher than those that affect photosynthesis. For example, Gauvrit and Rougetet (1983) investigated the effect of 23 substituted ureas on the growth of non-photosynthetic tissues using excised roots of tomato plants. It was concluded that oxidative phosphorylation had been disrupted, possibly as a result of a more general interference with respiration. Similarly, Foissner (1984) reported that diuron inhibited oxygen uptake by mitochondria of *Nitella* spp.

Acute toxicity of ureides to mammals is usually low (table 1.2). On the other hand low concentrations of some ureides have been known to induce back-mutations in *Salmonella typhimurium* in the Ames test and also to inhibit testicular DNA synthesis in mice (Seiler, 1979). Since both the Ames test and a test based on the inhibition of DNA synthesis can reveal potential carcino-genicity, there is a possibility that diuron (and perhaps other ureides) may be metabolised to an active carcinogen or mutagen. Seiler presented evidence for believing that the reaction sequence leading from herbicide to the induction of mutagenic effects might involve *N*-hydroxylation, followed by acetylation of the hydroxyl group.

15.2 TRIAZINE HERBICIDES

Most herbicides based on the symmetrical triazine nucleus have alkyl-substituted amino groups in positions 4 and 6 (figure 15.3) and either a chlorine group or a methylthio group in position 2. The compounds containing a chlorine atom have names terminating in -azine and those containing a methylthio group end in -etryn(e). A small third group contains substances that have a methoxy group in position 2 and have names that end in -ton (e.g. prometon).

Triazine herbicides are solids with low vapour pressures at room temperature and with aqueous solubilities that mostly vary within the range of 5–

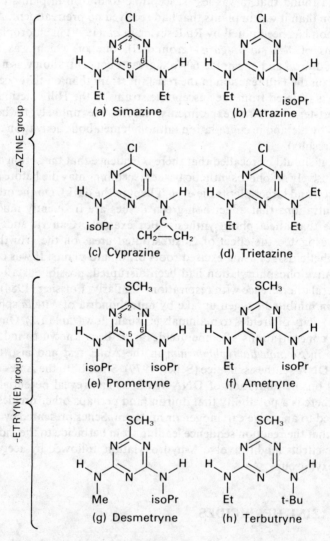

Figure 15.3 Some triazine herbicides: (a) 2-chloro-4,6-bis(ethylamino)-1,2,4-triazine; (b)–(h) are named similarly

500 ppm. **Simazine** and **cyprazine** are among the less soluble, **ametryne** and **desmetryne** among the more soluble. Solubility in suitable organic solvents is insufficient to allow ready formulation as emulsifiable liquids. They are therefore usually marketed as wettable powders comprising up to 80 per cent of active ingredient supplemented with detergents and, sometimes, diluents such as clay. Some are also formulated as granules.

Some crops are tolerant of specific triazines. However, for most crops, apparent selectivity in the field largely depends on the fact that the crop is large-seeded, or consists of bulbs, corms, etc., and in consequence is more deeply placed in the soil than are the seedling weeds. Depth protection also explains the use of simazine in well established asparagus beds and below certain fruit trees in orchards. They are also sometimes soil-incorporated before a crop is planted (e.g. maize) or used pre-emergence of both weeds and crop. Some can be applied as directed sprays to control weeds post-emergence of some crops (e.g. ametryne in maize and prometryne in cotton). In addition, several triazines are used at higher application rates for non-selective and long-term control in non-crop situations. Some of the varied uses of soil-acting triazines are shown in table 15.3. To this list should be added **prometon**, a 2-methoxytriazine, which is moderately soluble in water and is used for non-selective pre-emergence treatment.

Metribuzin, an asymmetric triazine, is also worthy of mention; it is used by soil incorporation but also as a foliage spray on potatoes. With regard to the latter use, Friessen and Wall (1984) tested the response of 22 cultivars of potatoes to an application of 1 kg/ha. Reduced yield occurred for some cultivars, the number of tubers per plant being lower than for the controls. This Canadian work also showed that cases of the growth disorder 'hollow heart' were increased in two cultivars after metribuzin treatment. Another asymmetric triazine, metramitron, is widely used for weed control in sugar beet in Europe.

Triazines have a wide spectrum of activity, killing many annual grasses as well as such annual dicotyledonous plants as chickweed, groundsel, ragweed and nightshade. Some perennial weeds, including *Agropyron repens*, are also controlled at higher rates of application.

Triazine herbicides can **persist** for many months in some soils and seasonal carry-over can sometimes cause difficulties. Carry-over is, naturally, most likely to occur when high application rates are used. Cyanazine is one of the less persistent members of the group and is often used in soils where carry-over could have serious consequences. The effectiveness of triazine herbicides is dependent on soil type and rainfall (section 13.5). For a similar herbicidal effect, much less is normally needed in sandy soils and when rainfall is high than in organic soils and when rainfall is low during the first few weeks after application. The toxicity of ureides to the crop also tends to be much higher in sandy soils than in organic soils, especially when rainfall is high. The effect on phytotoxicity of soil organic matter is illustrated by the work of Rahman *et al.*

Table 15.3   Uses of some triazine herbicides

Herbicide	Uses
Simazine	Total weed control on paths Control of germinating grass and broad-leaved weeds before planting, pre-emergence or early post-emergence Seedling weeds, in beans, sweet corn; in established rhubarb and hops Around a variety of fruit bushes, canes and trees Seedling weeds in alfalfa, pineapples, sugar cane
Atrazine	Weed seedlings in maize, pineapples, sorghum, sugar cane, raspberries, roses, young forest trees
Cyanazine	Annual dicot seedlings and annual meadow grass in peas Annual weed seedlings pre-emergence of potatoes (in mixtures with linuron) Post-emergence dicot weed control in cereals (in mixtures with MCPA or with mecoprop)
Prometryne	Germinating annual weeds pre-emergence of peas, potatoes Post-emergence many vegetables including carrots, celery In cotton, pre-emergence and directed post-emergence
Ametryne	Germinating annual weeds pre- and post-emergence potatoes Ditto in bananas, sugar cane; in pineapple soon after planting Some foliage activity on emerged weeds
Cyprazine	Newly emerged weeds in maize Germinating weeds pre-emergence of peas, potatoes (often in mixtures with linuron or simazine)
Desmetryne	Fat hen and other seedlings in many brassicas; when used post-emergence, the crop must have three true leaves
Terbutryne	Blackgrass and dicot seedlings pre-emergence of early drilled winter wheat, barley Seedling weeds in sorghum, peas, potatoes Filamentous algae in watercourses

(1978), who showed that the equitoxic dose of **atrazine** increased nearly three-fold as the content of organic matter increased from 8 to 19.3 per cent. Numerous studies have been made of the way that such properties as persistence, adsorption and effectiveness in the field are influenced by variation in soil moisture, pH and organic content. A collaborative venture on behalf of the European Weed Research Society illustrates the complexity of the problem for the case of simazine (Walker and Hance, 1983). In another investigation, atrazine was applied in Canada for 20 consecutive years to a field planted to maize (Khan and Saidak, 1981). Samples taken six and 12 months after the last application showed that both atrazine and a mono-*N*-dealkylated 2-hydroxy derivative were present.

Uptake of triazines is usually by the roots and movement is apoplastic. The use of ^{14}C-labelled triazines has shown that uptake from nutrient solutions occurs readily in both tolerant and susceptible plants. Moreover, radioactivity can usually be detected in shoots within an hour of application to roots. Upward movement is in the transpiration stream and factors that favour high transpiration usually favour rapid movement of triazines. As was mentioned for the ureides, such factors include elevated temperature and reduced environmental humidity (section 13.4). However, work of this kind does not prove that unchanged triazines accumulate in leaves. Additional experiments involving partition into solvents followed by chromatographic separation of the extracted substances are needed to distinguish between unchanged herbicide and its metabolites. This and similar work has demonstrated that most triazines are quite rapidly metabolised to both water-soluble and chloroform-soluble metabolites. Often, but not always, plants that are able rapidly to metabolise triazines prove to be relatively tolerant of them.

Metabolism of triazines proceeds by one or more of three major routes. These will first be described and then the probable relevance of each to plant tolerance will be considered. It should be remembered that any discussion about the importance to selectivity of the existence of different routes of metabolism is only meaningful in relation to the protection afforded against the effects of *equal concentrations of a herbicide entering the plant*, not to the *amount applied per square metre* of soil surface.

First, **chlorinated triazines** undergo non-enzymic but catalysed hydrolysis, the chlorine atom on C-2 being replaced by a hydroxyl group (figure 15.4). Some plants, including maize, contain non-enzymic catalysts that accelerate this reaction. Several related catalysts have been recognised but the best-known is benzoxazinone (DIMBOA, 2,4-dihydroxy-7-methoxy-1,4-benz-oxazine-3-one glucoside). The hydroxytriazine so formed has no herbicidal action, so that fraction of an absorbed dose of a triazine metabolised in this way is totally inactivated. **Methylthio-** and **methoxytriazines** are not metabolised at a significant rate by this route.

Secondly, some plants possess one or more glutathione-*S*-transferases (section 3.5), which allow glutathione to conjugate directly with herbicidal triazines of the **chlorotriazine** family. All glutathione conjugates are herbicidally inactive, so this pathway also leads to total detoxication of that fraction of an internal dose of triazine that is metabolised by this route. It is of interest that Guddewar and Dauterman (1979) have achieved a 61-fold purification of a glutathione-*S*-transferase (from mouse liver) which is capable of conjugating 2-chlorotriazines. It is a dimer, each of the two units of which have a molecular weight of about 23 000.

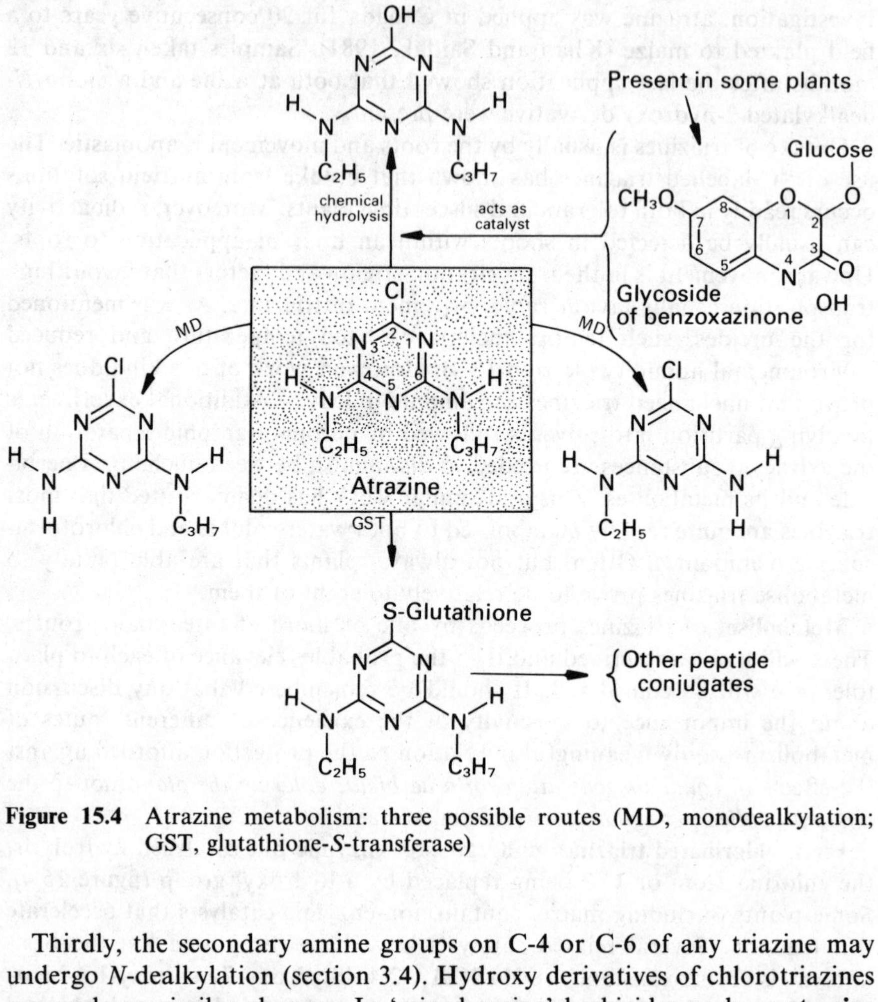

Figure 15.4 Atrazine metabolism: three possible routes (MD, monodealkylation; GST, glutathione-*S*-transferase)

Thirdly, the secondary amine groups on C-4 or C-6 of any triazine may undergo *N*-dealkylation (section 3.4). Hydroxy derivatives of chlorotriazines can undergo similar changes. In 'mixed amine' herbicides such as **atrazine** (figure 15.4), the ethyl group is removed from $-NHC_2H_5$ more rapidly than is the isopropyl group from $-NH.CH(CH_3)_2$. In suitable cases, further *N*-dealkylation can lead eventually to molecules containing only primary amine groups. Monodealkylated triazines are less effective herbicides than are the parent compounds but they do retain some activity; consequently, that fraction of a total dose metabolised by this route is not entirely inactivated. These partly dealkylated intermediates do not seem to conjugate rapidly with glutathione; perhaps for this reason their activity, although limited, often tends to be rather long-lasting.

In relation to the importance to selectivity of the three routes of metabolism described above, little correlation has been observed between tolerance of chlorotriazines and the presence of **benzoxazinone**. Maize, for example, is resistant and wheat is not, yet both contain catalysts of the benzoxazinone type. Conversely, Hamilton (1964) found that a maize mutant with a low benzoxazinone content was no less resistant to atrazine than were ordinary lines of maize. On the other hand, there may be a partial correlation between the ability of a plant to dealkylate a triazine and its resistance to it. Species such as peas and cotton that are of intermediate tolerance may owe that tolerance, in part, to the presence of this system (Shimabukuro and Swanson, 1970).

In contrast, there is evidence that an efficient glutathione-*S*-transferase system is well developed in many plants that can tolerate higher-than-average take-up amounts of triazine. The system is well developed in maize, sugar cane and sorghum, all of which are tolerant, but is poorly developed in wheat, barley and pea, which are of low or moderate tolerance (Frear and Swanson, 1970). Naturally, if plants well-endowed with the transferase system also possess high hydrolytic activity, the latter degradative route may well play a significant additional role in ensuring rapid detoxication of chlorinated triazines.

The **mode of action** of triazines resembles that of ureides (section 15.1). Briefly, electrons from photosystem II are prevented from entering the electron transport system of the chloroplast, probably as a result of the herbicide blocking the pathway at position B in figure 14.2. It has been suggested that this leads to the formation of superoxides, which give rise to peroxides, and that these probably attack unsaturated membrane lipids and destabilise chloroplastic membranes. Seedlings usually emerge before showing serious toxic symptoms, possibly because they are still largely living off food reserves in the cotyledons. Symptoms include chlorosis and desiccation, especially at the edges and tips of the leaves.

As was seen above, **selective action** is sometimes made possible because metabolic reactions proceed at different rates or by different routes. There is, however, increasing evidence that some species are tolerant of triazines because the site of action has become modified in some way (some authors refer to *tolerance* when metabolism is involved but *resistance* when the site of action is modified as a result of long-term contact with a toxicant). In an early investigation, Radosevich and Devilliers (1976) noted that uptake and internal distribution of atrazine were similar in atrazine-sensitive (S) and atrazine-resistant (R) biotypes of *Senecio vulgaris*; however, it was evident that photochemical activity of isolated chloroplasts from the S biotype was inhibited by atrazine concentrations that had no effect on the activity of chloroplasts from the R strain. It was later shown (Radosevich *et al.*, 1979) that a 3200-fold difference in concentration of ametryne had quantitatively similar effects on the Hill reaction in chloroplasts from R and S biotypes of *Senecio vulgaris*.

Some 30 weed species are now known to have produced triazine-resistant biotypes, among them being *Amaranthus retroflexus*, *Chenopodium album* and

Brachypodium distachyon. Gressel *et al.* (1983) reported that roadside populations of the last of these three weeds contained R biotypes after repeated treatment of roadsides in Israel with triazines over a number of years. Some metabolic differences did in fact exist, but the authors pointed out that the Hill reaction in chloroplasts isolated from R and S plants responded differently *immediately* upon exposure to atrazine, a circumstance that seems to exclude a predominant role for metabolism. Similarly Yaacoby *et al.* (1986), also in Israel, collected S and R biotypes from roadsides that had been repeatedly sprayed with triazine herbicides. They reported that the Hill reaction in chloroplasts of S plants was inhibited by 1 µM atrazine whereas the reaction in R types was not inhibited at all. The same authors demonstrated that the Hill reaction in atrazine-resistant chloroplasts was *nevertheless inhibited by diuron*, implying that site modification may sometimes be a very specific adaptation to the action of one particular toxicant.

15.3 URACIL AND PYRIDAZINONE HERBICIDES

Both of these small groups of herbicides contain substances whose molecules are based upon six-membered heterocyclic rings with two nitrogen atoms. Structures of selected members of the two groups are shown in figure 15.5. The basic ring structure of the uracils is that of pyrimidine and this provides an alternative name for the group.

The uracil herbicides were introduced in 1961, the three commonest members in current use being **bromacil**, **terbacil** and **lenacil**. They are less selective than are the ureides (which they otherwise resemble in application and mode of action) and are therefore used on a less wide range of crops and in non-crop situations. The crops are usually deep-rooted perennials such as citrus and other fruit trees (terbacil, bromacil) or cane fruits (bromacil, lenacil) or various kinds of beet (lenacil). Some examples are provided in table 15.4. Arnold and Aldrich (1979) found mixtures of terbacil with other compounds to be very effective in the control of bermuda grass (*Cynodon dactylon*) and purple nutsedge (*Cyperus rotundus*) growing in well established pecan (*Carya*) and peach. Various terbacil mixtures were reported by the same authors to provide some control of yellow nutsedge, dog fennel, camphor weed and large crabgrass.

Uracil herbicides are normally formulated as wettable powders but granules are also available. As with many ureides and triazines, a proportion of a total toxic dose enters emerged seedlings through their leaves, a fact that may determine whether the presence of a surfactant is desirable (if many of the seedling weeds have emerged through the soil, spray contact is increased by use of a spreading agent whereas, for non-emerged weeds, this form of adjuvant may not be necessary).

At standard application rates of 2–4 kg/ha most uracils persist in many soils

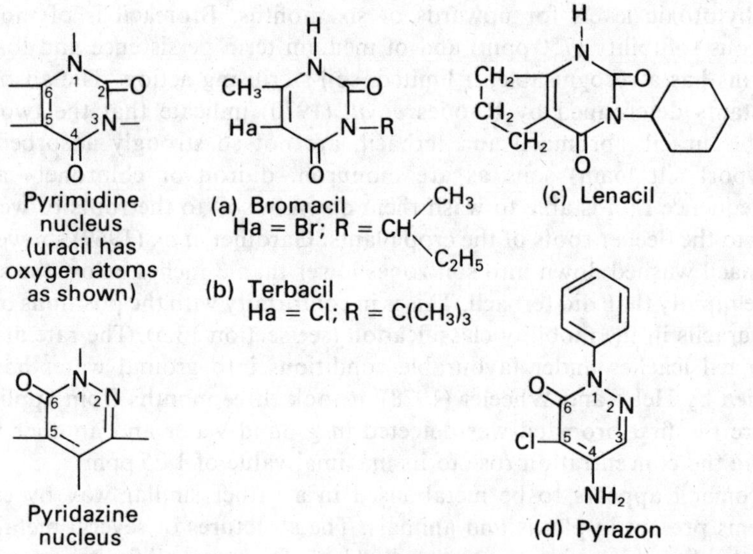

Figure 15.5 Uracil (pyrimidine) and pyridazinone herbicides: (a) 5-bromo-3-sec-butyl-6-methyluracil; (b) 5-chloro-3-tert-butyl-6-methyluracil; (c) 3-cyclohexyl-5,6-trimethylene uracil; (d) 4-amino-5-chloro-1-phenyl-6-pyridazinone

Table 15.4 Uses of uracil (pyrimidine) and pyridazinone herbicides

Substance	Uses
Bromacil	At low rates of application seedling weed control in citrus, cane fruit and pineapple
	At high rate of application can bring about soil sterilisation and total weed control in non-crop situations
	Some perennial weeds controlled by high application rates[a]
	Some brushwood species controlled by very high application rates
Terbacil	Annual weed control in strawberry, peaches, citrus, apples
	Ditto in sisal and sugar cane
	Winter weed control in dormant alfalfa
	Some perennial weeds controlled by high application rates[a]
Lenacil	Pre-emergence control of seedling weeds in sugar beet, mangolds
	Post-planting for strawberries, bulbs, some ornamentals
Pyrazon	Seedling weeds, pre-emergence sugar beet, fodder beet, red beet, mangolds

[a]Higher-than-normal concentrations are not necessarily compatible with use in crop situations.

at phytotoxic levels for upwards of six months. Bromacil is of moderate aqueous solubility (750 ppm) and of medium-term persistence and for these reasons has a recognisable, if limited, soil-sterilising action. The adsorption constants determined by Rhodes *et al.* (1970) indicate that the two more soluble uracils, bromacil and terbacil, are not so strongly adsorbed onto (Keyport silt loam) soils as are monuron, diuron or chloroneb, and in consequence rain is able to wash them down in soil to the roots of weeds or even to the deeper roots of the crop plants. Gardiner *et al.* (1969) showed that bromacil washed down into soil zones lower than 3 inches below the surface more rapidly than did terbacil. This is in conformity with the positions of these two uracils in the mobility classification (see section 13.5). The rate at which bromacil leaches under favourable conditions into ground water has been studied by Hebb and Wheeler (1978); it took three months from application before the first bromacil was detected in ground water and another month before the concentration rose to its maximal value of 1.25 ppm.

Bromacil appears to be metabolised in a rather similar way by enzyme systems present in plants and animals. The structures of several metabolites (isolated from the urine of rats that had been fed bromacil for one month) are such that it is likely that microsomal mono-oxygenases are involved in their formation (figure 15.6a). Thus hydroxylation occurred on the C-6 methyl group and in two different positions in the sec-butyl group attached to the N-3 nitrogen atom. The metabolism of terbacil appears to be essentially similar except that a complication occurs in the form of oxidative cyclisation involving the tert-butyl group on the N-3 nitrogen atom (figure 15.6b). The main metabolite in alfalfa was found by Rhodes (1977) to be metabolite C, but in work with animals quoted by Menzie (1974) metabolite A predominated.

It is very probable that the primary mode of action of the herbicidal uracils is the same as that of the ureides and triazines, namely that they interfere with electron transport at the reducing end of photosystem II. Concentrations of the order of $1–5 \mu M$ inhibit the Hill reaction of isolated chloroplasts by 50 per cent. Hoffman (1971) found that the toxic effects of monuron and bromacil to photosynthesising *Chlorella* were additive, indicating the probability of a common mode of action*. Moreover, monuron-resistant strains of *Euglena* were also resistant to bromacil, while in the dark neither resistant nor sensitive strains of *Euglena* were damaged by bromacil. It should perhaps be added that, despite the similarity of herbicidal uracils to the pyrimidines present in DNA and RNA, bromacil does not become incorporated into DNA and no mutagenic effects have been recorded.

Pyrazon (figure 15.5) is the commonest pyridazinone herbicide. It is of

---

*The concepts of similar and independent action of poisons is of importance in relation to possible harmful effects arising from the use of mixtures of compounds with a related mode of action. Similar and independent action is precisely defined mathematically and can be tested by applying mixtures of pesticides under controlled conditions. Reference should be made to chapter 8 of Finney (1947).

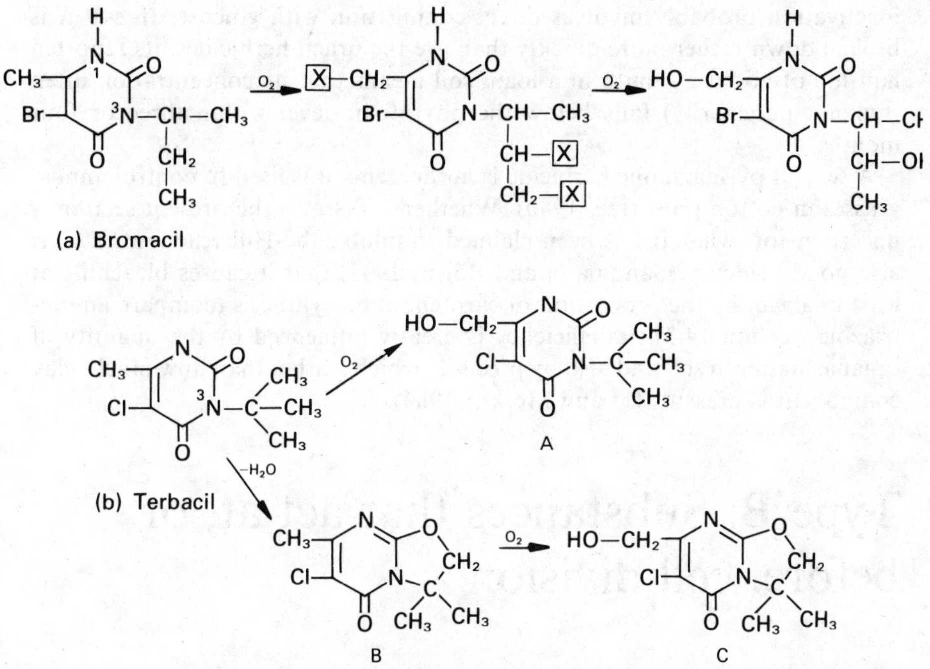

Figure 15.6 Metabolism of bromacil and terbacil. (a) Any of the three positions, X, can be hydroxylated in different metabolites (the other two being hydrogen. (b) A is the main primary metabolite in the dog; in one study C was the main metabolite in alfalfa

particular value for the pre-emergence control of annual broad-leaf weeds in various kinds of beet (it may control some seedling grasses but the level of control is variable). It enters any weeds that have emerged at the time of application via the shoot as well as entering all weed seedlings through the roots. It is sometimes mixed with diallate for use as a treatment before sowing beet in ground heavily infested with wild oats (*Avena fatua* and *A. ludoviciana*).

In contrast to most uracil herbicides, pyrazon binds somewhat strongly to constituents of organic and heavy soils. Its availability at different depths in the soil depends on soil type and its use on sandy soils is often inadvisable (section 13.5). On the other hand its strong adsorption on organic matter may lead to decreased weed control if the organic content is high. It is translocated apoplastically from the roots of plants to their leaves. For a given amount absorbed it accumulates in some plants and is inactivated in others, a difference that probably accounts, at least in part, for its selectivity. Beet can be damaged when the transpiration rate is very high since in this circumstance uptake may proceed faster than inactivation. The principal method of inactivation probably involves direct conjugation with glucose. In soil it is broken down rather more quickly than are the uracil herbicides; its reported half-life of about a month in a loam soil means that its concentration often (but not necessarily) falls below the phytotoxic level within three or four months.

A second pyridazinone herbicide is **norflurazon**; it is used to control annual grasses in cotton (Hawtree, 1980). Whether it fits into the present section is uncertain for, while it has been claimed to inhibit the Hill reaction, there is also good evidence (Sandmann and Böger, 1983) that it causes bleaching at least in algae, by the prevention of carotenoid biosynthesis (compare amino-triazole, section 14.3). Its efficiency is greatly influenced by the quantity of organic matter in soil and also by precisely which (rather than how much) clay component is present (Lo and Merkle, 1984).

Type B: Substances that act at, or before, cell division

15.4 PHENYLCARBAMATE DERIVATIVES

Esters of phenylcarbamic acid were originally introduced as a possible means of controlling monocotyledonous weeds in broad-leaved crops, i.e. to complement the action of the very successful phenoxyalkanoic acids (section 14.4). This early promise was, in fact, not fulfilled, for although seedling grasses succumb, established grasses usually do not. It was, however, soon evident that some crops are moderately resistant to carbamates at dosages, or under conditions, that destroy seedling grasses and some other weeds.

Phenylcarbamic acid esters are compounds in which a phenyl (or substituted phenyl) group has replaced an amino hydrogen atom in aminoformic acid. The structures of several important members of the group are shown in figure 15.7. They should be distinguished from the aryl esters of alkylcarbamic acid and phenylamides, which have other uses in crop protection:

(a) Phenyl–NH–COO–R (e.g.   R esters of phenylcarbamic acid
     propham)

(b) Alkyl–NH–COO–Aryl (e.g.   Aryl esters of alkylcarbamic acid
     carbaryl)

(c) Phenyl–NH–CO–R (e.g. propanil)   Not esters; phenyl-substituted amides

The phenylcarbamates used as soil-acting herbicides are solids with moderately low vapour pressure, although appreciable amounts may volatilise when

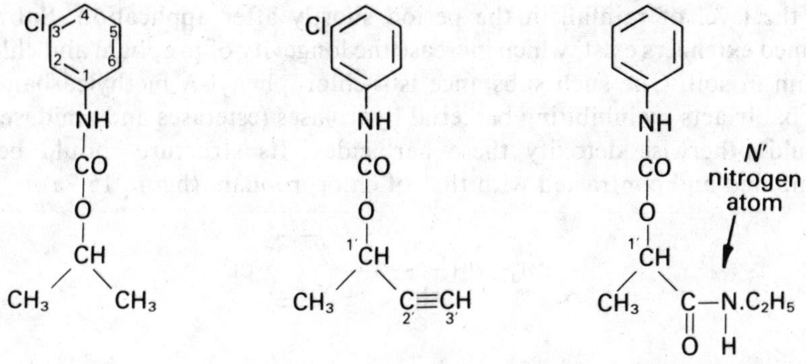

(a) Chlorpropham   (b) Chlorbufam   (c) Carbetamide

Figure 15.7 Some herbicidal carbamates: (a) isopropyl-*N*-(3-chlorophenyl)carba-
mate; (b) 1'-(methylprop-2'-ynyl)-*N*-(3-chlorophenyl)carbamate; (c) 1'-
(*N*'-ethylcarbamoyl)ethyl-*N*-phenylcarbamate. Propham resembles (a)
but lacks the C-3 chlorine; swep resembles (a) but has a second chlorine
on C-4

application is made to a soil surface. They are soluble in organic solvents such
as acetone and benzene. Their solubility in water is slow but variable.
Examples are chlorpropham, 90 ppm; chlorbufam, 540 ppm; carbetamide,
3500 ppm.

Phenylcarbamates are adsorbed onto soil colloids and especially onto soil
organic matter. In this respect they resemble the ureides and the same
considerations apply as were outlined in sections 13.5 and 15.1. In general, the
less water-soluble members including **chlorpropham** tend to be more strongly
adsorbed and to wash down more slowly than those that are more water-
soluble. This, it will be recalled, is the rationale underlying **positional selectivity**, for large-seeded crops such as peas and beans are planted deeply
compared to the location of most of the competitive weed seedlings (section
13.2). In addition, the extent of adsorption can affect both their herbicidal
efficiency and the time that they persist at herbicidal concentrations. Chlorpropham is in group 2 (low mobility) of the classification of Helling (1971).
Toxicity to crop plants is similarly influenced by the extent of adsorption onto
soil constituents. McGrath and McCormack (1979) have shown that the
phytotoxicity to sugar beet of chlorpropham (and also of atrazine and
linuron) is strongly and negatively correlated with the amount and type of soil
organic matter, but that soil pH and soil texture are of minor importance.

Herbicidal effectiveness is usually greatly increased by working these
substances into the soil to an appropriate depth, either by mechanical means
or by irrigation. In loam soils the half-life of many carbamates is of the order
of 2–5 weeks when used at normal herbicidal levels, but this range is greatly
influenced by soil temperature, by the type and numbers of soil microflora and

by the level of rainfall in the period shortly after application. Substances termed **extenders** exist, which increase the longevity of propham and chlorpropham in soil. One such substance is 4-chlorophenyl-*N*-methylcarbamate. It probably acts by inhibiting bacterial hydrolases (esterases and amidases) that would otherwise detoxify these herbicides. Its structure should be both compared and contrasted with that of chlorpropham (figure 15.7a).

$$CH_3-NH-\underset{\underset{O}{\|}}{C}-O-\text{⟨ring⟩}-Cl$$

4-Chlorophenyl-*N*-methylcarbamate

Some selective herbicidal uses of soil-acting carbamates are summarised in table 15.5. **Chlorpropham**, the most widely used member of the group, is extensively employed in Europe for the control of established chickweed (*Stellaria media*). In addition, it controls germinating weeds in many crops, some of which are listed in the table. It is frequently used in conjunction with other soil-acting substances, including diuron, fenuron, linuron and propham (MAFF, 1985). In the USA it is registered for the control of annual grasses and of some annual broad-leaved weeds in about 20 crops (Klingman and

Table 15.5   Some uses of carbamate herbicides

Substance	Uses
Chlorpropham	Established chickweed in bulbs, fruit bushes, dormant strawberries[a]
	Germinating weeds and established chickweed pre-emergence of broad beans, field beans, peas
	Weed seedlings in alfalfa, blueberries, cranberries, soybeans
	Post-harvest inhibition of sprouting of potato tubers
Propham	Germinating weeds, esp. wild oats, pre-emergence of peas, sugar beet
	Germinating weeds pre-emergence of sugar beet, fodder beet, mangolds
	Weed seedlings in alfalfa, lentils, safflower
Chlorbufam	Germinating weeds pre-emergence of sugar beet, some vegetables and some bulbs[a]
Carbetamide	Winter treatment of land later to be sown with brassicas, to control annual grasses, chickweed, speedwells
Swep	In Asia, against annual grasses in transplanted rice

[a]Often in mixtures with other herbicides.

Ashton, 1975). An important non-herbicidal use of chlorpropham is to prevent sprouting in ware potatoes. The uses of some other carbamates are also given in the table.

Carbamates readily enter seedling weeds through both roots and shoots. Once within plants, apoplastic translocation is usually rapid in sensitive plants. On the other hand, some tolerant species may owe this tolerance, at least in part, to restricted movement caused by limited binding to root components. **Swep**, for example, appears to be incorporated as the intact carbamate into the macromolecular structure of the plant. In other cases rapid metabolism in the roots of tolerant species may prevent extensive upward movement, either by direct detoxication or by the formation of metabolites that are bound to root components. In all of these cases, differential metabolism appears to be at least partly responsible for selective phytotoxicity, the enzymes in tolerant plants being more active, or more strategically located, or more capable of catalysing alternative routes of degradation, than the enzyme systems in sensitive species.

Some of the observations in the preceding paragraph are illustrated by the work on soybean plants by Still and Mansager (1973). These workers demonstrated that chlorpropham was changed first to polar products and then to insoluble residues, the proportion of the latter increasing with time. Polar metabolites were rapidly formed in roots and did not move upwards to the shoot, and were later bound to unknown root constituents. The apparently vulnerable ester and amide linkages do not appear to be rapidly attacked in plants, for the main polar products identified were 2- and 4-hydroxypropham and their *O*-glucosides.

Data relating to the metabolism of chlorpropham and propham by animals and by microorganisms have been collated by Menzie (1974, 1978). In rats, up to 30 per cent of an oral dose of chlorpropham was split by hydrolysis to give chloroaniline and its *N*-acetylated derivative (figure 15.8). However, as in plants, 4-hydroxychlorpropham was a major product in most animal species investigated by various authors: both this substance and its *N*-acetylated hydrolysis product (3-chloro-4-hydroxyacetanilide) are found in rat urine in the form of their glucuronide and sulphate conjugates. In addition, some authors have suggested that the isopropyl moiety can be hydroxylated and that the new –CH_2OH group can then be converted to carboxyl.

A very characteristic effect of carbamates on germinating rye grass or wild oats is to stunt growth and to cause the development of a bulbous shoot apex. Cells of affected apices contain swollen cells with giant nuclei. It is widely accepted that the most obvious general effect of phenylcarbamates at low concentrations is to act as inhibitors of mitosis (Yoshida *et al.*, 1983). Propham concentrations below 6 µM have been shown to prevent cell division whereas concentrations approaching 100 µM are required to inhibit the Hill reaction by 50 per cent. Herbicidal action is almost certainly linked to these effects on mitosis.

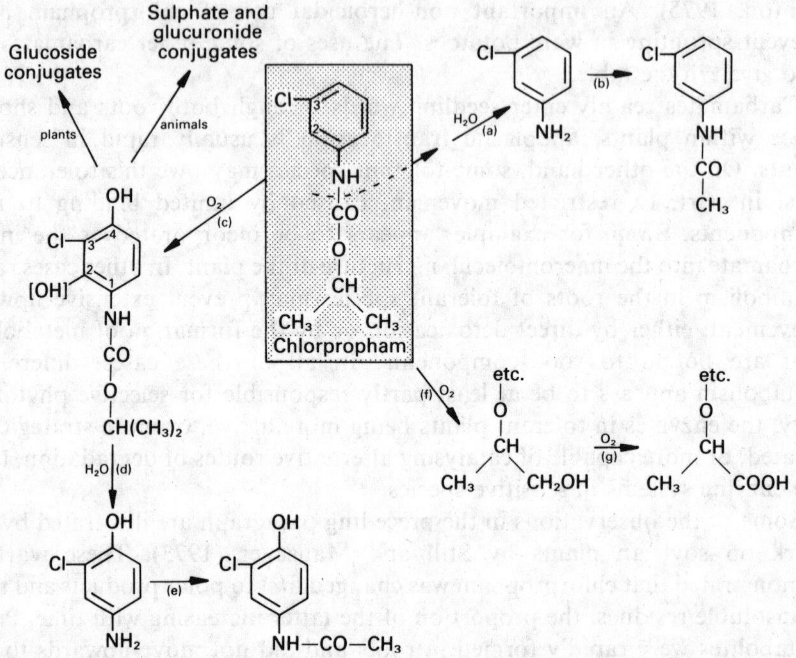

Figure 15.8   Metabolism of chlorpropham. Chlorpropham can be hydrolysed (a) and the product acetylated (b); in one study 30% was so metabolised by rats. Hydroxylation in the 4- or 2-position (c) is common in plants and in animals; the product(s) can be hydrolysed (d) and acetylated (e). There have been reports that the isopropyl group can also be oxidised (f) and (g)

The electron micrographs of Hepler and Jackson (1969) show that 55 µM propham affects within 2 h the organisation of the microtubules of the spindle fibres. These comprise a globular protein (tubulin) and their function is to separate the daughter chromatids. The existence of a cytoskeleton is mentioned in section 12.2, as is the role of microtubules in cell division. It will be recalled that microtubule fibrils contain tubulin, the molecule of which comprises two chains of amino acids. It is the assembly and disassembly of these tubules that leads, *inter alia*, to the separation of chromosomes during cell division. The assembly of the tubulin complex is carried out in regions termed **microtubule organising centres**. If these centres are damaged, microtubules are not assembled correctly and cell division is impaired. When this occurs, cells with abnormal numbers of chromosomes and multinucleate cells are often evident. The phenylcarbamates are believed to interfere with microtubule organising centres because experiments have shown that these herbicides have little binding affinity for tubulin. In contrast, it will be recalled that the benzimidazole fungicides prevent microtubule assembly by becoming attached to the β-tubulin subunit.

While the phenylcarbamates shown in figure 15.7 probably act predominantly as mitotic inhibitors, this is not necessarily true for other phenylcarbamates. Compounds such as phenmedipham (section 14.14) can in some circumstances act as uncouplers of oxidative or photosynthetic phosphorylation. Mona *et al.* (1987) studied a range of substituted phenylcarbamates and found that suitably substituted substances prevented light-driven electron transfer in thylakoid membranes. Several potent uncouplers of oxidative phosphorylation in potato mitochondria and of photophosphorylation in spinach chloroplasts were discovered; highly lipophilic molecules that also contained an acid-dissociable group were found to be particularly good uncouplers, acting in the concentration range of 1–10 µM. Such compounds do not appear to have a direct effect upon mitosis.

15.5 SULPHONYLUREA HERBICIDES

This relatively new group of weedkillers has aroused considerable interest because some members are actively herbicidal at less than 100 g/ha whereas many earlier substances doing somewhat similar tasks required the presence of kilograms per hectare. In addition, the structure is such that small modifications can lead to large differences in stability and solubility; consequently, different members of the group persist for very different periods of time in soil. The best-known compound in the group is chlorsulfuron but sulfometuron-methyl has also been marketed and many others are being actively investigated. They are variously used pre-plant, pre-emergence of crop or shortly after emergence.

Chlorsulfuron acts at an application rate as low as 10–100 g/ha, a principal use being to control a wide range of annual and some perennial broad-leaf weeds in small grain cereals such as wheat and barley. It also controls some annual grass weeds, including *Alopecurus myosuroides*. It can be used pre-emergence in winter wheat but it is usually used post-emergence, after the crop has developed three leaves but before the weeds have attained 5 cm in height. It is often used in conjunction with triallate (section 16.1) for the control of wild oats, but it is not recommended for use in very wet soil nor in light soil; it should not be followed by sugar beet, a crop that is readily damaged by it. It is also formulated in mixtures, e.g. with methabenzthiazuron (MAFF, 1986). When mixed with surfactant, applications of up to 140 g/ha give acceptable control of Russian thistle (Young and Gealy, 1986) and of bracken (Williams and Davies, 1987), although in the latter case considerable post-treatment management is also necessary. It enters both roots and shoots and is translocated to meristems where it interferes with cell division and plant growth; after about two weeks plants usually lose vigour, turning reddish in colour. Necrosis eventually develops and progresses away from the meristematic regions.

Sulfometuron is a sulphonylurea herbicide with similar agricultural uses to those of chlorsulfuron but with different crop specificity. In addition, it has proved valuable for the maintenance of a sward of centipedegrass (*Eremochloa ophiuroides*), keeping it free from undesirable intruders such as bahia-grass (*Paspalum notatum*—a preferred amenity grass in parts of the USA for growing on roadsides and on railway embankments, because it has a low growth habit and is tolerant to drought). *E. ophiuroides* is apparently tolerant of sulphometuron because it metabolises this substance rapidly. Thus Baird *et al.* (1989) found that it enters centipedegrass readily through both the shoot and the root but that 69 per cent of a foliar-applied dose is metabolised within 72 h of application.

A third example of a sulphonylurea herbicide is **chlorimuron**, 2-[[[[(4-chloro-6-methoxy-2-pyrimidinyl)amino] carbonyl] amino] sulphonyl] benzoic acid. It is a broad-spectrum selective herbicide used for soil incorporation before planting soybeans as well as for pre-emergence and post-emergence weed control in specified crops. Its phytotoxicity to the nutsedges (*Cyperus* spp.) has proved to be of particular interest because these weeds are difficult to control on account of the longevity of their tubers and the tendency of these tubers to sprout several times. Reddy and Bendixen (1988) reported that a foliar application of 20 g active ingredient per hectare gave, after 28 days, 84 per cent control of the yellow nutsedge and 100 per cent control of the purple nutsedge. In both species, 12 per cent of an applied dose was absorbed within 1 day and 15 per cent of that 12 per cent was translocated away from the treated area. Later, the same authors showed that it decreased shoot growth of *Cyperus esculentus* and *C. rotundus* by at least 85 per cent at rates as low as 10 g/ha. They also showed that chlorimuron absorbed by the tuber tended to remain in that organ whereas that absorbed by roots translocated to the shoots (Reddy and Bendixen, 1989). Nandihalli and Bhowmik (1989) showed that absorption of the ethyl ester of chlorimuron by root tissue of velvetleaf (*Abutilon theophrasti*) reached a maximum 2 h after application and that its uptake was inhibited by metabolic inhibitors and by anaerobic conditions. Wilcut *et al.* (1989) reported that, for five species investigated, tolerance of chlorimuron was directly correlated with the amount of chlorimuron metabolised in 72 h. Thus the rate of metabolism was greatest in soybean and peanut, whereas Florida beggarweed (*Desmodium tortuosum*) metabolised it more slowly; it was also observed that both the tolerance shown by peanuts towards chlorimuron and the rate at which they metabolise this substance increase as the plants get older.

Chlorsulfuron is representative of sulphonylurea herbicides and its structure is shown in figure 15.9. It can be regarded as a substituted urea, with a triazine group attached to one of the nitrogen atoms and an arylsulphonic acid attached to the other; variation of substituents in either the heterocyclic ring or the aryl ring results in analogues that have different rates (and sometimes routes) of metabolism, as well as different strengths as acids, different

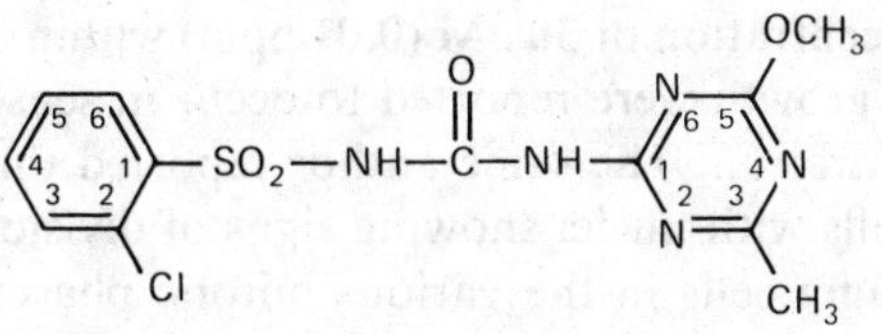

Figure 15.9 Structure of chlorsulfuron

solubilities and different degrees of sorption onto soil particles. Chlorsulfuron itself is slightly water-soluble (about 3000 ppm at room temperature), has a pK_a value of 3.8 and undergoes hydrolysis in acidic solution.

In soil, it is destroyed by living organisms and it leaches with water. Its persistence therefore depends on applied dose, soil type, pH, temperature and rainfall. Some care is necessary, for reports have appeared showing that 'carry-over' from one year to the next can occasionally result in damage to succeeding sugar beet (and sometimes other crops). Smith and Hsiao (1985) studied its persistence in prairie field soils; 45 weeks after use at a fairly high application rate, radioactivity studies showed that some 7 per cent of the chlorsulfuron was unchanged and another 15 per cent had been hydrolysed to 2-chlorobenzenesulphonamide. After 95 weeks some 2 per cent of the radioactivity was still in the form of chlorsulfuron. They also showed that 3–16 per cent of herbicide applied in May of one year was still detectable in the top 10 cm of soil a year later. Thirunarayanan *et al.* (1985) studied the effects of temperature and pH on adsorption and degradation of chlorsulfuron in soils. Adsorption was higher at 8°C than at 30°C and an inverse relation existed between pH and degradation rate, with a half-life of 88 days at pH 6.2 at 20°C. They reported that a rapid disappearance of chlorsulfuron took place for the first 15 days; after this time the herbicide disappeared more slowly, probably because the moisture content of the soil was also decreasing.

Joshi *et al.* (1985) demonstrated that soil sterilisation reduced the rate at which chlorsulfuron disappeared and that reinoculation of soil with indigenous soil organisms restored the higher rate of degradation. *Streptomyces*, *Aspergillus* and *Penicillium* species all destroyed it. These workers also showed, however, that significant *chemical* hydrolysis also occurred in acidic soils. Nicholls *et al.* (1987) measured the rate of degradation of chlorsulfuron in five soils of different pH values and at three depths. A half-life of longer than 600 days was recorded in some soils with pH values above 7.0; they ascribed subsequent sugar beet damage to persistence of chlorsulfuron on sites that were poorly drained. Beyer *et al.* (1987) concluded that chemical hydrolysis was the predominant cause of herbicide degradation in acidic soils, whereas in alkaline soils microbial attack was important. Breakdown was most rapid in warm, moist, light-textured soils of low pH.

With regard to the mode of action of chlorsulfuron, early studies showed that it decreased plant growth and inhibited cell division (Ray, 1982). In one study, for example, plant cell division was reduced to 20 per cent of normal by a chlorsulfuron concentration of 30 nM (0.01 ppm) within 8 h of treatment. In addition, effects on growth were reported to occur in sensitive plants at one-tenth of this concentration. The same author reported that, while it reduces the percentage of cells with nuclei showing signs of division, the *frequency of distribution* of dividing cells in the various mitotic phases (prophase, meta-phase, telophase) remains indistinguishable from the frequency observed in untreated specimens. These observations were taken to imply that chlorsul-furon probably blocks some mechanism of importance *prior to* cell division, rather than directly inhibiting cell division itself.

Using chlorsulfuron, sulfometuron-methyl and other sulphonylureas, various groups of investigators, including La Rossa and Schloss (1984), Chaleff and Mauvais (1984) and Ray (1985) have all demonstrated that the site at which the highly specific action of these herbicides is manifest is acetolactate synthase (ALS). This is the enzyme that catalyses the first step in the synthesis of the branched-chain amino acids, valine and isoleucine (figure 15.10). Addition of these acids to cells whose growth had been inhibited by chlorsulfuron resulted in a complete reversal of the inhibition. It will be recalled that vertebrates cannot synthesise valine or isoleucine, so there is no comparable system in animals for sulphonylureas to attack. Rubin and Casida (1985) postulated that this direct effect upon the synthesis of branched-chain amino acids leads to a reduction in the rate at which cells divide, although the precise mechanism remains uncertain.

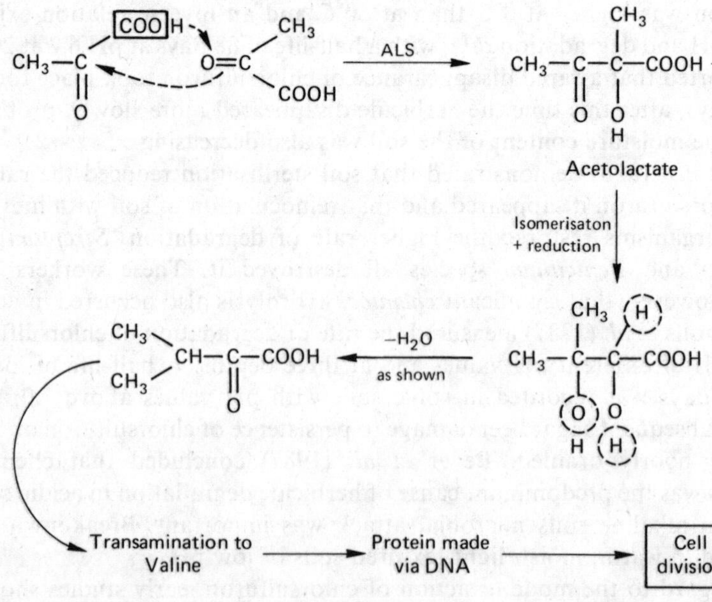

Figure 15.10   Role of acetolactate synthase (ALS) in the biosynthesis of valine in plants

It has also been shown that acetolactate synthase from a wide range of weeds and crop plants was almost equally sensitive to inhibition by sulphonylureas. For example, the I_{50} for chlorsulfuron varied only three-fold between the most sensitive and most tolerant of the plants investigated by Ray (1985). This strongly suggests that the several thousand-fold difference in herbicidal LD_{50} between the most sensitive and most tolerant plants so far studied is not due to differences in target site sensitivity. On the other hand, several reports have appeared showing that resistant mutants can be made in which the resistance must be ascribed to altered target site sensitivity; indeed such resistance has been used as a device to confirm that herbicidal effectiveness in the field really is a consequence of the ability of sulphonylureas to inhibit acetolactate synthase (Chaleff and Mauvais, 1984).

Sweetser *et al.* (1982) demonstrated that the remarkable differences in sensitivity of various weeds and crops was not caused by dramatic differences in sulphonylurea uptake by different species. They then provided evidence that the major factor governing differences in sensitivity was degradative metabolism. They established that a direct relationship existed between the rate of metabolism of ^{14}C-labelled chlorsulfuron and the sensitivity of the plant to this substance. When cotton, soybean and sugar beet (all of which are sensitive plants) were treated with chlorsulfuron, analyses carried out after 24 h showed that 80 per cent of the radioactivity was still associated with unchanged chlorsulfuron. On the other hand, less than 10 per cent was present in unchanged chlorsulfuron in wheat, barley and wild oats (all of which are tolerant).

Similarly, Hageman and Behrens (1984), who had earlier observed a 20 000-fold difference in tolerance of chlorsulfuron between velvetleaf (*Abutilon theophrasti*, sensitive) and Eastern black nightshade (*Solanum ptycanthum*, tolerant), found that 81 per cent of an absorbed dose was metabolised in three days by the first but only 7 per cent was metabolised by the second. Such results should be compared with those obtained using plant cell cultures; Swisher and Weimer (1986) found that all of a circumambient dose had been metabolised within 72 h by *Euphorbia esula* (tolerant) but only 2 per cent had been metabolised by *Cirsium arvense* (sensitive). A few reports have provided evidence that the rate of metabolism may be greater when uptake is via roots than it is when the substance enters through the leaves (Petersen and Swisher, 1985).

It is of interest that the precise metabolic process conferring tolerance appears to be different in tolerant grasses and in tolerant broad-leaf plants. Remembering that relatively few species have so far been investigated, it seems possible that the major metabolic route in tolerant dicotyledons (e.g. *Linum usitatissimum* and *Solanum ptycanthum*) involves oxidative attack upon the methyl group in the 3-position of the *triazine* ring. This attack leads to the formation of a hydroxymethyl group and of a substance that probably possesses residual toxicity; in practice, however, the oxidative product is rendered harmless by the formation of a glycoside (Hutchinson *et al.*, 1984). On the other hand, in tolerant cereals, Swisher and Weimer (1986) have reported that hydroxylation occurs in the 5-position of the *phenyl* ring, and that the phenol is then converted to a glycoside.

Substances termed **herbicidal antidotes** (section 16.1) confer on certain crop cultivars a degree of immunity from damage that specified herbicides possessing only marginal selectivity would otherwise cause. It is therefore of interest that at least one of these 'safeners' (*N,N*-diallyl-2,2-dichloroacetamide) can protect maize from adverse effects of chlorsulfuron (Sweetser, 1985). It has been shown that the use of this safener increases several-fold the rate at which chlorsulfuron is metabolised by maize, whereas the rate of metabolism in (sensitive) broad-leaf weeds growing in that crop is apparently unaffected. How antidotes achieve this protection is uncertain, although in the presence of cycloheximide (an inhibitor of protein synthesis) their beneficial action is not realised. The safener does not reverse the *in vitro* inhibition of acetolactate synthase in maize, but it does increase both the *in vivo* activity of this enzyme and the concentration of glutathione (chapter 3). Either of these effects could contribute to the antidotal effect (Rubin and Casida, 1985).

Mention has been made elsewhere of the possibility of creating crop cultivars by inserting genes that confer, for some reason or other, a level of immunity from the effects of a herbicide. In the case of sulphonylureas, Falco *et al.* (1987) isolated a plant gene encoding for a form of acetolactate synthase that was insensitive to sulfometuron-methyl and used it to transform herbicide-sensitive crop plants into resistant strains. Theoretically, other possibilities would be to insert into prized but sensitive cultivars multiple genes for the ordinary form of acetolactate synthase or multiple/modified genes for detoxifying enzymes. In the first case, overexpression of the gene for acetolactate synthase would presumably confer immunity by reducing the impact of small quantities of inhibitor.

Type C: Herbicides that disrupt membranes

15.6 DIPHENYL ETHERS WITH LIGHT-DEPENDENT ACTION

These substances, like those in section 14.9, are aromatic ethers, but they differ from them profoundly in regard to both their field uses and their mode of action. The aryloxyphenoxy derivatives, it will be recalled, affect fatty acid biosynthesis in grasses and are foliar-applied. The present substances are used pre- or post-emergence of the crop to control annual broad-leaf weeds and a few types of annual grasses; moreover, their toxic action is dependent on the presence of light and they are not translocated within the plant. The structures of two diphenyl ether herbicides are shown in figure 15.11.

The diphenyl ether herbicides enter weeds through the leaves or shoots. They do not normally enter through roots, yet they are often soil-applied. This apparent contradiction is explained by the fact that any part of an applied dose that misses weed foliage and lands on the ground remains at the soil surface and attacks the foliage of newly germinating weed seedlings as they emerge through the soil. As they do so, they also become exposed to light and suffer symptoms of wilting and leaf scorch within a day or two. At normal rates of application the diphenyl ethers remain herbicidally effective for 1–4 months. They are fairly persistent because they are strongly adsorbed onto soil colloids, are not very volatile and are not readily leached from the soil. Unlike some of the herbicides mentioned in the next chapter, these substances, for the reason stated above, should not be mixed with soil but should be left as an undisturbed surface layer. They are not very toxic to mammals but Draper and Casida (1983) have reported the formation of mutagenic metabolites when incubated under anaerobic conditions with rat liver.

Nitrofen (figure 15.11a) was one of the first diphenyl ethers (DPEs) to be introduced. Other examples are **acifluorfen** (figure 15.11b), fluorodifen and oxyfluorfen. Acifluorfen is used both as its sodium salt and as its methyl ether. Except for the salts of acifluorfen the solubility in water of these substances is less than 1 ppm. Various diphenyl ethers have found use for weed control in most major crops including soybean, rice, wheat, cotton, peanuts and sunflower, as well as various types of trees (Ensminger *et al.*, 1985). Except for trees and some other established perennials, they are usually applied pre-emergence of the crop but some post-emergence treatments are also possible; sometimes placement techniques are used to avoid crop damage. Their primary use is to kill annual broad-leaf weeds such as many members of the Crucifer family and the Polygonum family. Usually, the weeds should be treated before they have developed four true leaves. However, even within a botanical group a wide divergence of sensitivity exists; for example, *Spergula arvensis* is a very susceptible member of the Caryophyllaceae but chickweed, another member, is outstandingly resistant (Richardson, 1984). Small-seeded grasses are often susceptible (e.g. *Poa annua*) whereas larger-seeded grasses such as *Avena fatua* are much more tolerant. Fortunately, *Echinochloa crusgalli* is susceptible, a fact that explains the extensive use of diphenyl ethers in rice crops. Barker *et al.* (1984) described experiments to control five species of *Ipomoea* (morning glory) and concluded that the best overall result was

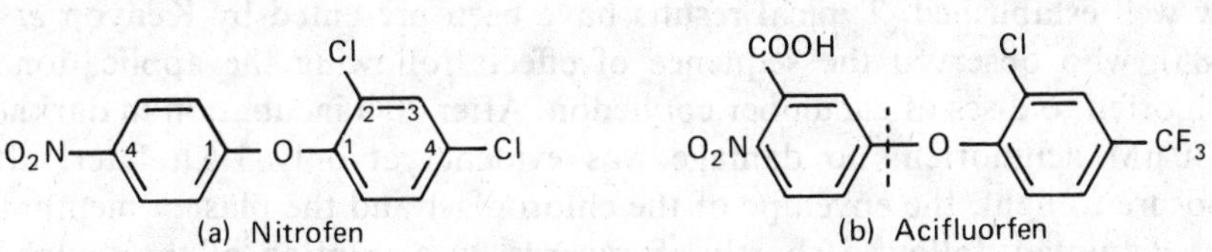

(a) Nitrofen   (b) Acifluorfen

Figure 15.11 The structures of two diphenyl ether herbicides

obtained using a tank mixture of bentazon (section 13.7) with acifluorfen (about 0.6 kg/ha of each).

The overall effect of diphenyl ethers on weeds is to disrupt cellular and subcellular lipoprotein membranes, so that they lose their selective permeability, leak their contents and cause the cell or plant to die. This was demonstrated for nitrofen and oxyfluorfen by Pritchard *et al.* (1980) and for acifluorfen by Orr and Hess (1981). In all cases light proved to be essential for activation of the disruption process; indeed, it was shown as early as 1969 that strains of rice were tolerant of nitrofen if kept in the dark but were highly susceptible if brought out into the light. Moreover, albino rice seedlings are also tolerant in light (Matsunaka, 1969).

The role played by light is still uncertain, but the two main theories are summarised by Gillham and Dodge (1987a, b). The first, supported by Kunert and Böger (1981), suggests that a functional photosynthetic electron transport system activates the diphenyl ether molecules, leading to the formation of free radicals that attack polyunsaturated fatty acids in lipoprotein membranes. One piece of evidence supporting this suggestion is that ureides such as monuron (section 15.2), which inhibit the photosynthetic electron transport system, also decrease the injury inflicted by diphenyl ethers. The alternative theory, supported by Orr and Hess (1982), proposes that carotenoids, a major normal role of which is to protect chlorophyll from photo-oxidation (section 14.3), activate diphenyl ether herbicides so that they initiate lipid peroxidation. Evidence supporting this view includes the observation that diphenyl ethers are phytotoxic in mutants that lack chlorophyll but not in mutants that lack both chlorophyll and carotenoids. A second piece of evidence is that pretreatment with fluridone, which inhibits carotenoid biosynthesis, protects plants from injury by diphenyl ethers (Orr and Hogan, 1983). More recently, several workers have provided evidence that diphenyl ether herbicides interfere with the metabolism of tetrapyrroles (e.g. Lydon and Duke, 1988; Matringe and Scalla, 1988). The latter authors demonstrated that diphenyl ethers cause protoporphyrin IX to accumulate in non-chlorophyllous soybean cells. They pointed out that acifluorfen acts as a photosensitiser but, since it does not absorb light in the visible region, some cell photo-receptor that is activated by light must participate in the toxic mechanism. An argument against the involvement of carotenoids is that diphenyl ether toxicity is induced by red light at a wavelength outside the absorption range of these pigments.

Whatever the precise role of light, the consequences of its intervention are now well established. Typical results have been presented by Kenyon *et al.* (1985), who observed the sequence of effects following the application of acifluorfen to discs of cucumber cotyledon. After 20 h incubation in darkness in 30 µM acifluorfen, no damage was evident yet only 1.5 h later, after exposure to light, the envelope of the chloroplast and the plasma membrane were disrupted, followed shortly afterwards by disruption of the thylakoid membrane. At this point, oxygen evolution that is dependent on carbon dioxide ceased and, within 2 h, malondialdehyde was recognised in the medium (a sure sign that lipid peroxidation had taken place). It was further shown that electrolytes leaked within 1 h of the discs being exposed to light, which led the authors to conclude that loss of membrane integrity precedes most of the other symptoms of damage caused by these herbicides. Ultrastructural alterations brought about by contact with acifluorfen have been described by Derrick *et al.* (1988), their article being illustrated by electron micrographs. 100 µM acifluorfen, in the presence of light, caused chloroplasts to swell and their membranal envelopes to distort. By 15 h, lysis of the tonoplast was evident and the plasmalemma disrupted after 30 h.

The oxidation of polyunsaturated fatty acids in membranes probably involves participation of superoxide ions, which in turn may be generated by organic free radicals. What remains uncertain is exactly how the diphenyl ethers fit in; the free radicals might be derivatives of these substances or the diphenyl ethers may initiate free-radical formation from carotenoids or other endogenous substances in the presence of light. A few examples will illustrate the present uncertainty.

Böger (1984) reported that the existence of free radicals of diphenyl ethers after activation by red light can be demonstrated using electron spin resonance techniques. These free radicals have direct or indirect peroxidative properties, which inhibit the formation of carotenoid precursors as well as damaging unsaturated fatty acids. Ensminger *et al.* (1984, 1985), while studying the effect of acifluorfen on *Chlamydomonas*, confirmed that free radicals played a role in the toxic process by demonstrating that free-radical scavengers such as ethanol diminished toxicity. Moreover, these workers also reported that toxicity is also decreased in anaerobic conditions. On the other hand, using analogues of herbicidal diphenyl ethers that contain chlorine instead of the nitro group, the same workers came to the conclusion that free radicals, if they were formed, did not require the presence of a nitro group (as others had earlier assumed to be the case). Orr and Hogan (1983) showed that two redox dyes were reduced by nitrofen concentrations as low as 17 µM in the presence of light, whether or not oxygen was present. Both Orr and Hogan (1983) and Ensminger *et al.* (1985) concluded that the diphenyl ethers are activated by the action of light upon yellow plant pigments and that these activated molecules then initiate a free-radical chain reaction involving polyunsaturated fatty acids in lipoprotein membranes.

It seems increasingly likely that some form of chloroplastic electron movement is involved in the activation of the diphenyl ethers (or, of course, that diphenyl ethers deflect the electrons so as to lead to the formation of damaging free radicals). One such theory is proposed by Gillham and Dodge (1987a,b). These workers showed that neither acifluorfen-methyl nor oxyfluorfen at 50 µM affected non-cyclic electron flow but that both repressed ferredoxin-dependent NADP reduction by illuminated chloroplasts. They suggested that reduced ferredoxin, formed in light at the reducing end of photosystem I in chloroplasts, passed its electrons to the herbicides instead of to NADP, this process somehow leading to damaging free-radical formation (compare, for example, section 14.1). They demonstrated that lipid peroxidation was promoted in thylakoids in light by acifluorfen-methyl but that this effect was abolished by washing the thylakoids prior to use; upon addition of exogenous ferredoxin, the toxicity of the herbicides was restored. On the other hand Alscher and Strick (1984), working with three species of varying sensitivity to diphenyl ether herbicides, concluded that the herbicidal effect was not diminished in the absence of full photosynthetic function. Using dark-grown and aetiolated plants, in which the photosynthetic apparatus was not fully developed, the diphenyl ether herbicides were found still to be highly toxic in light.

The metabolism of acifluorfen has been studied in excised leaf tissue of the soybean, a tolerant plant, by Frear *et al.* (1983). It was shown that the molecule was rapidly cleaved on the side of the ether linkage nearest to the nitrated ring, giving rise, *inter alia*, to a cysteine conjugate. Such cleavage could have been brought about by a glutathione transferase reaction (section 3.5). The newly formed phenolic group on the halogenated side of the original molecule of acifluorfen reacted to form a malonyl glucoside. About 90 per cent of the total acifluorfen absorbed was metabolised to these and other products within 24 h.

REFERENCES

Alscher, R. and Strick, C. (1984). *Pestic. Biochem. Physiol.*, **21**, 248
Arnold, C. E. and Aldrich, J. H. (1979). *Weed Sci.*, **27**, 638
Atkin, J. C. and Turner, M. T. F. (1982). *Proc. Br. Crop Prot. Conf., Weeds*, p. 637
Baird, J. H., Wilcut, J. W., Wehtje, G. R., Dickens, R. and Sharpe, S. (1989). *Weed Sci.*, **37**, 42
Barker, M. A., Thompson, L., Jr and Godley, F. M. (1984). *Weed Sci.*, **32**, 813
Beyer, E. M., Brown, H. M. and Duffy, M. J. (1987). *Proc. Br. Crop Prot. Conf., Weeds*, p. 531
Böger, P. (1984). *Pestic. Sci.*, **15**, 526
Cabanne, F., Gaillardon, P. and Scalla, R. (1985). *Pestic. Biochem. Physiol.*, **23**, 212
Camilleri, P., Bowyer, J. R., Gilkerson, T., Odell, B. and Weaver, R. C. (1987). *J. Agric. Fd Chem.*, **35**, 479
Chaleff, R. S. and Mauvais, C. J. (1984). *Science*, **222**, 1443
Derrick, P. M., Cobb, A. H. and Pallett, K. E. (1988). *Pestic. Biochem. Physiol.*, **32**, 153
Draper, W. M. and Casida, J. E. (1983). *J. Agric. Fd Chem.*, **31**, 1201
Ensminger, M. P., Hess, F. D. and Bahr, J. T. (1984). *Pestic. Sci.*, **15**, 526
Ensminger, M. P., Hess, F. D. and Bahr, J. T. (1985). *Pestic. Biochem. Physiol.*, **23**, 163
Falco, S. C., Knowlton, S., Larossa, R. A., Smith, J. K. and Mazuir, B. J. (1987). *Proc. Br. Crop Prot. Conf., Weeds*, p. 149
Finney, D. J. (1947). *Probit Analysis*. Cambridge Univ. Press, Cambridge
Foissner, I. (1984). *Pestic. Biochem. Physiol.*, **22**, 346
Frear, D. S. and Swanson, H. R. (1970). *Phytochemistry*, **9**, 2123

Frear, D. S., Swanson, H. R. and Mansagar, E. R. (1983). *Pestic. Biochem. Physiol.*, **20**, 299

Friessen, G. H. and Wall, D. A. (1984). *Weed Sci.*, **32**, 442

Gardiner, J. A., Rhodes, R. C., Adams, J. B. and Soboczenski, E. J. (1969). *J. Agric. Fd Chem.*, **17**, 980

Gaur, B. L., Gupta, P. C. and Sharma, D. D. (1986). *Trop. Pest Managem.*, **32**, 267

Gauvrit, C. and Rougetet, E. (1983). *Weed Res.*, **22**, 221

Geissbühler, H., Martin, H. and Voss, G. (1975). *Herbicides: Chemistry, Degradation and Mode of Action*, 2nd edn, vol. 1, eds P. C. Kearney and D. D. Kaufman, chap. 3. Marcel Dekker, New York

Gillham, D. J. and Dodge, A. D. (1987a). *Pestic. Sci.*, **19**, 19

Gillham, D. J. and Dodge, A. D. (1987b). *Pestic. Sci.*, **19**, 25

Green, M. B., Hartley, G. S. and West, T. F. (1977). *Chemicals for Crop Protection and Pest Control*. Pergamon, Oxford

Gressel, J., Shimabukuro, R. H. and Duysen, M. E. (1983). *Pestic. Biochem. Physiol.*, **19**, 361

Gross, D., Laanio, T., Dupuis, F. and Esser, H. O. (1979). *Pestic. Biochem. Physiol.*, **10**, 49

Guddewar, M. B. and Dauterman, W. C. (1979). *Pestic. Biochem. Physiol.*, **12**, 1

Hageman, L. H. and Behrens, R. (1984). *Weed Sci.*, **32**, 162

Hamilton, R. H. (1964). *Weeds*, **12**, 27

Hawtree, J. N. (1980). *Outl. Agric.*, **10**, 184

Hebb, E. A. and Wheeler, W. B. (1978). *J. Environ. Qual.*, **7**, 598

Helling, C. S. (1971). *Soil Sci. Soc. Am. Proc.*, **35**, 737

Hepler, P. K. and Jackson, W. T. (1969). *J. Cell Sci.*, **5**, 727

Hoffman, C. E. (1971). *Proc. 2nd Int. IUPAC Congr. Pestic. Chem.*, vol. 5, p. 65

Hutchinson, J. M., Shapiro, R. and Sweetsar, P. B. (1984). *Pestic. Biochem. Physiol.*, **22**, 243

Joshi, M. M., Brown, H. M. and Romesser, J. A. (1985). *Weed Sci.*, **33**, 888

Kenyon, W. H., Duke, S. O. and Vaughn, K. C. (1985). *Pestic. Biochem. Physiol.*, **24**, 241

Khan, S. U. and Saidak, W. J. (1981). *Weed Res.*, **21**, 9

Klingman, G. C. and Ashton, F. M. (1975). *Weed Science: Principles and Practices*. Wiley, New York

Kozak, J. and Weber, J. B. (1983). *Weed Sci.*, **31**, 368

Kunert, K. J. and Böger, P. (1981). *Weed Sci.*, **29**, 169

La Rossa, R. A. and Schloss, O. V. (1984). *J. Biol. Chem.*, **259**, 8153

Lo, C.-C. and Merkle, M. G. (1984). *Weed Sci.*, **32**, 279

Lydon, J. and Duke, S. O. (1988). *Pestic. Biochem. Physiol.*, **31**, 74

McGrath, D. and McCormack, R. J. (1979). *Ir. J. Agric. Res.*, **18**, 89

MAFF (1985). *Approved Products for Farmers and Growers. Reference Book 380/85.* UK Ministry of Agriculture, Fisheries and Food. HMSO, London

MAFF (1986). *Pesticides, 1986. Pesticides Approved under the Control of Pesticides Regulations 1986. Reference Book 500.* UK Ministry of Agriculture, Fisheries and Food. HMSO, London

Matringe, M. and Scalla, R. (1988). *Pestic. Biochem. Physiol.*, **32**, 164

Matsunaka, S. (1969). *J. Agric. Fd Chem.*, **17**, 171

Menzie, C. M. (1974). *Metabolism of Pesticides: An Update*, US Dept Interior, Fish and Wildlife Service, Special Scientific Report, Wildlife no. 184, Washington DC

Menzie, C. M. (1978). *Metabolism of Pesticides: Update II*, US Dept Interior, Fish and Wildlife Service, Special Scientific Report, Wildlife no. 212, Washington, DC

Mona, S., Ravanal, P., Chérade, X. de, Bergon, M., Calmon, J.-P. and Tissut, M. (1987). *Pestic. Biochem. Physiol.*, **27**, 261

Müller, F. and Frahm, J. (1980). *Med. Fac. Landbouww. Rijksuniv. Gent*, **45**, 1017
Nandihalli, U. B. and Bhowmik, P. C. (1989). *Weed Sci.*, **37**, 29
Nicholls, P. H., Evans, A. A. and Walker, A. (1987). *Proc. Br. Crop Prot. Conf., Weeds*, p. 549
Orr, G. L. and Hess, F. D. (1981). *Pestic. Biochem. Physiol.*, **16**, 171
Orr, G. L. and Hess, F. D. (1982). *Plant Physiol.*, **69**, 502
Orr, G. L. and Hogan, M. E. (1983). *Pestic. Biochem. Physiol.*, **20**, 311
Owen, W. J. and Donzel, B. (1986). *Pestic. Biochem. Physiol.*, **26**, 75
Petersen, P. J. and Swisher, B. A. (1985). *Weed Sci.*, **33**, 7
Pritchard, M. K., Warren, G. F. and Dilley, R. A. (1980). *Weed Sci.*, **28**, 640
Radosevich, S. R. and Devilliers, O. T. (1976). *Weed Sci.*, **24**, 229
Radosevich, S. R., Steinback, K. E. and Arntzen, C. J. (1979). *Weed Sci.*, **27**, 216
Rahman, A., Dyson, C. B. and Burney, B. (1978). *NZ J. Exp. Agric.*, **6**, 69
Reddy, K. N. and Bendixen, L. E. (1988). *Weed Sci.*, **36**, 707
Reddy, K. N. and Bendixen, L. E. (1989). *Weed Sci.*, **37**, 147
Ray, T. B. (1982). *Pestic. Biochem. Physiol.*, **17**, 10
Ray, T. B. (1985). *Proc. Br. Crop Prot. Conf., Weeds*, p. 131
Rhodes, R. C. (1977). *J. Agric. Fd Chem.*, **25**, 1066
Rhodes, R. C., Belasco, I. J. and Pease, H. L. (1970). *J. Agric. Fd Chem.*, **18**, 524
Richardson, W. G. (1984). *Pestic. Sci.*, **15**, 526
Rubin, B. and Casida, J. E. (1985). *Weed Sci.*, **33**, 462
Ryan, P. J. and Owen, W. J. (1982). *Proc. Br. Crop Prot. Conf., Weeds*, p. 317
Sandmann, G. and Böger, P. (1983). *Weed Sci.*, **31**, 338
Santakumari, M. and Das, V. S. R. (1978). *Pestic. Biochem. Physiol.*, **9**, 119
Schuphan, I. and Ebing, W. (1978). *Pestic. Biochem. Physiol.*, **9**, 107
Seiler, J. P. (1979). *Pestic. Biochem. Physiol.*, **12**, 183
Shimabukuro, R. H. and Swanson, H. R. (1970). *Weed Sci.*, **18**, 231
Smith, A. E. and Hsiao, A. I. (1985). *Weed Sci.*, **33**, 555
Still, G. G. and Mansager, E. R. (1973). *Pestic. Biochem. Physiol.*, **3**, 87
Sweetser, P. B. (1985). *Proc. Br. Crop Prot. Conf., Weeds*, p. 1147
Sweetser, P. B., Schow, G. S. and Hutchinson, J. M. (1982). *Pestic. Biochem. Physiol.*, **17**, 18
Swisher, B. A. and Weimer, M. R. (1986). *Weed Sci.*, **34**, 507
Takemoto, I., Yoshida, R., Sumida, S. and Kamoshita, K. (1985). *Pestic. Biochem. Physiol.*, **23**, 341
Thirunarayanan, K., Zimdahl, R. L. and Smika, D. E. (1985). *Weed Sci.*, **33**, 558
Utulu, S. N., Akobundu, I. O. and Fayemi, A. A. A. (1986). *Crop Prot.*, **5**, 129
Walia, U. S. and Gill, H. S. (1985). *Trop. Pest Managem.*, **31**, 226
Walker, A. and Hance, R. J. (1983). *Weed Res.*, **23**, 373
Wilcut, J. W., Wehtje, G. R., Patterson, M. G., Cole, T. A. and Hicks, T. V. (1989). *Weed Sci.*, **37**, 175
Wessels, J. S. C. and van der Veen, R. (1956). *Biochim. Biophys. Acta*, **19**, 548
Williams, G. H. and Davies, D. H. K. (1987). *Proc. Br. Crop Prot. Conf., Weeds*, p. 765
Yaacoby, T., Schonfeld, M. and Rubin, B. (1986). *Weed Sci.*, **34**, 181
Yoshida, Y., Nakamura, K. and Hiura, A. (1983). *Cytologia*, **48**, 707
Young, F. L. and Gealy, D. R. (1986). *Weed Sci.*, **34**, 318
Zwick, W., Menck, B.-H. and Nuyken, W. (1985). *Proc. Br. Crop Prot. Conf., Weeds*, p. 85

16 Soil-applied herbicides often used in the absence of annual crops

There is no absolute distinction between the substances considered in this chapter and in the last. It is nevertheless convenient to subdivide the many different herbicides that act on seedling plants or on rhizome buds, and one way to do this is to consider their use in relation to the seasonal planting of annual crops. Essentially, the substances described in the last chapter can be (although not necessarily are) used around the time of crop emergence and, to achieve best results, are usually applied to the soil surface. Those described in the present chapter are often soil-mixed and therefore applied prior to planting or seeding the crop. Moreover, their action is often indiscriminate, with the result that any seedling plant with which they come into contact is likely to be damaged. Most, but not all, show little selectivity between monocotyledonous and dicotyledonous plants. They have little or no action on foliage of seedling weeds but enter roots or other subterranean parts of the plant. An important use of many of the substances in the groups listed in table 16.1 is that they are able to suppress the development of buds on rhizomes of perennial grasses; this is of considerable practical importance since it limits the vegetative spread of a group of weeds that has become increasingly troublesome as the control of broad-leaf plants has been perfected. Some substances described below (in common with many that were mentioned in the last chapter) have been used for weed control in established perennial crops such as fruit trees and bushes, although sometimes directed spraying is necessary.

Table 16.1 Soil-acting herbicides, often soil-incorporated prior to planting or sowing a crop

---

Type A: Substances that disrupt lipid biosynthesis
  Section 16.1 Thiolcarbamates (e.g. EPTC, diallate, butylate)

Type B: Substances that affect meristematic growth
  Section 16.2 Dichlobenil and chlorthiamid
      16.3 Chloroacetamides (e.g. alachlor, metolachlor)
          Other amides (e.g. diphenamide)
      16.4 Dinitroanilines (e.g. trifluralin, pendimethalin)

Type A: Substances that disrupt lipid biosynthesis

16.1 THIOLCARBAMATES

Although chemically related to the carbamate herbicides (section 15.4), the thiolcarbamates differ from them in respect to their physical properties and their method of application in the soil. In addition, their phytotoxic mode of action is different. These herbicides are by preference termed *thiol*carbamates rather than *thio*carbamates since the sulphur atom is invariably in a position corresponding to the oxygen of the –OH group and not to that of the C=O group of the parent carbamic acid.

$$H_2N-\overset{\overset{\displaystyle O}{\|}}{C}-OH$$

Formulae and names of some members of this group appear in figure 16.1.

Most thiolcarbamates are yellowish liquids with vapour pressures ranging from 10^{-1} to 10^{-3} mmHg at 20°C. Most of them are therefore more volatile than herbicidal carbamates and a few of them are, compared with most pesticides, very volatile indeed. This property greatly influences how they must be used in agriculture if good field results are to be achieved. In view of the importance of volatility it is essential that the vapour pressures of thiolcarbamates should be known accurately. For example, Grover *et al.* (1978) reported that the vapour pressure of triallate is 1.08×10^{-4} mmHg at 20°C and can be calculated at other temperatures using

$$\log_{10} P = 11.05 - (4401/T) \tag{16.1}$$

where T is the temperature on the absolute scale and P is the vapour pressure (mmHg). Their aqueous solubilities are quite variable, ranging from 4 to 900 ppm.

Thiolcarbamates normally only kill weed seeds at the time of germination; they have very little effect once the plants have emerged. They are particularly useful for the control of seedling grasses and some annual broad-leaf plants. Examples are troublesome grasses such as wild oats (*Avena* spp.), blackgrass (*Alopecurus myosuroides*) and barnyard grass (*Echinochloa crus-galli*); susceptible broad-leaf weeds include chickweed (*Stellaria media*) and shepherd's purse (*Capsella bursa-pastoris*). Importantly, however, some thiolcarbamates can be successfully used against certain established perennial weeds, a fact that is explained by their ability to attack non-dormant buds on subterranean parts

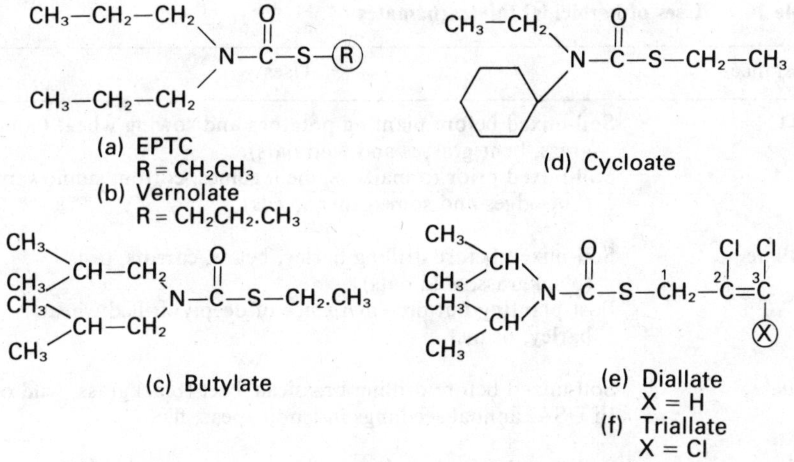

Figure 16.1 Some herbicidal thiolcarbamates: (a) *S*-ethyl-*N*,*N*-dipropylthiolcarbamate; (b) *S*-propyl-*N*,*N*-dipropylthiolcarbamate; (c) *S*-ethyl-*N*,*N*-di-isobutylthiolcarbamate; (d) *S*-ethyl-*N*-ethyl-*N*-cyclohexylthiolcarbamate; (e) *S*-(2,3-dichloroallyl)-*N*,*N*-di-isopropylthiolcarbamate; (f) *S*-(2,3,3-trichloroallyl)-*N*,*N*-di-isopropylthiolcarbamate

of perennials, thus restricting new vegetative growth. Cultivation that breaks up rhizomes stimulates the sprouting of vegetative shoots and for this reason is found frequently to enhance the effectiveness of thiolcarbamates. Important examples of perennials suppressed in this way are bermuda grass (*Cynodon dactylon*), couch or quack grass (*Agropyron repens*) and nutsedges (*Cyperus* spp.).

As well as being volatile, thiolcarbamates are somewhat unstable chemically and not strongly adsorbed onto soil constituents. In consequence they are ideal substances to perform the often tricky task of delivering a 'short, sharp, shock'—and then partially disappearing before a somewhat tolerant crop is drilled or planted days or weeks later (table 16.2). Nevertheless, this same volatility also dictates the manner of their application, for they must normally be **worked into the soil** to a suitable depth, and not merely applied to the soil surface. The effectiveness of soil incorporation is greatly improved if the soil surface is dry. Once within the soil, the more volatile substances (e.g. EPTC) evaporate into the air spaces within the soil, an effect that further improves distribution. Sometimes irrigation water can replace cultivation as a means of soil incorporation. It should be noted that an exception exists to the customary soil incorporation, namely that some members of the group are formulated as granules intended for surface application.

EPTC, ethyldipropylthiolcarbamate (figure 16.1a) is the most volatile member of the group (10^{-1} mmHg at 20°C) and its rapid incorporation into the soil is especially necessary. This should be done within 15 min of

Table 16.2   Uses of herbicidal thiolcarbamates

Substance	Uses
EPTC	Soil-mixed before planting potatoes and sowing wheat (couch grass, bent grasses and wild oats) Soil-mixed prior to maize, some legumes, cotton, sunflower (nutsedges and some other weeds)
Triallate	Soil-mixed before drilling barley, beans, carrots, peas (blackgrass, wild oats) Post-planting but pre-emergence of deeply drilled wheat, barley, beans[a]
Diallate	Soil-mixed before drilling brassicas, beet (blackgrass, wild oats) In USA, annual seedlings in lentils, peas, flax
Cycloate	Soil-mixed 3 weeks before drilling beet, mangolds (wild oats and other annual weeds)[b]
Pebulate	Soil-mixed before planting beet, tomatoes and before transplanting tobacco (annual grasses, nutsedges, hairy nightshade)
Vernolate	Soil-mixed before planting or transplanting peanuts, soybeans, sweet potatoes, tobacco (annual grasses, nutsedges)
Butylate	Soil-mixed before sowing maize (annual weeds, including grasses, nutsedges)
Molinate	Soil-mixed before planting rice (barnyard grass, annual grasses)
Benthiocarb	Pre- or post-planting rice (barnyard grass)

[a]Often mixed with lenacil.
[b]The seed must be below the depth of incorporation of herbicides.

application. Its solubility is about 350 ppm, which is sufficient to ensure that it can leach into soil below weed depth after heavy rain. In soil, it has a half-life of a week or two, which means that effective concentrations are present for from two to six weeks. When EPTC is soil-incorporated prior to sowing wheat, two passes should be made at a wide angle using a straight-toothed harrow (Fryer and Makepeace, 1978). In Britain, it is worked into the soil to a depth of 15 cm about two weeks before planting potatoes.

EPTC is used before planting maize, potatoes, sugar beet and sunflower, as well as pre-plant of certain leguminous crops. It is also used under established perennials such as woody ornamentals. In conjunction with a safener or antidote (see end of this section and section 15.5), EPTC has proved useful for the control of troublesome weeds in maize. Moyer and Dryden (1979) reported that good control of wild oat (*Avena* spp.) was obtained with little subsequent crop damage when soil-incorporated before seeding. Hemp dog-bane (*Apocynum cannabinum*) can be controlled for up to two months after soil incorporation prior to sowing maize. Similarly Ogg and Drake (1979) found that a mixture of EPTC and a safener gave 95 per cent control of barnyard grass (*Echinochloa crus-galli*) as well as control of fat hen (*Chenopodium album*), redroot pigweed (*Amaranthus*) and yellow foxtail (*Setaria lutescens*) when incorporated into soil before planting maize; no loss of yield, quality or succulence of maize was evident.

EPTC has also been employed for the control of proso-millet (*Panicum miliaceum*) in maize (Ezra and Stephenson, 1985). The difference in sensitivities of crop and weeds was attributed to the low level of glutathione-*S*-transferase in the millet compared to that in the tolerant maize. Good results against proso-millet were also obtained initially by Harvey *et al.* (1986) but these workers noted that the level of control diminished when a mixture of EPTC and dichlormid (a safener) was applied for two consecutive years to the same soil. Microbial enrichment (section 12.5) was probably responsible for this loss of effectiveness; the extent to which it occurs varies even for closely related substances, for, using the same soils, Harvey *et al.* (1986) found that the enrichment effect was much less noticeable when a mixture of cycloate (figure 16.1d) and dichlormid was applied to the soils for two succeeding years.

The persistence and rate of degradation of EPTC was studied by Lode and Skuterrud (1983) in three soils. It was observed that decomposition was greater at pH 7 than at pH 5, probably because the microorganisms present were more numerous or were qualitatively different at the higher pH. At pH 5 the duration of phytotoxicity was two or three weeks longer than at pH 7, and in very acid soils the herbicide could persist long enough to damage later crops. Presumably for similar reasons, (alkaline) ash from rice stubble rapidly inactivates molinate, another thiolcarbamate.

Diallate and **triallate** (figure 16.1) are also somewhat volatile and need to be incorporated into soil as soon after application as possible. Diallate is used pre-planting of beet and brassicas, particularly for the control of blackgrass (*Alopecurus myosuroides*) and of wild oats (*Avena fatua* and *A. ludoviciana*). Triallate is frequently used to control the same two weeds in cereals, although in this case the cereals must be drilled deeply and not undersown with grasses (Fryer and Makepeace, 1978). In appropriate circumstances it can be used both before and after drilling wheat and barley; in the case of spring wheat, for example, triallate can be incorporated between 3 days and 3 weeks before drilling. Zemanek and Kovar (1978) reported that triallate and TCA showed synergistic action, with the result that the application rate of triallate could be halved yet the toxicity to wild oats maintained.

Butylate (figure 16.1c) is often mixed with atrazine and is primarily useful for weed control in maize, especially to suppress rhizome bud development of nutsedge and bermuda grass. When mixed with a safener it gives good but temporary control of hemp dogbane (*Apocynum cannabinum*). Viable tubers of yellow nutsedge (*Cyperus esculentus*) were reduced by 96 per cent in two years when it was used on ground to be double cropped with barley and maize (Keeley *et al.*, 1979). Several groups of workers have shown that the breakdown of butylate is enhanced in soils that have a history of prior exposure to this or other thiolcarbamates. Wilson (1984) demonstrated accelerated degradation in such circumstances for butylate, vernolate, cycloate and EPTC. Similarly Obrigawitch *et al.* (1983) showed that butylate metabolised rapidly on a loam soil previously exposed to EPTC. Conversely, Obrigawitch found that its persistence in such soils was increased by use of **diethylphenylphosphorothioate**. The latter has a synergistic effect and is called an **extender**. Miaullis *et al.* (1982) ascribed the synergistic action of extenders to a prolongation of the life in soil of the thiolcarbamate by the inhibition of microbial enzymes that would otherwise degrade this herbicide. In an extensive investigation, Tuxhorn *et al.* (1986) studied the persistence of butylate in three soils previously treated for two years with one of four thiolcarbamates. Butylate was found to degrade most rapidly in soils previously treated with a mixture of butylate and the dichlormid safener.

Vernolate is frequently employed as a component of a mixture containing trifluralin. Mixed with an antidote, Ogg and Drake (1979) found, it did not reduce yield or quality of maize but greatly reduced the incidence of barnyard grass (*Echinochloa crus-galli*). In the USA it has been recommended for pre-planting incorporation before soybeans and peanuts.

Vernolate shares with other thiolcarbamates a propensity towards enhanced degradation in soils that have had a history of treatment with thiolcarbamate herbicides. Tal *et al.* (1989) have drawn a distinction between self-enhancement (in which soils treated with vernolate in earlier years degraded this substance more rapidly in the current year) and cross-enhancement (in which soils treated earlier with vernolate were found to degrade EPTC or butylate more rapidly in the current year). As little as 5 per cent of a soil with a history of vernolate treatment, when added to an 'un-enriched' soil, was sufficient to accelerate thiolcarbamate degradation. Tal *et al.* (1989) also provided references to several publications that consider the subject of enhanced degradation.

Miaullis *et al.* (1982) have investigated the use of diethylphenylphosphorothioate as an extender to delay the degradation of thiolcarbamates in soil. This extender (R33865) enhances the value of some thiolcarbamates for the control of late-germinating weeds, including perennial grasses. Whether all extenders have the same mode of action (the inhibition of microbial enzymes) is unclear. The metabolism of vernolate in soybeans has been studied by Wilkinson (1983).

Molinate and **benthiocarb** are employed to control germinating weeds in rice. Molinate is rapidly leached from soil and it also breaks down quickly. In consequence, little normally remains in soil a month after application. Both substances are used against barnyard grass. Molinate applied into flood water after emergence of rice seeded into water may damage the crop; a safer procedure is to apply after flooding dry-seeded rice.

The thiolcarbamates are essentially **inhibitors of shoot growth**, preventing cell elongation rather than cell division, and, in grasses, the first leaves are badly formed and have difficulty leaving the coleoptile. A typical action on susceptible plants is to cause their leaves to have very thin cuticles, a change which, when herbicide combinations are being used, facilitates the entry of other soil-acting poisons (by increasing water loss and thereby increasing transpiration). The affected leaves tend to be dark green and shiny.

Wilkinson and Smith (1975) suggested that the shortage of cuticular wax may only be a rather obvious consequence of a more general interference with lipid biosynthesis. This suggestion is gaining support, for it is now clear that the synthesis of certain fatty acids is affected, and this can lead to a widespread effect on lipid metabolism, including a shortage of phospholipids for the synthesis of lipoprotein membranes (Rivera and Penner, 1979). It has, however, been shown that the thiolcarbamates do not necessarily cause a decrease in the uptake of acetate for fatty acid biosynthesis. The main effect appears to be upon the biosynthesis of **fatty acids with 20 or more** carbon atoms in their molecules. It has also been suggested that thiolcarbamates inhibit the synthesis of gibberellic acid (Wilkinson, 1986). However, the precise connection between these biochemical events and the field effectiveness of thiolcarbamates remains uncertain; it is possible that the definitive action is upon the synthesis of some so far uninvestigated complex lipid.

Metabolism by microorganisms is probably a major factor determining the rate of disappearance of thiolcarbamates from soils, for in sterile soils they persist much longer. Nevertheless, factors considered elsewhere (section 13.5) also contribute. Volatilisation is greater from wet soils than from dry ones and persistence is longer in soils of high organic content than in those of a lower carbon content, while loss from damp soils is much more influenced by a raised temperature than is loss from dry soils. Above all, rate of loss from soil of volatile thiolcarbamates such as EPTC is greatly diminished if the substance is incorporated to a depth of at least 2 inches. The main degradative route probably involves hydrolysis of the thioester linkage to give a mercaptan, an amine and carbon dioxide:

$$\begin{array}{c} R' \\ \diagdown \\ \diagup \\ R \end{array} N{-}\overset{\displaystyle \overset{O}{\|}}{C}{-}S{-}R'' \quad \xrightarrow{\ H_2O\ } \quad \begin{array}{c} R' \\ \diagdown \\ \diagup \\ R \end{array} NH + CO_2 + HSR'' \qquad (16.2)$$

It was early established that metabolism of EPTC in plants often led to the thiol sulphur atoms eventually turning up in molecules of cysteine, methionine and cysteic acid. It is also known that plants that are tolerant of EPTC frequently metabolise it faster than plants that are sensitive to it. It now seems certain that a major route of degradation involves the glutathione transferase system, and the effectiveness of this metabolic system in different plants is probably an important factor determining species selectivity. Thus, for example, Ezra and Stephenson (1985) showed that the activity of the gluta-thione-S-transferase system in the shoot of (sensitive) proso-millet was only 10 per cent of that in the shoot of the (tolerant) maize. Moreover, the concentration of glutathione itself was twice as high initially in corn as in millet; however, only three days after applying EPTC with a herbicidal antidote the amount of glutathione (but not of its transferase) had increased greatly in the millet.

Another route of metabolism of thiolcarbamates involves the oxidation of the sulphide sulphur atom to sulphoxide and sulphone (compare table 3.1). The sulphoxides of the thiolcarbamates are more toxic than the parent substances whereas the sulphones are less toxic. It is possible that the sulphoxide may be the active molecular species at the site of action (Schuphan and Casida, 1979) and the action may be the consequence of a strong affinity of the sulphoxide for essential thiol groups at the site of action. Whether or not this is so, there is good evidence that it is the sulphoxide form of the herbicide that reacts with the thiol of glutathione during degradation.

In animals, hydrolytic breakdown of EPTC to a mercaptan is probably a major metabolic route, the thiol then being converted to propanol, which may be metabolised by the normal pathways of intermediate metabolism (e.g. converted to propionic acid). Less unstable carbamates, such as cycloate, however, probably form sulphoxides and sulphones, after which glutathione-S-transferase cleaves the molecule. The rather incomplete evidence has been collated by Menzie (1978).

Most thiolcarbamates are of low acute toxicity to animals, their LD_{50} values mostly lying within the range 1400–2000 mg/kg body weight. This, when considered in conjunction with their low chemical stability, suggests that any residue hazards are indirect. It should, however, be added that various pesticides containing chloroallyl, chlorovinyl or similar groups have been shown to be mutagenic in tests in which *Streptomyces coelicolor* and *Salmonella typhimurium* were test organisms (Carere *et al.*, 1978). Of the various types of pesticides tested by these authors, dichlorvos and triallate caused mutations in *Salmonella* and diallate and triallate were mutagenic in *Streptomyces*. They concluded that the presence of chlorinated vinyl or chlorinated allyl groups in pesticide molecules could cause the substances to induce point mutations in the two genera.

It is of interest that compounds are known that can diminish the toxic effect of thiolcarbamates in maize and wheat (crops other than these two do not seem to benefit to any significant degree). Such compounds are variously known as **safeners** (in the USA) and as herbicidal **antidotes** (in Britain). They should not be confused with extenders, which act as synergists and were referred to previously. An example of a safener is DDCA, *N*,*N*-diallyl-2,2-dichloroacetamide (often called R25788 or dichlormid). This protects maize from soil-applied butylate, EPTC and vernolate and, as a seed treatment, protects wheat from triallate. These safeners are of considerable commercial importance, because, although different thiolcarbamates do differ in their crop specificity, it often happens that little margin of safety exists between the concentration needed to control perennial grasses and the concentration that damages the crop. Literature on the role of safeners has been reviewed by Cole *et al.* (1987). It is not certain how 'herbicidal antidotes' function (or, indeed, whether the many safeners now known achieve their purpose in the same way). However, it has been observed that they prevent a thiolcarbamate-induced aggregation of epicuticular wax in certain crops, an aggregation that exposes the underlying tissues of the plant and causes rapid transpiration. Whatever their effect may be, an intriguing and important aspect of their action, so far unexplained, is that they offer protection to tolerant plants (the crops maize and wheat, for example) but do not normally increase the tolerance of susceptible weeds*.

Type B: Herbicides that affect meristematic growth

16.2 DICHLOBENIL AND CHLORTHIAMID

Dichlobenil (figure 16.2a) is a soil-acting benzonitrile derivative. Structurally, it is similar to bromoxynil and ioxynil (section 14.6) but its field use is quite different from that of these foliar-applied herbicides. **Chlorthiamid** (figure 16.2b) is a thioamide but it and dichlobenil are appropriately considered together since chlorthiamid actually breaks down to give dichlobenil after application. The difference between these two substances relates to their method of application because dichlobenil is somewhat volatile (vapour pressure, about 10^{-3} mmHg, at 25°C) and it is rapidly lost from some soils unless it is either irrigated into the soil or applied in the form of granules. Chlorthiamid, on the other hand, is much less volatile and it is not necessary to work it into the soil.

Both substances are marketed as granules and both are used for non-selective weed control (table 16.3). In addition, chlorthiamid is used to control troublesome perennial weeds, including established couch grass, ground elder (*Aegopodium podagraria*), nettles (*Urtica* spp.) and thistles (*Cirsium* spp. and

---

*The pesticidal equivalent of 'To him that has, more shall be given', so to speak. But how? To use the phraseology of a famous statesman in a different context, 'It boggles my mind!'

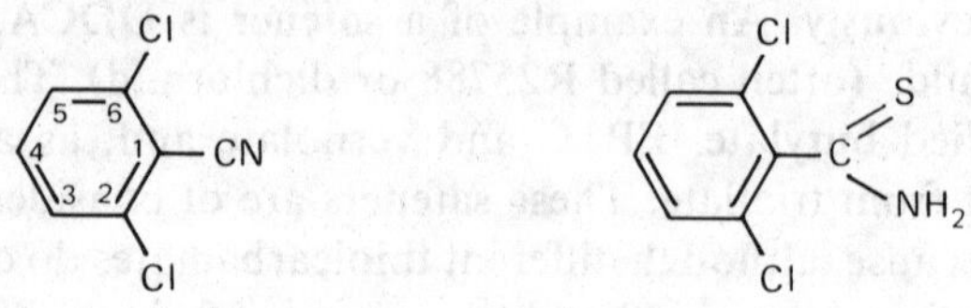

(a) Dichlobenil   (b) Chlorthiamid

Figure 16.2   Structures of dichlobenil and chlorthiamid

Carduus nutans) on ground not immediately to be used for crops (MAFF, 1985). This use may at first seem surprising since chlorthiamid and dichlobenil, like many other soil-acting compounds, kill seedlings. The reason is that both chlorthiamid and dichlobenil disrupt growth of sprouting underground buds, although neither affects dormant buds on rhizomes and tubers. In some crops (usually well established fruit trees or bushes) it is possible at carefully chosen application rates to obtain selective control of some perennial species (Fryer and Makepeace, 1978). In such cases, 'selectivity' is dependent on location of the roots of the plant to provide the necessary protection (sometimes called depth protection). The use of dichlobenil as a soil-residual herbicide to control aquatic weeds has been described by Bowmer (1987).

Dichlobenil is strongly adsorbed on lignin and humus, with the result that it does not readily leach in soils with a high organic content. It is this property which enables it to be employed for selective weed control in some deep-rooted trees and shrubs. Chlorthiamid persists longer than dichlobenil in most soils because it is less volatile; typically, it has a half-life of about a month in dry soils. Its effectiveness in damp soils is much less because of the effect of microorganisms and partly because water competes with it for binding sites on soil constituents (compare section 13.5).

Apoplastic movement of dichlobenil in plants following root uptake is restricted because of its affinity for lignin. The symptoms of its toxic action

Table 16.3   Uses of dichlobenil and chlorthiamid

Substance	Uses
Dichlobenil	Soil-mixed (unless granular) in non-crop situations, against grass and other weeds (seedling and established) and bracken
	In established fruit, rose, forestry trees and in some canes and bushes
	Kills aquatic weeds through soil contact
Chlorthiamid	As dichlobenil (in which form it acts)
	Granular forms used against established couch grass, ground elder, nettles and thistles

have been compared to those caused by boron deficiency, for in both cases there is an inhibition of growth followed by blackening of tissues. Sometimes a melanin-like pigment has been observed deposited in the region of the apical meristem and in the phloem. Leaves tend to be dark because of an elevated chlorophyll content while cell division in active tissues may be greatly diminished, the nuclei appearing granular and the chromosomes blotchy.

The precise mode of action of dichlobenil remains uncertain, for, although its overall effect is evidently to suppress apical growth, the primary effect is not upon cell division itself but upon some cellular event consequent upon cell division. A likely target is some stage in the biosynthesis of cellulose, for Meyer and Herth (1978), using tobacco callus cells, observed that the formation of new cell walls was totally prevented by 1 ppm dichlobenil.

Much of the loss of dichlobenil from both plants and soil can sometimes be by volatilisation, but metabolism also occurs. In plants, it was originally reported that the nitrile group was hydrolysed so that 2,6-dichlorobenzoic acid was the final product. More recently, some doubt has been cast on this observation. It now seems more likely that the major metabolic route, as is so often the case, is a microsomal oxidation. This results in the formation of two isomeric hydroxydichlorobenzonitriles from which two corresponding hydroxydichlorobenzamides appear to be formed by hydrolysis. Each of these four products may then, in plants, be conjugated with glucose.

16.3 α-CHLOROACETAMIDES; OTHER AMIDES

The α-chloroacetamide group, comprising several closely related amides, contains compounds based upon the configuration, $Cl-CH_2-CO-N<$. Most, but not all, are chloroacetanilides, i.e. they have a phenyl ring attached to the amide nitrogen atom. The structures of some of them are shown in figure 16.3. Two other members of the group are propachlor and allidochlor (CDAA). Allidochlor, N,N-diallyl-2-chloroacetamide, is the only important non-phenyl member of the group and its structure is similar to the safener R25788 mentioned in the previous section. Both propachlor and allidochlor are relatively volatile compared to other members of the group.

The α-chloroacetamides are used pre-emergence of certain crops to control germinating grass weeds and some annual broad-leaf weeds before they break through the soil surface. Examples are barnyard grass (*Echinochloa crus-galli*), foxtails (*Setaria* spp.), nightshade and purslane. In addition, if soil-incorporated before the crop is planted, they check the spreading of nutsedges (*Cyperus rotundus* and *C. esculentus*) by inhibiting sprouting from underground buds.

Different crops show varying levels of tolerance to different α-chloroacetamides. **Alachlor** is not only used pre-plant of maize and soybeans but preemergence of maize, soybeans, sugar cane, groundnuts, potatoes and cotton. **Propachlor** is used pre-emergence of onions, leeks, brassicas and sweet corn.

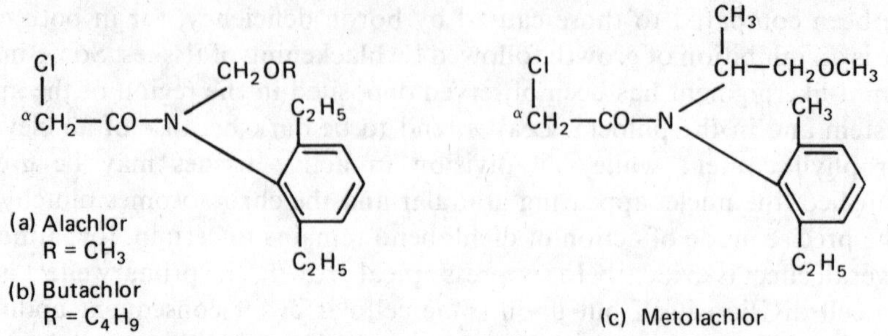

Figure 16.3   Structures of three α-chloroacetamides

Butachlor is incorporated into soil before planting rice or, sometimes, pre-emergence of a rice crop. **Metolachlor** is pre-plant incorporated into soil before maize and soybeans. **Allidochlor** is used pre-emergence of various beans and brassicas as well as pre-emergence of sugar cane, soybeans and sweet potatoes. In addition, most of the α-chloroacetamides can be applied by directed spraying around specified established perennial plants; examples are woody ornamentals and fruit trees.

Allidochlor and propachlor are not only more volatile than other α-chloroacetamides but also more soluble in water (500–2000 ppm). This explains why simple watering (or even relying on rain water) can sometimes replace physical incorporation into the soil. For others, pre-plant incorporation is often recommended although, according to Fryer and Makepeace (1978), alachlor and butachlor often perform most satisfactorily as surface pre-emergence applications unless the moisture content of the soil is low. Sorption on soil organic matter is variable, the least soluble being the most strongly adsorbed. The effective soil life of most α-chloroacetamides is of the order of 6–12 weeks (i.e., in many crops they can provide season-long protection). Their toxicity to man is low, but the more volatile members of the group (and especially allidochlor) can cause irritation to the skin and eyes.

α-Chloroacetamides enter germinating seedlings through shoots or roots but translocation is limited. Typical symptoms of poisoning are inhibition of root development and a stunting of growth; in grasses, malformed leaves fail to emerge from the coleoptile. In laboratory tests, a time lag of several hours exists before growth effects are evident. Early physiological effects are changes in membrane permeability and membrane leakage. In the presence of gibberellic acid (a growth regulator that stimulates plant cell growth) there is a decrease in the length of the lag phase before alachlor action is manifest. This observation has led to the suggestion that α-chloroacetamides act upon some aspect of cell division or growth. The effect is, however, almost certainly indirect and possibly involves some (as yet unknown) step in protein synthesis (Deal *et al.*, 1980). Wilkinson (1988) reported that metolachlor inhibited the activity of α-amylase and that this effect was reversed by gibberellic acid. As is well known, gibberellic acid induces the synthesis of enzymes needed for starch degradation or for the β-oxidation of lipids. He concluded that alachlor and metolachlor inhibit the synthesis of gibberellic acid in seedling tissue; in consequence, there is a greatly decreased utilisation of food reserves stored in the seed and a failure of the seedling to become independent. On the other hand, Weisshaar *et al.* (1988) found that alachlor treatment greatly reduced the linoleic acid content of the alga *Scenedesmus acutus*, from which they suggested that alachlor inhibits the further elongation of chains of fatty acids containing more than 15 carbon atoms.

Feng and Patanella (1989) studied the metabolism of alachlor by liver microsomes from rats, mice and monkeys. They found that the same major metabolites were produced in all three species, the changes involving hydroxylation of the ethyl groups attached to the benzene ring, *O*-demethylation of the methyl ether attached to the amide nitrogen atom and *N*-dealkylation leading to elimination of the dimethyl ether moiety (figure 16.4).

Propachlor is rapidly metabolised in most plants to give water-soluble derivatives. Two of these have been identified by Lamoureux *et al.* (1971) and are conjugates in which the propachlor is attached to glutathione (or a peptide derived from it by partial breakdown). Other workers have confirmed a close connection between the metabolism of various α-chloroacetamides and the levels of glutathione or of its transferase (section 3.5). Stephenson *et al.* (1983)

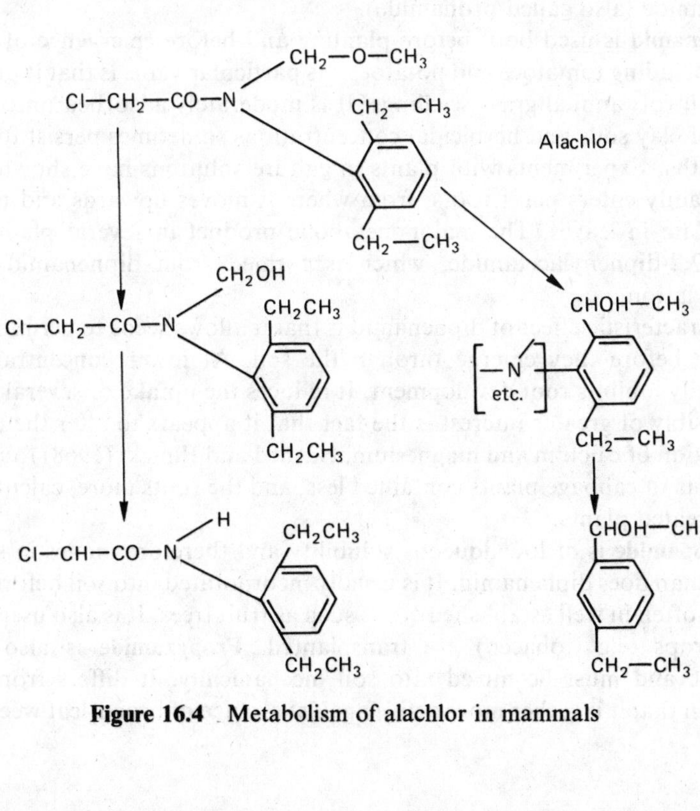

Figure 16.4 Metabolism of alachlor in mammals

observed that the treatment of maize seedlings with alachlor raised the levels of glutathione in the roots. Of possible importance is the observation of Ezra and Stephenson (1985) that maize plants pretreated with allidochlor for 2.5 days were subsequently in large measure protected from its action and that this protection was associated with a 50 per cent increase in the level of glutathione-*S*-transferase activity. Other workers have shown that another α-chloroacetamide, metolachlor, also increases the level of glutathione and the activity of glutathione-*S*-transferase in maize plants.

In animals, phenobarbital is one of several substances that can bring about an increase in the activity of certain enzymes. This effect is known as enzyme induction (sections 3.4 and 3.5). Relatively little is known about the induction of the corresponding microsomal systems in plants except that phenobarbital is not an inducer. It is has been suggested that, in this one particular respect, α-chloroacetamides may do in plants what phenobarbital does in animals. Another possibility is that exposure of a plant to α-chloroacetamide 'stress' results in some sort of feedback system that leads to the production of more glutathione and of its transferase; should this occur, the consequence would be that α-chloroacetamide could stimulate its own destruction in plants endowed with appropriate genes.

In addition to α-chloroacetamides, a few miscellaneous amides have found use as soil-acting herbicides. Examples are diphenamid, napropamide and propyzamide (also called pronamide).

Diphenamid is used both before planting and before emergence of certain crops, including tomatoes and potatoes. Its particular value is that it preferentially controls annual grass seedlings. It is moderately adsorbed onto constituents of clay soils and herbicidal concentrations sometimes persist for up to six months. Experiments with plants in culture solutions have shown that it quite readily enters plant roots, from where it moves upwards and tends to accumulate in leaves. The major metabolic product in several plants is *N*-methyl-2,2-diphenylacetamide, which is formed from diphenamid by *N*-demethylation.

A characteristic effect of diphenamid is that it allows seeds to germinate but they die before they emerge through the soil. At lower concentrations it powerfully inhibits root development. It reduces the uptake of several cations but possibly of greater interest is the fact that it appears to alter the internal distribution of calcium and magnesium. Nashed and Illnicki (1968) found that the shoots of cabbage plants contained less, and the roots more, calcium than did untreated plants.

Napropamide is of low aqueous solubility and therefore moves in soil less readily than does diphenamid. It is usually incorporated into soil before weeds emerge, often in well established crops such as fruit trees. It is also used before some crops (e.g. tobacco) are transplanted. **Propyzamide** is also nearly insoluble and must be mixed into soil mechanically. It differs from other amides in that it is rather more active against a range of broad-leaf weeds. It is often incorporated into soil before planting, or pre-emergence of, lettuce and certain legumes, as well as for weed control under forestry and some other trees.

16.4 DINITROANILINE HERBICIDES

This group of closely related soil-applied herbicides is used mainly in pre-plant or pre-emergence circumstances to control annual grasses and some broad-leaf weeds in a number of important crops. The structures of some typical members are shown in figure 16.5. Although some exceptions exist, most dinitroanilines work more efficiently if they are incorporated into the soil rather than being left on its surface; soil incorporation can be done mechanically or, in some instances, by irrigation. Sometimes it is possible to use dinitroanilines to suppress growth from buds on subterranean parts of perennial grasses, although this may require the use of higher concentrations in the soil, with risk of subsequent crop damage. They possess little foliar activity and are poorly translocated within plants. Their major effect is on the growth of roots; the shoots that emerge often appear quite normal, but soon die because of failure of secondary root development. Various crops show some tolerance to different members of the group.

Trifluralin (figure 16.5a) is a typical member of the nitroaniline group. It is a solid of low aqueous solubility (1 ppm). Although its acute toxicity to mammals is extremely low (oral LD_{50} 10 g/kg for rats), fish can be harmed by it. It is normally formulated as an emulsifiable liquid, which should be

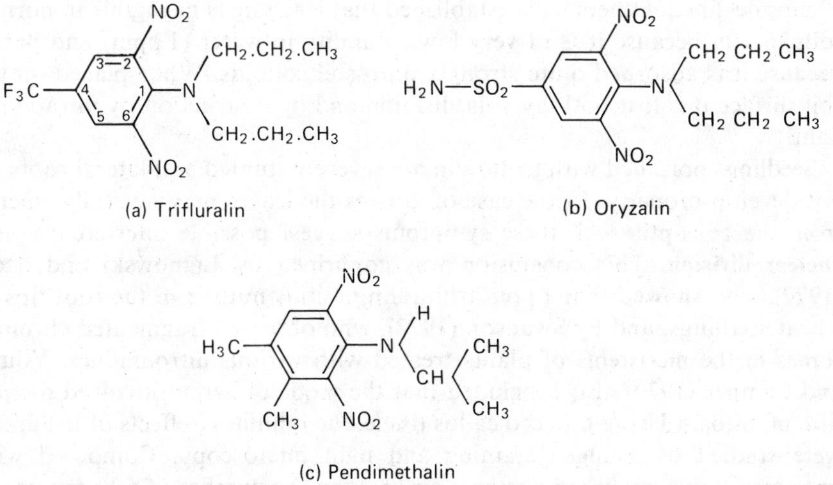

(a) Trifluralin

(b) Oryzalin

(c) Pendimethalin

Figure 16.5 Structures of some dinitroaniline herbicides

incorporated into the soil to an appropriate depth within 30 min of applying it. In Britain, its main use is to remove weeds from land into which cabbage, cauliflower, kale and sprouts are to be planted. It was, however, originally introduced for weed control in cotton and groundnuts as well as brassicas; now, mixed with linuron, it is often used to control weeds in winter barley and oats. Other uses include soil incorporation prior to planting or sowing carrots, swedes, turnips and beans (broad, field and runner), soybeans, peanuts and sunflowers. It is occasionally used pre-emergence of crop and rarely even post-emergence; an example of the latter is its use in sugar beet. In addition, this and other members of the group can be applied as directed post-emergence sprays in established perennials such as ornamental bushes, fruit trees and forestry plantations.

Trifluralin persists in soils from a few weeks to a few months at normal application rates. In common with other volatile compounds it is lost more rapidly from moist soils than from dry ones because it is more readily desorbed from soil constituents (section 13.5). A specific study has been undertaken by Solbakken *et al.* (1982) using Norwegian soils of various clay and organic matter content both in the field and in glasshouses. They applied 100 g/ha or 500 g/ha, with reapplication to half of the treated area the next spring before sowing crops on both halves of the area. Trifluralin was found to be more toxic on the retreated plots, suggesting that carry-over from year to year was a possibility, especially at higher application rates; soil properties were considered to have a greater effect on persistence than did climatic conditions. Laboratory studies showed that overall bacterial numbers were not affected by trifluralin but that the balance of species was altered; non-spore forms, Gram-negative bacteria and Actinomycetes increased in numbers but the numbers of organisms belonging to the coryneform and arthrobacter groups declined. Others have established that leaching is negligible in normal soils, partly because it is of very low solubility in water (1 ppm) and partly because it is adsorbed quite strongly onto soil colloids. When placed on the soil surface it is lost both by volatilisation and by destruction by ultra-violet light.

Seedlings poisoned with trifluralin are severely stunted and lateral roots do not develop properly. In the case of grasses the leaves may not fully emerge from the coleoptile. All these symptoms suggest possible interference with **nuclear division.** This conclusion was confirmed by Lignowski and Scott (1972), who showed that 1 ppm trifluralin inhibits mitosis in the root tips of wheat seedlings, and by Swanson (1972), who observed fragmented chromosomes in the meristems of plants treated with various nitroanilines. Young and Camper (1979) also concluded that the mode of action involved disruption of mitosis. Using tobacco callus tissue, the inhibitory effects of trifluralin were studied by Feulgen staining and light microscopy. Compared with untreated tissue a marked decrease occurred in the number of cells present at any one time in the anaphase and telophase states.

Precisely why trifluralin and other dinitroaniline herbicides affect nuclear division remains uncertain. After treatment with these herbicides, Parka and Soper (1977) reported that no microtubules could be detected in the root cells of affected grasses, implying an interaction with this system (microtubules in grasses appear to be more readily attacked by dinitroaniline herbicides than those in dicotyledonous plants). It will be recalled (section 15.4) that microtubules are hollow flexible cylindrical structures, visible in electron micrographs, that occur at various locations in a cell during cell division, and which are organised at microtubule organising centres (MTOCs). They are involved in redistribution of chromatin during cell division; in addition, however, it is probable that cortical microtubules, arranged near the plasmalemma, may be responsible for controlling the orientation of microfibrils of cellulose as new cell walls are formed.

Hertel and Marmé (1983) have observed that trifluralin and oryzalin inhibit energy-dependent calcium ion uptake by plant mitochondria at concentrations lower than those that inhibit ADP phosphorylation and lower than those that affect tubulin polymerisation. They have suggested that cytoplasmic calcium ion distribution forms a central physiological regulatory system and that its disruption leads to numerous abnormal effects, one of which could be disruption of the microtubule assembly system, possibly via interference with plant cell kinases (Nishida *et al.*, 1979).

Most of the routes by which trifluralin is metabolised are predictable (chapter 3). In carrots, for example, *N*-dealkylation is a major degradative pathway, although in addition, the nitro groups can be converted to amino groups and the $-CF_3$ group can be converted to carboxyl. Soil bacteria probably degrade it similarly, except that double *N*-dealkylation and reduction of both nitro groups can sometimes occur. In animals the $-CF_3$ group may not be readily modified; otherwise the primary metabolic changes are the same as in plants. The metabolism of trifluralin by rat liver microsomes has been studied by Nelson *et al.* (1977). These investigators confirmed that aliphatic hydroxylation, *N*-dealkylation and reduction of one nitro group had taken place to give three different metabolites. In addition, cyclisation had occurred to give a benzimidazole derivative.

Other dinitroaniline herbicides have somewhat similar uses and very similar soil properties to those of trifluralin. Among these substances are benfluralin (benefin), dinitramine, oryzalin (figure 16.5b), isopropalin and pendimethalin (figure 16.5c). So far as is known they all have an identical mode of action to that of trifluralin.

Benfluralin is soil-incorporated except, sometimes, when it is in the form of granules. It is used pre-plant of lettuce, of some legumes, and of transplanted tobacco. **Dinitramine** has been used pre-plant or pre-emergence of cotton, peppers and groundnuts. The effect of soil type upon its toxicity has been studied by Okafor *et al.* (1983). Adsorption on soil increased directly with soil organic matter content and inversely with the soil moisture content. Phytotoxicity to soybean was inversely related to soil organic matter, and toxicity to French bean was directly related to soil moisture content within the range 20–100 per cent field moisture capacity. Similarly, volatilisation was directly related to soil moisture content and inversely related to soil organic content.

Oryzalin (figure 16.5b) has a lower vapour pressure than most other dinitroaniline herbicides and can be applied to the soil surface, but best results are obtained if it is washed into the soil. It is used extensively as a pre-emergence treatment in soybeans and is also used as a directed spray pre-emergence of weeds in vines, ornamental bushes (e.g. roses) and fruit trees. The effects of temperature and irrigation upon its effectiveness have been described by Nelson *et al.* (1983). They found that the control of *Setaria* spp. and *Amaranthus* spp. increased with the thoroughness with which mechanical soil-mixing was carried out. However, the effectiveness of surface-applied oryzalin for this purpose increased with the volume of irrigation water until, eventually, toxicity to these species was the same as was obtained by pre-plant incorporation. The mode of action is probably the same as that described for trifluralin.

Pendimethalin (figure 16.5c) has a higher vapour pressure than oryzalin and is best incorporated into the soil mechanically or by irrigation. It has been used pre-plant of soybeans, cotton and tobacco. Van Hoogstraten and Fine (1982) reported it to be a useful herbicide for temperate and tropical regions, tolerant crops including, *inter alia*, maize, rice, groundnuts and sugar cane. In Britain it is used in specified winter cereals and in certain established fruit trees and bushes. As well as the normal range of weeds (e.g. meadow grass, blackgrass) it has been recommended for troublesome and refractory weeds such as *Rottboellia exaltata* (Van Hoogstraten and Fine, 1982), *Galium aparine* and *Viola* spp. In Britain, MAFF (1985) stress that its safe and successful use depends on soil type (too much organic matter can be detrimental) and on the absence of surface water; in addition, crops should be in good condition and not suffering from stress due to disease or drought.

Walker and Bond (1977) listed factors affecting the field effectiveness of pendimethalin and demonstrated that 60 per cent of an application was left in the soil in September after early-season incorporation into the soil but that only 20 per cent was left when a similar dose was left on the soil surface. Savage (1978) showed that pendimethalin, in common with other dinitroanilines, was dissipated faster if the soil is flooded and anaerobic than it is in soil maintained in a moist condition; the author used the word 'dissipated' because the loss was apparently not due to increased volatilisation nor to microbial action. Thus, it was demonstrated that the half-life of pendimethalin in Sharkey clay soil was 82 days when moist but 7 days when flooded, irrespective of whether the soil was natural or autoclaved; furthermore, he demonstrated that the volatilisation of several dinitroanilines from flooded soil was actually lower than it was from damp soil. Zimdahl *et al.* (1984) reported that the degradation of pendimethalin in three soils did not follow first-order kinetics (the latter relationship being a common observation for decomposition of pesticides in soil). They also found that, while the rate of its disappearance from soils was independent of soil water when the field water content was above 75 per cent capacity, it was less at moisture contents of around 50 per cent.

REFERENCES

Bowmer, K. H. (1987). In *Progress in Pesticide Biochemistry and Toxicology*, vol. 6, *Herbicides*, eds D. H. Hutson and T. R. Roberts, chap. 9. Wiley, Chichester

Carere, A., Ortali, V. A., Cardamone, G. and Morpurgo, G. (1978). *Chem. Biol. Interact.*, **22**, 297

Cole, D. J., Edwards, R. and Owen, W. J. (1987). In *Progress in Pesticide Biochemistry and Toxicology*, vol. 6, *Herbicides*, eds D. H. Hutson and T. R. Roberts, p. 57. Wiley, Chichester

Deal, L. M., Reeves, J. T., Larkins, B. A. and Hess, F. D. (1980). *Weed Sci.*, **28**, 334

Ezra, G. and Stephenson, G. R. (1985). *Pestic. Biochem. Physiol.*, **24**, 207

Feng, P. C. C. and Patanella, J. E. (1989). *Pestic. Biochem. Physiol.*, **33**, 16

Fryer, J. D. and Makepeace, R. J. (1978). *Weed Control Handbook*, 8th edn, vol. 2, *Recommendations*. Blackwell, Oxford

Grover, R., Spencer, W. F., Farmer, W. J. and Shoup, T. D. (1978). *Weed Sci.*, **26**, 505

Harvey, R. G., McNevin, G. R., Albright, J. W. and Kozak, M. E. (1986). *Weed Sci.*, **34**, 773

Hertel, C. and Marmé, D. (1983). *Pestic. Biochem. Physiol.*, **19**, 282

Keeley, P. E., Thullen, R. J., Miller, J. H. and Carter, C. H. (1979). *Weed Sci.*, **27**, 463

Lamoureux, G. L., Stafford, L. E. and Tonaka, F. S. (1971). *J. Agric. Fd Chem.*, **19**, 346

Lignowski, E. M. and Scott, E. G. (1972). *Weed Sci.*, **20**, 267

Lode, O. and Skuterrud, R. (1983). *Weed Res.*, **23**, 19

MAFF (1985). *Agricultural Chemicals Approval Scheme, Reference Book 380 (85)*, UK Ministry of Agriculture, Fisheries and Food. HMSO, London

Menzie, C. M. (1978). *Metabolism of Pesticides: Update II*, US Dept Interior, Fish and Wildlife Service, Special Scientific Report, Wildlife no. 212, Washington DC

Meyer, Y. and Herth, W. (1978). *Planta*, **142**, 253

Miaullis, B., Nohynek, G. J. and Pereiro, F. (1982). *Proc. Br. Crop Prot. Conf., Weeds*, p. 205

Moyer, J. R. and Dryden, R. D. (1979). *Can. J. Plant Sci.*, **59**, 383

Nashed, R. B. and Illnicki, R. D. (1968). *Proc. 22nd NE Weed Control Conf., USA*, p. 500

Nelson, J. E., Meggitt, W. F., Penner, D. and Ladlie, J. S. (1983). *Weed Sci.*, **31**, 752

Nelson, J. O., Kearney, P. C., Plimmer, J. R. and Menzer, R. E. (1977). *Pestic. Biochem. Physiol.*, **7**, 73

Nishida, E., Kumagai, H., Ohtsuki, J. and Sakai, H. (1979). *J. Biochem.*, **85**, 1257

Obrigawitch, T., Martin, A. R. and Roeth, F. W. (1983). *Weed Sci.*, **31**, 187

Ogg, A. G., Jr and Drake, S. (1979). *Weed Sci.*, **27**, 608

Okafor, L. I., Sagar, G. R. and Shorrocks, V. M. (1983). *Weed Res.*, **23**, 199

Parka, S. J. and Soper, O. F. (1977). *Weed Sci.*, **25**, 79

Rivera, C. M. and Penner, D. (1979). *Res. Rev.*, **70**, 45

Savage, K. E. (1978). *Weed Sci.*, **26**, 465

Schuphan, I. and Casida, J. E. (1979). *J. Agric. Fd Chem.*, **27**, 1060

Solbakken, E., Hole, H., Lode, O. and Pedersen, T. A. (1982). *Weed Res.*, **22**, 319

Stephenson, G. R., Ali, A. and Ashton, F. M. (1983). In *Pesticide Chemistry: Human Welfare and the Environment*, vol. 3, *Mode of Action, Metabolism and Toxicology*, eds S. Matsunaka, D. H. Hutson and S. D. Murphy, pp. 219–24. Pergamon, Oxford
Swanson, C. R. (1972). *Herbicides, Fungicides, Formulation Chemistry*, ed. A. S. Tahori, Proc. 2nd Int. IUPAC Congr., vol. 5, p. 87
Tal, A., Rubin, B., Katan, J. and Aharonson, N. (1989). *Pestic. Sci.*, **25**, 343
Tuxhorn, G. L., Roeth, F. W., Martin, A. R. and Wilson, R. G. (1986). *Weed Sci.*, **34**, 961
van Hoogstraten, S. D. and Fine, R. R. (1982). *Proc. Br. Crop Prot. Conf., Weeds*, p. 883
Walker, A. and Bond, W. (1977). *Pestic. Sci.*, **8**, 359
Weisshaar, H., Retzlaff, G. and Böger, P. (1988). *Pestic. Biochem. Physiol.*, **33**, 212
Wilkinson, R. E. (1983). *Pestic. Biochem. Physiol.*, **20**, 347
Wilkinson, R. E. (1986). *Pestic. Biochem. Physiol.*, **25**, 93
Wilkinson, R. E. (1988). *Pestic. Biochem. Physiol.*, **32**, 25
Wilkinson, R. E. and Smith, A. E. (1975). *Weed Sci.*, **23**, 90
Wilson, R. G. (1984). *Weed Sci.*, **32**, 264
Young, L. W. and Camper, N. D. (1979). *Pestic. Biochem. Physiol.*, **12**, 117
Zemanek, J. and Kovar, J. (1978). *Ochr. Rostl.*, **14**, 143 (in Czech; quoted from abstract)
Zimdahl, R. L., Catizone, P. and Butcher, A. C. (1984). *Weed Sci.*, **32**, 408

Epilogue

In the preceding chapters reference has been made to many of the major developments in the chemistry of pest control that have occurred during the last decade or so. Not only have new groups of pesticides been introduced to tackle problems not resolved by the use of earlier compounds, but also for many substances, old and new, there has been a dramatic deepening of insight into how they affect target organisms. Mechanisms of metabolism are now sufficiently well understood to enable predictive statements to be made as to the probable routes of degradation of named substances in specified organisms or in a soil environment. In some cases, enzymes responsible for metabolic changes have been recognised as products of specific genes, a circumstance which, in turn, has thrown light on the causes of some types of resistance that have developed in insects and in fungi. For both of these, the introduction of techniques of resistance management has led to a diminution in the incidence of resistance, and to a decrease in the rate at which new cases of resistance have developed. These successes, partial though they frequently are, provide the backcloth against which to assess the possibilities for the future.

Legislation and more rigorous registration requirements at the national level, associated with international recommendations, have improved safety of usage and greatly reduced the likelihood of toxic amounts of substances being present in food at the time of consumption. In many countries, media attention has increased public awareness of dangers inherent in contamination of food with pesticides. In most respects this is greatly to be praised but it is a truism that bad news is both interesting to readers or viewers and profitable to report. Potential dangers in food supply or in water can create much emotion, and emotional matters can be handled by the publicity media in ways that distort the inherent dangers *vis-à-vis* other dangers in life. This, in turn, can lead to imbalances in political responses. In Africa, for example, illness caused by contaminated water or protein deficiency is widespread, yet the author has met politicians and their advisers who profess to being deeply disturbed about whether a named pesticide might, just might, be a cause for concern.

When making scientific judgements about the possible ill-effects of small amounts of residues in food, experts are confronted with a dilemma. It is this: in this matter (and perhaps in all matters), no scientist can ever prove a negative; it is never possible to say with certainty that traces of pesticides are absolutely safe to all people and at every stage of their lives. In practice, no useful purpose is served by considering dangers inherent in the use of pesticides as a subject divorced from a wider scenario which considers equally honestly the possible consequences of their *non-use*. For example, in absence of pesticides, biological residues such as insect excreta and fungal toxins could prove health-threatening. In this regard it is not facetious to point out that fewer people have seen visions since rye bread contaminated with ergot has become rare (ergot produces alkaloids similar to lysergic acid diethylamide, LSD). Furthermore, there is another danger: if attempts to achieve unrealistic safety limits were to lead to heavy-handed legislation, costly legal complexities or bureaucratic muddle, it could remove incentives to do the very research that is essential in order that newer, safer compounds should eventually reach the market.

Among insecticides, the acylureas, formamidines and avermectins cause behavioural changes in insects and interfere with various stages in their life cycle. These effects sometimes occur at very low concentrations and are often a consequence of interference with hormones or enzymes that regulate various aspects of insect behaviour, ecdysis or metamorphosis. Investigations into pheromones, food and sex attractants, as well as into the neurophysiological roles of octopamine and GABA, have frequently been regarded as the province of insect physiologists and biologists, many of whom are avowed proponents of pest control by 'non-chemical' means. Evidently, a convergent evolution of thought has been taking place and has led to an erosion of strict barriers of demarcation. This coincidence of interest is likely to occur increasingly in the future as more is discovered about the mechanisms whereby insect growth and behaviour are regulated.

A bonus sometimes accruing from the use of behavioural toxicants (the very word 'insecticide' is often now inappropriate) is that insects, mites and nematodes may cease to eat almost immediately after coming into contact with the toxicant, even though they may remain alive for weeks thereafter. A toxicant with these characteristics may not only decrease crop damage due to the invertebrate but reduce the incidence of virus transmission by invertebrate vectors. Evidence for this already exists not only in relation to insect vectors but also to vectors that are mites or nematodes (chapter 8). Development of this approach can be expected to lead to useful advances in plant virus control.

As knowledge increases concerning, on the one hand, how pesticides function and, on the other, how stages in the life cycles of pests are controlled, there will be an increasing tendency for chemicals to be used as part of a wider pest management programme in which the contributory effects of chemical, biological and cultural methods are optimised, often by the use of computer-determined predictions arising from the application of databases to each new pest management problem. Integrated pest management programmes of varying degrees of comprehensiveness do, of course, exist already, both for insect control and, more especially, for the control of fungi. Partially integrated systems, such as that referred to as supervised pest control (where more or less empirical decisions of experts are acted upon) are already in *de facto* existence in some countries. Supervised pest control could transform efficiency and safety in developing countries if only trained people were in the right place at the right time. It is therefore a pity that, in the author's experience, too many of those who come for training to Europe or the USA use their higher degrees for personal administrative advancement. I would like to see such people spend more time on the farm and less time on the telephone. Above all I strongly recommend regular in-service training courses or workshops, done in the home country with (if need be) expatriate specialists attending by invitation.

The use of pathogenic microorganisms and their toxins is another technique already in use in pest management programmes. The best-known and most commercially exploited organism so far is *Bacillus thuringiensis*, which has been used for decades to control larvae of Lepidoptera. In the case of *B. thuringiensis*, concentrates containing spores, with protein (referred to as 'crystal') deposited around them, are sprayed onto plants infested with lepidopteran larvae (Dubois and Lewis, 1981). The protein is termed delta-endotoxin and the lethal agent is part of its molecule; the active toxin is released by enzymic action in the insect gut (a change that provides a further example of lethal metabolism). It is unfortunate, but an arbitrary line must be drawn somewhere between chemical and biological control; for this reason the uses of *B. thuringiensis* have not been discussed in this book. Useful data on many aspects of microbial control of pests and diseases has been edited by Burges (1981). However, it is relevant to point out the similarity between the use of toxins in living preparations and of antibiotics such as kasugamycin (chapter 12); in the latter case, a metabolite is extracted in a commercial laboratory and formulated for spraying whereas in the case of delta-endotoxin the whole *biological* laboratory is, so to speak, sprayed intact. Progress in genetic engineering raises the prospect of the construction of pathogens to specification, increasing both the spectrum of action and the toxicity to insects of 'living' insecticides.

Finney (1988), in an article entitled 'Demisting the crystal ball', has predicted that real growth in pesticide usage during the next few years is likely to be rather low in those countries which now use them most and in which specific facets of the market are nearly saturated (section 1.3). On the other hand, some market growth is to be anticipated in the USSR and Italy, and even higher usage is to be expected in Brazil and India. Moreover, the use of herbicides is likely to increase considerably in those developing countries where rural populations are beginning to migrate to towns. Finney also predicts that biological products will only contribute about 5 per cent to the total agrochemical market by the year 2000, but that plant breeding techniques, including genetic engineering, may lead to a decline in the use of insecticides and fungicides. The same author has predicted that considerable advances will be made in cognate technologies, enabling optimal use to be made of substances that are highly toxic at low application rates. In addition, pesticide safety is likely to be increased by the introduction of highly sensitive new methods of analysis. Of particular importance, immunochemical methods are likely to be used routinely to detect and to quantify residues in food and in the environment. Already, diagnostic kits based on immunoassay have been introduced for many pesticides, including aldicarb, atrazine, benomyl and diclofop (Wraith and Britton, 1988).

Many of the older non-systemic fungicides are proving to be good work horses; among them are the dithiocarbamates and phthalimides. The success of new systemic fungicides should not detract from the fact that, for decades now, these non-systemic fungicides have protected valuable crops, including potatoes and fruit, without many serious incidents of resistance. Nowadays, a non-systemic and systemic fungicide are often applied together, since, in many cases, resistance does not develop to the systemic component as rapidly when used as a component of a mixture as it does when it is used alone. An example is the use of a dithiocarbamate mixed with metalaxyl (chapter 12). If, as sometimes happens, the systemic and non-systemic components of a mixture attack the fungus at different stages of its life cycle, this also militates against the development of resistance. In addition, components of mixtures some-times act synergistically, the mixture being more toxic than can be accounted for by the toxicity of the components when they act separately. The use of poorly systemic imidazoles such as prochloraz (chapter 11), which is able to control certain Oomycetes (and especially strains of *Pseudocercosporella*) that have developed resistance to benzimidazoles, is likely to increase and to be extended to other pathogens.

Understanding of the fundamental biochemistry of systemic fungicides has increased enormously in the last few years, allowing a more rational classification of the type shown in chapter 12. Seen in 'pure' academic terms the light that fungicide studies has focused on fungal biochemistry is exciting; however, like the academic studies on insect biochemistry mentioned earlier, such advances will inevitably result in commercial spin-offs, not only by pointing to the design of a wider armoury of weapons, but also to provide weapons less likely to recoil on the user by causing the development of resistance. Systemic fungicides have now been found that target almost all kinds of fungi, although those that attack Oomycetes are still limited in number (see chapter 12).

In the first edition of this book less than a decade ago, the author is on record as warning that the extensive use of systemic fungicides might lead to the development of an unacceptable level of resistance. In practice, fungicides belonging to several of the more recently developed systemic groups have not so far been compromised in this manner in field conditions. The same is true of some members of two older systemic groups, the morpholines and oxathiins (especially carboxin) (chapter 12). It appears that systemic fungicides that are mainly used as seed protectants are much less likely to cause resistance to develop than are substances that are used as foliar sprays. For example, carboxin (a seed protectant) has caused less problems than foliage-applied oxycarboxin. No doubt for this reason, many of the new systemic fungicides are, in fact, applied so that they are taken up by plant roots or are used as seed treatments. Their lower tendency to cause resistance when used in mixtures was mentioned above.

As the mechanisms, biochemical and genetic, that enable insects and fungi to develop resistance become better understood, it is to be anticipated that such knowledge will suggest ways in which the problem of resistance can be minimised. As was seen in chapter 8, one common cause of resistance to insecticides is the presence in resistant strains of detoxication systems that are superior to those in less resistant strains. Resistance to fungicides can also be caused in this way (chapter 11). A knowledge of which enzymes are present in increased amount (or modified form) in specified resistant strains could lead to the development of synergists of a more specific nature than those currently employed. Similarly, when resistance to insecticides and fungicides is due to changes in the target enzyme or receptor, a deeper understanding of which molecular alterations elicit this tolerance could provide clues about the use of adjuncts to minimise the chances of selection or mutation.

As was already clear by the early 1980s, the action of phenoxyacetic acid and other herbicides that specifically kill dicotyledonous weeds encouraged the spread of perennial grasses, which, in the absence of competition, could grow unchecked. A new dimension in weed control has been opened up by the discovery of 'graminicides', or substances that specifically control grasses. Examples are fluazifop and sethoxydim, which control such problem grasses as *Agropyron repens*, *Cynodon dactylon* and *Echinochloa crus-galli* (chapter 14). It is likely that future work will aim, not just to add new members to this and similar groups, but to develop compounds that can be used to solve grassy weed problems in specified grassy crops. Moreover, the antagonism that exists between members of this and the auxin group of weedkillers offers an interesting scientific problem, especially in relation to the field compatibility of mixtures containing aryloxyphenoxy compounds for use in mixed weed situations. Of great scientific interest is the reason why fatty acid synthetase in grasses is affected by the aryloxyphenoxy herbicides while that in dicotyledonous weeds is not. There seems scope for such 'pure' studies as this to be translated into practical utility by an alteration of crop cultivars by genetic engineering.

A related herbicide problem that has a component of both commercial and theoretical interest is the need to identify the precise site of action that is attacked by the ureide and triazine herbicides (chapter 15). Except in general terms, very little is known about the modification that occurs in those strains of weeds that show target site resistance to these herbicides. A clearer picture might well indicate a genetic involvement capable of exploitation to render specific crop cultivars less sensitive to soil-applied herbicides. A second type of investigation that could pay dividends would be further to explore the role of microtubules and their organising centres both in plant cell division and in the initiation of cellulose deposits in newly formed cell walls (chapters 15 and 16).

An investigation with commercial implications which is already in progress relates to the part played by certain adjuncts or supplements that are added to some pesticide formulations. For example, the mode of action of safeners such as diallyl dichloroacetamide is still imperfectly understood, as is the reason why inhibitors of protein synthesis prevent or diminish their beneficial action (chapter 16). Conversely, there is still much to be learnt about how the longevity of action of a soil-applied herbicide can be optimised by addition to the formulation of synergists that inhibit enzymes in soil microorganisms. One such substance, diethylphenylphosphorothiolate, probably prolongs the life of thiolcarbamates in soil by inhibiting microbial hydrolases (chapter 16). The full potential of this technique does not seem yet to have been realised.

One spin-off of modern studies on herbicide action is worthy of comment. Two types of herbicides are believed to exert their effect by direct disruption of protein biosynthesis in plants; glyphosate blocks the shikimate pathway by which plants synthesise aromatic amino acids (chapter 14) while chlorsulfuron blocks acetolactate synthase which catalyses a step in the synthesis of branched-chain amino acids (chapter 15). It has probably not escaped the attention of those familiar with the biochemistry of vertebrates that both of these pathways are absent in animals; indeed, it is for this reason that animals depend on plants and microorganisms for their *essential* amino acids. With tongue not too firmly in cheek, it could be said that, in this one respect, these herbicides render the biochemistry of plants more like that of higher animals. Herbicides could possibly become useful instruments with which to investigate plant protein chemistry.

It often happens that crop cultivars, bred specifically for the quality or yield of their produce, are more prone to attack by invertebrates or fungi than are lesser-yielding varieties. With the advent of genetic engineering, attention has therefore been focused on the prospect of manipulating genes of prized cultivars, to make them better able to withstand attack from pests and diseases. Such an approach could reduce the number of occasions during a growing season on which pesticides need to be applied. Somewhat similarly, gene manipulation could lead to the insertion into a crop cultivar of genes (or of additional genes) for products that alter the plant–pest relationship. Several variants of this approach can be visualised. One of these would be the insertion into the genome of cultivars of genes that code for products that repel pests or that diminish the ease with which fungi establish themselves on plants. Remembering the pesticidal attributes of some Compositae and Leguminosae (chapters 7 and 8), an alternative approach might be to try to insert into a crop plant a gene coding for an endogenously produced substance with pesticidal or pest-repellant properties. Yet another variant would be to remove from the crop plant's genome genes coding for the unique feature that causes pests to be attracted to one particular crop rather than another.

In a rather similar way, genetic engineering clearly has a major role to play in the protection of crop plants from the action of herbicides. If the mode of action of a herbicide is known it may be possible to locate, in a resistant strain of some species of plant or microorganism, a gene coding for a target site protein. Hopefully, that gene could then be isolated and transferred from the resistant species to cell cultures of a (susceptible) crop cultivar from which clones of whole plants can be generated. An example is illustrated by the work of Falco and colleagues on mutant tobacco cells resistant to sulphonylurea herbicides (chapter 15). Others have suggested that, rather than to isolate the gene(s) coding for an altered protein located at a resistant target site, a gene at a susceptible site could perhaps be isolated and modified in transit so that the target site containing it is herbicide-resistant. As well as resistance being caused by altered proteins at target sites, it can be due to alteration in activity or quantity of pesticide-metabolising enzymes. Genes coding for these can also be isolated; it would be a solution of considerable elegance if artificial gene amplification in prized cultivars could result in both the more rapid (oxidative) detoxication of herbicides and simultaneously in the (oxidative) activation of plant-protecting insecticides and fungicides (chapters 4, 12 and 15).

Pesticide science is a multidisciplinary subject and a book such as this must therefore be wide-ranging and introductory, although, one would hope, never consistently elementary to any one reader. The writer would in any case like to believe that some specialists with sharply focused interests may have widened their outlook by looking up from the microscope for a while. On the other hand, an attempt has been made, no matter how imperfectly, to present sometimes complex scientific ideas sympathetically rather than to blind with an exaggerated use of scientific terminology. As I have said to my students over many years, it is as necessary in science as in retailing to package the product attractively if one wishes to interest others in it. I hope that the non-specialist will have appreciated my not-too-serious approach.

The road to discovery and exploitation in the pesticide field is long but a quotation from Robert Louis Stevenson's *El Dorado* epitomises the challenge to those who follow on:

'It is true that we shall never reach the goal; it is even more than probable that there is no such place. Soon, soon, it seems to you, you must come forth on some conspicuous hilltop, and, but a little way farther, against the setting sun, descry the spires of El Dorado. Little do you know your own blessedness; for to travel hopefully is a better thing than to arrive, and the true success is to labour.'

That is my message to the next generation.

REFERENCES

Burges, H. D. (1981). *Microbial Control of Pests and Plant Diseases, 1970–1980*. Academic Press, London

Chaleff, R. S. and Mauvais, C. T. (1984). *Science*, **224**, 1443

Finney, J. R. (1988). *Proc. Br. Crop Prot. Conf., Pests and Diseases*, p. 3

Dubois, N. R. and Lewis, F. B. (1981). *J. Arboricult.*, 7, 233

Wraith, M. J. and Britton, D. W. (1988). *Proc. Br. Crop Prot. Conf., Pests and Diseases*, p. 131

Appendix: Some proprietary products containing active ingredients mentioned in the text

Only a few of the thousands of proprietary formulations can be included. Excluded are tradenames that reflect common names (e.g. Smith's parathion) or are serial numbers (e.g. Brown's B237). Where, after such exclusions, several proprietary products remain, products have been chosen at random. Parentheses imply the presence of more than one active ingredient; with exceptions, mixtures have been awarded low priority for entry. Presence in the list does not imply that a product is currently available nor that it is currently approved in any particular country. While care has been taken with the preparation of the list, it is for information not trade; no product should be used without checking accuracy against literature supplied by the manufacturer.

SECTION A: INSECTICIDES AND RELATED COMPOUNDS

Common name	Some tradenames
Aldicarb	Temik, (Sentry)
Aldrin	Aldrex, Soildrin
Allethrin	Pynamin, Floret Fly and Wasp Killer
Amitraz	Mitac, Taktic
Azinphos-methyl	Gusathion, Guthion
Bendiocarb	Delta Insect Powder, Ficam, Garvox, Seedox
Bioresmethrin	Cooper Garden Spray
Bromophos	Ficare Insecticide, Hybrom, Nexion, Springspray, Bromotex
Carbaryl	Savit 4F, Microcarb T, Sevin, Thinsec, Murvin 85
Carbofuran	Yaltox, Furadan, Nex, Carbosip 5G
Carbosulfan	Marshal 10G
Chlorfenvinphos	Birlane, Sapecron

Chlorpyrifos	Dursban 4, Spannita, Talon, (Chlorophos), (Twinspan)
Chlorpyriphos-methyl	Graincote, Reldan
Clofentezine	Apollo
Cyhexatin	Acarstin L, Plictran, (Murfite)
Cypermethrin	Ambush C, Cyperkill 5, Cymbush, Ripcord, Toppel
DNOC	Sandolin A, (Winter Wash)
DDT	Gesarol
Deltamethrin	Decis, Crackdown, Thripstick
Demeton-S-methyl	DSM, Persyst, Azotox 580, Duratox, Metasystox, Mifatox
Diazinon	Basudin, Root Guard, Flytrol, Ant/Crawling Insect Spray
Dichloropropene	Telone, (D-D)
Dichlorvos	Vapona, Nuvan, Sectovap, Nerkol, (Farmyard Fly Spray)
Dicofol	Kelthane, (Childion)
Dieldrin	Dilstan, Octalox
Diflubenzuron	Dimilin
Dimethoate	Rogor, Cygon, De-Fend, Roxion, (Bio Long Last)
Disulfoton	Disyston, Parsolin, Solvigran, (Twinspan), (Doubledown)
Endosulfan	Thiodan, Malix
Fenitrothion	Sumithion, Dicofen, Folithion, Fentro
Fenvalerate	Sumicidin
Formothion	Anthio
Lindane	Gamma-Col, Gammasan, Hexaflow, (Sentry), (Gammalex)
Malathion	Karbophos, Cythion, Malastan, (Crop Saver)
Metaldehyde	Slugit, Slugoids
Metalkamate	Bux
Methiocarb	Draza, Mesurol
Methomyl	Lannate, (Fly Belt)
Methyl parathion	Dalf, Metron, Nitrox
Mevinphos	Phosdrin
Nicotine	XL All
Oxamyl	Vydate
Oxydemeton-methyl	Metasystox R
Parathion	Thiophos, Phoskil
Permethrin	Ambush, Fumite 3000, Permasect, Permit, Picket, (Dragon S)
Phorate	Thimet, Granutox, Terrathion

Phosphamidon	Dimecron, Dicron
Pirimicarb	Pirimor, Aphox, Abol G, (Roseclear)
Pirimiphos-methyl	Actellic, Blex, Sybol 2, (Kerispray)
Propoxur	Baygon, Blattanex
Pyrethrin	Pyro Fog 100, (Marstan Fly Spray)
Pyrethrin (synergised)	(Lindane Pybuthrin), (Kerispray), (Ficam Plus)
Resmethrin	(Tubair Kilsect Super), (Pynosect)
Rotenone	Derris Dust, (Hexyl)
Tetradifon	Tedion, Duphar, (Acarstin Combi), (Murfite), (Childion)
Tetramethrin	Neopynamin, Pesguard, (Dragon S), (Pynosect 40)
Triazophos	Hostathion
Trichlorphon	Dipterex, Anthon
Vamidothion	Kilval, Trucidor

SECTION B: FUNGICIDES

Common name	Some tradenames
Benomyl	Benlate
Binapacryl	Morocide, Ambox, Acricid, Endosan
Bupirimate	Nimrod, (Roseclear)
Captafol	Difolatan, Sanspor, Sufenimide, Folcid, Conquest
Captan	Orthocide, (Bromotex T), (Kapitol)
Carbendazim	Derosal, Bavistin, Carbate, Delsene, Hinge, Maxim
Carboxin	Vitavax, (Murganic)
Chloranil	Spergon
Chlorthalonil	Bravo, Termil, Daconil, Repulse, Bombardier, (Accolade)
Copper compounds	Burcop, Wetcol, Cuprosana, Kocide, Cuprokylt
Cycloheximide	Acti-Dione
Dazomet	Mylone, Crag Nemacide
Dichlofluanid	Elvaron, Euparen
Dichlone	Phygon, Quintar
Dicloran	Allisan, Botran, Ditranil
Dimethirimol	Milcurb
Dinocap	Karathane, Crotothane, Mildex, Arathane, Caprane
Dodemorph	Meltatox, Milban

Dodine	Cyprex, Melprex, Radspore, (Pummel)
Ethirimol	Milstem, Milgo, (Junospor), (Ferrax)
Fenarimol	Rubigan
Fenoprop	Kuron, Kurosal
Fenpropimorph	Corbel, Mistral, (Sirocco)
Fentin	Farmatin, Du-Ter, Tubotin, Tinmate, (Astaman), (Brestan)
Ferbam	Fermate, Ferradow
Flutriafol	Impact, Mitre
Folpet	Folpan, Phaltan
Fosetyl-Al	Aliette, (Hy-Cote)
Fuberidazole	(Baytan IM)
Imazalil	Fungaflor, (Cerevax Extra)
Iprodione	Rovral
Mancozeb	Dithane, Karamate N, Penncozeb, (Galben), (Recoil),
Maneb	Manzate, Tubothane, Dithane M22, X-Spor, Farmaneb
Mercuric oxide	Santar
Mercurous chloride	Cyclosan, M-C, Calomel
Metalaxyl	Apron 350, Subdue, (Ridomil-MBC), (Fubol)
Nabam	Dithane, Parzate, (X-Spor)
Nuarimol	Triminol, (Kapitol), (Accolade)
Organomercury compounds	Agrosan, Ceresol, Ceresan, Panogen M, (Mergamma)
Oxadixyl	(Recoil)
Oxycarboxin	Plantvax
Phosetyl-Al	Aliette
Prochloraz	Octave, Sportak, (Sporgon)
Propiconazole	Radar, Tumbleblight, Tilt 250, (Hispor), (Tilt Turbo)
Propineb	Antracol
Pyrazophos	Afugan, Pokon Mildew Spray
Quintozene	Botrilex, Bras-sicol, Folosan, PCNB, Tritisan/
Streptomycin	Agrimycin, Agri Strep, Streptorex
Sulphur	Kuron, Kurosal, Aquilite, Super Six, Elosal, Thiovit, Solfa, Kumulus S, Magnetic 6, (Bolda), (Senator)
Tecnazene	TCNB, Fusarex, Hytec, Folosan, Easytec, Nebulin
Thiabendazole	Storite, Tecto, Arbotec, Mintezol, Thiaben, Ceratotect
Thiophanate-ethyl	Topsin E

Thiophanate-methyl	Mildothane, Cercobin M, Topsin M, Mildothane
Thiram	Tripomol, Fernasan, Arasan, Pomarsol, Nomersan, Hysede
Triadimefon	Bayleton
Triadimenol	Bayfidan, (Baytan), (Dorin)
Tridemorph	Beacon, Calixin, Bardew, Ringer, (Cosmic), (Dorin)
Triforine	Saprol, Funginex, (Nimrod T), (Brolly), (Roseclear)
Vinclozolin	Ronilan, Apex
Zineb	Dithane Wettable, Tiezene, Lomacol, Parzate
Ziram	Cuman, Fuklasin, Milbam, Zerlate

SECTION C: HERBICIDES

Common name	Some tradenames
Alachlor	Lasso
Alloxydim	Clout, Weed Out
Ametryne	Evik, Gesapax
Aminotriazole	Weedazol, Azolan, (Clearway), (Atlazin), (Primatol AD)
Asulam	Asulox, (Graslam)
Atrazine	Gesaprim, Weedex A4FG, Borocil A, Residox, (Atlazin)
Barban	Carbyne, Oatax
Benfluralin	Balan, Quilan, Benefin
Bentazon	Basagran, (Topshot), (Triagran), (Acumen)
Benthiocarb	Saturn
Benzoylprop-ethyl	Suffix
Bromacil	Hyvar X, Phytar, Croptex, Onyx, (Borocil K), (Hydon)
Bromoxynil	Buctril, (Asset), (Glean TP), (Vulcan), (Certrol E)
Butachlor	Machete
Butylate	Sutan
Carbetamide	Legurame, Carbetamex, (Pradone Plus)
Chloramben	Amiben, Naptol, Vegiben
Chlorbromuron	Bromex, Maloran
Chloridazon	Gladiator, Pyramin, Trojan, (Alicep), (Destral)
Chlormequat	Farmacel, Stabilan, Titan, Arotex Extra,
Chloroneb	Demosan, Tersan

Chloroxuron	Tenoran, Norex, (Mosskiller), (Tumblemoss)
Chlorpropham	Furloe, CIPC, Mirvale 500 HN, (Quartet), (Herald)
Chlorthiamid	Prefix
Chlorsulfuron	(Glean), (Finesse)
Chlortoluron	Dicurane, Hyvena S, Talisman
Cyanazine	Fortrol, (Holtox), (Topshot), (Cleaval), (Envoy)
Cycloate	Ro-Neet, Eurex
Cyprazine	Outfox
2,4-D	Shell D, Palormone D, Planotox, Weedon, Destox, Fernimine, Syford, Dicotox, (Weedazole Total), (Atlavar), (Butoxone), (Verdone), (Atladox)
2,4-DB	Embutox, (Legumex Extra), (Topshot), (Butoxone)
Dalapon	Dowpon
Desmetryne	Semeron
Diallate	Avadex, (Pyradex)
Dicamba	Banvel, (Mephetol Extra), (Emblem), (Field Marshall), (Cornox Plus), (Paddox), (Quad-Ban), (DiFarmon M)
Dichlobenil	Casoron, Prefix D, (Fydulan)
Dichlorprop	Redipon, Polytox-K, (Basagran DP), (Cornoxynil), (Certrol E), (Tetrone), (Mephetol Extra)
Diclofop-methyl	Hoegrass
Difenzoquat	Avenge
Dinitramine	Cobex
Dinoseb	Dinosol, Haulmex, Haulmone, Ivosit
Diquat	Reglone, (Cleansweep), (Weedol), (Pathclear)
Diuron	Karmex, (Orchard Herbicide), (Residuren Extra)
EPTC	Eptam 6E
Fenoprop	(Estermone)
Fenuron	(Herald), (Quartet), (Barrier), (Profen), (Quintex)
Flamprop-methyl	Lancer
Flamprop-isopropyl	Commando
Fluazifop-butyl	Fusilade
Fluorometuron	Cotoran, Lanex
Fluorodifen	Soyex, Preforan
Glyphosate	Roundup, Sonic, Sting, Tumbleweed, (Rival)
Ioxynil	Totril, Actrilawn, (Asset), (Deloxil), (Stellox 400), (Glean TP), (Crusader), (Certrol-E), (Advance)
Isoproturon	Arelon, Tolkan DF, (Astrol), (Dictator), (Stomp)
Lenacil	Venzar, Vizor, (Advizor), (Varmint), (Lanslide)

Linuron	Afalon, (Alibi), (Profalon), (Alistell), (Lanslide), (Broadcide 20), (Tempo), (Janus), (Warrior), (Pre-Empt)
MCPA	Agricorn, Agroxone M, Phenoxylene, Shell M, Agritox, (Legumex), (Acumen), (Buctrilin), (Tetrone), (Minerva), (Butoxone), (Emblem), (Field Marshall), (Paddox)
MCPB	Tropotox, Bellmac Straight, (Acumen), (Trifolex-Tra)
Mecoprop	Clovotox, Methoxone M, Clenecorn, Iso-Cornox 57, Hymec, CMPP, Propal, (Crusader), (Sydex), (Verdone), (Sydex)
Metham-Na	Vapam, Vitafume
Metoxuron	Deftor, Dosaflo, (Hermes)
Metribuzin	Sencorex
Metsulfuron	(Finesse)
Molinate	Ordram, Hydram
Monolinuron	Arresin, (Broadcide), (Gramonol 5)
Monuron	Telvar, Karmax W
Neburon	Kloben
Nitrofen	Tok-E, Nip, Tokkorn
Napropamide	(Devrinol T)
Oryzalin	Surflan
Paraquat	Dextrone, Grammoxone, Scythe, Speedway, (Groundhog), (Pathclear), (Cleansweep), (Weedol), (Soltair)
Pendimethalin	Stomp 330, (Stomp/IPU)
Phenmedipham	Betanal E, Fender, Goliath, Pistol 25, Beetomax, Gusto
Picloram	Tordon, (Diadon), (Atladox)
Prometryne	Gesagard 50, (Peaweed)
Propachlor	Albrass, No-Weed, Ramrod, Sentinel, (Decimate)
Propanil	Rogue, Stam F
Propham	IPC, (Herald), (Quartet), (Barrier), (Murbeetol), (PCF Beet Herbicide), Profen, Quintex
Propyzamide	(Matrikerb)
Sethoxydim	Checkmate
Simazine	Gesatop 50, Syngran, Weedex, (Alcatraz), (Clearway), (Primatol SE), (Total Weed), (Pathclear), (Rival), (Weedazin), (Hermes), (Remtal), (Hytrol)
2,4,5-T	Brushwood Killer, (Kilnet)
2,3,6-TBA	Trysben, (Touchweeder), (Cambiline), (Camtox)
TCA	Varitox, Tecane

Terbacil	Sinbar
Terbutryne	Clarosan, Prebane, (Tempo), (Peaweed), (Opogard 500)
Triallate	Avadex, (Trigger)
Trietazine	(Bronox), (Pre-Empt), (Remtal), (Aventox)
Trifluralin	Digermin, Marksman 2, Treflan, Trigard, Tristar, (Masterspray), (Pre-Kite), (Fallclene), (Chandor), (Janus), (Linnet), (Warrior), (Pre-Empt), (Lextra)
Vernolate	Vernam

Index

abaxial deposition   44, 47
abortions   133
Abutilon spp   464, 467
acaricidal action   170, 177, 210, 217, 219, 345
acaricides   111, 224–228, 283, 302
accelerated degradation, *see* Enhanced degradation
acceptable daily intake (ADI)   15
accidents, level of risk in   16
accumulation   57, 267, 273
acephate   118
acetate metabolism   282, 328, 421
acetoacetate   102
acetolactate synthase (ALS)   466, 468, 501
acetyl coenzyme A   397
acetylation   92
acetylcholine   89–93, 177, 223
acetylcholinesterase   92–96, 100, 115, 118, 131, 138
   modified   251–254
acetyldopamine   172
acetylthiocholine   252
Achillea spp   409
Achromobacter   141
acid equivalents   401
acifluorfen   439, 468–472
Actinomycetes   148, 490
action potential   90, 159–163
activation of pesticides   72, 103, 112, 116, 139, 245–247
activators   49, 370
active ingredient   32, 34, 37
activity coefficient   434
Aculus spp   219
acute toxicity   10, 97, 98
acyl coenzyme A derivatives   428
acylalanines   265, 350–354
acylurea insecticides   208–214, 496
adenosine deaminase   349
adenylate cyclase   220, 231
ADI, *see* Acceptable daily intake
adjuvants   26, 40, 42, 47–50
adrenaline   219

adsorption   385
   on plant constituents   371
   on soil constituents   320, 372–377, 441–443, 450, 459, 484, 488, 490, 492
adsorption constants   376, 546
adverse effects, of o/p compounds   97–100
Aedes spp   138, 254, 256
Aegopodium spp   393, 483
aerosols   34, 119
A- and B-esterases   61–62, 241
affinity constant, K 95
after-potential   161, 165, 202–203
ageing of blocked enzyme   96, 100
agent orange   403
agonistic effect   220
Agropyron spp   386, 391–392, 396, 415, 419–420, 449, 477, 499
Agrostis spp   417, 419
air impulsion   41
airborne pathogens   263–264
aircraft   20, 36, 99, 399
alachlor   6, 475, 483–489
alanine ester fungicides   351
aldicarb   38, 73, 126–127, 130, 144–149, 230
aldimorph   332
aldrin   34, 72, 158, 173–175
aldrin dihydrodiol   176
alfalfa   450, 455, 460
alfalfa weevil   130, 150
algae   450, 458, 487
aliphatic hydroxylation   68–69
alkanes   433
alkoxy groups, removal of   62, 70
alkoxyalkylmercury compounds   276
alkyl chlorides   433
alkylmercury compounds   276
allethrin   190–191
allidochlor   486, 488
Allium cepa   279
alloxydim   418
Alopecurus spp   415, 422, 441, 445, 463, 476, 479

Alternaria spp   273, 287, 290, 311, 322, 333
alternating spray application   354
aluminium phosphide   33
Amaranthus spp   409, 414, 454, 479, 492
ambimobile   392
Ames test   16, 99, 180, 447
ametryne   397, 447–454
amidases   60, 62, 127, 241, 427
amide herbicides   423
amine oxide   69, 332
amine salts of herbicides   400, 429
amino acid exudates   271
aminoacyl tRNA   350
2-aminobenzimidazole   321
γ-aminobutyric acid   91–92, 204
aminoformic acid   126, 458
aminopyrimidine fungicides, *see*
    Hydroxyaminopyrimidine fungicides
aminotriazole   40, 376, 378, 383, 390, 395–399
amitraz   217–222
amitrole   395–399
Ammania spp   414
ammonium thiocyanate   396–399
amphipathic ion   50
amplification of genes   367–368
amplitude reduction   201
Amsinckia spp   411
amylase   486
anabasine   222
anaerobic conditions   169, 175, 214, 275, 471
anaerobic soils   147–149, 152, 214, 492
anaesthesia   97, 433
anaesthetic action, of formamidines   220
analysis, new methods of   498
anaphase   490
animal dips   175, 179
animal fats   168, 175, 180
animal parasites   122
anionic sites   92–94
anionic surfactants   50–51
annual dicots, control of   468
annual grasses, control of   460, 488
Anopheles spp   138, 242, 252
anorexia   164, 217, 221, 232, 346
antagonism between herbicides   418, 499
antestis bug   86
anthelmintics   230
Anthemis spp   408, 411
Anthonomus spp   209
anthracnose disease   320

anthranilate   394
antibiotics   349–350
antidotes   96, 468, 482
antilymphocytic action   281
antimetabolite   281
antimycin A   329
anti-oxidants   188–189
antiserum techniques   243
ants   129, 158, 174
Apanteles spp   199
aphids   83–86, 103, 106, 113, 122, 130, 138, 150, 158–159
    resistant strains of   197, 241–242
apical growth   392–394, 424, 485
Apocynum spp   404, 480
apoplastic movement   324, 328, 343, 345, 348, 352, 355, 370–371, 392, 451, 461, 484
apple canker   276
apple moth   248
apple scab   276, 283, 290, 298, 309
application, of pesticides   34–47
appressorium   348
aquatic animals   389
aquatic weed control   385, 484
arachnids   76
Archachatina spp   234
armyworms   114, 130, 135, 158
aromatic amino acid synthesis   393–395
aromatic hydroxylation   69–70, 444
arousal system   220
Arthrobacterium spp   337, 490
artificial respiration   98
aryl carboxylamidase   63
aryl epoxides   64
aryl methylcarbamates   126, 133–139
arylmercury compounds   276
aryloxyphenoxy herbicides   416–422, 499
arylsulphonic acid herbicides   463–468
Ascochyta spp   292, 307, 319–320
Ascomycetes   263–264, 309, 315, 319, 336, 338, 343
ascorbate peroxidase   387
aseptate hyphae   267, 341, 350
asparagus   385, 450
aspartic acid   408
Aspergillus spp   267, 294, 324, 427, 465
asphyxiation   98
assimilates   370
3-ATAL   396
ataxia   133, 201
Atherigona spp   144

atomising jet   45
ATPase   162, 165
atrazine   6, 71, 73, 75, 364, 375, 379,
    396, 410, 439, 448, 450, 452–453
atropine   96, 98, 132
attapulgite   34, 37
Autobasidiomycetes   269
autonomic nervous system   88
auto-oxidation   387
autoradiography   404, 443
autumn control of weeds   369
auxins   405–406
avalanching neurotoxicity   177
Avena spp   415, 422–423, 425–426, 440,
    469, 476, 479
avermectins   230–232, 496
avocado   86, 355
axial bonds   171–172
axonic membranes   87–90, 165, 203
axonic transmission   159–163
azinphos-methyl   82, 84, 112

Bacillus thuringiensis   497
bahia grass   402
baits   139, 158, 233
BAL   273
balance of nature   3
bamboo   416
banana fruit fly   213
bananas   86, 141, 293, 319, 392, 450
barban   423, 432
barley   159, 277, 291, 299, 322, 328, 332,
    337–338, 347–349
  weed control in   385, 424, 441, 445,
    453, 478–479, 490
barnyardgrass   426–427, 476, 479, 485
Basidiomycetes   264, 268, 309, 315, 319,
    330, 336, 338, 343
Batrachedra spp   35
beans   86, 117, 159, 230, 291, 319, 378,
    450, 460, 478, 486, 490, 492
bedstraws   408
bees   116, 134, 159, 339
beet   116–119, 143, 150, 230, 431, 455,
    457, 460
beet armyworm   208, 213, 215
beet cyst nematode   147
beet virus yellows   113, 197
beggarweed   465
behavioural abnormality   133, 180, 213,
    217, 219, 238, 496
bell peppers   151

Belonolaimus spp   146, 230
Bemisia spp   197, 218
benalaxyl   293, 351
beneficial organisms   113, 155, 198–199,
    210, 224, 232
benefin   491
benefit-to-cost ratio   8, 292
benfluralin   491
benomyl   268, 278, 293, 307, 315,
    318–326, 498
bent grass   478
bentazon   383, 414, 418
benthiocarb   478, 480
benzene   435
benzimidazoles   2, 263, 308, 316,
    318–326, 333, 345
benzoic acid auxins   408–410
benzonitriles   483–485
benzoxazinone   452–453
benzoylphenylurea insecticides   208–216
benzoylprop-ethyl   424
bermuda-grass   415, 454, 477, 480
B-esterases, A-esterases   60–62
between-crop application   385
BHC   171–174
  see also HCH
big bud   177, 283
bilharzia   129, 233
biliary excretion   143
bimodal curve   214, 322
binapacryl   226, 265, 287, 291, 302–304,
    430
binding
  to cell constituents   323, 337
  to receptors   254
  to soil constituents   25
  see also Adsorption, on plant
    constituents
bioactive amines   91–92, 204, 219
bioallethrin   191
biodegradable pesticides   3, 64
biological magnification   179
biological pesticides   497
biological residues   496
biological spectrum   158
biomagnification factor   179
Biomphalaria spp   234
biophase   433–435
bioresmethrin   190–191
bipyridinium herbicides   384–389
birds   99, 139, 177, 181, 197, 278
birth defects   429
bisdithiocarbamates   289, 293, 295, 297

bisulphate, as activator   49
bitertanol   336
bitter rot   299
black bindweed   409
black rot   290
black spot   291, 299, 338
blackcurrants   177, 283
blackgrass   415, 441, 476–479
blackpod disease   8
blasticidin S   349
bleaching   458
Blissus spp   112
blockade of transmission   202–203, 224
blood plasma   58
blood pressure   97
blossom weevils   158
blotch diseases   338
blowflies   158–159, 175
blue mould   322
blueberries   460
blurred vision   132
boll weevils   158, 198, 213
bollworms   86, 130
borates   378, 485
Bordeaux mixture   1, 269–275
Bothynoderes spp   144
Botrytis spp   263, 265, 268, 291, 299,
     301, 311–312, 333, 336, 339, 356
Brachiaria spp   418
Brachypodium spp   454
bracken   484
Brassicas   116, 121, 143, 276, 305, 319,
     374, 419, 431, 449, 460, 478,
     485–486, 490
break-even point   8
Bremia spp   352, 354
broadleaf weed control   399–415,
     428–432, 468–472
bromacil   68, 375–376, 439, 454–458
bromophos   82, 121
bromoxynil   410–413, 483
Bromus spp   419
broncho-constriction   97
brown rot   320
brown rust   357
brushwood control   402, 455
buds, effect on rhizome   416
build-up, of soil herbicides   372–373
bulb flies   113, 116
bulb nematodes   229
bulbs   379, 449, 455, 460
bunt diseases   273, 277, 315, 322, 327,
     337

bupirimate   316, 347
buthiobate   316, 344
butonate   84
butoxyethanol   40
butylate   7, 475, 478–479, 483
4-n-butyltriazole   357
butyrolactones   350, 354
butyrylcholine   252

C-14 demethylation inhibitors   335–347
cabbage family, *see* Brassicas
cabbage root fly   110, 118, 121, 130,
     141, 143, 158, 177, 276
Cajanus spp   290
calabar bean   125
calcium ions   89–90, 178, 204–205, 390,
     393, 415, 488, 491
calcium-dependent ATPase   165
calcium-/magnesium-dependent
     ATPase   178, 205
callose   266
callus cells, callose   266, 485, 490
calmodulin   162–163
calomel   276
Calonectria spp   323
Calystegia spp   409
camomile   409
camphorweed   454
Canada thistle   414
cancer   64, 469
  of the prostate   346
cane borer   129
cane fruits   112, 291
cantaloupe   151
Capsella spp   476
capsid bugs   106, 113–115
captafol   287, 291, 298, 301, 349
captan   6, 33, 287, 291, 298–302, 308,
     343, 352
carbamate herbicides   2, 374, 383,
     422–424, 435, 439, 458–463
carbamate insecticides   62, 70, 94, 96,
     125–152, 245, 254–257
carbamate-type organophosphorus
     insecticides   115–116
carbamoyl compounds   318
carbamylation of
     cholinesterase   131–133
carbaryl   9, 64, 70, 77, 126–128,
     133–138, 239, 427, 458
carbendazim   265, 293, 310, 316–317,
     322–326, 333, 338, 352

carbetamide 459–460
carbofuran 6, 71, 126–128, 130,
 140–144, 228–230
carbon disulphide 229, 297
carbon monoxide 65, 169, 343
carbonyl sulphide 301
carbosulfan 130, 143–144
carboxamides, *see* Oxathiins
carboxin 263–264, 268, 278, 316, 327,
 330, 499
carboxylesterase 62–63, 85, 103–105
 in R strains 240–245
carcinogenic effects 14, 99, 120, 138,
 180, 222, 447
carotenoids 397–398, 470
carrier 34–36, 40–42
carrot root fly 36, 86, 110, 113, 121
carrots 147, 230, 319, 323, 417,
 431–432, 478, 490
carry-over, from year to year 490
Carya spp 454
Caryophyllaceae 469
casein 49
casparian strip 371
catecholamines 219
caterpillars 1, 158
cation exchange capacity 385
cationic detergents 308
cattle tick 197
cattle, weed palatibility to 402
cauliflower mosaic virus 368
CCPR 17
CDA 43
CDAA 485
celery 319, 379, 431
celery fly 86
cell fractionation 59
cell growth, herbicides and 439,
 458–468, 481, 484–486
cell membrane damage 267, 343,
 356–357, 427
cell wall abnormality 339, 344, 357,
 485, 491
cellulose 266, 350
cellulose biosynthesis 485
cement layer 29
centipedegrass 464
central nervous system (CNS) 164
centrifugal energy 40, 45–46
Cephalosporium spp 214
Cerastium spp 409, 411
Cercospora spp 308, 319, 323, 338–339
cereal nematodes 129, 228

cereals 86, 265, 277, 291, 299, 315, 319,
 323, 328, 332, 337–338, 344
 weed control in 401, 409, 428, 441,
 450, 463, 467, 479, 492
certificate of competence 20
cetyl trimethylammonium bromide 51
chafer grubs 122, 158
Chara spp 389
charged droplets 44
chelation complexes 266, 271, 273–274
chemical hydrolysis 465
Chenopodium spp 222, 414, 431, 453,
 479
cherry 319
Cheshunt compound 269–270
chickens 197, 301
chickweed 402, 409, 411, 450, 460, 469,
 478
chiral centre 406
Chironomus spp 205
chitin 28–30, 208, 210–212, 266, 300,
 333, 339, 350
Chlamydomonas spp 280, 471
chloramben 409
chlorbenside 225
chlorbenzilate 164, 170
chlorbromuron 441–442
chlorbufam 459–460
chlordane 2, 158, 176
chlordimeform 217–222
Chlorella spp 274, 416
chlorfenprop 383, 425–426
chlorfenquat 425–426
chlorfenson 225
chlorfenvinphos 84, 121
chlorfluazuron 209, 215
chloride ion channels 204–206
chloride ion uptake 172, 178, 204, 232
chlorimuron 464
chlorinated allyl groups 482
chlorinated amino compounds 287
chlorinated aromatic fungicides 287,
 305–308
chlorinated benzoic acids 383, 408–410
chlorinated cyclodienes 174–178
chlorinated nitrocompounds 286
chlorinated quinones 286
chlorinated triazines 451
α-chloroacetamides 475, 485–489
chloroacetanilides 485–489
chloroaniline 214, 423, 462
2-chlorobenzenesulphonamide 465
p-chloromethylaniline 344

chloroneb   70, 263, 265, 268, 316, 356
chlorophenoxy-3-methylbutyric
    acid   198
4-chlorophenyl-N-methylcarbamate   460
chlorophenylurea   214
chlorophyll content   485
chlorophyll-free mutants   470
chloropicrin   229, 266
chloroplast disruption   414, 427, 453,
    470
chloroplast electron transport   387, 399,
    446, 456
chloroplast membranes   421
chlorosis   273, 386, 398, 412, 425, 453
chlorothalonil   287, 291–292, 307, 312,
    350
chloroxuron   379, 440–443
chlorpropham   70, 431, 439, 458–463
chlorpyrifos   8, 35, 111, 121, 242, 244
chlorsulfuron   439, 463–468, 501
chlorthiamid   77–78, 378, 475, 483–485
chlortoluron   440–447
cholesterol   442
cholinergic nerves   91
cholinesterase inhibition   92–97, 112,
    246
chorismate   395
chromatids   462
chromophores   189
chromosome abnormality   424, 485, 490
chronic toxic effects   10, 14–17, 97–100,
    133, 180, 296
chronological selectivity   365
chrysanthemic acids   187–190, 192
cinerins I and II   186
cinnamic acid fungicides   358
Cirsium spp   391, 409, 467, 483
cis-crotonanilides   327
citrus   86, 150, 225, 319, 355, 392, 455
Cladosporium spp   319, 324
clams   179
clay, adsorption to   34, 306, 320, 393
cleavage, of ester linkages   75, 194
cleavers   402, 409, 431
clofentezine   219, 226
cloning   367
closed community   182
closed spray systems   47
Clostridium spp   279
clubroot   276
CNS   87–91, 172, 177, 220
cocklebur   414
cocoa   272, 338, 352

Codex Alimentarius Commission   17
Codex Committee on Pesticide Residues
    (CCPR)   17–19
codling moth   86, 112, 129, 139, 150
coenzyme Q binding protein   329
coffee   86, 140, 210, 272, 336, 338
Coleopteran larvae   193, 199–200, 209
coleoptiles   366, 415, 421, 481
Collembola spp   178
Colletotrichum spp   296, 319–320, 345,
    356
colloidal sulphur   281–284
Colorado beetle   1, 130, 143, 158, 200,
    205
colour coding   278
combinant DNA   243
combined sprays, see Mixtures, of
    fungicides
competitive disadvantage   440
competitive inhibition   132
competitive vigour   347
complementary DNA   368
complexes   294
computerisation   13, 46, 496
concentration gradient   267
conditioning of insects   239
conduction, axonic   90, 160–162
conformations, ion gate   161–162, 166
conidia   264–266
conifers   355
conjugation reactions   56, 75–79, 194,
    397
connectives   91
consecutive applications   258
contact action   27–29
contact fungicides   262–266
contact herbicides   369, 384
contact o/p insecticides   87, 100–102
contact pre-emergence   378
containers, safe disposal of   21
controlled droplet application
    (CDA)   43–45
controlled release from granules   37
conventional sprays   40, 42
Convolvulus spp   393, 409
convulsions   132, 164, 172, 201, 205
cooking, effect on residues of   189
copper carbonate   270
copper fungicides   263, 265, 269–275
corms   379
corn, see Maize; Sweet corn
corn borer   221
corn earworm   130

corn marigold 411–412
corn rootworm 130
corrosion, of cans 292, 302
cortical microtubules 491
corticosteroids 346
corticum 328
coryneform bacteria 338, 490
Corynespora 272
cosolvents 39
cotton
   fungicides for 332, 356
   insecticides for 117–118, 134, 139,
      146, 158, 210, 218
   weed control in 419, 431, 442, 449,
      458, 467, 478, 485, 491
cotton boll weevil 209, 213, 218
cotton leafworm 195, 208
couch grass (quack grass) 386, 396, 415,
      477–478, 483
covered smut 277
cowpea 328
cowpea mosaic virus 197
cow's milk 181, 197
crabs 179
cranberries 460
crawlers 231
crayfish 166
crickets 158
crop candidosis 346
crop canopy problems 42–47
crop competition 424
crop rotation 3, 362
crop stress 492
cross-enhancement 480
cross-resistance
   to fungicides 308, 317, 325, 331, 347,
      354
   to insecticides 105, 111, 173, 210,
      239, 254–259
   negative 318, 325, 331
crown rot disease 352, 355
crucifers 469
cucumber 319, 347, 357, 414
cucumber mosaic virus 113
Cucurbitaceae 159
Culex spp 242, 245, 254, 258
cultivation, in weed control 415–417
cuprous oxide 269–270, 272
currants 319
Curvularia spp 344
cuticle 25–31, 239, 319, 432
cuticle/injection ratio 31
cutworms 112, 122, 158, 200

cyanazine 378, 450
α-cyano pyrethroids 191–192, 196–199,
      201–205
cyclic AMP 219–220
cyclic catalysis 388
cycloate 477–478
cyclodienes 156, 158, 174–178, 239
cycloheximide 468
cycloprate 225–226
cyclopropane carboxylic acid 190–193
cycloxydim 418
cyfluthrin 205
cyhexatin 226, 227
cymoxanil 293, 316
Cynodon spp 393, 415, 417, 419, 427,
      454, 477, 499
cypermethrin 196–205, 258
cyperquat 384
Cyperus spp 385, 391–392, 454, 464,
      477, 480, 485
cyprazine 431, 448, 450
cyprofuram 350, 354
cyst nematode 150, 228–230
cysteine 79, 247, 273, 295, 322, 481
cytochrome P_{450} 59, 66, 108, 116, 135,
      246, 302, 310, 340–342, 399, 408
cytokinesis 279
cytoskeleton 324, 461–463
cytosol 60, 267

2,4-D 62, 371, 376, 399–408, 419
dalapon 40, 383, 401, 415–416
damping-off 305, 319
databases 496
date moth 35
day-flying moths 218
dazomet 142, 229
2,4-DB 364, 401, 428–429
D-D mixture 33, 146, 228–229
DDA 169
DDD 164, 168–169
DDE 167–168
DDT 2, 105, 155–156, 158–160,
      163–172, 179, 181, 203, 226,
      238–240, 253–256, 435
debilitation, as virus control factor 197
decamethrin 199
decarbamylation 131–133
DEF 196, 243–244
de-esterification ambiguity 425
de-ethyl diazinon 249
defence mechanisms 57–58

defoliant action 431
dehydrochlorinase 167, 250
dehydrochlorination 167–168, 250–251
dehydrogenation, of terpenes 397–399
delayed neuropathy 100, 133
delayed release from granules 37
Delia spp 122
delta-endotoxin 497
deltamethrin 191–192, 199, 253
demethyl chlordimeform 221
demethyl dichlorvos 119
demethyl fenitrothion 109
demethyl trichlorphon 118
demeton-*S*-methyl 72, 82, 84, 100, 114,
    229
demyelination 133
dendrites 87–89
dephosphorylation of enzyme 61,
    94–96, 100
depletion, transmitter vesicle 204
depolarisation of axon 160–163, 165,
    201–205
deposition of droplets 44–47
depth protection 484
dermal application 31
dermophytosis 346
Deroceras spp 139
derris dust 223
desiccation 217, 386, 431, 453
desmetryne 431, 448–450
Desmodium spp 464
detergents 50–53, 308, 319
detoxication of pesticides 57–79, 499
Deuteromycetes 263–264, 267, 303, 309,
    319, 331, 336, 338, 343
Diabrotica spp 141
diagnostic kits 498
dialkyl dithiocarbamates 289, 291–293
diallate 375, 476–483
diamond back moth 150, 199, 210, 240
diatomaceous earth 34–36, 41
Diatraea spp 221
diazinon 74–75, 83–84, 99, 110–112,
    122, 248–249
1,2-dibromo-3-chloropropane 34, 229
dicamba 376, 401, 406, 408–410
di-n-butyl tin 280
dicarboximides 287, 311–312
dichlobenil 77–78, 364, 372, 376, 378,
    475, 483–485
dichlofluanid 263, 265, 291, 298, 312
dichlone 267, 287, 291, 308
dichlormid 479

dichloroacetaldehyde 119
3,4-dichloroaniline 63, 427
2,6-dichlorobenzoic acid 485
3,5-dichloronitrobenzene 74
2,4-dichlorophenoxyacetic acid
    (2,4-D) 62, 371, 376, 399–408, 419
2,4-dichlorophenoxybutyric acid
    (2,4-DB) 428–429
1,2-dichloropropane 146
1,3-dichloropropene 34, 229
dichlorovinyl derivatives 119–120, 192,
    194
dichlorprop 400–402, 412
dichlorvos 76, 81, 84, 100, 482
diclobenil 475, 483–485
diclobutrazole 316, 337
diclofop 2, 416–422, 500
dicloran 265, 287, 291, 306–307
dicofol 16, 159, 163, 168, 170, 226
dicrotophos 118
Didymella spp 299, 311
die-back disease 354
dieldrin 72, 105, 158, 173–176, 239, 256
Diels–Alder reaction 174
diesel oil 432
diet, effect on toxicity 110
diethyl ethylphosphonothioate 92
diethyl phenylphosphorothioate 480,
    500
difenzoquat 385, 425–426
diflubenzuron 2, 208–215, 245, 257
difluorobenzoic acid 214
trans-dihydrodiols 64, 176
dihydronaphthols 137
DIMBOA 451
dimethirimol 316, 347–349
dimethoate 63, 81–84, 115
dimethomorph 358
dimethyl dithiocarbamates 287–290
dimethyl silicones 53
dimethylaniline 222
dimethylcyanoformamide 151
dimethylformanilide 222
dimethylphenylcarbamates 135
dimethylsulphamoyl ethirimol 347
dinitramine 491
2,4-dinitro 6-alkylphenols 2, 264,
    302–304, 429–431
dinitroaniline herbicides 475, 489–493
dinitrocyclohexylphenol 226
dinocap 264, 287, 291, 302–304, 429
dinoseb 303, 429–431
diols 137

dioxin 403
diphenamid 475, 488
diphenyl ethers 468–472
diploid nuclei 279
dipping, for fungal control 320, 322
Diptera, control of 200, 208
diquat 367, 378, 383–389
direct drilling 386
directed spray 386
directives, EEC 20
dispersing agents 40, 48
dissociation constant 95
distribution of tolerances 12
disulfiram 297–298
disulfoton 84, 114–115, 122
disulphides 301
dithiocarbamates 264, 279, 287–298
Ditylenchus spp 129, 141, 147, 228, 230
diuron 72, 365, 375, 440–447, 454
DNA synthesis inhibition 405, 447
docking disorder 129, 150, 230
docks 409
dodemorph 316, 331–335
dodine 287, 291, 308–309
dog fennel 454
dopamine 172
dormant season application 368
dosage–response curves 10–13, 227
downy mildews 263–265, 269, 291–292,
    299, 319, 350, 352, 355–356
DPEs 469
drainage water 179
drazoxalon 265
drip irrigation 151
droplet size 41–47
Drosophila spp 168, 237, 253
drought stress 420
dry and moist soil, herbicides in 484,
    490
dry rot 291, 322
dusts 32, 34–36
Dutch elm disease 118

ear tags 198
early blight 351
earthworms 134, 144, 158, 178–180, 339
earwigs 128
ecdysis 210–214
Echinochloa spp 417, 427, 469
economic dosage 364
economics, of pesticide use 7–10, 219
ecto-ATPase 165–167

ectoparasites of animals 158, 224
ectoparasitic fungi 262, 266
EDTA 273, 390
EEC regulations 277
efflux, of fungicides 267, 269
eggs 99, 182, 197, 219
electrodyne sprayer 47
electro-encephalographs 98
electron microscopy 266, 280, 339, 344,
    348, 357, 386, 395, 413, 471
electron paramagnetic resonance 329
electron spin resonance 471
electron transport 412, 415
electronegativity 275
electrophilic attack 93
electrostatic effects 35, 44, 46–47
Eleusine spp 419
elm bark beetles 158
Elodea spp 279
Elymus spp, *see Agropyron* spp
embryotoxic 180
emergency medical action 22
emulsifiable concentrates 40–42
emulsifiers 47–54
encapsulation 339
end feet 88–90
end-foot vesicles 204
endocuticle 28–31
endogenous compounds 58
endoparasitic fungi 263–265
endoparasitic nematodes 146–149
endoplasmic reticulum 59, 300, 310, 339
endosulfan 158, 173–174
endothall 431
endrin 158, 173–175
enhanced degradation 122, 142,
    147–148, 235, 312, 373, 404, 480
enolpyruvyl shikimate
    phosphate 394–395
enrichment, *see* Enhanced degradation
enterohepatic circulation 143
environmental contamination 156–157,
    178–182
Environmental Protection
    Agency 19–20
enzyme blocking 95
enzyme induction, *see* Induction, of
    enzymes
enzyme–inhibitor complex 94–96
epicuticle 28–31
epicuticular wax 483
epidermal cells 28–29
epinasty 404

EPN   243–244
epoxidation   69, 72, 137, 175
epoxide hydrolase   137
EPSP synthase   395
EPTC   475–483
equatorial bonds   172
equilibrium   434
Equisetum spp   396
Eremochloa spp   464
ergosterol   335, 340–342
ergosterol biosynthesis inhibitors (EBIs),
     see C-14 demethylation inhibitors;
     Morpholines
Erica spp   355
Erysiphe spp   196, 198, 200–201, 211,
     214, 265, 268, 280, 283, 315, 319,
     331, 336–339, 347, 349
erythrose-4-phosphate   394–395
Escherichia spp   301
ester cleavage   198–199, 248–249
ester hydrolysis   60–62
esterases   60–62, 127–128, 136–137,
     195–196
ester-forming site   92–94
etaconazole   339
ethirimol   70, 316, 339, 347–349
ethyldipropylthiocarbamate
     (EPTC)   478
ethylene bisdithiocarbamate   288–290
ethylene dibromide   229
ethylene thiourea   296–297
ethylene thiuram disulphide   296–297
ethylphosphonates   316, 354–356
ethylsuccinate linkage   62, 103–104, 242
Euglena spp   456
eukariotes   349
Euphorbia spp   467
excitability,
     formamidine-induced   218–221
Exobasidium spp   331
exocuticle   29–30
exocytosis   89
extenders   460, 480
exudates   271
eye-spot disease   198, 309, 321, 346

face fly   198
FAD-containing enzyme   65, 68
false positive results   16
FAO Guidelines on Pesticides   17–19
farnesyl pyrophosphate   397–398
Fasciola spp   233

fat bodies   116, 220
fat hen   431, 449, 479
fatty acid biosynthesis   412, 421–422,
     481–483, 487
fatty acid desaturase   341, 346
Federal Register of Tolerances   19
feed-back effects   247, 394
fenarimol   304, 316, 343–344
fenchlorphos   121
fenitro-oxon   109
fenitrothion   35, 82, 84, 103, 106–109
fenoprop   400
fenpropimorph   332
fentin derivatives   266, 280
fenuron   441
fenvalerate   8, 191–193, 198, 203, 205,
     246, 256–258
ferbam   289
ferredoxin   329, 384–387, 472
fertility, of birds   181–182
fiddleneck   411
field water capacity   420, 492
FIFRA   19
fillers   34–36, 41
Fimbristylis spp   427
fireflies   220
first-order reactions   147, 493
flamprop   423–424
flare-up   113
flavin   66
flax   410, 478
flea beetles   143, 158
fleas   158–159, 188
flour beetles   62, 106, 111
fluazifop   383, 416–422, 499
flufenoxuron   210
fluometuron   440–443
fluorescence   445–446
fluorodifen   469
flusilazol   339
flutriafol   349
fodder beet   55, 457, 460
foetotoxicity   120, 149
foliar herbicides   383–435
folpet   287, 298, 302
Food and Drugs Administration   19–20
Food and Environment Protection
     Act   19–20
food chain effect   156, 181–182
forage quality   402
forestry trees   386, 392, 450, 484–485,
     489
forget-me-not   411

formaldehyde 229
formamidine insecticides and
    acaricides 217–222, 496
formulation of pesticides 25, 31–44
fortified oils 432
fosetyl-aluminium, *see*
    Phosetyl-aluminium
foxtails 479, 485
free radicals 387–388, 446, 470–471
freight wagons 33
Frescon 233–234
Freundlich isotherm 376
frit fly 114
froghoppers 157–159
fruit bushes 272, 283, 291, 322, 368,
    378, 386, 416, 450, 460, 484
fruit canes 322, 368, 449–450, 454, 484
fruit flies 86, 121, 128–130, 139,
    143–144, 158
fuberidazole 318, 323
Fucus spp 181
fuel costs 40–42
fumigant action 33–34, 81, 87, 119, 144,
    159, 222, 229, 282, 288
fumitory 321, 411
Fungi Imperfecti, *see* Deuteromycetes
fungicides
    classification of 264
    selectivity of 267–269
fungistatic action 273, 353
furalaxyl 350
furyl-3-methanol derivatives 192
Fusarium spp 141, 214, 264, 268–269,
    271, 277, 291, 299, 319

GABA (γ-aminobutyric acid) 92, 172,
    204
GABA receptors 172, 178, 232
galactosyl diacyl triglycerides 421
Galeopsis spp 411
Galium spp 402, 409, 431, 492
gall mite 177, 283
Gambusia spp 170
ganglia 87–92, 97
gates, for ion movement 161–162,
    165–167, 178
gelatin 273
gene amplification 242–245, 247, 405,
    501
genetic engineering 243, 367, 468, 495,
    500
genetic variation 237

geranyl geraniol 398
germ tube 266
germinating weeds 448, 450, 458
giant nuclei 461
giberellic acid 481, 486
gipsy moths 158
glasshouse 119, 122, 292, 311, 321, 349,
    490
global weed control 362
Globodera spp 141, 150, 230
Gloeosporium spp 299, 319
Glossina spp 240
glucose conjugates 76–78
glucosides 76, 139, 356, 424
glucuronides (*S*- and *O*-) 59, 76, 139
glume blotch 265, 291, 299
glutamate, as neurotransmitter 220
glutathione 73–76, 109, 247, 300, 308,
    322, 387, 468, 482, 487
glutathione reductase 387
glutathione-*S*-transferases 73–76, 109,
    116, 119, 167, 175, 247–251, 451,
    472, 487
glycine 76–77, 271, 390
glycogen phosphorylase 219
glycoprotein 165
glyphosate 378, 383, 390–395
goitrogenic effects 296
gooseberry 303
grain 86, 109, 120
grain pests 106, 158, 209
graminicides 416–422, 499
Gram-negative bacteria 490
Gram-positive bacteria 346
granular formulations 32, 34–36, 144,
    147, 379, 389, 449, 455, 483, 491
grapes 291, 311, 319, 338, 354
grass, weed control in 401
grass-hoppers 158
grassland renovation 386
grassy weed control 397–399, 415–427
green foxtail 427
green mould 323
grey mould, *see* *Botrytis* spp
ground area coverage 41–42
ground elder 393, 483–484
groundnuts 119, 146, 307, 319, 464,
    469, 478, 485, 490, 492
groundsel 411, 447
growth-regulating effects 339, 424,
    486–487
guanidine derivatives 287
gummosis 355

gums   49

haem protein   59, 135, 340–342
haemolymph   219–220
half life, of pesticides in soil   214, 419,
    465, 479, 492
haloxon   229
haloxyfop   421
hard granules   36–39
haustoria   262
γ-HCH   155, 157–158, 171–174, 179,
    239
headaches   132
heart rot   355
heavy metal fungicides   263, 265,
    269–281
Heliothis spp   110, 209, 213, 218, 237,
    243
Helminthosporium spp   277, 311
Hemileia spp   338
Hemiptera   158, 218
hemp dogbane   404, 479–480
heptachlor epoxide   173, 175
heptane   433
herbicidal antidotes   468, 479, 482–483
heterocyclic carbamate
    insecticides   140–144
heterocyclic leaving groups   110, 125
heterocyclic methyl carbamates   140–144
Heterodera spp   147, 150, 230
Heteronychus spp   143
hexachlorobenzene   278
hexaconazole   338
hexahydrophthalic acid   431
high boiling point solvent   34
high density lipoprotein   62
Hill reaction   386, 414, 435, 446, 454,
    456, 458, 461
Hirschmanniella spp   131, 230
HLB (hydrophilic–lipophilic
    balance)   41, 50, 55
homoeostasis   402
homogenate, liver   59
homologous chromosome
    mismatch   243
homozygous individuals   256–259
hops   139, 150, 291–292, 357, 450
horn fly   198
horn worms   164
horsetails   396
houseflies, resistant strains of   216, 239,
    241–242, 245–249, 252–256

human milk   181
humectant   49
hydraulic spray systems   40–42, 44–47
hydrocarbon oils   383, 432
hydrogen peroxide   387–388
hydrogen sulphide   11, 281–282
hydrolases   60–64, 215, 243–245, 460
    inhibitors of   243–245
hydrolysis, of choline esters   94–96
hydrolysis theory, of sulphur action   281
hydrolytic dealkylation   139
hydrophilic–hydrophobic balance
    (HHB)   42, 50, 55
hydrophobic mycelium   262, 263
hydrophobic regions   330, 370
hydroprene   216
hydroxyaminopyrimidine
    fungicides   347–349
4-hydroxycarbaryl   137
3-hydroxycarbofuran   142–143
hydroxydichlorobenzonitrile   485
hydroxydieldrin   176
hydroxyl groups, metabolic insertion   69
hydroxymethyl conjugates   444
hydroxymethylation of pyrethrin   189
hydroxypropham   461–462
5-hydroxypropoxur   139
hydroxypyrimidine fungicides, *see*
    Hydroxyaminopyrimidine fungicides
hydroxythio-oxamidate   151
Hymenoptera   158
hyperexcitability   160–161, 164,
    172–173, 201–204, 220
hyperplasia   180, 403
hyperpolarisation   161
hypersensitivity   220
Hypochnus spp   327
hypoxanthine   349

I_{50} 11, 135, 414, 467
iatrogenic effect   322
IBP   316
ideal solution   434
imazalil   287, 309, 316, 338, 346
imidazole fungicides   287, 309, 316, 335,
    344–346
immune chemistry, aspects of   12, 17,
    99, 243, 389, 498
impaction of droplets   43–47
impaired senses   98–100
impulses   159–163, 201–204
impulsion, of spray droplets   40–43

impurities, in malathion 104–105
inactivated conformation 160–163
inactivation, of glyphosate 390
incorporation into soil, of
    herbicides 476–479
independent action 456
Indian buffaloes 181
indigo carmine 386
indolylacetic acid 393, 397, 405
induction, of enzymes 168, 180, 253,
    310, 338, 346, 488
industrial accidents 16
inert diluent 34–37, 40–42
infants 181
infection, time after 338
influx, of fungicides 266–267
infrastructure, and role of pesticides 9
inhibition constant, K_i 96
inhibitor–enzyme complex 95–96
inhibitors, of enzymes 62, 67, 73, 135,
    188, 195–196, 244
inhibitory neurotransmitter 172
inorganic fungicides 262–276, 281–284
insect cuticle 28–31
insect growth regulators
    (IGRs) 210–217
insect integument 28–30
insect life cycle 210
insect resistance to insecticides 135, 155,
    158, 218, 231, 237–259
insecticide–herbicide interactions 427
insensitivity, *see under* Resistance
instars 199, 210, 213, 216, 237
integrated pest management 210, 218,
    224, 258
intensive agriculture 3
interconversion, of forms of
    mercury 279–280
intermembrane space theory 166–167,
    171
international safety arrangements 17–19
intrinsic toxicity 433
in vitro and *in vivo* studies 246
ion channels 159–163, 203–204, 253
ion pumps 159–163, 203
ioxynil 410–413
Ipomoea spp 391, 414, 469
iprodione 311–312, 333
Irish potato famine 265
iron in soil 149, 152, 390, 393
iron–sulphur clusters 330
irrigation, to incorporate
    herbicides 478–479

iso-anaesthetic concentrations 432–434
isodrin 174–175
isofenphos 121–122
isoleucine synthesis 465–467
isomalathion 104
isopentenyl pyrophosphate 397
isopropalin 491
isopropanol 39–41
isoproturon 441
isothiocyanates 293, 297
isotoxic concentrations 433–435
isozymes, of cytochrome P_{450} 66
ivermectins 230–232

Japanese quail 279, 338
jasmolins I and II 187
jets, spray 40–42, 45–47
Johnson grass 393, 417
Juncus spp 396
Juniperus spp 392
juvenile hormone 210–212

K_m values 242–243, 253
K_{ow} (the oil–water partition coefficient,
    also referred to as P) 28, 112–113,
    266, 370, 376
kale 370, 385, 396, 489–490
kaolin 34, 37
kasugamycin 316, 350, 497
kdr strains of houseflies 253–254
3-keto-carbofuran 142
ketoconazole 316, 345–346
2-keto-dieldrin 176
kinetic constants 242–243, 253
knock-down effect 185, 191, 205, 254
knotgrass 402, 409, 411

lag phase 141–142, 148
Lagenidium spp 300
land clearance, by herbicides 364, 377
lanosterol 333–334, 338, 341–343
Laodelphax spp 197
large-seeded crops 365–366, 449, 459
late broods 182
latency of pathogens 338
lawns, weeds in new 410–413
LC_{50} 10–12
LD_{50} 10–12
LD_{95}, for cyhexatin 227
leaching 37–39, 147, 396, 443

leaf blight 291
leaf blotch 291, 299, 333
leaf cuticle 26–27
leaf hoppers 130, 139–140
leaf miners 86, 106, 113, 116, 118, 128–130, 146, 158, 252
leaf mould 269, 292, 299
leaf spot diseases 265, 269, 272, 277, 291–292
leaf stripe disease 277
leafrollers 197, 215
learning ability 132
leatherjackets 34, 86, 129, 158, 177
leaving group (*X*) 83, 94, 102
leeks 299, 485
legumes 116, 291, 307, 364, 428–431, 478, 489, 491
lenacil 454–456
lentils 460, 478
Lepidoptera 158, 193, 200, 209, 218, 496
Leptinotarsa spp 199
leptophos 100
lethal metabolism 58, 72, 304, 429, 497
lettuce, weed control in 291, 299, 306, 319, 345, 352, 489
leucine 421
lice 159, 175, 188
life cycles, importance of 218, 224, 228, 496
ligaments 45
ligands, for copper 271
light reactions, of photosynthesis 385–389, 445–447
light sensitivity, of pyrethrins 189
light-dependent reactions 385–389, 397–399, 414, 468–472
lignin 328
Ligustrum spp 392
lime-sulphur 1, 281–284
Limnaea spp 233
lindane 34, 138, 157, 171–174
linoleic acid reduction 487
linuron 440–445
lipid composition, *Ustilago* spp 343
lipid metabolism 225, 307, 481
lipid peroxidation 312, 343, 445–447, 453, 470
lipids in cuticle, resistance and 239–240
lipophilic–hydrophilic balance 55, 406, 446
lipoprotein membrane disruption 161, 167, 213, 265, 309, 339, 343, 356, 432–435, 469–472, 481

lipoproteins 28–30, 412–414
high density 62
liver enlargement 338, 346
liver fluke 233
lobsters 92
loco-systemic action 28, 82, 87, 102–112
locusts 158, 175
Lolium spp 388, 418, 443
Lonchocarpus spp 223
long-chain fatty acids 481
looper caterpillars 86
loose smut 266, 277–278, 320, 329
loss of food, after harvesting 120
low-boiling-point solvents 34
low-volume formulations 40, 42
lucerne 214
Ludwigia spp 414
lung cell proliferation 388
lycoprene 397–398
lysosomes 211

machinery, for applying pesticides 44–47
magnesium ions 162, 488
magnesium-dependent ATPase 166, 344
maize
fungicidal use in 277, 290
insecticide use in 36, 210, 230
weed control in 385, 396, 409, 414, 421, 431, 449–450, 452, 468, 478, 480, 485
maize rough dwarf virus 197
malaoxon 103–104, 246
malaria 4, 155, 157
malathion 62, 82, 99, 103–104, 254–256
analogues of 104–105
resistance to 240–244, 246–247
malathion carboxylesterase 241–244
malformation 389, 486
malonyl glucoside 472
management, of resistance 256–259, 317, 324, 349, 354
mancozeb 287, 289, 291–292, 352
maneb 7, 266, 278, 287, 291, 352
manganese 310, 432
mangold fly 86
mangolds 455, 460, 478
markets, for pesticides 4, 8, 497
Matricaria spp 409, 411, 413
matrix of granules 37
maximum residue limits 17
mayweeds 409, 411, 413

MCPA 396, 400–402, 412, 423
MCPB 428
meadow grass 450
mealy bug 86, 106, 128, 146
mecoprop 400–402
medical uses, of pesticides 233–234
Mediterranean sea 179
Megaselia spp 119
melanin 29–30, 485
Meloidogyne spp 129, 147, 150, 228, 230
membranes
    disruption in 356, 432, 439, 447, 470, 486
    see also Lipoproteins; Phospholipids; Fatty acid biosynthesis
    ion pumps in 204
menazon 82, 110, 112
mepronil 327
mercapturic acid 78
mercuribenzoate 75
mercury compounds 275–280
mesh size 39
mesocotyl elongation 366
metabolism, principles of 57–79
metalaxyl 264–265, 272, 293, 316, 350–354
metaldehyde-bran baits 232–233
metalkamate 130
methabenzthiazuron 463
methamidophos 118, 258
metham-sodium 229, 289
methiocarb 126, 130, 133, 139
methionine 481
methomyl 126, 130, 132, 145, 149–150, 237
methoprene 216–217, 245
methoxychlor 158, 164, 169–170
methoxy-ureides 444
methyl bromide 120, 229, 266
methyl cellulose 139
methyl isocyanate 228, 290, 296
methyl mercury chloride 278–280
methyl parathion 74, 102, 105, 107, 112, 242, 245
methyl sterols 341
methyl viologen 384, 387–388
2-methyl-4-chloroaniline 222
methylene dioxyphenols 67, 128, 135, 188, 245
methylthiotriazines 451
metobromuron 441–442
metolachlor 475, 485–488

metoxuron 440–442
metribuzin 449
mevalonic acid 397
mevinphos 100–102
miconazole 346
microsacs in rat brain 204
microsomal oxidases, *see* Mono-oxygenases
microsomes 59, 65–67, 143
microtubule disruption 424, 462, 491
migratory nematodes 146–148
milk, pesticides in 181, 197, 200
millipedes 129, 143, 146, 158
minimal cultivation farming 362–363, 386, 417
mipafox 100
mirex 175
mites 111–112, 158, 170, 176–177, 224–228, 283, 302
mitochondria 162, 165, 224–225, 267, 282, 300, 304, 327–331, 339, 349, 357, 388–389, 426–427, 447, 463, 491
mitotic inhibitors 279, 326, 461–462, 490–491
mixed function oxidases, *see* Mono-oxygenases
mixtures, of fungicides 272, 292, 328, 333, 354–355
mobilisation of copper, from fungicides 270–272
mobility of herbicides, in soil 374–377
moisture, effect on toxicity 151, 348, 492
molinate 478, 480
molluscicides 126, 129–130, 139, 141, 232–234, 280
Monilinia spp 282, 307, 319, 339
monoamine oxidase 220
monocrotophos 40, 118, 197
monoculture 399
mono-demethylated ureides 444
monolinuron 440–447
mono-oxygenases 59, 65–76, 85, 107, 112, 139, 143, 188, 194, 199, 245–247, 335, 340, 344, 346
mono-substituted dithiocarbamates 288–290
montmorillonite 189, 385
monuron 373–375, 440–447
morning glory 391, 414, 469
morphogenesis 211
morpholines 316, 331–335, 339
mosquitoes 36, 105, 158, 185, 189, 242, 252–256

moth larvae   158
motor nerve terminals   201, 253
moulting   210–212
mouse-ear   409
MRLs (maximum residue limits)   17
Mucor spp   266, 356
multiple discharges   161, 164, 201–203
multiple forms, of cytochrome P_{450} 67
multiple genes   468
   see also Resistance
multiple resistance   256
multiple sites, of fungicidal action   264
mushrooms   119, 121, 292–293, 310
mustards   411
mutagenic effect   13, 16, 64, 99, 301,
   326, 447, 456, 482
mutant genes   63, 237, 241, 367–368
myclobutanil   339
Mycogone spp   310
Mycosphaerella spp   319, 331
myelinated nerves   87–91
Myosotis spp   411
Mytilus spp   181
Myzocallis spp   238
Myzus spp (as a vector)   197
   see also Aphids

nabam   263, 289
N-acetyl cysteine   78
N-acetyl glucosamine   29, 211
nap gene   254
naphthenic acids   270
α-naphthyl acetate   241, 243
napropamide   488
narcissus   147, 229
narcosis   432–435
Nardus spp   386
national arrangements for
   pesticides   19–20
natural enemies, of pests   151
natural pyrethroids   185–190
Natural Resources Defense Council   20
N-dealkylation   69, 71, 111, 128, 221,
   444, 491
near-red light   445–446
neburon   444
necrosis   412, 414
Nectria spp   276
negative cross-resistance   317–318, 325,
   331, 349
negative temperature coefficient   159,
   196, 205

nematicides   126, 129–130, 141,
   150–152, 228–230, 306
neonatal stages   231
Nephotettix spp   139–140, 256
Nernst equation   160
nerve cells   88–89, 159–162, 219
nerve-muscle preparations   202
net blotch   310
nettles   483–484
neuroeffector junctions   88–92
neurohormones   92, 219
neurological symptoms, o/p insecticide
   poisoning   97–99
neuromotor junctions   88–91, 97–99,
   201
neuronal sensitivity, reduced   253–254
neurons   88–92, 100, 159–162, 219
neuropathy target esterase   100, 118
neuroreceptors, for lindane   172
Neurospora spp   267, 274, 282, 305
neurotransmitters   87–92, 162, 202–205,
   217–219
N-glycoside   77
N-hydroxylmethyl carbofuran   142–143
N-hydroxymethyl carbaryl   137
NIA 16388 (hydrolase inhibitor)   196
niclosamide   233–234
nicotine   1, 222–223
nightshade   414, 449, 467, 478, 485
Nitella spp   447
nitrifying organisms   148, 344
nitrites   138
Nitrobacter spp   134
4-nitro-*m*-cresol   66
nitrofen   469
nitro-group reduction   59, 304, 307, 491
nitrophenol   109
p-nitrophenyl butyrate   243
nitrophenyl ethers, *see* Diphenyl ethers
N-methyl carbamate esters   125–127
N-methyl-4-carboxypyridinium ion   389
N-methyl-2,2-diphenyl acetamide   488
N,*N*-diallyl-2-chloroacetamide   485
N,*N*-diallyl-2,2-dichloroacetamide   468,
   483
N-nitrosocarbaryl   138
non-cyclic
   photophosphorylation   445–447
non-haem iron   328–330
non-ideal solutions   434
non-ionic surfactants   52–53
non-myelinated axons   160
non-persistent viruses   197

non-selective weed control 363, 377, 483
non-specific sites of action 264
non-systemic fungicides 262, 286
nor-adrenaline 88–92, 204, 219
nor-epinephrine, *see* Nor-adrenaline
normal distribution 11
no-till farming, *see* Minimal cultivation
    farming
N-triphenylmethyl morpholine 233
nuarimol 316, 343–344
nucleophilic attack 96
nucleoside diphosphate monomer 211
nutsedges 414, 464, 477–478, 480, 485
nymphal stages, of mites 224–226

oats 277, 328, 421–427, 490
occupational hazards 21–22
octanoic acid 410
octopamine 92, 220
n-octylamine 67
O-dealkylation 69–70, 102, 170,
    188–189, 247
oestradiol 346
oestrus cycle 133
ofurace 316, 351
Oidium spp 319
oil palms 392
oil seed rape 386, 416–417
oil-soluble emulsifiers 41
oil-water partition coefficient 28,
    112–113, 266, 376
omnivorous species 181–182
onchocerciasis 4
Oncobasidium spp 338
Oncopeltus spp 212
onion fly 276
onions 86, 159, 230, 276, 292, 323, 370,
    412, 485
Oomycetes 196–198, 200, 236–237, 239,
    257, 263–268, 309, 315–316, 319,
    341, 349–354, 356–358
open configuration 161
Ophiocephalus spp 111
opium poppy 441
opportunistic fungi 129
oral toxicities 12
organic matter, in soil 321, 376–377,
    442–443, 449
organochlorine insecticides 155–182,
    238, 253, 256
organomercury fungicides 2, 263, 266,
    276–280, 308, 336

organophosphorus compounds,
    synergistic use of 194, 197
organophosphorus fungicides 357
organophosphorus herbicides 390–395
organophosphorus insecticides 2, 61,
    69, 81–123, 129, 241–256
organotin compounds 280–281
ornamental plants 225, 291, 299, 319,
    332, 455, 478, 490, 492
oryzalin 489, 492
Oscinella spp 144
ovicides 224–226, 432
ovipositing 209, 231
ovulation delay 181–182
oxadiazon 383, 425–426
oxadixyl 293, 316, 351, 354
oxamyl 126, 129, 144, 150–152, 229–230
oxathiins 268, 316, 327–331
oxazole ketones 350–351
β-oxidase 428–429
oxidative activation 246–247
oxidative desulphuration 69, 72
oxidative phosphorylation 166, 280,
    304, 427, 429–431, 435, 447
oxime carbamates 73, 127, 144–152
oxirane rings 69, 72, 175–176
oxycarboxin 316, 327–331, 358
oxyfluorfen 469

paddy blast disease 350
paddy water 218
PAM 96
Paniculum spp 418
Panicum spp 479
pantothenic acid 416
PAPS 77
paraoxon 72, 242
paraoxonase 242–243
paraquat 39, 364, 383–389
parasympathetic nerves 88
parathion 72, 84, 102–103, 106–109,
    229
parsley 432
parsnips 431–432
particle size 35–36, 39, 213
partition coefficient (K_{ow} or P) 112, 434
pasture renovation 393
pathogens (borne by air, seed and
    soil) 263
PCNB 305–306
pea 86, 114, 117, 290, 320, 323, 356,
    385, 414, 417, 450, 453, 459–460, 478

pea midges   116
pea moth   86, 130
peach   111, 324, 455
peach leaf curl disease   269, 283, 299
peanuts, *see* Groundnuts
pear   86, 111, 319, 454
pear psyllid   210
pear scab   291
pebulate   478
pecan   454
pectic acid   26
pectin methyl esters   405
peel, residues in citrus   225
Pegomya spp   144
pellets, granule   34–39, 139
Pellia spp   395
penconazole   339
pendimethalin   475, 489, 491
Penicillium spp   141, 214, 300, 320, 465
pentachloroaniline   305
pentachlorophenol   234, 280
pentanochlor   431
peppers   491
peptidyl transferase   350
perennial grass control   390–399,
    415–422, 476–483, 499
perennial weeds, control of   369,
    377–379, 390–399, 410
perfect solutions   435
peripheral nerves   91, 160, 164, 232
perithecia   320
permeability, of membranes   340
permethrin   190–196, 201–205, 239–240,
    254–255, 258
Peronosclerospora spp   352
Peronospora spp   350–351
peroxidation of lipids   343, 387–389,
    412–413
persistence   73, 81, 110, 155, 159, 256,
    262, 372–377, 449, 465, 480
persistent auxins   404–405
persistent contact insecticides   87,
    102–112
personal safety measures   21
pest management programmes   256, 496
petroleum spirit   432
Petunia spp   368
pH   116, 127, 222, 370, 401, 450, 459,
    465, 479
Phalaris spp   422, 441
phase distribution   432–435
Phaseolus spp   394
phenmedipham   431, 463

phenobarbital   488
phenolic nitriles   383, 410–413
phenoxyacetic acid herbicides   365, 383,
    399–408, 499
phenoxyacetic-resistant weeds   411
phenoxyalkanoic acids   399–408, 428
phenoxybenzyl alcohol   191–193
phenoxybenzyl cyanhydrin   200
phenoxybutyric acid herbicides   383, 428
phenylalanine–ammonia lyase   394
phenylamide fungicides   316, 350–354
phenylcarbamate herbicides   439,
    458–463
phenylmercury chloride   276
phenylpyrrole fungicides   358
phloem   151, 345, 355, 370
Phoma spp   311, 319, 333
phorate   82, 84, 113–115, 122, 232
phorids   119
phosalone   110
phosetyl-aluminium   262, 354–356
phosphamidon   117
phosphatases   60–62, 83, 162–163, 241,
    248
phosphatidyl glycerol   421
phosphine   33, 120
phosphites   356
phosphoenol pyruvate   394
phosphofructokinase   330
phospholipids   66, 453, 481
    see also Lipoprotein membrane
        disruption
phosphonates   84, 118
phosphorothioates   83–84
phosphorothiolthionates   83–84
phosphorothionates   83–84
phosphorous acid   356
phosphorylation, cholinesterase   93–96
phosphotriesterases   241
Photinus spp   221
photoassimilates   392
photo-oxidation   399, 412
photophosphorylation, inhibition
    of   280, 412
photosensitiser   470–472
photostable pyrethroids   190–200
photosynthesis
    disruption of   386–389, 432, 440–458
    factors favouring   404
photosynthetic electron transport   427,
    463, 470–472
photosynthetic products   370
photosystem I   387, 472

photosystem II   387, 412, 426, 445, 453, 456
Phragmites spp   396
phthalimide fungicides   263–265, 286, 298–302, 350
Phyllonorycter spp   252, 255
physical toxicity   167, 432–435
physiological changes and resistance   238
physostigmine   125
phytin   398
phytoene   397–398
phytophagous mites   217–219
Phytophthora spp   263, 265, 268, 292, 299, 305, 307, 319, 350, 351–357
phytoseiid mites   232
phytotoxicity   272, 283, 374, 424
phytyl alcohol   399
picloram   410
pineapple   319, 355, 379, 450, 455
pink bollworm   198
piperazine fungicides   316, 344–347
piperonyl butoxide   67, 135–136, 143, 188, 194, 199, 215, 221, 245
pirimicarb   34, 130, 140, 144
pirimiphos-methyl   16, 82, 84, 111, 120
placement selectivity   367
placement techniques   39, 378
placental transfer   149, 181
plankton   156
plant breeding and pest control   497
plant cell cultures   367
plant cell kinases   491
plant leaf cuticle   26–28
planthopper   197
plasma membrane and auxin   405
plasmadesmata   370
plasmid   279
Plasmodiophora spp   276
Plasmopara spp   265, 350–351, 354
plastic strips   119
plastocyanin   387
plastoquinone   387, 399, 412, 427
Platynota spp   215
ploughing, in weed control   364, 416
plum   227, 319
Plutella spp   210, 240, 258
PMA   276
Poa spp   419, 469
pod midges   158
Podosphaera spp   303, 319, 343, 347
poisoning, emergency measures after   22
polarity   57, 77, 274, 370

polycyclic compounds   64
polyethylene oxide derivatives   41, 52–53
Polygonum spp   393, 402, 409, 411, 431–432, 469
polymerisation, degree of   27
polyoxins   212
polyphenols   29
polysulphides   281–284
polyunsaturated fatty acids   471
pome fruits   349
poppy   411
pore size   39
porosity modifiers   37
porphyrin derivatives   65–66, 340
positional selectivity   365
positive temperature coefficient   202, 205
post-emergence weed control   368, 463
post-harvest protection
   by fungicides   292–293, 306, 320, 351
   by insecticides   106, 111, 120, 209, 214
post-synaptic membranes   88–91, 178, 219, 232
potassium ions   159–163, 415
potato cyst nematode   129–130
potato haulms   386
potato root nematode   228–230
potato virus   197
potatoes
   fungicides for   291–293, 299, 302, 319, 322, 352
   insecticides/nematicides for   86, 122, 146–147, 150
   weed control in   396, 417, 419, 431, 449–450, 478, 485, 488
potentiation   104
powdery mildews   263, 265, 280, 283, 291, 302–303, 310, 331–332, 335–339, 343–344, 347–349, 357
pralidoxime   96, 98, 132
Pratylenchus spp   146, 230, 306
pre-emergence weed control   368–369, 385–386, 390, 392, 419, 440, 449, 454, 460
prephenate   395
pre-planting treatments   377–379, 415–416, 475–493
pre-sowing grass killers   415–416
pre-synaptic membranes   88–90, 177, 203
pre-synaptic vesicles   89–90, 162
primary metabolism   57
probit analysis   12–13
problem soils   373

procaine 220
prochloraz 287, 309–310, 316, 322, 338, 346
procuticle 29
procymidone 311
productivity, of farm workers 9
progesterone 344
prokariotes 349
prometon 449
prometryne 431, 448, 450
promycelium 339
pronamide 488
propachlor 485–489
propanil 63, 425, 427, 458
propham 458–463
propiconazole 265, 316, 337–343
propoxur 126, 128, 130, 133, 138–139
propylene glycol 49
prop-2-ynyl phenylphosphonate 196
propyzamide 488
prosobranch snails 234
proso-millet 479, 482
protective fungicides 265
protein biosynthesis 350, 393, 424, 468, 500
protein, in diet, effect on pesticides 132
protein kinase 162
prothiocarb 316, 355, 357
protoporphyrin IX 470
pruning cuts 323
Pseudocercosporella spp 263, 265, 309, 318, 321, 336, 338, 346
pseudocholinesterase 91
Pseudomonas spp 122, 138, 279, 321, 337
Pseudoperonospora spp 292, 350–351, 357
Pseudoplusia spp 195, 199, 232
psyllids 210
Puccinia spp 307, 337, 339, 357
pumice 34
Puntius spp 133
pupae 213
pupil, of eye 97
purines 349
purple blotch disease 287–288
purple nutsedge 454, 485
   see also Nutsedges
purslane 485
pyracarbolid 327
pyrazon 439, 455–458
pyrazophos 303, 316, 357
Pyrenophora spp 264, 309

pyrethrins I and II 186–187, 189
pyrethroids 34, 68, 165, 185–190, 253–254, 256, 258
pyrethrolone 186
Pyricularia spp 315, 350, 357
pyridazinone herbicides 456–458
pyridine fungicides 316, 335, 344–347
pyridine-2-aldoxime methiodide 96
pyridinium surfactants 51
pyrimidine fungicides 316, 335, 341, 343–344
   (for the ethirimol group of pyrimidine derivatives, see Hydroxyaminopyrimidine fungicides)
pyrophosphoramides 84
Pythium spp 263–264, 268, 319, 322, 341, 356

Q (electron acceptor) 445
quack grass, see Couch grass
Quadraspidiotus spp 111, 232
quasi-systemic, see Loco-systemic action
quaternary ammonium compounds 2, 384–389
quenching 446
Quercus spp 408
quinones 31, 356
quintozene (PCNP) 278, 287, 305–306
quizalofop 418

R25788 (a safener) 483
R33865 (an extender) 480
radioisotope techniques 109, 143, 148, 197–198, 391, 404, 410, 418, 420, 421, 426, 443, 465
ragwort 401, 449
rainfall, effect on soil pesticides of 374, 443, 449, 460
Ranvier, nodes of 88
Raphanus spp 431
raspberries 227, 320
rat brain, synaptosomes of 204
rate constants 61, 93–96
receptors 90, 165–167, 201–204, 254
recommendations, on pesticide storage 18–19
reconstituted systems 405
recovery, of blocked esterase 93, 96
red core disease 299, 355
red flour beetle 254

red light 470
red spider mite 86, 103, 112–113, 117, 291, 302, 345
redcurrants 407
redox potential 384, 387
redroot pigweed 479
redshank 402, 409, 411
reduction of nitro-groups 59, 307, 491
reductive dechlorination 167–168
reductive dehalogenation 168–169
reed canary grass 422
reeds 393, 396
reflex arc 165, 177
regenerated crop plants 368
relative saturation 433–435
release patterns 37
repetitive discharges 161, 201–204
residual herbicides 365–367
residues 17–19
  of DDT, in fat 156, 158
resistance
  to acaricides 224
  due to metabolism 58, 62
  to fungicides 286, 292, 299, 302, 307, 311, 316–317, 324–325, 329, 342, 347, 349, 354, 498
  to herbicides 368
  to insecticides 105, 108, 112, 128, 143, 168, 196, 215, 218, 227, 237–259
  at site of action 251–254, 325, 447, 454
resistance factor (or ratio), *RF* 210, 237, 245, 254, 257
resmethrin 191, 255
respiration, effects on 132, 329–330, 430, 447
resting conformation 161
resting potential 160
retention of deposit 34–37, 47, 269
R_f value 376
Rhizobium spp 148, 337
Rhizoctonia spp 70, 278, 296, 305, 307, 319, 327, 338, 356
rhizome bud development 391, 416, 420, 475, 479, 481, 484, 485
Rhizopus spp 306–307
Rhodnius spp 30–31
rhododendrons 355
Rhodotorula spp 214
rhubarb 386
Rhynchosporium spp 291, 299, 310, 332, 336, 338, 346
Rhyzopertha spp 209, 214

riboflavin 169
ribosomes 349
rice 63, 77, 139, 213, 414, 426–427, 460, 478, 480, 486, 492
rice blast disease 315, 350, 357
rice hoppers 252
rice root nematode 228, 230
rice tungro virus 129
rice water weevil 213
river blindness 155
RNA 307, 353, 405, 409
root development inhibition 488, 490
root dips 116, 129, 158–159, 175, 177, 230, 276, 351
root knot nematode 8, 129, 147, 150, 228
root lesion nematode 230
root uptake 113, 146, 320, 378, 475
root–rot diseases 291, 351, 355
root-systemic action 36–38
roses 265, 291, 299, 332, 450, 484, 492
rosette of leaves 366
rotary disc machines 45–47
rotenone 223, 329
roti 149
Rottboellia spp 492
Rotylenchus spp 147, 230
rumen organisms 181
Rumex spp 409, 411
ruminants 111
run-off 179
rushes 396
rust diseases 263, 291–292, 308, 315, 327, 331–332, 337–339, 344, 357
rust mites 219

safe storage 21, 149, 277–278
safeners 478–479, 482–483, 500
safety factor 14
salivation 191
Salmonella spp 16, 99, 447, 482
Salmonella/microsome mutagenicity test 16, 99
San José scale 111, 232
sarcomas, of soft tissue 403
sarin 81
saturation concentration 433–434
sawflies 106, 113, 158
scab diseases 263, 338, 343
scale insects 86, 103, 106, 128, 146, 158, 232
scarlet pimpernel 411

scavengers, free radical 471–472
Scenedesmus spp 487
schistocerca 220
Schistosoma spp 233–234
schradan 84
Schwann cells 88
Scirpus spp 414
Sclerospora spp 350, 352
sclerotin 29–30, 211
Sclerotinia spp 263, 311, 319, 339
sclerotinised proteins 29, 211
Sclerotium spp 300, 305, 312, 356
scorching of leaves 386
scorpions 158
scrub typhus 170
sealed units for ULV 44
second generation pesticides 4
secondary cell walls 26
secondary messenger 405
secondary metabolism 57, 76–79
sedimentation force 42–44
seed merchants 277
seed treatment
 with fungicides 266, 277–279,
  290–291, 322–323, 333, 337, 348,
  351–353, 356, 499
 with insecticides 122, 139, 141, 158,
  177
seed-borne fungi 263–264, 266, 290,
  305, 307–308
seedling blight 277
seedling grass control 416–422, 476–483
seedling weed control 364–367, 439,
  442, 450, 455, 460, 484
selection pressure 257–258
selective action, of fungicides 263–269,
  286–288, 315–318
Senecio spp 401, 409, 411, 447, 453
sensory nerve fibres 204
Septoria spp 263, 265, 290, 299, 309,
  319, 331, 336, 339, 358
sequestration, of copper 273–275
serine 61, 94, 396
sesamex 188, 215, 245
Setaria spp 420–421, 427, 479, 485, 492
set-aside 7
sethoxydim 383, 416–422, 424, 499
Seveso 403
sheep blowfly 243
sheep dips 158–159, 175
shepherd's purse 414, 476
shikimic acid pathway 393–395, 500

shoot growth abnormality 424,
  461–463, 481
sieve mesh 39
signal transmission block 203, 230–232
silicas 34
silver scurf 322
simazine 364, 396, 439, 447–450
similar action 456
single gene mutation 331
singlet oxygen 413
site of action modification 227,
  251–254, 447
site-specific action, of fungicides 331,
  347
Sitophilus spp 205, 209, 214, 240, 254
skin 57
skin spot 322
slipping clutch analogy 430
slow-release granules 37
slugs 129, 139, 179, 232–234
smoke formulations 33, 120, 144
smut diseases 263–264, 266, 268, 273,
  315, 327, 338, 344, 346
snails 129, 174, 232–234
snow mould 277
sodium chlorate 364, 378
sodium dimethyl dithiocarbamate 294
sodium ion channels 160–163, 166, 203
sodium pumps 159–163
soft granules 36–38, 389
soil application 129, 321, 351
soil constituent/pesticide
 interaction 214, 320, 323, 332, 345,
  384–385, 392, 459, 469, 477, 484
soil depth 366, 376
soil drenches 352, 356
soil moisture, and herbicides 372, 374,
  484, 490
soil nematodes 146
soil organic matter 374, 376, 377,
  442–443, 449, 456–457, 459, 484,
  486, 488, 490, 492
soil organisms, effect of pesticides
  on 121, 134, 158, 177–178
soil, persistence of herbicides
  in 374–377, 415, 442, 449, 456,
  460, 465, 484
soil sterilants 266, 290, 396
soil-applied herbicides 439–472,
  475–493
soil-borne infections 263, 265, 305–306,
  356–358

soil-incorporated herbicides   458,
    475–483, 486, 489
Solanum spp   409, 467
solubilisation, of copper   271
solvents, high boiling point   34
Sonchus spp   431
sorbitan alkanoic acids   53
sorghum   386, 417, 450, 453
sow thistle   431
soybean looper moth   195, 199, 209, 232
soybeans   7, 118, 291, 319, 356, 378,
    386, 409, 419, 421, 464, 467, 469,
    478, 480, 485, 492
specificity, fungicidal   262–269, 286–288,
    315–318
speedwells   411
Spergula spp   409, 469
Sphaerotheca spp   319, 347, 357
spider mites   158, 217–219, 224–228, 251
spike   161
spindle fibres   462
spiracles   29, 222
Spodoptera spp   114, 135, 208, 213, 215,
    218, 240, 244
spores   266–267, 271, 273, 282
sporulation inhibition   350, 353
spray adjuvants   47–53
spray drift   41–43, 399–400
spray machinery   44–47
spray operators   21, 98, 105
spray supplements (adjuvants)   47–53
spray tank dilution preparation   21
sprayer design   44–47
spreaders   42, 48, 50–53
spring-sown cereal fungicides   348, 396
sprouting of tubers   306, 460
spruce budworm   232
squalene   397–398
squalene epoxidase   341
stabilisers   48, 50
stability
    of chelates   271, 275
    of phosphorylated
        cholinesterase   93–95
stale seed-bed technique   365
stalk borer   86
starch   37, 269
steady state uptake   13–15
Stellaria spp   409, 411–412, 458, 460,
    476
stem borer   36, 86, 130
stem nematodes   129, 228, 230

stem rot   291, 305
Stemphylium spp   290
sterility   232
sterol demethylation   340–342
sterol synthesis inhibitors   309, 316,
    331–347
stoloniferous grasses   392, 396
stomach poisons   208
stomata   371, 414, 432, 443
Stomoxys spp   193
storage, diseases during   299, 306
stored product protection   21, 111, 120,
    214, 224
strawberries   227, 291, 293, 299, 303,
    312, 319, 355, 431, 455, 460
strawberry mite   177
Streptomyces spp   230, 349, 465, 482
streptomycin   316, 349
sub-clinical effects   97–100
subsidiary sodium channel   161–163
subsistence agriculture   9, 362
substrate specificity   57–58
subterranean tissue destruction   404,
    476–481, 483–493
succinate dehydrogenase   132, 269,
    328–329
succinate ester   103
sugar beet
    fungicides for   319, 323
    insecticides for   86, 143–144, 146, 150,
        158, 277, 280, 283
    weed control in   416, 420, 423, 431,
        449, 455, 459–460, 463, 465, 478, 490
sugar beet yellows virus   146
sugar cane   119, 140, 146, 319, 352, 386,
    450, 455, 485–486
suicide theory   271
sulfometuron-methyl   463–468
sulphate conjugates   76
sulphated alcohols   51
sulphenylated carbamates   144
sulphides   62, 283
sulphonated hydrocarbons   51
sulphones   69, 73, 306, 328, 482
sulphonylurea herbicides   439, 463–468
sulphotransferases   77
sulphoxides   69, 73, 114, 139, 148–149,
    225, 298, 306, 328, 482
sulphur fungicides   281–284
sulphydryl compounds   273
sunflower   386, 423, 478, 490
superoxide dismutase   388

superoxides 387, 453, 471
supervised pest control 496
supplements (adjuvants) 26, 47–55
surface tension 48, 54
surfactants 40–42, 47–48, 50–55
suspension concentrates 32
sward destruction 386
swedes 490
sweet corn 485
sweet potatoes 86, 478, 486
swep 460–461
sympathetic nerve fibres 88
sympathomimetic properties 219
symphilids 200
Sympiesis spp 151
symplast 345, 355, 369, 392
synapses 87–92, 201–205
synaptosomes 204, 232
synergism 104, 188, 196, 215, 396–397, 480
synergistic ratio 135
synergists 49, 128, 135–136, 188, 244–245, 258
synthetic pyrethroids 2, 190–205
systemic action 28
systemic fungicides 262–265, 315–358
systemic o/p insecticides 81–82, 112–118

t_{50} 147, 151, 215
2,4,5-T 400, 403
tabun 81
tainting 171, 292, 302, 432
tank mixing, of pesticides 20
tap roots 171, 370, 432
Taphrina spp 299
target site resistance 239, 251–254
target surfaces 25–31
2,3,6-TBA 408–410
TCA 415–416, 479
TDE 164
tea 319, 331
technology, in crop protection 44–47
tecnazene 218, 306
teflubenzuron 210
tefluthrin 200
temperature coefficient, negative 159, 166, 177, 205
Tenebrio spp 213, 215
TEPP 100
teratogenic effects 13, 99, 138, 227, 298, 326, 389, 403–404
terbacil 455, 457

terbinconazole 339
terbutryne 447–450
terminal velocity 43
termites 112, 158
terpenyl pyrophosphate 397–398
testosterone 346
tetrachlorvinphos 100–101
tetradifon 224
tetraethyl thiuram disulphide 297
tetramethrin 191, 201
Tetranychus spp 224–228
tetrapyrrole metabolism, disruption of 470
thermodynamic activity 167, 434
thermoplastic matrix granules 37
thiabendazole 263, 316, 318, 322, 349
thin cuticles 481
thin shells 182
thin-layer chromatography 376
thiobencarb 427
thiocarbonates 301
thioether family of systemic o/p insecticides 113–115
thioether oxidation 69, 72
thiofanox 144
thiohydroxyimidates 126, 145
thiol groups 75, 265, 276, 279, 293, 299, 301, 308
thiolcarbamates 372, 476–483
thiomethanol 152
thionazin 228–229
thiophanate-methyl 263, 316, 318, 323–324
thiophosgene 301
thiophosphates 72, 84, 106–107
thiosulphates 283–284
thiourea derivatives 293, 301
thiovamidothion 116
thiram 2, 265, 278, 287, 289–291, 328
thistles 483–484
three-point attachment theory 406–407
threshold daily dose 14
thrips 86
thylakoid membranes 421, 472
ticks 158, 170, 220, 230–232
tillage 392
Tilletia spp 305, 322
timber treatment 270
tobacco 86, 119, 150, 319, 321, 368, 419, 478, 485, 489, 491
tobacco budworm 110, 196, 198, 243–244
tobacco hornworm 130, 149

tolerance limits   19
tolerances   105, 215, 237–239, 252, 445, 453
   distribution of   12
tomatoes   86, 147, 230, 269, 272, 291–292, 299, 319, 321, 352, 478
tonnage, of pesticides used   3–5
tortrix moth   118, 130
toxaphene   158
toxicity scale   11
toxicology, of pesticides   10–17
toxophore   16, 327, 330
tractor vaporising oil   432
trains of impulses   160–163, 201–204
transcription/translation   405
transferases   73–76
transgenic plants   367–368
transition elements   274–275
translaminar movement   344
   see also Loco-systemic action
translocation   352, 369, 391, 401, 415, 443
   see also Systemic action
transmitter   90–92
transpiration, factors affecting   371, 412, 443
transportation costs   40
treated grain, precautions with   277–279
tremors   98–100, 164, 191
triadimefon   316, 336–337
triadimenol   264, 337
triallate   365, 476–483
triarimol   268, 343
triazine herbicides   2, 71, 375, 380, 431, 439, 447–454
triazole fungicides   316, 336–343
triazophos   110
Tribolium spp   189, 243, 254
S,S,S,-tributyl phosphorotrithioate   196, 215, 244–245
trichloroacetic acid   364, 375, 415–416
2,4,5-trichlorophenol   403
trichlorphon   84, 99, 117–118
tri(cyclohexyl) tin   226–227
tridemorph   316, 331–332
tridiphane   73
trietazine   448
trifluralin   7, 37, 375, 404, 475, 489–491
triforine   316, 344–345
O,O,S-trimethyl phosphorothioate   105
tri-orthocresol phosphate   62
Trioxys spp   210
triphenyl phosphate   243–244

triphenyltin fungicides   73, 280
Trombiculid spp   170
trophic level   181
trunk treatment   352
tryptophan   394
tsetse fly   158, 240
tubulin sub-units   323–324, 462–463, 491
tufted budworm   198
tulip fire   291
tulips   229
turbine blowers   35
Tylenchorhynchus spp   146, 306
Typhula spp   337, 356
typhus   155
tyrosine   357, 393–395

ubiquinone   329–331, 412
UDPG(A)   76–77
UDP-*N*-acetylglucosamine   211
ultra-low-volume (ULV) spray systems   40, 42–45
ultraviolet radiation   331, 389, 490
ULV   40, 42–45
Uncinula spp   339
uncropped land   396
undersown cereals   412, 430
uracil herbicides   439, 445, 454–458
urea herbicides (ureides)   375, 440–447
uridine   353
uridine diphosphate glucose (UDPG)   77
uridine triphosphate   211
Urocystis spp   264, 327
Uromyces spp   339, 357
Urtica spp   483
USA pesticide regulations   19–20
USA pesticide usage   7
Ustilago spp   319, 327, 337, 343

vaginal candidosis   346
valine synthesis   466
vamidothion   82, 115
Van der Waals forces   95
vapour drift   400
vascular streak dieback disease   338
vascular system, crushing of   404–405
vectors
   and alternate hosts   4, 129, 146, 155, 170, 189, 230, 233–234
   of plant viruses   113, 122, 129, 140, 146, 197, 199

velvetleaf   464, 467
Venturia spp   276, 292, 309, 319,
    324–325, 338, 343
vermiculite   37
vernolate   476–480
Veronica spp   411
Verticillium spp   119, 264, 268–269, 290,
    310, 321
vesicles at end-feet   89–90, 204
veterinary and medical uses   5, 193, 197,
    216, 223, 230, 233
Vietnam war   403
vigour tolerance   227
vinclozolin   287, 310–312, 317
vines   272, 311, 355, 419, 492
Viola spp   411, 413, 492
virus disease control   113, 122, 129, 140,
    146, 197, 199, 230, 496
volatility   336, 476–483
voltage clamp technique   161, 166, 201
voltage-dependent ion
    channels   159–163, 165–167,
    201–205
Voluntary Approval Scheme   20
vortex   45

walnut aphid   210
warehouses   120
wasps   128, 158, 231
water balance   231
water lillies   393
water requirement, of fungi   263
watering in, for soil
    incorporation   485–487
wax deposits   26–31
weathering, of sulphur deposits   283
weevils   86, 103, 106, 114, 130, 158
wettable powder (WP)   32, 40–41
wetting agent   48, 54
wheat
    fungicides for   265–266, 277–278, 291,

299, 310, 319, 328, 338, 347, 357
    insecticides used in   139
    protection by safeners   483
    weed control in   385, 410, 421–422,
        424–426, 442, 444, 450, 463, 469,
        478–479
white grubs   158
whiteflies   128, 138, 158, 197, 218
wild oats   366, 415, 421–422, 425, 442,
    460, 476, 478–480
wild radish   431
wild-type populations   257
wilt diseases   355
wing fanning   177
winter moths   112
wireworms   33, 129, 143, 158–159, 174,
    177, 200
woodlice   106
woody ornamentals, weed control
    in   486
woody weed control   402, 410, 441
woolly aphids   48, 113, 116
writhing syndrome   203–205

Xanthium spp   394, 414
xylem   368–371

yarrow   409
yeast   267, 296, 342, 349
yellow fever   155
yellow foxtail   479
yellow nutsedge   454, 478
    see also Nutsedges

zinc compounds   289–290, 294
zineb   265, 289
ziram   289
zoospores   263, 350, 353
zymogen   211